SOME PROBLEMS
OF CHEMICAL KINETICS
AND REACTIVITY

VOLUME 1

Revised and expanded by the author

Academician N. N. SEMENOV
Institute of Chemical Physics,
Academy of Sciences of the U.S.S.R.

Translated by

J. E. S. BRADLEY, B.Sc., Ph.D.

PERGAMON PRESS

LONDON · NEW YORK · PARIS · LOS ANGELES

1958

PERGAMON PRESS LTD.
4 & 5 *Fitzroy Square, London W.1*

PERGAMON PRESS INC.
122 *East 55th Street, New York 22, N.Y.*
P.O. Box 47715 Los Angeles, California

PERGAMON PRESS S.A.R.L.
24 *Rue des Écoles, Paris V^e*

Library of Congress No. 58–10936

Printed in Great Britain by the Pitman Press, Bath

CONTENTS

INTRODUCTION

THIS book was first published in 1954 by the U.S.S.R. Academy of Sciences, its history being as follows: The Chemistry Division of the Academy had arranged an All-Union Conference on Chemical Kinetics and Reactivity, to be held in 1955, and I was requested to present the opening paper; while working on this I came to the conclusion that it would be of value to produce a small book in which the published data and my personal views on the topics to be discussed could be presented. The book appeared in 1954, and a collection of 69 papers presented at the Conference by various Soviet workers was published by the Academy in the first half of 1955; the Conference was held on 20–25 June, 1955, being a general discussion on my book and on the papers in the collection. A number of important topics, touching on the development of studies in chemical kinetics and reactivity, were considered.

The book was produced only in small numbers, and the edition was soon sold out; I was requested by the Academy to prepare a second edition. Immediately afterwards I was requested to grant my permission for the book to be translated into English and German, by Pergamon Press and Princeton University, and by the Academy of Sciences of the German Democratic Republic, respectively. The book has been substantially enlarged for the second edition, fresh data appearing in the world literature or obtained at the Institute of Chemical Physics being incorporated. The book consists of various views and calculations developed by myself and certain colleagues at the Institute of Chemical Physics during the last 10–15 years from our experiments and from the published data on chemical kinetics. The book therefore presents a particular viewpoint, does not cover all work done on reaction mechanisms, and does not pretend to be a treatise or work of reference. The main topics considered are radical and radical-chain reactions. More than 20 years have passed since my previous book *Chain Reactions* appeared; meanwhile studies in chemical kinetics and chain reactions have developed enormously, vast numbers of papers have appeared, but it still seems as though the main problems are as yet not completely solved; the situation is very different from that in the physics of nuclear reactions, particularly chain fission, which was discovered in 1939 and since then has been so completely elucidated. The unsatisfactory situation in relation to reaction mechanisms has arisen, in my opinion, because the world's scientists have been occupied with isolated observations on particular reactions and have not undertaken a general all-round study. Such isolated observations are now quite inadequate in most cases, and can even be useless in developing the theory, either in relation to particular types of reaction, or to general problems in kinetics and reactivity. To undertake isolated studies unrelated to general problems is like determining particular points on a surface of which we wish to define the form; if the surface is complicated, knowledge about a few points tells us nothing about the form, and only enables us to reject unfounded hypotheses. Only the organized efforts of physical, organic and inorganic chemists directed to elucidating the general problems of mechanism, in relation to basic types of reaction and related reactivity problems, can lead to a decisive advance in chemistry.

Here, as in all other problems, from the fundamental political problems of the struggle for peace onwards, the united forces of the world's scientists are required. I shall be happy if this book is of interest to chemists, even if only slightly so, and if it directs attention to the solution of problems in chemical kinetics and reactivity.

I record my thanks to S. S. Polyak, A. B. Nalbandyan, N. S. Enikolopyan, D. G. Knorre, A. E. Shilov and several others of my colleagues at the Institute of Chemical Physics, and also to A. M. Pravednikov, who have all participated in writing the new chapters and in supplementing the previous chapters for the second edition.

N. SEMENOV.

PART I

RADICAL REACTIONS

(PROPAGATION AND BRANCHING OF CHAIN REACTIONS)

Chapter 1

UNIRADICAL REACTIVITIES

1. RADICAL REACTIONS: BASIC TYPES

THE reactions of univalent free radicals may be divided into three basic classes:

(1) Substitution:

$$\dot{R}_1 + R_2R_3 \rightarrow R_1R_2 + \dot{R}_3$$

where R_1, R_2, and R_3 are atoms or radicals. R_2 is a single atom in the majority of substitution reactions which have so far been studied.

(2) Addition at multiple bonds, or reaction with atoms which have unpaired electrons:

(*a*) $$\dot{R} + A_1{=}A_2 \rightarrow RA_1{-}\dot{A}_2$$

(*b*) $$CO + \dot{Cl} \rightarrow O{=}\dot{C}{-}Cl$$

A particular case of (*a*) is a polymerization, initiated by the radical $\dot{R}$:

$$\dot{R} + A_1{=}A_2 \rightarrow RA_1{-}\dot{A}_2$$
$$RA_1{-}\dot{A}_2 + A_1{=}A_2 \rightarrow RA_1{-}A_2{-}A_1{-}\dot{A}_2$$
$$RA_1{-}A_2{-}A_1{-}\dot{A}_2 + A_1{=}A_2 \rightarrow RA_1{-}A_2{-}A_1{-}A_2{-}A_1{-}\dot{A}_2, \text{ etc.}$$

(2′) Decomposition reactions (i.e. the inverse of addition):

(*a*) $$RA_1{-}\dot{A}_2 \rightarrow \dot{R} + A_1{=}A_2$$

(*b*) $$\dot{C}OCl \rightarrow CO + \dot{Cl}$$

(3) Isomerization, e.g.:

$$H_2\dot{C}{-}CH_2{-}CH_3 \rightarrow H_3C{-}\dot{C}H{-}CH_3$$

All these elementary reactions, except those of types 2(*b*) and 2′(*b*), involve breaking one of the bonds of the initial molecules, and result in the formation of a new bond.

1

The rates of all these processes are given by the formulae:

$$w_1 = a_1 \exp\left(-\varepsilon_1/RT\right)[\text{R}] \tag{1}$$

(unimolecular decomposition; isomerization), and

$$w_2 = a_2 \exp\left(-\varepsilon_2/RT\right)[\text{R}][\text{M}] \tag{2}$$

(bimolecular reactions; e.g. of radicals with molecules, either by substitution or addition).

The rate constant is a numerical expression of the reactivity of a molecule when its various bonds are subjected to attack by a radical.

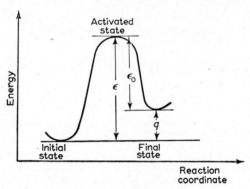

Fig. 1

The value of ε—the activation energy of the elementary process—indicates the minimum energy which the reacting system must possess in order that the reaction may take place. (The system may be a molecule or radical in unimolecular processes, or both the reacting particles in bimolecular processes.)

The state of the system may be represented graphically, taking the "reaction co-ordinate" as abcissa, and the potential energy of the reacting system as ordinate. Then the activation energy will be dependent on the height of the potential barrier that has to be surmounted during the reaction.

If, as is shown in Fig. 1, the reaction is endothermic, then the activation energy ε will be composed of two terms: firstly, ε_0, which is strictly the height of the potential barrier; and, secondly, the difference in energy between the final and initial states, i.e. the absolute value of the heat of reaction, $|q|$:

$$\varepsilon = \varepsilon_0 + |q| \tag{3}$$

If the process is exothermic (such as the reverse reaction to that of Fig. 1), then the activation energy will simply be equal to the height of the potential barrier ε_0. The difference in activation energy between the forward and back reactions is equal to the heat of the forward reaction. The factor a_1 is about 10^{13} sec^{-1} in many unimolecular reactions; this is of the order of molecular vibrational frequencies.

The values of a_1 for molecules and radicals are frequently assumed not to differ widely. In support of this assumption, we have the direct experiments of BUTLER and POLANYI [1], on the initial decomposition of iodides into two free radicals, and also the results of LADACKI and SZWARC [2] on the decomposition of a range of organic compounds; in these reactions, a_1 was found to be about 10^{13} sec^{-1}.

In bimolecular reactions a_2 is often close to the collisional frequency z (between molecules and radicals), i.e. about 10^{-10} cm^3/sec (or 10^{14} cm^3/mole-sec, depending on the unit of concentration used).

In fact, however, not every collision between a radical and a molecule leads to reaction, even if the energy of the colliding particles is sufficient; consequently, $a_2 = fz$, where f is the so-called steric factor ($f < 1$ normally). In most reactions $0 \cdot 1 < f < 1$. Latterly, it has been shown (mainly by STEACIE et al. [3, 4, 5]) that f falls to 10^{-3}–10^{-4} in some reactions of hydrocarbon radicals and hydrogen atoms with alkanes. The problem of the f-values in these reactions cannot yet be considered as definitely decided, however. Extensive experimental data on free radicals were presented at the Faraday Society Discussion in September, 1952. The results of different workers were sometimes inconsistent; e.g. according to BERLIE and LE ROY [6], ε is $6 \cdot 8$ kcal*, and $f = 4 \cdot 8 \times 10^{-3}$, in the reaction between atomic hydrogen and ethane. For the same reaction ($D + C_2H_6$) DARWENT and ROBERTS [7] found $\varepsilon = 9$ kcal, and $f = 0 \cdot 6$. We propose to use the latter values, since we can see no special theoretical reason for the occurrence of very small f-values in substitution reactions.†

Addition reactions (radicals or atoms) at double bonds would seem always to have low f-values (10^{-3}–10^{-5}). Numerous experimental

* For brevity, we use "kcal" to indicate "kilocalories per mole" throughout this book.

† More recently, some further results on substitution reactions have appeared, in which the authors stress the importance of steric factors of 10^{-3}–10^{-4}. The experimental data serve only to determine the a-factors, however, and these may be the product of the steric factors for a number of two-body collisions. The collisional frequency for a radical is calculated from gas-kinetic diameters of similar molecules: this may result in large errors. No theoretical basis for expecting small f-values in substitution reactions has been put forward, except by STEPUKHOVICH [8]: the arguments he uses do not appear very convincing to us, since a number of assumptions, for which there is little justification, are made in calculating the steric factors.

results, both direct and indirect, bear this out. Theoretical reasons may be advanced for the small f-values in reactions of this type; these are based on the statistical theory of the activated complex. It is found that, in this case, the activated complex, unlike in substitution reactions, does not decompose and its entropy is lower than that of the initial state. The smallness of f thus follows by analogy with corresponding data for the equilibrium constant in addition reactions: the equilibrium constant can be expressed with a degree of accuracy which is sufficient for this purpose, in the form: $K = A \exp\left(-Q/RT\right)$. In equilibria of the type $C_2H_4 + HBr \leftrightharpoons C_2H_5Br$, A is about 10^{27}, being equal to the ratio a_1/a_2 (the a-values for decomposition and addition respectively): $A = 10^{27} = a_1/a_2$. In many reactions, $a \simeq 10^{13}$, so $a_2 \simeq 10^{-14}$; consequently, $f \simeq 10^{-4}$.

By analogy with molecular additions, the steric factors in radical additions are supposed small.

In the gas phase, at pressures $\simeq 1$ atm, unimolecular reactions (decomposition or isomerization) proceed considerably more rapidly than bimolecular reactions (substitution or addition), temperature and activation energy being equal. The rates of unimolecular reactions are given by:

$$w_1 \simeq 10^{13} \exp\left(-\varepsilon_1/RT\right)c$$

where c is the number of molecules per cubic centimetre; c being about 10^{19} at atmospheric pressure. The rates of bimolecular reactions are given by:

$$w_2 \simeq 10^{-10} \exp\left(-\varepsilon_2/RT\right)c^2$$

Then, if $\varepsilon_1 = \varepsilon_2$ $\quad \dfrac{w_1}{w_2} = \dfrac{10^{13}}{10^{-10}c} = \dfrac{10^{13}}{10^{-10} \times 10^{19}} = 10^4$

i.e. under the same conditions, unimolecular reactions are about 10^4 times more rapid than bimolecular ones.

2. EXPERIMENTAL DETERMINATION OF ACTIVATION ENERGIES

The quantity $\exp\left(-\varepsilon/RT\right)$ in the expression for the rate constant will now be examined. The magnitude of this factor is determined by the value of ε. The latter quantity is, as we have seen above, equal to the potential barrier height ε_0 in exothermic reactions. When radicals react with molecules, or when radicals decompose, $\varepsilon_0 < 10$ kcal usually; most frequently, it lies in the range 3–6 kcal. Strongly endothermic radical reactions may have much larger activation energies. For instance, the decomposition of alkyl radicals to olefin + H (e.g. CH_3—$CH_2 \rightarrow C_2H_4 + H$) may involve an activation energy of about 40 kcal. These reactions are endothermic, the energy absorbed in the forward reaction being about 38 kcal. Now, according to (3), $\varepsilon_0 = \varepsilon - |q|$, so ε_0 is not great in these reactions, being only about 2 kcal. The reverse (exothermic) reaction—addition of a hydrogen atom at the double bond in olefins —has been found by direct experiment to have a very small activation energy, about 2–4 kcal [7, 9, 10].

The endothermic reaction $Br + H_2 \rightarrow HBr + H$ has an ε of 17·6 kcal: since we have, from (3), $\varepsilon = \varepsilon_0 + |q|$ and $q = -16·4$ kcal, $\varepsilon_0 = 1·2$ kcal.

Table 1 gives values of ε_0 determined for exothermic reactions of hydrogen atoms with various molecules. In Tables 2, 3, 4, and 5

Table 1. *Heat of reaction and activation energy for some elementary reactions involving hydrogen atoms*

Reaction	q^* (kcal)	ε_0 (kcal)	Reference
$H + CH_4 \rightarrow H_2 + CH_3$.	+ 2	13	[11]
$H + C_2H_6 \rightarrow H_2 + C_2H_5$	+ 5	9·5	[5]
$H + C_3H_8 \rightarrow H_2 + iso\text{-}C_3H_7$.	+ 13	8·5	[5]
$H + C(CH_3)_4 \rightarrow H_2 + CH_2C(CH_3)_3$.	+ 4	9·3	[5]
$H + CH_3CHO \rightarrow H_2 + CH_3CO$	+ 18	6	[12]
$H + CCl_4 \rightarrow HCl + CCl_3$	+ 33·5	3·5	[10]
$H + CHCl_3 \rightarrow HCl + CHCl_2$.	+ 28	4·5	[10]
$H + CH_2Cl_2 \rightarrow HCl + CH_2Cl$.	+ 24	6	[10]
$H + CH_3Cl \rightarrow HCl + CH_3$	+ 22	8	[10]
$H + C_2H_5Cl \rightarrow HCl + C_2H_5$.	+ 22	8	[10]
$H + C_2H_5Br \rightarrow HBr + C_2H_5$.	+ 20	6	[10]
$H + CH_3Br \rightarrow HBr + CH_3$.	+ 18	3–7	[10]
$D + CH_4 \rightarrow HD + CH_3$	+ 2	11	[10]
$D + C_2H_6 \rightarrow HD + C_2H_5$	+ 5	9	[7]
$D + C_3H_8 \rightarrow HD + iso\text{-}C_3H_7$.	+ 13	7·2	[7]
$D + iso\text{-}C_4H_{10} \rightarrow HD + tert\text{-}C_4H_9$.	+ 18	6·3	[7]
$H + D_2 \rightarrow HD + D$.	0	6·5	[13]
$D + H_2 \rightarrow HD + H$.	0	5	[14]
$H + Cl_2 \rightarrow HCl + Cl$.	+ 45	2	[13]
$H + Br_2 \rightarrow HBr + Br$.	+ 40	1·2	[13]
$H + I_2 \rightarrow HI + I$.	+ 35	0	[13]
$H + HCl \rightarrow H_2 + Cl$.	+ 1·1	4·5	[13]
$H + HBr \rightarrow H_2 + Br$.	+ 18	1·2	[13]
$H + HI \rightarrow H_2 + I$.	+ 33	1·5	[13]

* q is an expression of the thermochemical value of the reaction: for exothermic reactions it will therefore be positive.

Table 2. Heat of reaction and activation energy for some elementary reactions with hydroxyl radicals

Reaction	q (kcal)	ε_0 (kcal)	Reference
$OH + CH_4 \rightarrow H_2O + CH_3$	+ 16	8·5	[15]
$OH + C_2H_6 \rightarrow H_2O + C_2H_5$	+ 19	5·5	[15]
$OH + HCHO \rightarrow H_2O + HCO$	+ 38	0·5	[16]
$OH + CH_3CHO \rightarrow H_2O + CH_3CO$	+ 32	4·0	[16]
$OH + CO \rightarrow CO_2 + H$	+ 26	7·0	[17]

Table 3. Heat of reaction and activation energy for some elementary radical reactions

Reaction	q (kcal)	ε_0 (kcal)	Reference
$CH_3 + CH_4 \rightarrow CH_4 + CH_3$	0	11·2	[3]
$CH_3 + C_2H_6 \rightarrow CH_4 + C_2H_5$	+ 4	10·4	[3]
$CH_3 + C_4H_{10} \rightarrow CH_4 + iso\text{-}C_4H_9$	+ 11·5	8·3	[3]
$CH_3 + C_5H_{12} \rightarrow CH_4 + iso\text{-}C_5H_{11}$	+ 13	8·1	[3]
$CH_3 + C_6H_{14} \rightarrow CH_4 + iso\text{-}C_6H_{13}$	+ 14	8·1	[3]
$CH_3 + CH_3\text{—}CH\text{—}CH\text{—}CH_3 \rightarrow$ $\quad\;CH_3\;\;CH_3$ $\rightarrow CH_4 + CH_3\text{—}C\text{—}CH\text{—}CH_3$ $\quad\quad\quad\;\;CH_3\;CH_3$	+ 16	6·9–7·8	[3]
$CH_3 + iso\text{-}C_4H_{10} \rightarrow CH_4 + (CH_3)_3C$	+ 16	7·6	[3]
$CH_3 + (CH_3)_3CC(CH_3)_3 \rightarrow$ $\quad CH_4 + (CH_3)_3CC(CH_3)_2CH_2$	+ 4	9·5	[3]
$CH_3 + (CH_3)_2CH\text{—}CH\text{—}CH(CH_3)_2 \rightarrow$ $\quad\quad\quad CH_3$ $\rightarrow CH_4 + (CH_3)_2C\text{—}CH\text{—}CH(CH_3)_2$ $\quad\quad\quad CH_3$	+ 16	7·9	[3]
$CH_3 + (CH_3)_4C \rightarrow CH_4 + CH_2C(CH_3)_3$	+ 4·0	10·0	[3]
$CH_3 + C_3H_8 \rightarrow CH_4 + iso\text{-}C_3H_7$	+ 11·5	8	[10]
$CH_3 + CH_3Cl \rightarrow CH_4 + CH_2Cl$	+ 3·6	9·4	[18]
$CH_3 + CH_2Cl_2 \rightarrow CH_4 + CHCl_2$	+ 7·8	7·2	[18]
$CH_3 + CHCl_3 \rightarrow CH_4 + CCl_3$	+ 12	5·8	[18]
$CH_3 + CH_3Br \rightarrow CH_4 + CH_2Br$	+ 6	10·1	[18]
$CH_3 + CH_2Br_2 \rightarrow CH_4 + CHBr_2$	+ 13·3	8·7	[18]
$CF_3 + CH_4 \rightarrow CF_3H + CH_3$	+ 2	10·3–9·5	[19]
$CF_3 + C_2H_6 \rightarrow CF_3H + C_2H_5$	+ 5	7·5	[19]
$CF_3 + C_3H_8 \rightarrow CF_3H + iso\text{-}C_3H_7$	+ 14	6·5	[19]
$CF_3 + n\text{-}C_4H_{10} \rightarrow CF_3H + iso\text{-}C_4H_9$	+ 14	5·1	[19]
$CF_3 + iso\text{-}C_4H_{10} \rightarrow CF_3H + C(CH_3)_3$	+ 18	4·7	[19]
$CH_3 + CH_3CHO \rightarrow CH_4 + CH_3$	+ 16	6·8	[20]

the activation energies which have been determined for some other radical substitution reactions are given, together with the calculated values for the heats of reaction q.

Table 4. *Heat of reaction and activation energy for some elementary reactions with hydrogen or halogen atoms*

Reaction	q (kcal)	ε_0 (kcal)	ε (kcal)	Reference
$H + H_2 \rightarrow H_2 + H$ . .	0	$6 \cdot 2 \pm 1$	—	[13]
$D + D_2 \rightarrow D_2 + D$. . .	0	$6 \cdot 0$	—	[13]
$Cl + H_2 \rightarrow HCl + H$ . .	$- 1 \cdot 1$	$5 \cdot 6$	—	[13]
$Br + H_2 \rightarrow HBr + H$ . .	$- 16 \cdot 4$	$1 \cdot 2$	$17 \cdot 6$	[13]
$F + H_2 \rightarrow HF + H$ . .	$+ 31$	$7 \cdot 5$	—	[13]
$Br + CCl_3Br \rightarrow Br_2 + CCl_3$.	$- 4$	$2 \cdot 0$	$(6 \cdot 0)$	[10]
$I + C_2H_4I_2 \rightarrow I_2 + C_2H_4I$.	$- 11$	$*$	$(12 \cdot 0)$	[21]
$Cl + CHCl_3 \rightarrow HCl + CCl_3$.	$+ 13$	$8 \cdot 0$	—	[10]
$Cl + CH_4 \rightarrow HCl + CH_3$ . .	$+ 1$	$6 \cdot 2$	—	[10]
$Cl + C_7H_{16} \rightarrow HCl + C_7H_{15}$.	$+ 8$	$6 \cdot 0$	—	[10]
$Br + CHCl_3 \rightarrow HBr + CCl_3$.	$- 6^*$	4^*	$10 \cdot 0$	[10]
$Br + CH_3Br \rightarrow HBr + CH_2Br$.	$- 12^*$	$3 \cdot 6^*$	$15 \cdot 6$	[22]
$Br + CH_4 \rightarrow HBr + CH_3$.	$- 18^*$	$0^* (1 \cdot 4)$	$17 \cdot 8$	[22]
$Cl + Br_2 \rightarrow BrCl + Br$ . .	$+ 6$	0	—	[13]
$Cl + BrCl \rightarrow Cl_2 + Br$ . .	$+ 5 \cdot 7$	0	—	[13]

* Indicates that the value given was derived by indirect methods. Unreliable values are indicated by parentheses.

It is very difficult to measure the activation energies of elementary free radical reactions; much more so than for reactions between molecules. Free radicals are unstable, and disappear rapidly by combination, either on the walls of the vessel, or by homogeneous reaction. In consequence, it is very difficult to maintain a constant concentration of free radicals, and to measure it especially in the gas phase.

Free radicals are commonly obtained from electrical discharges in gases, by the action of ultra-violet light, or by pyrolysis of compounds that decompose to give free radicals (such as peroxides). Direct quantitative determination of the free radical concentration is usually extremely difficult, particularly as the concentrations normally encountered are very small indeed. For this reason, the concentrations and rates of reaction are usually deduced from the rates of formation of stable intermediates, or of final products. In addition to the primary reaction between the radical and molecule in question, secondary reactions (between the radicals resulting from the primary reaction and other molecules) also take place.

These difficulties make determination of the activation energies of radical reactions so troublesome that it has so far only been undertaken in a limited number of cases—principally for the simplest radicals. For some of these, the activation energies are known with a fair degree of precision (0·5–1 kcal). In other cases, various

Table 5. * *Heat of reaction and activation energy for some elementary reactions of sodium atoms*

Reaction	q (kcal)	ε_0 (kcal)	Reference
$Na + CH_3Cl \rightarrow NaCl + CH_3$ . . .	14·5	10·2	[24]
$Na + CH_2Cl_2 \rightarrow NaCl + CH_2Cl$ . .	19·5	8·2	[24]
$Na + CHCl_3 \rightarrow NaCl + CCl_2H$ . .	24·5	6·2	[24]
$Na + CCl_4 \rightarrow NaCl + CCl_3$ . . .	29·1	5·0	[24]
$Na + C_2H_5Cl \rightarrow NaCl + C_2H_5$ . .	17	9·7	[10]
$Na + C_3H_7Cl \rightarrow NaCl + C_3H_7$ . .	20	9·0	[10]
$Na + (CH_3)_3CCl \rightarrow NaCl + (CH_3)_3C$.	22·5	8·0	[10]
$Na + CH_2{=}CH{-}CH_2Cl \rightarrow$			
$\quad NaCl + CH_2{=}CH{-}CH_2$	39·5	5·3	[10]
$Na + CH_2{=}CHCl \rightarrow NaCl + CH_2{=}CH$.	11	10·0	[10]
$Na + CH_3Br \rightarrow NaBr + CH_3$ . . .	20	5	[10]
$Na + C_2H_5Br \rightarrow NaBr + C_2H_5$ . .	22·7	4·9	[10]
$Na + C_6H_5Br \rightarrow NaBr + C_6H_5$ . .	16·7	4	[10]
$Na + CH_2{=}CHBr \rightarrow NaBr + CH_2{=}CH$.	17·7	5·8	[10]

* Note that the reactions of sodium with bromine derivatives of hydrocarbons usually proceed rapidly; in Fig. 2, page 27, the experimental points usually lie in the vicinity of the lower limit of the straight line 1. (The equations for these lines are given by $\varepsilon_0 = A - \alpha|q|$.) Data for reactions of sodium with iodides always lie considerably below the limits of the band defined by the lines 1 and 3.

authors give differing results for the same reaction, the discrepancies being as large as 2–3 kcal. Let us take, for example, the results of AVRAMENKO and LORENTSO [15–17] on the activation energies when OH radicals react with various molecules. They used the line spectra of OH, observed in absorption, to determine [OH] under steady-state conditions. (This method was developed by KONDRATIEV [23] and his school.) The basic principle of the method is that the rate constant may be deduced from the decrease in [OH] which takes place when the substance under investigation is introduced. The OH radicals are produced by passing a steady stream of water-vapour through a discharge. The greater the rate at which the molecules introduced react with the OH radicals, the greater will be the reduction in [OH]. [OH] is determined with the compound both present and absent. Since this method of observing the changes in [OH] is largely specific to OH, it is not subject to interference from other atoms (such as oxygen or hydrogen) which may be present.

To determine the rate constant of the reaction, use is made of the formula that makes allowance for the homogeneous and heterogeneous reactions of OH. The rate constant for the recombination reaction has been given by KONDRATIEV and ZISKIN [25], and also by SMITH [26]. At each temperature, the rate constant for the reaction between OH and the substance in question was determined, and the activation energy deduced from the temperature coefficient of the rate constant.

In this way, the absolute values of the rate constants and the energies of activation were obtained for the reactions of free OH with hydrogen and CO [17], with CH_4, C_2H_6, C_2H_4 and C_2H_2 [15], and with HCHO and CH_3CHO [16].

The applicability of the method is limited by the need to work at low pressures when the radicals are produced in discharges. Photochemical methods are free from this disadvantage, but the radical concentration is small when light of ordinary intensities is used. The production of very high concentrations of radicals within extremely short periods of time was demonstrated by NORRISH and PORTER [27, 28], using flash photolysis. The use of very high light intensities (10^{21} quanta in 1 msec) enabled them to obtain large photochemical effects in a time comparable with the lives of radicals or of excited states of molecules.

The general arrangements used in flash photolysis are as follows: a quartz reaction vessel is illuminated by a discharge of very high instantaneous power (10,000 joules dissipated in 0·1–3 msec), giving about 10^{21} quanta per msec. The intensity is sufficiently high to dissociate the gas almost completely into atoms and radicals. Subsequent to the exciting flash, absorption spectra are taken at intervals of 10–100 msec, to investigate the kinetics of the radical reactions. The absorption spectra of a number of radicals were discovered by flash photolysis; those of C_3, NH_2, C, CH, CN, CS, SO, and ClO being amongst them [29]. The most detailed studies were those of PORTER and WRIGHT [30] on the reactions of ClO. This radical was formed by combination of chlorine atoms with oxygen, apparently according to the following scheme:

(1) $\dot{C}l + O_2 \rightarrow ClO\dot{O}$
(2) $ClO\dot{O} + \dot{C}l \rightarrow 2ClO\dot{}$

The amount of ClO formed did not depend on T in the range 25–300° C.

The ClO radicals then react:

(3) $\text{Cl}\dot{\text{O}} + \text{Cl}\dot{\text{O}} \rightarrow \text{Cl}_2 + \text{O}_2$

PORTER and WRIGHT showed that (3) was of second order, with a rate constant:

$$k = 1 \cdot 2 \times 10^{-16} \exp\left[-\left(0 \pm 650\right)/RT\right] \text{ cm}^3/\text{mole-sec}$$

Such a small steric factor (10^{-6}) is unusual in radical reactions.

Using flash photolysis, CHRISTIE et al. [31] studied the influence of different inert gases on the recombination of iodine atoms; in these experiments, the iodine was about 80 per cent dissociated. They found that I_2 is extremely effective in causing iodine atoms to recombine (see Chapter 4).

Flash photolysis enables us to investigate the constants of elementary reactions, the kinetics of complex reactions, and to discover new radicals and the modes of formation of excited molecular states.

3. BOND DISSOCIATION ENERGIES

The difficulties encountered in determining heats of reaction for radicals are considerably greater than for molecules. Direct thermochemical determination is practically impossible in the vast majority of cases. The heat of reaction, q, is therefore calculated as the difference between the energy liberated in the formation of the new bonds in the products, and the dissociation energies of the bonds in the initial molecules. For instance, q in $\text{H} + \text{Cl}_2 \rightarrow \text{HCl} + \text{Cl} + q$, is equal to $Q_{\text{H--Cl}} - Q_{\text{Cl--Cl}}$, where Q is the dissociation energy of the corresponding bond. The Q-values for the Cl—Cl and H—Cl bonds are well known, being derived from spectroscopic and thermodynamic data, and are 57 kcal and 102 kcal respectively. Consequently, q is $102 - 57 = 45$ kcal. Unfortunately, such direct methods of determining the Q-values of bonds are only applicable in the simplest molecules. Even in a molecule as simple as methane, it is difficult to deduce the Q-values of the C—H bonds. It is not permissible to use mean values for the bond energies in this case (all that can be deduced from the heat of combustion). It is well known that the energy absorbed by the abstraction of the first hydrogen atom differs substantially from the mean bond dissociation energy for all four hydrogen atoms. $Q_{\text{C--H}}$ for the "first" hydrogen atom must be determined by direct experiment. A number of different methods have been applied (photobromination of methane, pyrolysis of methyl iodide, electron impact, etc.), and it has been shown that Q_{CH_3-H} is 101 ± 2 kcal; i.e. it is larger than the mean energy of the four C—H bonds in CH_4.*

Q_{C-H} for the "first" hydrogen atom in CH_4 may be determined as follows. When small quantities of CH_3Br (mixed with an inert carrier gas), are passed through a tube heated to a high temperature, methyl radicals and bromine atoms are the only primary decomposition products; these products, of course, immediately begin to react. It may reasonably be assumed that this decomposition does not have a potential barrier ($\varepsilon_0 \simeq 0$), so that the activation energy† determined from the pyrolysis of CH_3Br is directly equal to Q_{C-Br}. Experiments on these lines gave [33] $Q_{CH_3-Br} = 67$ kcal. Thus we have:

$$CH_3Br \rightarrow CH_3 + Br - 67 \text{ kcal}$$

Since Q_{Br-Br} is $45 \cdot 2$ kcal, this may be written as:

$$CH_3Br \rightarrow CH_3 + \tfrac{1}{2}Br_2 - 44 \cdot 4 \text{ kcal}$$

From published tables [34]‡ of the heats of formation of compounds from their elements, we find $\Delta H_{CH_3Br} = -8 \cdot 10$ kcal; for bromine vapour $\Delta H_{Br_2} = 7 \cdot 59$ kcal, or $\Delta H_{\frac{1}{2}Br_2} = 3 \cdot 80$ kcal. Then, $-8 \cdot 10 = x + 3 \cdot 80 - 44 \cdot 4$, where $x = \Delta H_{CH_3}$. $\Delta H_{CH_3} = 32 \cdot 5$ kcal. Knowing this, it is easy to calculate Q_{CH_3-H}. ΔH_{CH_4} is $-17 \cdot 89$ kcal, and ΔH_H is 51.90 kcal. Then:

$$Q_{CH_3-H} = \Delta H_{CH_3} + \Delta H_H - \Delta H_{CH_4} = 102 \cdot 3 \text{ kcal**}$$

And so the energy required to abstract the first hydrogen atom from methane is 102 kcal.

Knowing ΔH_{CH_3}, Q_{C-C} in ethane may be evaluated, from $\Delta H_{C_2H_6}$. The dissociation energies of the C—Br bonds in CH_3Br, CH_2Br_2,

---

* If we take the heat of sublimation of carbon as 171 kcal, the value now commonly used [32], instead of 150 kcal (the value employed throughout this book), then the mean energy of the C—H bonds in methane works out at $99 \cdot 7$ kcal: but it has no influence on the basic conclusions. Q_{C-H} for the first hydrogen atom is well known to be 101 kcal; similarly, Q_{C-H} in the CH radical is accurately known from spectroscopic data (80 kcal). The sum of the Q-values for the other two C—H bonds in CH_4 would then be 218 kcal; this is difficult to reconcile with the value derived from a series of investigations, using electron impact methods, which gives 170–180 kcal if these values can be considered as quite accurate. If the heat of sublimation of carbon is 150 kcal the mean energy of the C—H bonds in methane should be 94 kcal.

† The activation energy was determined directly from the rate constant, and not from its temperature dependence, assuming the pre-exponential factors to be the same ($2 \times 10^{13} \text{ sec}^{-1}$) for all the methyl halides.

‡ In all future calculations, we shall use the data given by KOROBOV and FROST [34].

** ΔH_{CH_3} is $31 \cdot 5$ kcal if Q_{CH_3-H} is taken as 101 kcal in accordance with the value now accepted.

CHBr$_3$ and CBr$_4$ have been determined from decomposition experiments [33], and from these we may deduce the ΔH values for CH$_2$Br, CHBr$_2$ and CBr$_3$, in a similar fashion; and thus arrive at Q_{C-H} in the corresponding bromides without recourse to direct experiment.

Consider, for instance, the reaction CH$_3$Br $\rightarrow$ CH$_2$Br + H. ΔH_{CH_3Br} and ΔH_H are known from the tables. Since ΔH_{CH_2Br} is computed from experimental data on the decomposition of CH$_2$Br$_2$, we may also compute Q_{C-H} for the first hydrogen atom in CH$_3$Br.

The examples given suffice to show that, by determining the dissociation energy of a given bond in a compound, we are able to deduce the energies of the other bonds in the compound (and even the bond dissociation energies in some other compounds) from the thermochemical values for the heats of formation of compounds from their elements.

The strengths of C—I bonds have been obtained by the pyrolysis of organic iodides. By methods analogous to that given above, the C—H bond energies in various hydrocarbons were calculated. POLANYI [1] obtained 102·5 kcal for Q_{CH_3-H} in this way.

The most exact determinations of the C—H bond energies in CH$_4$, C$_2$H$_6$, and (CH$_3$)$_4$C are those by KISTIAKOWSKY, et al. [22, 35–37] from their photobromination. The activation energies of the forward and reverse reactions (ε_1 and ε_1') were determined.

(1) RH + Br $\rightarrow$ R + HBr + q
(1') R + HBr $\rightarrow$ RH + Br

q in (1) was equal to the difference between the activation energies: $q = \varepsilon_1 - \varepsilon_1'$. On the other hand, $q = Q_{RH} - Q_{HBr}$. Consequently,

$$\varepsilon_1 - \varepsilon_1' = Q_{R-H} - Q_{H-Br}$$

$$Q_{R-H} = Q_{H-Br} + \varepsilon_1 - \varepsilon_1'$$

Q_{H-Br} is taken from the tables. For CH$_3$Br, $\varepsilon_1 = 18$ kcal, and $\varepsilon_1' = 2$ kcal. Hence $q = 18 - 2 = 16$ kcal, at $453°$ K, and 15 kcal at $0°$ K. $Q_{H-Br} = 85·8$ kcal, so $Q_{CH_3-H} = 85·8 + 15 \approx 101$ kcal.

Bond dissociation energies are determined by electron impact methods [38, 39], by pyrolysis in a stream of toluene (SZWARC [40]), and by the use of metallic mirrors (RICE and DOOLEY [41]) spectroscopically and recently by ionic impact [42].

Molecular dissociation due to collision with electrons is observed in electron impact studies. The basic principles of the method were established by FRANK [43]. KONDRATIEV [44] was the first to use the mass spectrometer for this purpose. The changes that occur as the electron energy is varied are followed by mass-spectrometric methods; so-called ionization curves are drawn up, i.e. curves showing the ion current for a particular species as a function of the electron energy. The electron energy at which the spectrometer begins to register that ion current is called the appearance potential. When the ion is formed without dissociation, the appearance potential is equal to the ionization potential. When an ion R_1^+ is formed by dissociation of the molecule R_1—R_2 via the process:

$$R_1\text{—}R_2 + e \rightarrow R_1^+ + R_2 + 2e \ (e \text{ being an electron})$$

the appearance potential may be expressed in the form:

$$A_{R_1^+} = Q_{R_1-R_2} + I_{R_1} + K + W$$

where $A_{R_1^+}$ is the appearance potential for R_1^+, $Q_{R_1-R_2}$ is the dissociation energy of the bond R_1—R_2, I_{R_1} is the ionization potential of the fragment R_1, K is the kinetic energy carried off by R_1^+ and R_2, and W is the excitation energy of R_1^+ and the fragment R_2. Determination of K is always difficult, and demands special experiments; its value is always inaccurate. W can be determined only in rare, very simple cases [38]. Therefore, the value of $Q_{R_1-R_2}$ is never very accurate, even if I_{R_1} is known from other data.

Q may be determined from the appearance potentials in two different processes, e.g.:
(1) $C_2H_6 + e \rightarrow C_2H_5^+ + H + 2e$ and
(2) $C_3H_8 + e \rightarrow C_2H_5^+ + CH_3 + 2e$
q in $C_2H_6 + CH_4 \rightarrow C_3H_8 + 2H + q$ being known from thermochemical data, Q_{CH_3-H} may be deduced if we neglect possible differences in K and W in (1) and (2).

This is possible if different pairs of processes of types (1) and (2) give consistent results. The best accuracy attained was ~ 2 kcal.

Data on the dissociation energies of molecules and ions can sometimes be obtained by the "ionic impact method" suggested by TALROSE and FRANKEVITCH [42] in 1956, dissociation energies being evaluated by comparing various ion–molecule reactions occurring in the mass spectrometer ion source at 10^{-3}–10^4 mm Hg. This method was used for reactions of the type

$$RH^+ + M \rightarrow MH^+ + R$$

accompanied by proton or H atom transfer. Such reactions have no activation energy [45] (see paragraph 11) and the mere fact that the mass-spectrometer records "secondary" ions shows that the heat of reaction is positive or 0 ± 2 kcal

$$Q = P_M - Q_{R-H} + I_{RH} - I_H \geqslant 0$$

where P_M is the affinity of M for the proton. If secondary MH^+ from the $RH^+ + M$ collision is not found $Q < 0$. Two such processes have been shown to be possible where $MH^+(Q \geqslant 0)$ is observed in one and not in the other $(Q < 0)$. A limiting value can then be assigned to the heat of reaction if all other quantities are known.

Thus TALROSE and FRANKEVITCH [42] have shown that H_3O^+ ions are observed in

$$H_2O + H_2S^+ \rightarrow H_3O^+ + HS$$

and not observed in

$$H_2O + C_2H_2^+ \rightarrow H_3O^+ + C_2H$$

This means that the first process is exothermic and the second endothermic and the affinity of a proton for a water molecule will be

$$(a) \qquad Q_{H-SH} - I_{H_2S} + I_H \leqslant P_{H_2O} < Q_{C_2H-H} - I_{C_2H_2} + I_H$$

Substituting numerical values for the dissociation energies and ionization potentials into (a) ($Q_{H-SH} = 95$ kcal, $I_{H_2S} = 10 \cdot 48$ eV, $I_H = 13 \cdot 59$ eV, $Q_{C_2H-H} = 121$ kcal, $J_{C_2H_2} = 11 \cdot 43$ eV) we get the upper and lower limits for P_{H_2O}

$$167 \text{ kcal} \leqslant P_{H_2O} < 171 \text{ kcal}$$

Thus the affinity of a water molecule for a proton, obtained experimentally for the first time, proved to be 169 ± 2 kcal, i.e. much lower than the calculated value of $188 \cdot 6$ kcal.

(a) also gives a lower limit for Q_{C_2H-H} as 117 kcal/mole [46].

It has been shown that the radicals formed by decomposition of the compound in the toluene carrier method [40] react considerably more rapidly with the toluene itself than with its reaction products. This is due to the comparative ease with which toluene donates a hydrogen atom; low-activity benzyl radicals are formed, which mainly combine to dibenzyl. When organic bromides are pyrolysed, the amounts of HBr and dibenzyl formed, which should be equivalent in amount, and the temperature coefficients of their yields, determine the activation energy for the decomposition. Since $\varepsilon = 0$ for the dimerization of radicals formed in the decomposition of parent substances, ε for the decomposition is equal to Q for dissociation of the compound.

The metallic-mirror technique [41] for determining Q-values is as follows. The organic compound is decomposed to radicals by passing it, at a pressure between $0 \cdot 2$ and 2 mm, through a furnace heated to $950-1200°$ C. The contact time is about 1 msec. At different distances from the furnace, antimony mirrors are deposited, and the time the radicals take to remove these is measured. By extrapolation, the time required for removal at the outlet of the furnace may be calculated. In this way the (relative) radical concentrations may be determined at different temperatures. ε for the decomposition (derived from these measurements) is then equal to Q. Activation energies measured in this way have an error of about ± 3 kcal.

Tables 6 and 8 [from SZWARC] give the bond dissociation energies for a variety of compounds. These data were obtained either directly, using the methods outlined above, or by calculation from the experimental data in conjunction with thermochemical ΔH values. Those values followed by asterisks were obtained indirectly, and are therefore unreliable. Table 7 gives the heats of formation for some atoms and radicals.

In 1952, SZWARC et al. [67, 68] gave Q_{C-Br} in bromobenzene as 70·9 kcal, from their measurements. Combining this with thermochemical ΔH values, reliable Q-values may be derived for many bonds of the type C_6H_5—R. For this purpose, we need to know ΔH for bromobenzene. Using the data of ZILBERMAN-GRANOVSKAYA and SHUGAM [75] on the latent heat of evaporation of bromobenzene, HARTLEY et al. [76] showed that the heat content of bromobenzene in the vapour phase is 23·2 kcal. The bond-dissociation energies in compounds of the type C_6H_5—R may then be evaluated, as $\Delta H_{C_6H_5Br}$ and the Q_{C-Br} in bromobenzene (71 kcal) and $\Delta H_{C_6H_5R}$ are known. The heat of formation of the phenyl radical should be calculated for this purpose.

$$\Delta H_{C_6H_5} = \Delta H_{C_6H_5Br} - \Delta H_{Br} + 71$$
$$= 23 \cdot 2 - 26 \cdot 7 + 71$$
$$= 67 \cdot 5 \text{ kcal*}$$

Some examples are given below:

(1) Q_{C-C} of the phenyl–phenyl bond in diphenyl:

$$C_6H_5-C_6H_5 \rightarrow 2C_6H_5 - Q_1$$
$$\Delta H_{C_6H_5-C_6H_5} = 2\Delta H_{C_6H_5} - Q_1$$
$$41 \cdot 3 = 2 \times 67 \cdot 5 - Q_1$$
$$Q_1 = 93 \cdot 7 \text{ kcal}$$

(2) $Q_{CH_3-C_6H_5}$ in toluene:

$$C_6H_5CH_3 \rightarrow C_6H_5 + CH_3 - Q_2$$

* SZWARC and WILLIAMS [68] use 25·4 kcal for $\Delta H_{C_6H_5Br}$; using this value, ΔH for phenyl becomes 70 kcal. All the bond energies calculated below would accordingly be increased by 2·5 kcal.

Table 6. Dissociation energies o

R' \ R''	H	CH_3	C_2H_5	$CH_2{=}CH$	$CH{\equiv}C$
CH_3 . . .	101	83	82	90*	110*
C_2H_5 . .	98	82	82	90	109*
$CH_2{=}CH$ . .	104*	90*	90*	101*	—
$CH{\equiv}C$ . .	121*	110*	109*	—	—
$n\text{-}C_3H_7$.	95	79	79	87*	106*
$iso\text{-}C_3H_7$.	89*	74·5*	75*	85*	109*
$CH_2{=}CH{-}CH_2$.	77	60	60·5	68·5*	—
$n\text{-}C_4H_9$.	94	78	78	86*	—
$(CH_3)_3C$ . .	85*	74*	73*	81*	—
$CH_2{=}C(CH_3)CH_2$.	76*	60*	60*	—	—
C_6H_5 . .	104*	91*	91*	101*	119*
$C_6H_5CH_2$ . .	77·5	63	62	—	—
$o\text{-}CH_3C_6H_4CH_2$.	74	58	58	—	—
$m\text{-}CH_3C_6H_4CH_2$.	77·5	62	62·5	—	—
$p\text{-}CH_3C_6H_4CH_2$.	75	60	60	—	—

R' \ R''	H	$C_6H_5CH_2$	Cl	Br	I
CH_3 . . .	101	63	80	66–67	54–55
C_2H_5 . .	98	62	80	65	51–52
$n\text{-}C_3H_7$ . .	95	59	77	—	50
$iso\text{-}C_3H_7$ . .	89*	54·5*	—	—	46
$n\text{-}C_4H_9$ . .	94	57·5*	—	—	—
$(CH_3)_3C$ . .	85*	—	75*	61*	~ 45*
$CH_2{=}CH$ . .	104*	—	86*	—	55*
$CH_2{=}CH{-}CH_2$ . .	77	—	58	48	35–37
CHO . .	79*	—	—	—	—
CH_3CO . .	85*	—	82*	67*	51*
C_6H_5 . .	104*	76·5*	88*	—	57*
$C_6H_5CH_2$ . .	77·5	47	—	50·5	39*

bonds (from SZWARC [40]), *in kcal*

n-C_3H_7	iso-C_3H_7	$CH_2=CH-CH_2$	n-C_4H_9	$tert$-C_4H_9	C_6H_5
79	74·5*	60	78	74*	91*
79	75*	60·5	78	73*	91*
87*	85*	68·5*	86*	81*	101*
106*	103*	—	—	—	119*
76	72*	57·5	75	70*	88*
72*	66·5*	54·5*	71*	65*	83*
57·5	54·5*	38	56·5	—	—
75	71*	56·5	74	69*	87*
70*	65*	—	69*	60*	78*
—	—	—	—	—	—
88*	83*	—	87*	78*	103*
59	54·5*	—	57·5	—	76·5*
—	—	—	—	—	—
—	—	—	—	—	—
—	—	—	—	—	—

OH	NH_2	CN	CHO	$COCH_3$	NO_2
90	79	105	71–75	77*	57
90	78	—	71*	77*	52
92	77	—	71*	77*	—
~90	—	—	—	73*	—
—	—	—	—	—	—
91*	76*	—	—	—	—
—	—	121*	84*	—	—
71	64*	92*	50*	—	—
96*	89*	—	—	59*	—
102*	98*	—	59*	60	—
107*	94*	124*	83*	—	—
73*	59	95*	—	63	—

The ΔH's for $C_6H_5CH_3$, C_6H_5, and CH_3 are 11·95, 67·5, and 32·5 kcal respectively.

$$\Delta H_{C_6H_5CH_3} = \Delta H_{C_6H_5} + \Delta H_{CH_3} - Q_2$$

$$Q_2 = 67·5 + 32·5 - 11·95$$

$$= 88 \text{ kcal}$$

(3) Q_{C-H} in benzene:

$$C_6H_6 \rightarrow C_6H_5 + H - Q_3$$

$$\Delta H_{C_6H_6} = \Delta H_{C_6H_5} + \Delta H_H - Q_3$$

From the tables, $\Delta H_{C_6H_6}$ and ΔH_H are 19·82 and 52·0 kcal respectively. Therefore, we have:

$$Q_3 = 67·5 + 52·0 - 19·82 = 99·7 \text{ kcal}$$

(4) $Q_{C_3H_7-C_6H_5}$ in propylbenzene:

$$C_6H_5CH_2CH_2CH_3 \rightarrow C_6H_5 + CH_2CH_2CH_3 - Q_4$$

Table 7. Heats of formation of atoms and radicals at 25° C, in kcal

Radical	ΔH_f	Reference	Radical	ΔH_f	Reference
H . . .	52	[32]	tert.-C_4H_9 . .	4·5	[40]
F . . .	18·3	[32]	CH_3O . .	− 0·5	[50]
Cl . . .	29	[32]	C_2H_5O . .	− 8·5	[50]
Br . . .	26·7	[32]	n-C_3H_7O . .	− 13	[50]
I . . .	25·5	[32]	iso-C_3H_7O . .	− 18	[50]
O . . .	59·2	[32]	n-C_4H_9O . .	− 17	[50]
OH . . .	8	[47]	iso-C_4H_9O . .	− 18	[50]
SH . . .	33	[48]	$sec.$-C_4H_9O .	− 20	[50]
S . . .	53·2	[32]	$tert.$-C_4H_9O .	− 25	[50]
CN . . .	92	[40]	$tert.$-$C_5H_{11}O$.	− 30	[50]
NO . . .	21·6	[32]	C_6H_5 . .	67·5	[2]
NO_2 . .	8·1	[32]	$C_6H_5CH_2$ . .	37·5	[40]
NH_2 . .	41	[40]	$CH_2{=}CH{-}CH_2$.	30·0	[40]
HO_2 . .	5	—	$CH_2{=}C(CH_3)CH_2$	20	[40]
CCl_3 . .	13·9	—	HCO . .	− 1·5	—
CF_3 . .	− 117 ± 2	[49]	CH_3CO . .	− 10·8	[51]
CH_3 . .	31·5	[40]	C_6H_5CO . .	15·6	[52]
C_2H_5 . .	26	—	$C_6H_5CHCH_3$.	∼ 30	[53]
n-C_3H_7 . .	18·2	[40]	$CH_3C_6H_4CHCH_3$.	∼ 21	[53]
iso-C_3H_7 . .	12·2	[40]	$C_6H_5C{<}^{CH_3}_{CH_3}$.	∼ 22	[53]
n-C_4H_9 . .	12·0	[40]	$C_6H_5CO_2$ . .	− 10	[54]

Table 8. *Dissociation energies of bonds*

Compound	Bond	Q (kcal)	Reference
CCl₃Br	C—Br	49·0	[33, 55]
CBr₄	C—Br	49·0	[33]
CHBr₃	C—Br	55·5	[33]
CHCl₂Br	C—Br	53·5	[33]
CH₂Br₂	C—Br	62·5	[33]
CH₃Br	C—Br	67·5	[33]
CF₃Br	C—Br	64·0	[33]
(C₆H₅)₃C—C(C₆H₅)₃	C—C	11·0	[56]
C₆H₅CH₂—CH₂CH₃	C—C	57·5	[57]
C₆H₅CH₂—CH₃	C—C	63·2	[58]
C₆H₅CH₂—CH₂CH₂CH₃	C—C	65·0	[59]
C₆H₅CH₂—H	C—H	77·5	[57]
CH₃CO—COCH₃	C—C	60	[60]
C₆H₅CH₂—CH₂C₆H₅	C—C	47	[60]
C₆H₅CH₂—Br	C—Br	50·0	[61]*
CH₂=CH—CH₂Br	C—Br	47·5	[61]
C₆H₅CH₂NH₂	C—N	59·0	[63]
H₂N—NH₂	N—N	60·0	[64]
(CH₃)₃CO—OC(CH₃)₃	O—O	36·0	[65]
C₆H₅COBr	C—Br	57·0	[66]
β-C₁₀H₇Br	C—Br	70·0	[67]
α-C₁₀H₇Br	C—Br	70·9	[67]
C₆H₅Br	C—Br	70·9	[67, 68]
9-Bromophenanthrene	C—Br	67·7	[67]
9-Bromoanthracene	C—Br	65·6	[67]
n-C₃H₇SH	C—S	71·4	[69]
H₂S	S—H	92·2	[69]
CH₄	C—H	101·4	[70]
CH₃	C—H	85·3	[70]
CH₂	C—H	89·9	[70]
CH	C—H	80	[70]
CF₄	C—F	123 ± 2	[49]
CF₄	C—F	116	[71]
CF₃H	C—H	103 ± 4	[49]
CF₃Cl	C—Cl	83 ± 3	[49]
CF₃I	C—I	57 ± 4	[49]
CF₃CH₃	C—C	90	[49]
CF₃CF₃	C—C	97	[49]
CHCl₃	C—H	88·9 ± 3	[49]
CCl₃F	C—F	102 ± 7	[49]
CCl₄	C—Cl	67·9	[49]
CH₃SH	C—S	70	[71]
C₂H₅SH	C—S	69	[71]
tert-C₄H₉SH	C—S	65	[71]

* $Q_{C_6H_5CH_2—Br}$ given by LOSSING, INGOLD, and HENDERSON [62] is 44·7 ± 3 kcal.

Table 8.—continued

Compound	Bond	Q (kcal)	Reference
CH_3SCH_3	C—S	73	[71]
$C_2H_5SC_2H_5$	C—S	69	[71]
CH_3ONO	O—N	36·4	[72]
C_2H_5ONO	O—N	37·7	[72]
C_3H_7ONO	O—N	37·7	[72]
iso-C_3H_7ONO	O—N	37·0	[72]
n-C_4H_9ONO	O—N	37·0	[72]
iso-C_3H_7Cl	C—Cl	73·3	[73]
iso-C_3H_7Br	C—Br	58·8	[73]
iso-C_3H_7I	C—I	42·4	[73]
$CH\equiv C—CH_2Br$	C—Br	57·9	[73]
$CH\equiv C—CH_2I$	C—I	45·7	[73]
p-Fluorobromobenzene	C—Br	70·4	[74]
p-Chlorobromobenzene	C—Br	70·3	[74]
m-Chlorobromobenzene	C—Br	69·9	[74]
o-Chlorobromobenzene	C—Br	69·7	[74]
p-Dibromobenzene	C—Br	70·6	[74]
o-Dibromobenzene	C—Br	69·1	[74]
p-Bromotoluene	C—Br	70·7	[74]
m-Bromotoluene	C—Br	70·7	[74]
o-Bromotoluene	C—Br	70·1	[74]
p-Bromodiphenyl	C—Br	70·7	[74]
m-Bromodiphenyl	C—Br	70·1	[74]
o-Bromodiphenyl	C—Br	68·2	[74]
p-Bromophenyl cyanide . . .	C—Br	70·6	[74]
m-Bromophenyl cyanide . . .	C—Br	70·1	[74]
o-Bromophenyl cyanide . . .	C—Br	70·3	[74]
p-Bromophenol	C—Br	67·0	[74]
o-Bromophenol	C—Br	67·1	[74]
3-Bromopyridine	C—Br	75·9	[74]
2-Bromopyridine	C—Br	71·5	[74]
2-Bromothiophene	C—Br	68·5	[74]

From the tables, $\Delta H_{C_6H_5C_3H_7} = 1·87$ kcal, $\Delta H_{C_6H_5} = 67·5$ and $\Delta H_{n\text{-}C_3H_7} = 18·2$ kcal, therefore we have:

$$Q_4 = \Delta H_{C_6H_5} + \Delta H_{C_3H_7} - \Delta H_{C_6H_5C_3H_7}$$

$$= 67·5 + 18·2 - 1·87 \text{ kcal}$$

$$\simeq 84 \text{ kcal}$$

The results of the calculations set out above are tabulated in Table 9; some values calculated by VOEVODSKII from SZWARC's data on Q_{C-Br} values and from thermochemical data are given; these relate to Q_{C-H} values in bromomethanes. Q_{C-H} values cannot be calculated for chloromethanes, since ΔH for CH_2ClBr is not known. From the data of Table 8, it follows that replacement of H by Br in the bromomethanes changes Q_{C-Br} by the same amount in each case. The Q_{C-H} and Q_{C-Cl} values given in Table 9 were calculated by VOEVODSKII, on the assumption that the same gradation in bond energies also obtains in the chloromethanes.

Table 9. Bond dissociation energies

Compound	Bond	Q_{C-H} (kcal)	Q_{C-Cl} (kcal)
CH_3Br	C—H	95·2	—
CH_2Br_2	C—H	87·7	—
$CHBr_3$	C—H	80·2	—
CH_3Cl	C—H; C—Cl	97·4	83·5
CH_2Cl_2	C—H; C—Cl	93·2	78·5
$CHCl_3$	C—H; C—Cl	89	73·5
CCl_4	C—Cl	—	68·4
$C_6H_5-C_6H_5$ . . .	C—C	94·5	—
$C_6H_5-CH_3$ . . .	C—C	87·5	—
C_6H_6	C—H	99	—
$C_6H_5-CH_2CH_2CH_3$ . .	C—C	84·6	—

The accuracy of the bond energies thus obtained depends on the accuracy of the kinetic measurements and on that of the published ΔH values. Usually the kinetic measurements are carried out with an accuracy of 1–2 kcal.* From the calculated error of the thermochemical measurements, the error in Q may be shown to be 2–3 kcal.

---

* The Q-values for bonds, determined by direct experiment, are sometimes given widely different values by various authors; the differences may be as large as 4–5 kcal. For example, Q_{C-H} for the CH_3 groups of propane is given as 99–100 kcal by STEVENSON [69] and LEIGH and SZWARC [59], but as 95 kcal by BUTLER and POLANYI [1] (see Table 6). The bond energies $Q_{(CH_3)_2CH-H}$ and $Q_{(CH_3)_3C-H}$ are correspondingly increased. COTTRELL [77] also uses a high value for Q_{C-H} in C_3H_8 and isobutane and judging by these experiments considers this value as being quite correct. However, we think that this is not yet fully proved. From the theoretical point of view, it is not clear why Q_{C-H} in propane is greater than that in ethane. A decision on the true value of the bond energy can finally only be made from fresh experimental data. It should be noted, however, that the value 95 kcal is in close agreement with qualitative concepts in chemical kinetics and reactivity. For the sake of uniformity, we will use BUTLER and POLANYI's data [1] in this book.

Table 10. *Dissociation energies of bonds, obtained from spectroscopic data and from dissociation constants*

Compound						Bond	Q kcal	Reference
H_2 .	.	.	.	.	.	H—H	103·2	[78–79]
HD	.	.	.	.	.	H—D	104·05	[80]
D_2 .	.	.	.	.	.	D—D	105·02	[80]
O_2 .	.	.	.	.	.	O=O	117·96	[81]
OH	.	.	.	.	.	O—H	103	[82]
N_2 .	.	.	.	.	.	N≡N	225·09	[83]
NO	.	.	.	.	.	N=O	149·6	[83]
CO .	.	.	.	.	.	C=O	256	[83]
F_2 .	.	.	.	.	.	F—F	37·6	[84]
Cl_2 .	.	.	.	.	.	Cl—Cl	57·2	[78–79]
Br_2 .	.	.	.	.	.	Br—Br	45·4	[78–79]
I_2 .	.	.	.	.	.	I—I	35·5	[78–79]
ClBr	.	.	.	.	.	Cl—Br	52	[78–79]
ClI .	.	.	.	.	.	Cl—I	49·8	[78–79]
BrI	.	.	.	.	.	Br—I	42	[78–79]
S_2 .	.	.	.	.	.	S=S	83	[85]
SO .	.	.	.	.	.	S=O	119	[85]
P_2 .	.	.	.	.	.	P≡P	116	[78–79]
P_2 .	.	.	.	.	.	P—P	48	[77]
HF .	.	.	.	.	.	H—F	134	[78–79]
HCl	.	.	.	.	.	H—Cl	102	[78–79]
HBr	.	.	.	.	.	H—Br	86·5	[78–79]
HI .	.	.	.	.	.	H—I	70·5	[78–79]
Li_2 .	.	.	.	.	.	Li—Li	25	[78–79]
Na_2 .	.	.	.	.	.	Na—Na	17·5	[78–79]
K_2 .	.	.	.	.	.	K—K	11·8	[78–79]
NaCl	.	.	.	.	.	Na—Cl	97·5	[79]
NaBr	.	.	.	.	.	Na—Br	87·7	[79]
NaI	.	.	.	.	.	Na—I	70·7	[79]
NaH	.	.	.	.	.	Na—H	47	[78–79]
Se_2 .	.	.	.	.	.	Se=Se	65	[86]
Te_2 .	.	.	.	.	.	Te=Te	53	[86]
H_2O	.	.	.	.	.	H—OH	116	[79]
HO_2	.	.	.	.	.	H—O_2	47	[87]
H_2O_2	.	.	.	.	.	H—HO_2	89·5	[87]
NH .	.	.	.	.	.	N—H	88	[88]
NH_2	.	.	.	.	.	N—H	88	[88]
NH_3	.	.	.	.	.	N—H	100–104	[63–64]
N_2O_4	.	.	.	.	.	N—N	10·2	[89]
ONO	.	.	.	.	.	O—N	72	[77]
ClO_2	.	.	.	.	.	Cl—O_2	4·3	own calculation
$(CN)_2$	.	.	.	.	.	C—N	112	[77]
HgH	.	.	.	.	.	Hg—H	8·6	[78, 77]

Table 10.—*continued*

Compound	Bond	Q (kcal)	Reference
HgCl	Hg—Cl	23	[78, 79]
HgCl$_2$	ClHg—Cl	81	[90]
HgBr	Hg—Br	17	[78–79]
HgBr$_2$	BrHg—Br	72	[91]
HgI	Hg—I	7	[78–79]
HgI$_2$	IHg—I	60	[77]
Hg$_2$·	Hg—Hg	3·2	[92]
NOCl	N—Cl	36	[91]
NOBr	N—Br	28	[91]
Hg(CH$_3$)$_2$·	Hg—C	52·1	[93]
Hg(C$_2$H$_5$)$_2$	Hg—C	41·5	[93]

The bond-dissociation energies given in Table 10 are derived from basic optical data, as well as from measured equilibrium constants of dissociation.

The bond dissociation energies are of very great interest in theoretical chemistry in connexion with structural theories. They are a quantitative measure of the mutual influence of atoms, which as we shall see below, is quite large. For instance, while Q_{C-H} in CH_4 is 101 kcal, in the CH_3 groups of long-chain n-alkanes it is 93–94 kcal. For the CH_2 groups in these alkanes the value becomes 88 kcal, and for tertiary C—H bonds in alkanes it is reduced to 86 kcal.

Q_{C-H} in ethane is 98 kcal, but in acetaldehyde, for the –CHO group, it becomes 80–84 kcal. This reduction in Q_{C-H} arises from the addition of the oxygen atom. Q_{C-Br} in n-C_3H_7Br is about 60 kcal, while Q_{C-Br} for the same group in allyl bromide, $CH_2BrCH{=}CH_2$ is 47 kcal. This reduction is due to the double bond in the α-position.

The same effect on Q_{C-H} may be found in CH_3 groups which are α with respect to a double bond. Q_{C-H} for a CH_3 group in propane is 95 kcal, but Q_{C-H} for the CH_3 group in propylene is 77 kcal.

The presence of a benzene ring also reduces Q_{C-H} in CH_3 groups. Thus, in toluene Q_{C-H} for the "first" hydrogen atom in the methyl group is 77·5 kcal, while Q_{C-H} in ethane is 98 kcal. The following curious result is then obtained: the presence of a large system of conjugated bonds, as in the benzene nucleus, has the same effect on Q_{C-H} in a CH_3 group as does the single double bond in propylene.

Q_{C-H} in CH_3Br is 95 kcal; in CH_2Br_2 it is 88 kcal; and in $CHBr_3$ it is reduced to 80 kcal. In this case, the reduction in Q is a quantitative indication of the influence of bromine on the bond strengths. It is interesting to observe that each fresh bromine atom introduced reduces Q by the same amount (about 7 kcal), while the corresponding value for chlorine is 4 kcal.

By analysing the influence of fluorine on the dissociation energies of a number of different bonds, VEDENEEV and PURMALYA (Institute of Chemical Physics, Moscow) were able to evaluate Q_{CH_3-F}. Lack of data as to ΔH_{CH_3F} prevented Q_{C-F} being calculated by thermochemical methods. Electron impact gave Q_{CH_3-F} as 107 ± 12 kcal [94]. The large error in Q_{CH_3-F} is due to the determination of the appearance potential of $CH_3{}^+$ from CH_3F being inaccurate.

Table 11*

Bond	Q (kcal)	Method of determination	ΔH_{CF_3} (kcal)	Q_{calc} (kcal)	Reference
1	2	3	4	5	6
CF_3—H	102 ± 2	Electron impact	-119	103	[49]
	103	Pyrolysis of acetone-d_6 in presence of CF_3H	-118	—	[95]
CF_3—F	123 ± 2	Electron impact	-113	118	[49]
CF_3—Cl	80 ± 2	From difference of activation energy in the reactions $Na + CF_3Cl$ and $Na + CH_3Cl$	-120	82	[96]
CF_3—Br	$64{\cdot}5 \pm 3$	Pyrolysis of CF_3Br	—	—	[33]
CF_3—I	57 ± 4	Electron impact	—	—	[49]

* The appearance potential of $CF_3{}^+$ was measured using CF_3Cl, CF_3Br, and CF_3I in reference [49]. However, the authors consider these values unreliable, and do not use them in calculating the corresponding bond dissociation energies. Q_{CF_3-I} was determined from the appearance potential of I^+.

Q_{CH_3-F} may be calculated as follows. Consider the data given in the second column of Table 11. ΔH for CF_3H, CF_4, and CF_3Cl are given as -169 kcal [49]†, -218 ± 2 kcal [97], and -171 ± 1 kcal [97] respectively.

† ΔH_{CF_3H} in [49] is referred to as being from a personal communication.

These may be used to calculate ΔH_{CF_3}. The calculated values are given in the fourth column of Table 11. Taking into account the errors in Q-values and also the errors in the ΔH values used, the values of ΔH_{CF_3} may be considered as in satisfactory agreement. Taking -118 kcal for ΔH_{CF_3}, the values of Q_{CF_3-X} obtained are given in column 5 of Table 11.

These latter, taken in conjunction with some other experimental bond dissociation energies [77], enable us to perform some interesting comparisons (see Table 12).

Table 12

$Q_{R_F-X} - Q_{R_H-X}$	ΔQ (kcal)
$Q_{CF_3-H} - Q_{CH_3-H}$ . . .	$+1$
$Q_{CF_3-Cl} - Q_{CH_3-Cl}$ . . .	$+1$
$Q_{CF_3-Br} - Q_{CH_3-Br}$ . . .	-2.5
$Q_{CF_3-I} - Q_{CH_3-I}$ . . .	$+4.0$
$Q_{p-FC_6H_4-Br} - Q_{C_6H_5-Br}$ . .	-0.5
$Q_{o-fluoroC_6H_4CH_2-H} - Q_{C_6H_5CH_2-H}$.	$+0.5$
$Q_{p-fluoroC_6H_4CH_2-H} - Q_{C_6H_5CH_2-H}$.	$+0.5$
$Q_{m-fluoroC_6H_4CH_2-H} - Q_{C_6H_5CH_2-H}$.	$+0.5$

Allowing for the errors in the determinations, it is clear that replacing hydrogen by fluorine makes no difference in practice to the strength of the bond.*

It is therefore clear why no material change in the activation energy was found when the compounds CF_3Cl, CF_2HCl, CFH_2Cl, and CH_3Cl were treated with sodium atoms [103]. This fact may be used to deduce Q_{CH_3-F} very simply. It follows that it should be equal to Q_{CF_3-F}, i.e. 118 kcal, or perhaps 1–2 kcal lower.

Thus C—F bonds in F-substituted hydrocarbons should be stronger than corresponding C—H bonds by about 15–17 kcal.

Results contradicting the above statement that Q_{C-X} in practice does not vary on replacing H by F can be found in literature.

---

* The discrepancy between the experimental values for Q_{C-H} in the CH_3 groups of propane was noted above. This value was determined by electron impact, together with data from the pyrolysis of n-C_3H_7I, and by the toluene carrier method. It is not possible to calculate this quantity from the photobromination of propane, since this bromination yields primarily *iso*propyl bromide. It would be interesting to study the bromination of $CH_3CF_2CH_3$. The strength of the bond is not changed by substituting fluorine for hydrogen, but bromination only takes place in the methyl groups.

For instance COTTRELL [77] gives $Q_{CF_3-CF_3}$ and $Q_{CF_3-CH_3}$ as 124 and 117 kcal respectively, while observing that they seem to be too high. These values were calculated by DIBELER et al. [98] from mass-spectrometric determination of the CF_3^+ and CH_3^+ appearance potentials using C_2F_6 and CF_3CH_3. The ionization potential of CF_3 was calculated from the above data and found to be 8·8 eV. They [99] ascribe a too high value (143 kcal) to Q_{CF_3-F}. To calculate Q_{CF_3-F}, DIBELER et al. determined A_{CF_3} for the following compounds

Compound	CF_4	CF_3Cl	CF_3Br	CF_3I
$A_{CF_3^+}$ (eV)	16·0	12·7	12·2	11·4

However, in calculating Q_{CF_3-F} they did not use their 1952 value for $I_{CF_3^+}$ but preferred to make the calculation from $Q_{CF_3-Cl} \approx 80$ kcal and $Q_{CF_3-Br} \approx 65$ kcal (Table 11) and the corresponding A_{CF_3}. They found that $I_{CF_3^+}$ was 9·3 eV. Q_{CF_3-F} was calculated from this to be 143 kcal.*

However it is easy to show that there is a thermochemical contradication in $Q_{CF_3-Cl} \approx 80$ kcal and $Q_{CF_3-F} = 143$ kcal. ΔH for CF_3Cl and CF_4 are -171 kcal and -228 kcal. If we start from $Q_{CF_3-Cl} \approx 80$ kcal, ΔH_{CF_3} should be ≈ 120 kcal. Further calculation of Q_{CF_3-F} gives 116 kcal, a value much lower than 143 kcal. Direct mass-spectrometric determination of $A_{CF_3^+}$ also gave 10·1 eV as compared with DIBELER's 1952 value of 8·8 eV.

All this shows that DIBELER's appearance potentials are not very accurate and the calculated values of $Q_{CF_3-CF_3}$, $Q_{CF_3-CH_3}$ and Q_{CF_3-F} cannot be considered as reliable.

4. THE CORRELATION OF ACTIVATION ENERGIES WITH HEATS OF REACTION

We now return to the discussion of Tables 1–5. In Fig. 2, the data from these tables are plotted as graphs of ε_0 vs. q; all reactions are included except those involving halogen atoms, the reaction $H + H_2 \rightarrow H_2 + H$ and analogous reactions with deuterium. The striking fact emerges that almost all the points lie within a band defined by the two parallel straight lines $\varepsilon_0 = 10 - \alpha q$ (line 1) and $\varepsilon_0 = 12·7 - \alpha q$ (line 2), where $\alpha \simeq 0·23$. Comparatively few points lie above the upper line; these fall in the band between lines 2 and 3, the equation for line 3 being $\varepsilon_0 = 13·6 - \alpha q$. The scatter of the points arise from the experimental errors (1–2 kcal) and is connected with certain variations of A in the equation for these few compounds.

* Allowing 0·5 eV as kinetic energy.

If the errors in ε_0 (1–2 kcal) and in q (2–3 kcal) are taken into consideration, it may be assumed that all reactions for which the points lie between lines 1 and 2 on Fig. 2 will be in agreement with the following approximate relationship:

$$\varepsilon_0 = 11\!\cdot\!5 - 0\!\cdot\!25|q|$$

For exothermic reactions, this becomes $\varepsilon_0 = 11\!\cdot\!5 - 0\!\cdot\!25q$ and for endothermic reactions, $\varepsilon_0 = 11\!\cdot\!5 + 0\!\cdot\!75q$.

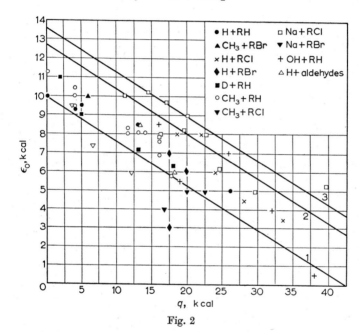

Fig. 2

This equation applies to reactions of radicals such as H, Na, CH_3, and OH with a variety of molecules, e.g. with derivatives of methane (including chloromethanes and bromomethanes), aldehydes, ethylene, and propylene. In other words, the reactivities in these diverse reactions are all determined by the energies of formation and rupture of the bonds. The bond energies depend essentially on the structures of the reactants. The direct connexion between structure and reactivity is thus made clear.

EVANS and POLANYI [100] were the first to demonstrate the existence of the relationship $\Delta\varepsilon_0 = -\alpha\Delta q$ for exothermic reactions.

They discussed it from a theoretical point of view and checked it later from reactions between atomic Na and homologous hydrocarbons. The relationship found was similar to

$$\varepsilon_0 = A - \alpha q \tag{4}$$

where A is a constant for a given homologous series. However, at that time (1938) insufficient data were available for the general validity of the equation to be verified.

BAGDASARYAN [101] and TIKHOMIROVA and VOEVODSKII [102] improved these concepts considerably, and verified formula (4) for a range of experimental values. The reactions of a given radical with a homologous series of compounds were studied; e.g. TIKHIMIROVA and VOEVODSKII [102] compared the reactions of CH_3 with alkanes, and the reactions of sodium atoms with chloromethanes, etc. In this way they showed that (4) was always satisfied, but that the values of A and α were different for the differing series. A ranged from 10 to 15, and α from 0·2–0·4. Since the accuracies of ε_0 and q were low, however, and the number of points in any given case only covered a small range q, the values of A and α given by TIKHIMIROVA and VOEVODSKII are not completely reliable. Fig. 2 therefore appears to us a more convincing way to plot the various values of ε_0 and q, since, within the limits of error of experiment, they fall close to the same straight line for a large range of q-values.

It is not asserted, however, that if ε_0 and q were more accurately known, A and α would still be the same for different homologous series. It is only supposed that A and α would not be greatly altered by the use of more accurate data; and that, to a first approximation, we may regard them as being constant for the purpose of illustrating the general relation of ε_0 to q.

It should be appreciated that the supposed relationship between ε_0 and q is still regarded as an hypothesis, since the number of reactions studied is still very small. However, some deviations from this empirical rule are already apparent, e.g. reactions involving halogen atoms, for which a similar relation does not appear to apply. If such a relation does apply to the halogen-atom reactions, the values of the A's must certainly be appreciably lower than those given above. It is also possible that similar exceptions will be found for some other strongly electronegative radicals.

In conclusion, it should be once again noted that (4) is only approximate. Negative values of ε_0 are meaningless but (4) would predict their occurrence for sufficiently large q. It also seems likely that ε_0 will not be given accurately when $q = 0$.

In the main, theoretical considerations do not lead to exactly the formula given. They only give a qualitative statement that ε_0 will fall as the absolute value of q, $|q|$, increases, for some range of values of q. This follows from a very simple treatment. The activation energy of $\dot{A}_1 + A_2A_3 \rightarrow A_1A_2 + \dot{A}_3$ is determined to a first approximation by the ordinate of the point where the curve for the repulsion between $\dot{A}_1$ and A_2A_3 cuts the curve for the attraction between $\dot{A}_2$ and $\dot{A}_3$ in A_2A_3. If the heat of reaction is zero, then the curves of attraction and repulsion may be as in Fig. 3, where the

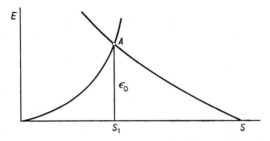

Fig. 3. Potential curve intersection for a thermally neutral reaction

potential energy E is plotted as ordinate and the "reaction co-ordinate" as abscissa; the curves then cross at some point A.

The ordinate at A is approximately equal to ε_0. If there is a heat of reaction q, then the curves will be as shown in Fig. 4. This change in the relative positions of the curves leads to a reduction in ε_0, this reduction being larger, the greater the value of q.

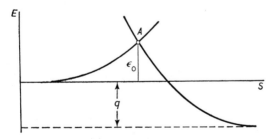

Fig. 4. Potential curves for a reaction with a non-zero q

As in the discussion of the linear relation between ε_0 and q, the principal assumption is that, in passing from one substance to another, the curves will only be altered as regards the co-ordinate q. In reality there is a simultaneous change in the co-ordinate S, so the above argument only represents a first rough approximation to the actual state of affairs.

As to what determines the difference in reactivity of radicals in their interactions with various molecules, or with different bonds in the same molecule, this might perhaps be one of the most fundamental problems in the theory of chemical transformations. Is the difference determined by the magnitude of A, or by the magnitude of q? In fact, both these quantities are important. At present, the changes in A between radical reactions are obscure. The connexion between ε and q is somewhat better understood. Methods of determining these quantities have been established, and their relationship defined. It is quite clear that differences between the heats of reaction with the various bonds determine to some extent the course of the reaction and the nature of the products. The question then reduces to a consideration of the magnitude of the changes in A. As Fig. 2 shows, A does not change considerably from one reaction to another, and allowing for experimental errors it is permissible to develop chemical kinetics from an approximate hypothesis as to the constancy of A and from the known effect of q on the course that the reaction will take. This is one of the basic assumptions in this book. Results obtainable from this approach are in agreement with qualitative kinetic data. However, it is essential to extend the range of experimental data in order to determine to what degree the assumptions agree with quantitative kinetic experiments in organic chemistry.

Only after the subject has been carefully studied will it be possible to discover discrepancies and inconsistent features, and thus to elucidate the role of A. This should also indicate which physical and chemical properties influence A, and thus enable one to establish the connexion between reactivity and structure. A serious lack of data on heats of reaction and activation energies also exists for ionic reactions; these reactions are also involved in a very wide range of chemical changes, as are radical reactions. We shall try to illustrate the possible influence of the chemical structure on A in Section 11.

5. RADICAL AND MOLECULAR ACTIVITIES

We consider now the substitution reactions of a series of different radicals R_1, R_2, R_3, R_4, etc., with some given compound $R'X$, where R' and X are any radicals.

$$R_1 + R'X \rightarrow R_1X + R' + q_1'$$
$$R_2 + R'X \rightarrow R_2X + R' + q_2'$$
$$. \quad . \quad . \quad . \quad . \quad . \quad . \quad . \quad . \quad . \quad . \quad .$$
$$R_i + R'X \rightarrow R_iX + R' + q_i'$$

(5)

The series R_1, R_2, R_3 is chosen such that all the R_i have their free valence attached to one and the same element, e.g. to carbon in one series, to oxygen in another, etc.

The q-values are given by $q_i' = Q_i - Q'$, where $Q_i = Q_{R_i-X}$ and $Q' = Q_{R'-X}$. If $q_1' > q_2' > \ldots > q_i'$, then it follows from (4) that $\varepsilon_1' < \varepsilon_2' < \ldots < \varepsilon_i'$; consequently if the series R_1, R_2, R_3, R_4 is arranged in order of decreasing q, it is evidently also arranged in order of decreasing chemical activity. The activity of a radical may thus be characterized by its heat of reaction with some standard molecule $R'X$.

It is convenient to consider relative rather than absolute activities, by comparing the activity of the radical in question with that of some standard radical. In the case of radicals in which the free valence is attached to a carbon atom, we shall in what follows always take CH_3 as the standard radical (R_1). As a measure of the relative activity of the radical R_i we may take the difference $q_i' - q_1'$, which serves to define the difference in the activation energies $\varepsilon_1' - \varepsilon_i'$. The latter determines the relative rate of the reaction between $R'X$ and R_i as compared with that of the standard radical R_1 (if the pre-exponential factors are equal):

$$\frac{R_i}{R_1} = \frac{\exp\left(-\varepsilon_i'/RT\right)}{\exp\left(-\varepsilon_1'/RT\right)}$$

The difference $q_i' - q_1' = Q_i - Q_1 = L_i$ is the heat of the reaction

$$R_i + R_1X \rightarrow R_iX + R_1 + L_i \tag{6}$$

By computing the heat of reaction from bond dissociation energies we can obtain L_i, which is characteristic of the relative activity of R_i. The relative activity of R_i will be smaller the smaller L_i.*

Such estimates of radical activities are of material interest only if they are peculiar to the radicals, and do not depend, in a first approximation, on the properties of $R'X$. It is clear from (6) that L_i does not depend on the properties of R', since R' does not appear

---

* It is important to remember that activities determined in this way depend upon the assumption that A and α in (4) change only slightly. We suppose that any change in these will be relatively small; this supposition is justified in many instances by the observations that the quantitative aspects of various radical activities correspond with their experimental kinetic behaviour. Apart from this, the activity so defined will depend upon the pre-exponential factors being equal, i.e. upon all changes being in ε alone. Only in some uncommon instances, such as substitution reactions, are the pre-exponential factors greatly altered. For example, STEACIE et al. [3, 4, 5] demonstrated that the pre-exponential factors were low in a series of reactions of hydrocarbons with CH_3 and H atoms. However, we consider these low values to be not very reliable.

in the reaction used to determine L_i. But it is not clear that L_i does not depend on the properties of X in R_1X. On the contrary, it follows from current ideas in theoretical organic chemistry that L_i must depend on the nature of the substituent X. However, it has been shown experimentally, at least in the cases we have investigated, that if L_i does depend on X, the effect must be very small, and lie within the limits of ± 2 kcal. Consequently, we may assert that, to a first approximation, L_i does not depend on the nature of X, and is a measure of the activity of R_i; it is defined solely by the properties of R_i, and its interest to theoretical chemistry stems from the latter fact.

We may now investigate the activities of various molecules R_1X, R_2X, R_3X, . . . R_iX as shown in their reactions with some given radical R':

$$R' + R_1X \rightarrow R'X + R_1 - q_1'$$
$$R' + R_2X \rightarrow R'X + R_2 - q_2'$$
$$\cdot \quad \cdot \quad \cdot \quad \cdot \quad \cdot \quad \cdot \quad \cdot \quad \cdot \quad \cdot \quad \cdot \quad \cdot \quad \cdot \tag{7}$$
$$R' + R_iX \rightarrow R'X + R_i - q_i'$$

Since these reactions are the reverse of those in (5), their heats of reaction will be the same in absolute magnitude as those of (5), but with the signs reversed. The relative activity of R_iX, as compared with that of R_1X, will be given by $-(q_i' - q_1') = -L_i$.

The relative activity of R_i will be smaller, the smaller L_i. The relative activity of R_iX will be smaller the lower $-L_i$, i.e. the greater L_i. If we arrange the R_i in a series descending with respect to L_i, i.e. in a series in which the activities of R_1, R_2, R_3, . . . R_i diminish in sequence, R_1X, R_2X, R_3X, . . ., R_iX will be arranged in ascending order of activity. So the greater the activity of R_i, the lower will be the activity of R_iX; this relation is independent of the nature of X.

To conclude these general remarks, we may observe that in exothermic reactions ($\varepsilon_0 = A - 0.25q$) a change of 4 kcal in L_i produces a change in ε_0 of about 1 kcal. So if L_i changes by 4 kcal, the rate of the reaction will alter by a factor $\exp(1/RT)$, i.e. at room temperature ($300°$ K) the change will be 5-fold. A change of 8 kcal in L_i will produce a 25-fold change and so on. In endothermic reactions ($\varepsilon_0 = A + 0.75q$), if L_i changes by 4 kcal, then this changes the rate by a factor $\exp(3/RT)$, or at $300°$ K more than 100-fold.

We shall now show that the relative activity of R_i, as compared with the standard radical CH_3, also does not depend on the nature of X, within the limits of ± 2 kcal. For this purpose we consider the heat L_X as found in the reaction $R + CH_3X \rightarrow RX + CH_3 + L_X$ for different substituents X.

(1) $R = \text{allyl}$, $CH_2 = CH—CH_2$.

$L_X = Q_{C_3H_5-X} - Q_{CH_3-X}$; Q is taken from Table 6, page 16.

Table 13. Heats of reaction for the allyl radical

$$CH_3X + CH_2 = CH—CH_2 \rightarrow CH_3 + CH_2 = CH—CH_2X + L_X$$

X	L_R (kcal)
C_3H_7 . . .	− 21·5
CH_3 . . .	− 23
Cl	− 22
I	− 19
$CH_2=CH—CH_2$.	− 21·5
CHO . . .	− 23
OH . . .	− 19
H	− 24

The mean value of L_R is $− 21 \cdot 6 \pm 2 \cdot 5$ kcal. Note that $L_R = − 24$ kcal, i.e. it is lower than the other values of L_R.

(2) $R = n\text{-propyl}$, $n\text{-}C_3H_7$.

$$\dot{C}_3H_7 + CH_3X \rightarrow \dot{C}H_3 + C_3H_7X + L_X$$

Table 14. Heats of reaction for the n-propyl radical

X	L_R (kcal)
CH_3 . . .	− 4
Cl	− 3
I	− 4
OH . . .	− 2
NH_2 . . .	− 2
$CH_2=CHCH_2$ . .	− 2·5
H	− 6

The mean value of L_R is $− 3 \pm 1$ kcal. An exception is $L_{R_H} = − 6$ kcal.

(3) R = phenyl, $\dot{C}_6H_5$.

Table 15. *Heats of reaction for the phenyl radical*

$$\dot{C}_6H_5 + CH_3X \rightarrow C_6H_5X + \dot{C}H_3 + L_X$$

X	L_R (kcal)
Br	+ 5
C_6H_5 . . .	+ 5·3
CH_3 . . .	+ 2·7
C_3H_7 . . .	+ 3·8
H	− 3·7

The mean value of L_R is $4 \pm 1\cdot3$ kcal. The exception is L_{R_H}, at − 3·7 kcal.

(4) R = benzyl, $C_6H_5\dot{C}H_2$.

Table 16. *Heats of reaction for the benzyl radical*

$$C_6H_5\dot{C}H_2 + CH_3X \rightarrow C_6H_5CH_2X + \dot{C}H_3 + L_X$$

X	L_R (kcal)
CH_3 . . .	− 19
C_3H_7 . . .	− 17
Br . . .	− 16
NH_2 . . .	− 20
$C_6H_5CH_2$ . .	− 16
H	− 24

The mean value of L_R is $- 17\cdot4 \pm 1\cdot5$ kcal. The exception is L_{R_H} at − 24 kcal.

(5) R = vinyl, $CH_2 = \dot{C}H$.

All the data given above were computed from bond dissociation energies in the corresponding radicals. In the case of the vinyl radical sufficiently reliable data on the bond dissociation energies in $CH_2 = CH—X$ are not available for any substituent X. In Table 6 the vinyl values are followed by asterisks, since they were obtained by indirect methods. The values given below in Table 17 are consequently not quite reliable.

Table 17. *Heats of reaction for the vinyl radical*

$$CH_2 = \dot{C}H + CH_3X \rightarrow CH_2 = CHX + \dot{C}H_3 + L_X$$

X	L_R (kcal)
CH_3 . . .	+ 7
$CH_2{=}CH$ . .	+ 11
C_3H_7 . . .	+ 8
C_6H_5 . . .	+ 10
CHO . . .	+ 11
H	+ 3

The mean value of L_R is $9 \cdot 4 \pm 2$ kcal. The exception is L_{R_H} at approximately 3 kcal.

The activity of $n\text{-}C_3H_7$, having its free valence on the terminal carbon, was considered above. For this radical, $L_R = -3$ kcal. The activity of $iso\text{-}C_3H_7$ will now be considered. There are no thermochemical data of sufficient accuracy for this radical. The appropriate values in Table 6 were derived by indirect means, and are given with an asterisk. Using those figures, the values in Table 18 are obtained.

Table 18. *Heats of reaction for the* iso*propyl radical*

$$CH_3\dot{C}HCH_3 + CH_3X \rightarrow CH_3CHXCH_3 + \dot{C}H_3 + L_X$$

X	L_R (kcal)
CH_3 . . .	− 7·5
$n\text{-}C_3H_7$ . . .	− 7
$C_6H_5CH_2$ . .	− 8·5
$iso\text{-}C_3H_7$. . .	− 8
H	− 12

The mean value of L_R is $-7 \cdot 8 \pm 1$ kcal. The exception is L_{R_H} at − 12 kcal.*

* It is seen that the activity of the $iso\text{-}C_3H_7$ is 4·8 kcal less than that of the $n\text{-}C_3H_7$. Correspondingly, when a terminal C—H bond in propane is subjected to radical attack, its activity is 4·8 kcal less than that of C—H bond attached

The divergence between L_{R_H} and the mean value of L_R which occurs in practically all the instances given here seems to be explained by our taking CH_3 radical as standard. But the divergence from the law of addition of bonds is greatest in the paraffin hydrocarbons for the energies of the methane C—H bonds. If we were to take as standard a radical with a greater number of carbon atoms, their divergence would be considerably less.

L_i evidently does not depend on X to a first approximation in all the cases quoted, being determined only by the nature of R_i and by the standard radical R_1.

We note that a number of the systems also had fairly strongly conjugated double bonds, e.g.

$$C_6H_5 + C_6H_5CH_3 \rightarrow C_6H_5C_6H_5 + CH_3$$

producing two conjugated benzene rings. Similarly,

$$CH_2{=}CH + CH_2 = CH{-}CH_3 \rightarrow CH_2{=}CH{-}CH{=}CH_2 + CH_3$$

gives the conjugated molecule butadiene.

The values of L_R for a few radicals, CBr_3, $CHBr_2$, CH_2Br, C_2H_4Cl are set out below:

$$CBr_3 + CH_3Br \rightarrow CBr_4 + CH_3 + L \qquad (L = + 49 - 66)$$

$$L_{CBr_3} = - 17 \text{ kcal}$$

$$CHBr_2 + CH_3Br \rightarrow CHBr_3 + CH_3 + L \qquad (L = + 55 - 66)$$

$$L_{CHBr_2} = - 11 \text{ kcal}$$

$$CH_2Br + CH_3Br \rightarrow CH_2Br_2 + CH_3 + L \qquad (L = + 62 \cdot 5 - 66)$$

$$L_{CH_2Br} = - 3 \cdot 5 \text{ kcal}$$

$$CH_3CHCl + CH_3H \rightarrow CH_3CH_2Cl + CH_3 + L \qquad (L = + 92 - 101)$$

$$L_{C_2H_4Cl} = - 9 \text{ kcal*}$$

---

to the central carbon atom; in other words, the reaction $\dot{R} + CH_3CH_2CH_3 \rightarrow RH + \dot{C}H_2CH_2CH_3$ proceeds with greater difficulty than $\dot{R} + CH_3CH_2CH_3 \rightarrow RH + CH_3\dot{C}HCH_3$.

This is still more clearly shown in the compound $CH_2{=}CH{-}CH_3$ where L_{R_H} for the CH_2 group is 27 kcal less than for the CH_3 group, which is α with respect to the double bond. In other words, the activity of C_3H_6 when reacting with R is 27 kcal less for the CH_2 group than it is for the CH_3 group.

* $Q_{C_2H_4Cl-H}$ was obtained indirectly via the endothermic decomposition of C_2H_4Cl ($C_2H_4Cl \rightarrow C_2H_4 + Cl - 26$ kcal). $\Delta H_{C_2H_4}$ and ΔH_{Cl} are known from the tables. From these we may compute that $\Delta H_{C_2H_4Cl} = 12 \cdot 5 + 28 \cdot 5 - 26 = 15$ kcal. From the tables we may also get $\Delta H_{C_2H_5Cl}$ and ΔH_H, so we may put $C_2H_5Cl \rightarrow C_2H_4Cl + H$ in the following form: $-25 = 15 + 51 \cdot 9 - Q$, whence $Q \simeq 92$ kcal.

All the radicals considered are arranged in order of decreasing L_R in Table 19; i.e. in order of decreasing activity. The activity of a radical (relative to CH_3) does not depend to a first approximation on the structure of the substituent X.

Table 19. *Relative radical activities*

R	L_R (kcal)
$CH_2{=}CH$ . .	$+$ 9·4
C_6H_5 . . .	$+$ 4
CH_3 . . .	0
C_3H_7 . . .	$-$ 3
CH_2Br . . .	$-$ 3·5
C_2H_4Cl . . .	$-$ 9
$CHBr_2$ . . .	$-$ 11
CBr_3 . . .	$-$ 17
$C_6H_5CH_2$ . .	$-$ 17·4
$CH_2{=}CH{-}CH_2$.	$-$ 21·5

Table 19 shows how much the activities of radicals may differ. When L_R changes by 30 kcal, the corresponding change in ε is 7·5 kcal for exothermic reactions, and 22·5 kcal for endothermic ones. Kinetic measurements show that the radical activities correspond with the series arrangement given.

For instance, the benzyl radical is of exceptionally low activity. This has been particularly clearly demonstrated by RAZUVAEV, OLDEHOP and VYAZANKIN [103–105] and by SZWARC [40]. RAZUVAEV *et al.* investigated the photolysis of mercury diphenyl, mercury ditolyl, and mercury dibenzyl in solution, and showed that the radicals from the first two compounds reacted with the solvent, giving the corresponding mercurichlorides, as well as benzene and toluene. Benzyl radicals were also produced with mercury dibenzyl, but these did not react with the solvent; instead, they combined to dibenzyl. SZWARC [40], who studied the decomposition of various organic compounds in the vapour phase in admixture with toluene, showed that the benzyl radicals produced by the toluene reacting with radicals were also converted quantitatively to dibenzyl.

Hitherto we have only investigated radicals in which the free valence resides on a carbon atom and have found their activities relative to CH_3 in different reactions with molecules. Other series of radicals exist, for instance NH_2 and NO_2, which the free valence is on the nitrogen atom, or radicals such as OH, HO_2* and RO_2 in which the valence is on an oxygen atom, etc. Unfortunately, there is an almost complete absence of experimental data on the Q-values for bonds in these radicals, and only in extremely few instances have values been derived by indirect methods. In each such series we must select some one radical as a qualitative standard. For example, one can take OH as standard, and define the activities of HO_2, RO_2 and RO relative to this. The relative activity of HO_2 is determined from the reaction:

$$HO_2 + XOH \rightarrow HO_2X + OH + L_{HO_2}$$

Suppose X = H. Then we have:

$$HO_2 + H_2O \rightarrow H_2O_2 + OH + L_{HO_2}$$

From indirect data it is known that ε is 24 kcal for the reaction $HO_2 + H_2 \rightarrow H_2O_2 + H + q$. Since ε_0 does not usually exceed 12 kcal, $q < -12$ kcal, and $Q_{HO_2-H} = 103 + q < 103 - 12 = 91$ kcal. On the other hand, $Q > 103 - 24 = 79$ kcal. The high value is the more likely one, and we also prefer it.

In that case $L_{HO_2} = -117 + 91 = -26$ kcal, which is in agreement with the very low activity of HO_2, as compared with OH.

The data on the activities of alkoxy and peroxy radicals, RO and RO_2, are scarce. Qualitatively speaking, the alkoxy radicals are highly active (like H), while the peroxy radicals are relatively inactive (like HO_2).

The activities of alkoxy radicals relative to CH_3 when C—X is C—H may be estimated from GRAY's thermochemical data [50] on the O—H bond-energies in alcohols

$$CH_3O + CH_4 \rightarrow CH_3 + CH_3OH - 1 \ (101-100) \ \text{kcal}$$
$$C_2H_5O + CH_4 \rightarrow CH_3 + C_2H_5OH - 2 \ (101-99) \ \text{kcal}$$
$$n\text{-}C_3H_7O + CH_4 \rightarrow CH_3 + n-C_3H_7OH \sim O \ (101-101) \ \text{kcal}$$
$$iso\text{-}C_3H_7O + CH_4 \rightarrow CH_3 + iso\text{-}C_3H_7OH - 1 \ (101\text{-}100) \ \text{kcal}$$

Thus the activities of alkoxy radicals are sufficiently high and comparable with that of CH_3.

The activity of NO_2 relative to NH_2 may be estimated from the reaction

$$NO_2 + CH_3NH_2 \rightarrow CH_3NO_2 + NH_2 + L_{NO_2}'$$

---

* Up to the present, no experimental proof that the HO_2 radical exists has been available, although it has been postulated to occur in many oxidations. The recent work of FONER and HUDSON [106] has shown that HO_2 (detected with the mass spectrometer) is produced by combination of H atoms with O_2 in a discharge in an inert-gas carrier.

$(L_{NO_2}' = -79 + 53 = -26$ kcal). It follows that the activity of NO_2 relative to NH_2 is small.

We will now investigate the theoretical interpretation of the results so far obtained. We have seen above that L_i is practically independent of the structure of the substituent X, and very greatly dependent on the structure of R_i. The heat of the reaction $R + CH_3X \rightarrow RX + CH_3 + L_R$ is $Q_{R-X} - Q_{CH_3-X}$. X may be any radical, e.g. $X = CH_3$. R may have any structure, provided only that the free valence is attached to a carbon atom. In particular, we may suppose that R is a hydrocarbon radical. It may be seen from Table 6 that Q_{R-CH_3} for different hydrocarbon radicals may range from 90 kcal for vinyl or 83 kcal for CH_3 to 60 kcal for allyl, $CH_2{=}CH{-}\dot{C}H_2$. This change of 30 kcal in Q_{C-C} as a function of the structure may appear surprising at first sight, for we know that the so-called mean energy of the C—C bond, as found in different molecules, changes only a few kilocalories for different classes of compound (law of bond-addition). Consequently, the cause of the large changes in Q_{R-X} (some tens of kilocalories) must be sought in the differences in the free radicals R, and not in the properties of the molecules R—X. The radical R, when part of the molecule RX, may have quite a different electron-density distribution from that in the free state. The "free" electron in the free radical interacts considerably more strongly with all the atomic cores and electrons which may constitute the particle R than it does when coupled to the electron from the particle X to form the bond R—X.

It is, of course, fairly obvious that, since the electron is not so bonded or so fixed in position in the free radical as it is in RX, it is transferred considerably more readily.

The process $RX \rightarrow R + X$ may be divided conceptually into two distinct stages:

(1) The bond R—X is broken, but the electron-density distribution and the atomic configurations are maintained the same in R and X as in the molecule R—X.

From the law of addition of bonds, we may assign to this process one and the same energy E_{C-X}', without regard to the structures of R and X; which is correct to the same degree as the law of bond-addition.

(2) The radicals obtained from the first stage are transformed to their actual form and real electron-density distribution. This liberates energy $B_R + B_X$, which is determined only by the properties of the isolated radicals R and X.

The energy B, due to the change to the radical configuration and to the interaction of electrons and atomic cores, we shall provisionally term the conjugation energy of the "free" electron in the radical.

4

Since the total energy required is independent of the route taken, $Q_{R-X} = E_{R-X'} - (B_R + B_X)$.*

Expressing in terms of L_R, we have:

$$L_R = Q_{R-X} - Q_{CH_3-X}$$
$$= E_{C-X'} - E_{C-X'} - (B_R + B_X) + (B_{CH_3} + B_{BX})$$
$$= - B_R + B_{CH_3}$$

Thus expressed, L_R is the difference between the conjugation energies of the "free" electron in the radicals CH_3 and R, as well as being the relative activity of R. Naturally, this quantity is independent of the nature of X within the limits of accuracy set by the law of addition of bonds.†

The difference between the dissociation energies $Q_{CH_3-CH_3}$ and $Q_{(CH_2=CH-CH_2)-CH_3}$ (equal to $83 - 60$, i.e. 23 kcal) is due to the conjugation energy of the free electron in $CH_2=CH-CH_2$ being 23 kcal greater than that for CH_3. The law of additivity of bonds is accurate within a few kilocalories, and even for strongly conjugated systems the deviation from the value calculated from single bonds does not usually exceed 6 kcal. This is why L_R is independent of X within a few kilocalories. However, thermochemical observations are often of no greater accuracy.

It is important to remember that in fairly strongly conjugated systems, such as $C_6H_5-C_6H_5$, where the energy of conjugation is estimated to be 6·8 kcal, no material deviation from additivity is observed. Consequently, Table 15 shows that L in the reaction $C_6H_5 + CH_3X \rightarrow C_6H_5X + CH_3 + L$ is 2·7 kcal when $X = CH_3$, but 5·3 kcal when $X = C_5H_5$. The difference (2·6 kcal) is considerably less than 6·8 kcal. We have the impression from the cases we have investigated that the conjugation energy is less than

* In any particular case, e.g. C—H, E' is greater than the mean bond energy E. The mean bond energy in this instance may be evaluated from ΔH_{CH_4}. Taking the heat of sublimation of carbon as being 150 kcal, ΔH is 375 kcal. Hence $E_{C-H} = 375/4 \simeq 94$ kcal.

E' is given by $(\Delta H + K)/4$, where K is the energy required to transform the carbon atom to its quadrivalent state. K is not accurately known, but it is $\not< 100$ kcal. Then, since $E' = E + K/4 = 94 + K/4$, E' is not only greater than E, but also greater than Q_{CH_3-H} in methane (101 kcal). Thus the energy yield in the hypothetical second stage, B_{CH_3} in methane is $B_{CH_3} = 94 + (K/4) - 101 = (K/4) - 7$.

† The heat of reaction between two molecules having all their valence bonds saturated will be zero within the accuracy of the law of additivity of bonds, if the bonds in the reaction are of the same type; e.g. if the bonds R_1-X and R_2-Y in the reaction $R_1X + R_2Y \rightarrow R_1Y + R_2X$ are both C—C bonds.

that given in the literature. This may possibly be connected with the marked deviation from the mean L when $X = H$. This deviation is found in all the cases we have investigated, and the reason for it is not adequately clear.

The activities, relative to CH_3, of radicals having the free valency attached to atoms other than carbon, e.g. O, N, etc., will now be considered.

Let us denote by Y the atom in R which has the free valency. In the reaction $R + CH_3X \rightarrow RX + CH_3 + L$, L is then $B_{CH_3} - B_R + E_{Y-X}' - E_{C-X}'$, and $\Delta E' = E_{Y-X}' - E_{C-X}' \neq 0$. The value of $\Delta E'$ will depend upon which atom in R has the free valency. If C—X is C—C, then $\Delta E' = E_{Y-C}' - E_{C-C}'$. This quantity will be independent of the nature of X, so L will be constant, but only on condition that C—X remains a C—C bond. If C—X is C—H, then $\Delta E'$, and consequently L, will take some other value, and so on.

In each case, the activity relative to CH_3 will have one value when CH_3—X is C—C, a second value when it is C—H, a third value when it is C—N, etc.

Let us first consider those reactions where C—X = C—C. The activity of H relative to CH_3 may be determined from the data given below:

$$H + CH_3\text{---}CH_3 \rightarrow CH_4 + CH_3 + 18\ (101 - 83)\ \text{kcal};$$

$$H + CH_3\text{---}C_3H_7 \rightarrow C_3H_8 + CH_3 + 16\ (95 - 79)\ \text{kcal};$$

$$H + CH_2\text{=}CH\text{---}CH_3 \rightarrow CH_2\text{=}CH_2 + CH_3 + 14\ (104 - 90)\ \text{kcal};$$

$$H + CH_3CH_2CH\text{=}CH_2 \rightarrow CH_3CH + CH_2 + \\ + CH_3 + 17\ (77 - 60)\ \text{kcal};$$

$$H + C_6H_5CH_3 \rightarrow C_6H_6 + CH_3 + 14\ (100 - 86)\ \text{kcal}.$$

Thus the relative activity of H with respect to C—C bonds is 16 ± 2 kcal, and does not depend on the nature of X, if the free valency in X is attached to a carbon atom.

The following set of reactions may be used to determine the relative activity of NH_2:

$$NH_2 + CH_3\text{---}CH_3 \rightarrow CH_3NH_2 + CH_3 - 4\ \text{kcal}$$

$$NH_2 + C_3H_7CH_3 \rightarrow C_3H_7NH_2 + CH_3 - 2\ \text{kcal}$$

$$NH_2 + C_6H_5CH_2CH_3 \rightarrow C_6H_5CH_2NH_2 + CH_3 - 4\ \text{kcal}$$

It follows that $L_{NH_2} = -3 \pm 1$ kcal.

The relative activity of NO_2 may be estimated from the equation $NO_2 + CH_3\text{---}CH_3 \rightarrow CH_3NO_2 + CH_3 - 30\ (53 - 83)\ \text{kcal}.$

The activity of OH relative to CH_2 may be estimated on the basis of the equation:

$$OH + CH_3CH_3 \rightarrow CH_3OH + CH_3 + 7 \ (90 - 83) \ \text{kcal}$$

When C—X is C—H, the activities of radicals may be determined from their reactions with methane:

$$H + CH_4 \rightarrow H_2 + CH_3 + 2 \ \text{kcal}$$

$$NH_2 + CH_4 \rightarrow NH_3 + CH_3 - 16 \ \text{kcal}$$

$$OH + CH_4 \rightarrow H_2O + CH_3 + 16 \ \text{kcal}$$

A short summary of activities of radicals relative to CH_3 is given in Tables 20 and 21.

Table 20.   *Activities of radicals relative to CH_3 for reactions at C—C bonds*

R	L_R (kcal)
H	16 ± 2
OH . . .	7
NH_2 . . .	-3 ± 1
NO_2 . . .	-30

Table 21.   *Activities of radicals relative to CH_3 for reactions at C—H bonds*

R	L_R (kcal)
OH . . .	16
H	2
NH_2 . . .	-16

We shall now consider the problem of the nature of the inter-action between the free electron, and the other electrons and atomic cores which may comprise a radical R, for the general case of a complex radical.

The action of removing X from the molecule RX changes the shape of the particle R, and also changes its electron-density distri-bution. These changes also effect B_R, which is a measure of the absolute activity of R. The difference $B_R - B_{CH_3}$ is a measure of the activity of R relative to that of the standard radical CH_3. The process by which the shape of the radical changes as a result of valence-electron density redistribution may be investigated in the formation of CH_3 from methane.

The CH_3 radical in the intact methane molecule has the form of a symmetrical pyramid the vertices of which are arranged round the carbon atom. The free radical takes the form of an equilateral triangle, with the hydrogen atoms at the vertices and the carbon atom at the centre.* In CH_4 the fourth valence electron of carbon takes part in the CH_3—H bond. The corresponding electron-density distribution forms a lobe with its axis along the CH_3—H axis, normal to the base of the pyramid. In the free radical the fourth electron is distributed between two lobes, one on each side of the plane containing the atoms, with their common axis perpendicular to the plane.

The process of abstracting the hydrogen atom from CH_4 may be imagined as divided into two stages: (a) the C—H bond is broken, while maintaining the pyramidal form of the CH_3 fragment; this absorbs an amount of energy E': and (b) rearrangement of the pyramidal fragment into the planar radical, this step yielding the energy B. The heat of the reaction, Q, $_{CH_3—H}$ is then:

$$Q_{CH_3—H} = E_{C—H}' - B$$

Note that in the abstraction of an H atom from any compound in which carbon is quadrivalent, and in which there consequently are four σ-bonds, B may be considered as the sum of two parts. The first (B') may be considered as the energy involved in the transition from the valency state with sp^3 hybridization to that having sp^2 hybridization. Naturally, this quantity does not depend on the nature of the substituent. The second part (B'') may be considered as the energy arising from the interaction of the free valence with the rest of the bonds in the radical, i.e. the influence of the substituent.

When a hydrogen atom is abstracted from ethylene, the shape of the resulting radical differs but little from that of ethylene itself; consequently, $B_{CH_2=CH} < B_{CH_3}$. This explains why the activity of $CH_2=CH$ is greater than that of CH_3. The relative activity of $CH_2=CH$ is given by:

$$L = B_{CH_3} - B_{CH_2—CH} = + 9 \text{ kcal}$$

The redistribution of electrons that occurs in the transition bonded radical → free radical has been suitably determined in a few instances. The best instance of this is the formation of the free radical NO. Two electrons from the N atom and two from the O atom form the N=O bond in a compound of the type RNO; e.g. $(CH_3)_3CNO$.

* According to the latest investigations [107] the CH_3 radical is not planar.

The third electron from the N atom, together with that from $(CH_3)_3C$ form the strong N—C bond. When NO is produced by the rupture of this bond, this third electron is drawn in between the N and O atoms and strengthens the N=O bond. In fact, the "free" electron interacts with the two non-bonding electrons on the oxygen atom, with the formation of a third (three-electron) bond between N and O: N≡O; the dissociation energy of this bond, i.e. the energy evolved in the transition N≡O → N=O is also determined by conjugation of the free electron with the other electrons in the radical.

The O—H bonds in hydrogen peroxide are identical, and their energies are very close to the bond-energy in the OH radical. When a hydrogen atom is removed to give H—O—Ȯ, the electron cloud becomes redistributed as a result of the interaction of the "free" electron with the non-bonding electrons on the free oxygen atom. The energy B evolved in the formation of this three-electron bond reduces the activity of the HO_2 radical.

When the allyl radical is produced, e.g. by the abstraction of a hydrogen atom from propylene, the "free" electron, via its interaction with the bonds, produces a conjugated bond system $CH_2\!\cdots\!CH\!\cdots\!CH_2$, with strengthened bonds. The energy B evolved in $CH_2\!=\!CH\!-\!CH_2 \to CH_2\!\cdots\!CH\!\cdots\!CH_2$ defines the consequent reduction in the allyl radical activity L. Strongly electronegative groups (Br, OH, etc.), with strong electron affinities, often interact substantially with the "free" electron (particularly if they are attached to the carbon atom) which also liberates energy and consequently reduces the free radical activities.

Although this free-electron coupling to interatomic bonds, with resultant bond strengthening produces the largest effect on the energy and activity, it is by no means the only way in which the electron density may become redistributed in free radicals. In many cases the redistribution amounts to the free valence interacting with neighbouring C—C and C—H bonds; this alters the shape of the radical and the electron distribution relatively little, the free-electron orbital interacting with the electron-orbitals of adjacent σ-bonds.

This type of interaction is undoubtedly responsible for the reduction in activity observed on passing from CH_3 to C_4H_9 in aliphatic radicals; and upon increased branching in the hydrocarbon. In such cases one cannot say the free electron is drawn into an interatomic bond, with evolution of conjugation energy.*

Whether the so-called "static conjugation" in molecules is an electron delocalization or an interaction of localized electrons with

* Neglecting small effects such as σ–p and σ–σ conjugation.

a subsequent change in molecular shape, it cannot have any important effect on the course and rate of a reaction. This effect is small as compared with the effect of a "free" electron interacting with other bonds in a free radical. Organic chemists themselves have often remarked that static conjugation by itself cannot explain well-known facts about the major influence of structure on reactivity. This is why the concept of "dynamic conjugation" was put forward, the effect being shown in the actual instant of reaction, when one bond is broken and another formed. However, this concept is not notable for its clarity.

The concept that the energy of interaction between the free electron and the bonds in complex radicals is the determining factor in the chemical kinetics of complex reactions is developed here. It follows that the presence of this interaction in radicals (or ions) will accordingly determine the reaction rate, in as far as chemical reactions occur via free radicals (or ions). It is the cause of major structural influences on reactivity.

All the activities given above are derived from substitution reactions. These concepts can also be applied readily to radical additions at double bonds. The analogous theory for polymerizations has been developed during the past few years by BAGDASARYAN. VOEVODSKII has expressed similar ideas for individual substitution reactions.

In developing the above concepts as to radical and molecular reactivities, we have limited the discussion to the case where ε for a radical reaction depends only upon q, assuming that A and α are almost constant. A may evidently vary by ± 2–2.5 kcal for other classes of reaction, however. We have shown there is a large change in A when the electronegative atoms Cl and Br are involved. Other cases of noticeable variation in A will probably come to light on further investigation, and an improvement in the data discussed here will result. The variation of A and α with a variety of features peculiar to the bonds involved (many of which have been determined spectroscopically) will undoubtedly become obvious with further accumulation and systematic comparison of experimental results. If this is successfully carried out, it will enable us to develop radical and molecular reactivity theory and to extend BUTLEROW's theory considerably, as well as elucidate the relationship between ε and q. Only after such a theory has been developed from formal hypotheses (derived from quantitative experimental data) will we be able to develop the electronic theory of molecular structure on a sufficiently firm basis, without tending to lapse into speculation.

The very large body of chemical data on reactivity cannot confidently be used in developing an electronic theory of structure at the present time, since it does not admit of kinetic analysis; consequently, the reacting particles responsible for the reactivity as established in organic chemistry are not known—they may be ions, molecules, complexes, or radicals.

The type of investigation suggested here opens up the very widest perspectives for the development of chemistry.

6. EMPIRICAL FORMULAE FOR COMPUTING BOND-ENERGIES IN ORGANIC MOLECULES

The great difficulties encountered in determining bond-energies by experiment naturally impel us to seek empirical or semi-empirical formulae to derive them approximately.

The data of HINSHELWOOD et al. [108] on the oxidation of paraffins and their chloro-derivatives throw some light on the effect of molecular structure on Q_{C-H} in paraffins. They showed the oxidation rate to increase with chain-length in the n-series and to decrease with increase in the degree of branching within families of isomers. They explained this by methyl groups exerting a greater stabilizing influence, giving lower reactivities. So the primary oxygen-molecule attack (and hence radical attack) occurred at the C atom furthest from all CH_3 groups. The maximum oxidation rate for a paraffin or its chloroderivative was assumed some inverse function of the stability factor S, computed as follows. S for a group adjacent to CH_3 is assumed unity; if one C atom intervenes, $\frac{1}{3}$; if two C atoms, $\frac{1}{9}$, etc.

By plotting log (relative rate)* vs. S for the group furthest from all CH_3 groups a single curve was obtained for both n- and branched-chain paraffins, as well as for their monochloro derivatives, if additional allowance was made for the chlorinated group.

VOEVODSKII [109] used the methyl group stabilization concept to derive an empirical formula for paraffin Q_{C-H} values.

His basic assumptions were:

(a) The Q_{C-H} for primary, secondary and tertiary carbon atoms in molecules with infinite side-chains differ by a constant B, i.e.

$$A_{\text{tert}} = A_{\text{sec}} - B = A_{\text{pri}} - 2B.$$

(b) As a CH_3 group approached Q_{C-H} increased, the increase being proportional to α^n, where n is the number of C atoms in the side-chain.

In the most general case VOEVODSKII's formula can be put as

$$Q_{C-H} \approx A_X + B\Sigma\alpha^{n_i} \tag{1}$$

---

* Relative to that for n-pentane, taken as 1.

where i is the number of the methyl group, n_i the distance from the C—H bond to the ith CH_3 group, in C atoms. The summation is carried over all CH_3 groups in the molecule (of course if a primary C—H bond is involved the summation is over all other CH_3 groups). A_x depends on the bond broken (primary, secondary, tertiary).

With secondary C—H bonds, for instance, the general formula becomes

$$Q_{C-H} = A_{sec} + B(\alpha^{n_1} + \alpha^{n_2})$$

α, B and A_X are found from experimental data: $\alpha = 0.4$, $B = 8$ kcal, $A_{sec} = 85.6$ kcal. VOEVODSKII's formula is satisfactory for C—H bonds in paraffins of the most varied structure (save cyclic).

In essence VOEVODSKII's formula is implied by HINSHELWOOD's $\log \omega_{rel}$ vs. S relation. The curvature of this latter relation is in essence due only to the two points corresponding to n-C_8H_{18} and n-$C_{10}H_{22}$. The others fall on a straight line.

Consider the n-alkanes. The CH_2 groups of minimum S will be the first to be attacked by oxygen and chain-carrier radicals. This implies Q_{C-H} is least here, so Q_{C-H} and S must be related, and a first rough approximation is the linear relation

$$Q_{C-H} = a + bS* \tag{1'}$$

* In fact to a first approximation

$$\log \omega_{rel} \approx \frac{\Delta \varepsilon}{2.3RT}$$

where $\Delta \varepsilon$ is the difference between the chain-propagation activation energies for the given hydrocarbon and n-pentane.

Applying POLANYI's rule we get

$$\log \omega_{rel} = - \frac{\Delta \varepsilon}{2.3RT} = - \frac{\alpha \Delta H}{2.3RT} = - \frac{\alpha(Q_{C-H} - Q_{C-H}')}{2.3RT}$$

where Q_{C-H} and Q_{C-H}' are the values for the least stable CH_2 groups in the hydrocarbon and n-pentane respectively.

Since $\log \Delta$ vs. S is approximately linear

$$\log \omega_{rel} \approx a' + b'S$$

So

$$-\frac{\alpha(Q_{C-H} - Q_{C-H}')}{2.3RT} \approx a' + b'S$$

or

$$Q_{C-H} = a + bS$$

where

$$a = Q_{C-H}' + \frac{a' \times 2.3RT}{\alpha}$$

and

$$b = \frac{b' \times 2.3RT}{\alpha}$$

where a and b are constants. S may be put as $(\tfrac{1}{3})^{n_1} + (\tfrac{1}{3})^{n_2}$ where n_1 and n_2 are the distances from the two CH_3 groups in C atoms (if the CH_2 is adjacent to a CH_3, $n = 0$).

If, following FRANKLIN, we assume that these remain unchanged in free radicals, we may calculate ΔH for groups with a free valency, e.g. $\Delta H_{C_2H_5}$ is $- 25$ kcal. Then $25 = \Delta H_{CH_3} + \Delta H_{CH_2} = - 10{\cdot}1 + \Delta H_{CH_2}$ so $\Delta H_{CH_2} = + 35{\cdot}1$ kcal. From the ΔH's for other radicals we may calculate $\Delta H_{CH}\ \Delta H_C$, etc. To calculate ΔH for any radical we need to know the ΔH's for all the groups in it.

The principal shortcoming of FRANKLIN's method lies in its prediction that the ΔH values for radicals which contain the same number of identical groups, e.g. o-, m-, and p-chlorophenyl, should be identical. If ΔH is calculated for o-, m-, and p-(ClC_6H_4X) after FRANKLIN [11!], the values should be identical, which is contrary to experiment. FRANKLIN's method allows us to estimate ΔH for complex organic radicals containing a variety of atoms and groups, but with an unknown degree of accuracy. However, it is necessary to know ΔH for the corresponding molecules to calculate Q-values; data on these heats of formation are in any case largely lacking. This is why ΔH must be obtained by FRANKLIN's method, when we have to calculate the Q of any bond in such a molecule. It is quite impossible to estimate in advance the error involved in such calculations.

VOEVODSKII's formula deals only with Q_{C-H} for alkanes, so it only has a limited range of applicability. VEDENEEV (Institute of Chemical Physics, Moscow) has used the above assumptions (that Q for a molecular bond is determined by the free-electron conjugation in the radical) to derive a semi-empirical formula for Q applying to a very wide range of organic compounds.

As was shown on page 40 Q_{R-X} in the RX molecule may be expressed as

$$Q_{R-X} = E_{R-X}' - (B_R + B_X) \qquad (3)$$

If X is a single atom, $B_X = 0$, and (3) may be rewritten:

$$Q_{R-X} = E_{R-X}' - B_R \qquad (4)$$

Then (1') can be written as

$$Q_{C-H} \approx a + b\{(0{\cdot}33)^{n_1} + (0{\cdot}33)^{n_2}\} \qquad (2)$$

Thus we get a formula exactly corresponding with VOEVODSKII's.

FRANKLIN has attempted to compute heats of formation for radicals (and hence bond-energies) from additivity concepts [110]. The following example illustrates FRANKLIN's method. Since $\Delta H_{C_2H_6} = - 20{\cdot}2$ kcal the fractional ΔH assigned to each CH_3 group is $\tfrac{1}{2}(- 20{\cdot}2 \text{ kcal}) = - 10{\cdot}1$ kcal, i.e. $\Delta H_{CH_3} = - 10{\cdot}1$ kcal. ΔH_{CH_2}, ΔH_{CH}, etc., can be calculated from other molecules.

E_{R-X}' is characteristic of the bond type, e.g. C—C, C—H, C—Br, etc., and within the limits of additivity, it is constant. B_R is the "free" electron conjugation energy in R, i.e. it is the energy evolved in going from its state in RX to the free state. As was noted above, this change is due to the free valency interacting with the bonds in R. VEDENEEV assumed that the interaction with any bond of the jth type attached to the nth carbon atom ($n = 0$ for the carbon atom with the free valency) took the form:

$$B_. = \alpha_j \exp\left(-\beta_n\right) \tag{5}$$

where α_j and β are coefficients related to the interaction.

Summing over all the bonds in R, we obtain:

$$B_R = \varepsilon_n N_j \alpha_j \exp\left(-\beta_n\right) \tag{6}$$

where N_j is the number of bonds of the jth type attached to the nth carbon atom.

Combining (6) and (4) we obtain:

$$Q_{R-X} = E_{R-X}^1 - \varepsilon_n N_j \alpha_j \exp\left(-\beta_n\right) \tag{7}$$

Interaction between all the bonds in R except the ordinary C—C bonds and the free valency should be allowed for.*

Consider the case X = Br. To determine the coefficients in (7) we may use the following experimental data:

$$Q_{CH_3-Br} = 67 \text{ kcal} \qquad Q_{C_2H_5-Br} = 65 \text{ kcal}$$
$$Q_{CH_2Br-Br} = 62 \text{ kcal} \qquad Q_{CH_2BrCH_2-Br} = 63 \text{ kcal}†$$

The set of simultaneous equations from which the coefficients are to be determined then becomes:

$$67 = E_{R-Br}' - 3\alpha_{C-H}$$
$$62 = E_{R-Br}' - 2\alpha_{C-H} - \alpha_{C-Br}$$
$$65 = E_{R-Br}' - 2\alpha_{C-H} - 3\alpha_{C-H}\exp(-\beta)$$
$$63 = E_{R-Br}' - 2\alpha_{C-H} - (2\alpha_{C-H} + \alpha_{C-Br})\exp\left(-\beta\right)$$

* It is not necessary to take account of ordinary C—C bonds, when Q is calculated for hydrocarbons and their derivatives, since the value they introduce into the general interaction is automatically allowed for in the other α_j.

† Calculated from the data of SCHUMACHER et al. for the photo-bromination of ethylene [112].

This set of equations gives $\exp(-\beta) = 0.4$, $\alpha_{C-H} = 10$ kcal, $\alpha_{C-Br} = 15$ kcal, $E_{R-Br}' = 97$ kcal. (7) takes the form

$$Q_{R-Br} = 97 - \Sigma N_j \alpha_j (0.4)^n \qquad (8)$$

The free valency interaction with π-bonds is regarded as being like that with any other bond. Also, only when the free valency in the "π-state" (as in CH_3 for instance—see page 43) is α to the π-bond has the conjugation energy E_{conj} to be allowed for by comparison with experiment. From $Q_{CH_2:CBr-Br}$ and $Q_{CH_2:CHCH_2-Br}$, which are 63 and 46 kcal respectively, we may deduce that $\alpha_\pi = 11$ kcal and $E_{conj} \approx 19.4$ kcal.

To calculate Q_{C-Br} for aryl bromides, we use α_B, i.e. the α_j appropriate to the free valency interaction with the C—C bonds in the benzene ring. For this purpose we take $Q_{C_6H_5-Br} = 71$ kcal. Then we have

$$71 = 97 - B_{C_6H_5}$$

$$B_{C_6H_5} = 2\alpha_B + (2\alpha_{C-H} + 2\alpha_B) \times 0.4 + (2\alpha_B + 2\alpha_{C-H})$$
$$\times 0.16 + \alpha_{C-H} \times 0.064$$

$$= 3.12\,\alpha_B + 11.8$$

Thus

$$\alpha_B = 4.6 \text{ kcal.}$$

Finally we obtain for Q_{R-Br} the expression:

$$Q_{R-Br} \simeq 97 - \Sigma N_j \alpha_j (0.4)^n - E_{conj} \qquad (9)$$

α_j may be α_{C-H}; α_B; α_{C-Br} or α_n. E_{conj} 19.4 kcal when the bond in question is α to a π-bond or a benzene ring.

Values of Q_{R-Br} derived from (9) are given in Table 22 for various brominated hydrocarbons, and are there compared with experimental values.

VEDENEEV has derived similar formulae for the cases $X = R$ (where R is a hydrocarbon radical), Cl, I, CN, and other substituents. The formula is precisely the same as VOEVODSKII's in the case of alkanes.

It is of course clearly understood that calculation of distances from number of carbon atoms is a first, and very rough, approximation. A more accurate calculation would be premature while our Q-values are so inaccurate, and any results would only be premature and misleading.

The existence of various empirical or semi-empirical formulae for Q should not allow one to neglect development of a rigorous theory. Since a rigorous theory is not available, however, they are sometimes

Table 22

R—Br	Q_{calc} (kcal)	Q_{exp} (kcal)
CH_3—Br .	67	67
CH_2Br—Br	62	62
$CHBr_2$—Br	57	55
CBr_3—Br	52	49
CH_2:CH—Br .	68	—
CHBr:CH—Br	66	—
CH_2:CBr—Br .	63	(63)
C_2H_5—Br	65	(65)
CH_2BrCH_2—Br	63	(63)
CH_3CHBr—Br.	60	—
n-C_3H_7—Br .	64·2	63·4*
iso-C_3H_7—Br .	63	62·5
$CH_3CHBrCH_2$—Br .	62·2	—
$\begin{array}{l}CH_3 \\ \quad\diagdown \\ \qquad CH\text{—Br} \\ \diagup \\ CH_2Br\end{array}$	61	—
n-C_4H_9—Br .	63·9	—
iso-C_4H_9—Br .	62·2	—
$tert.$-C_4H_9—Br .	61	60·6*
CH_2:CHCH$_2$—Br .	46	(46)
$\begin{array}{l}CH_2{=}C\text{—Br} \\ \qquad | \\ \qquad CH_3\end{array}$	66	—
CH≡C—CH$_2$—Br .	52	58
C_6H_5—Br .	71	(71)
$C_6H_5CH_2$—Br .	47·1	45–50
o-$CH_3C_6H_4$—Br .	70·2	70·1
m-$CH_3C_6H_4$—Br .	70·7	70·7
p-$CH_3C_6H_4$—Br .	70·9	70·7
	69·5	69·2
	70·3	70
	67·8	66
	69	68

* The values bracketed were used to compute the coefficients in (9). The starred values were obtained from thermochemical data   Heats of formation are derived from [111].

extremely useful, as in the calculation of unknown bond-energies; also, it allows one to analyse the large amount of conflicting experimental data from a unitary point of view.

7. ADDITION AT MULTIPLE BONDS

Reactions of types (2) and (2′) (page 1) will now be considered; radical addition to molecules with double bonds (reaction (2)), and the reverse reaction, radical decomposition, forming double bonds (reaction (2′)), e.g.:

(2) $H + CH_2 {=} CH_2 \rightarrow CH_3 {-} \dot{C}H_2 + q$

(2′) $CH_3 {-} \dot{C}H_2 \rightarrow CH_2 {=} CH_2 + H - q$

ε_0 must certainly be the same for the forward and reverse reactions. If (2) is exothermic, then (2′) will be endothermic. The activation energy for (2) will be ε_0, and for (2′) it will be $\varepsilon = \varepsilon_0 + q$.

It has been noted above that addition reactions are characterized by low steric factors. Such reactions only occur readily when ε is small. If additions involve activation energies as great as, or greater than, those in other reactions, then as well as reactions such as (2) above, metathetical reactions would occur concurrently, e.g. $H + C_2H_4 \rightarrow C_2H_3 + H_2$, with rates which might be much greater than that of the addition; i.e. it would be extremely difficult to detect the addition. But the majority of additions at double bonds involve only very low activation energies; consequently, at low temperatures, their rates exceed those of competing metathetical reactions very considerably, and the situation is reversed only at very high temperatures—substitution then becoming dominant.

Measurement of ε for a radical reaction is always difficult, and it is even more difficult for additions than for substitutions. If addition is sufficiently rapid at room temperature, ε_0 is very small ($\sim$ a few kilocalories). Since the accuracy with which activation energies are measured is usually not much higher, the relative error in ε_0 is very large. On the other hand, if ε is large enough for the relative error to be small, then it is difficult to measure, owing to competition by substitution.

The addition of hydrogen atoms to double bonds usually occurs very readily. For example, the rate constant for (2) is 9×10^{-13} cm³/mole-sec [9]. $\varepsilon \not> 2$ kcal, apparently.

Similarly, hydrogen atoms combine with ethylene, benzene, and some other compounds with double bonds at low temperatures—even as low as the boiling-point of nitrogen. Combination of atomic H with O_2 occurs readily at the latter temperature. Reactions of hydrogen atoms at triple bonds always have low activation energies. For example, HCN reacts readily at the $C{\equiv}N$ bond, giving $H_2C = N$ as the primary product. Cyanogen, $(CN)_2$, and azomethane also react rapidly at room temperature. The first step appears to be addition at the N=N bond:

$$H + CH_3N{=}NCH_3 \rightarrow CH_3NH{-}\dot{N}CH_3$$

All the above reactions of atomic hydrogen are quite strongly exothermic. Taking the bond energies as being N=N $\sim$ 80 kcal; N—N $\sim$ 60 kcal [64]; and N—H $\sim$ 85 kcal, we may estimate the energy liberated when hydrogen atoms combine with azomethane as $85 - 80 + 60 = 65$ kcal.

The energy liberated in $H + O_2 \rightarrow HO_2 + q_A$ may be estimated as follows: since ε for $HO_2 + H_2 \rightarrow H_2O_2 + H + q_B$ is about 24 kcal, and ε_0 can scarcely exceed 12 kcal, if we take $\varepsilon_0 = 12$ kcal q_B is $- 12$ kcal, i.e. $Q_{HO_2-H} - Q_{H-H} = - 12$ kcal. Hence $Q_{HO_2-H} = 103 - 12 = 91$ kcal.

$\Delta H_{H_2O_2}$ is 33 kcal, so q_A may be determined from the thermochemical equation $Q_{H-O_2} + Q_{HO_2-H} - Q_{H-H} = 33$ kcal, so $Q_{H-O_2} = 103 + 33 - 91 = 45$ kcal.*

Additions of CH_3 (and other alkyl radicals) at double bonds have been studied but little. Very varied qualitative data make it clear that these radicals combine readily with O_2: $R + O_2 \rightarrow RO_2$. $\varepsilon < 4$ kcal. At room temperature, radicals containing the phenyl group (e.g. $(C_6H_5)_3\dot{C}$) take up oxygen while in the liquid phase; the primary product is a peroxide radical like $(C_6H_5)_3COO$. ΔH is not known for such peroxide radicals, but it can hardly be doubted that their heats of formation are considerable but less than that for HO_2.

The nitrogen diphenyl radical [114] (free valency on the nitrogen atom), does not combine with free oxygen, unlike triphenyl methyl, and solutions of $(C_6H_5)_2N{-}N(C_6H_5)_2$ do not oxidize at 100° C. Q_{N-O} is appreciably less than Q_{C-O}, so the formation of $(C_5H_5)_2NOO$ would be appreciably endothermic.

Insufficient study has been made of alkyl radical addition at double C=C bonds. Quantitative data on the activation energies do not exist, although ε_0 is undoubtedly $\leqslant 5$ kcal.

The most reliable data on alkyl radical additions concern dienes and molecules with conjugated double bonds generally. Such sub-

---

* Q_{HO_2-H} was determined experimentally by FONER and HUDSON [87] in 1955. Mass-spectrometric analysis was used: large amounts of HO_2 were produced by reaction between H_2O_2 and radicals generated in a discharge in water vapour. Q_{HO_2-H} was determined from the difference between the appearance potential of HO_2^+ and the ionization potential of HO_2; it was found to be 89·5 kcal. Using this in combination with thermochemical data Q_{H-O_2} was calculated to be 47·1 kcal. The values calculated above from kinetic data for these two quantities (91 and 45 kcal respectively) are thus in quite good agreement with experiment.

stances polymerize readily (e.g. styrene, butadiene, vinyl acetate, chloroprene, etc.).

The primary radicals needed in polymerization are produced by adding peroxides, hexaphenyl ethane, etc., which readily decompose to free radicals. A radical, once produced, combines with a monomer molecule (at a double bond) to give a new radical; this latter then undergoes addition at another double bond, and so on. In this way a long polymer chain may be produced. The activation energy for chain propagation ε_p is known. All the elementary reactions are identical, since propagation is scarcely affected by molecular length. For instance, in the polymerization of butadiene

$$RCH_2{=}CH{-}\dot{C}H_2$$

reacts with a butadiene molecule to produce

$$RCH_2CH{=}CHCH_2CH_2CH{=}CH{-}\dot{C}H_2$$

which is formally identical with

$$RCH_2CH{=}CH{-}\dot{C}H_2$$

If the hydrogen atoms are replaced by chlorine, or the $CH_2{=}CH$ group is replaced by some other group which also contains a double bond, e.g. $CH_3{-}\overset{\displaystyle O}{\underset{\displaystyle O-}{C{\Big\langle}}}$ as in vinyl acetate $CH_3\overset{\displaystyle O}{\underset{\displaystyle O-CH{=}CH_2}{C{\Big\langle}}}$ the polymerization can still proceed. $C{=}C$ double bonds are always converted into $C{-}C$ single bonds in polymerizations.

The energy liberated in chain growth is determined by the difference between the Q-values of the $C{-}C$ bonds and those of the $C{=}C$ bonds. Such chains usually liberate 13–22 kcal, depending on the monomer.

Some heats of polymerization and ε_p values are given below. Experiment usually gives the temperature variation of the ratio (rate constant for chain propagation):(rate constant for chain termination)$^{\frac{1}{2}}$. Termination is by free radical combination or disproportionation. The observed activation energy, ε_0, is then $\varepsilon_0 - \frac{1}{2}\varepsilon_T$, where ε_T is the activation energy for termination.

For the substitution reactions which have been investigated, $\varepsilon_T = 0$. Many workers have assumed that the same is true for polymerizations, where the radicals themselves are long-chain. However, some recent experiments have shown that ε_T may range from 1–3 kcal, so the true ε_p values may differ from the observed values by 0·5–1·5 kcal.

We shall assume that $\varepsilon_T = 0$, and will calculate ε_p directly from the temperature coefficient of the over-all photoreaction. Table 23 gives q, ε_0, and ε_p for a few polymerizations.

Table 23. *Heats of reaction and activation energies*
*for some polymerizations**

Compound	q (kcal)	ε_0 (kcal)	ε_p (kcal)
Vinyl acetate	21	4·5	4·5
Methyl acrylate	19	4·4	5·2
Styrene	16·1	5·5	6·9
Methyl methacrylate . . .	13	5·1	5·7
Butadiene	17·8	5·4	—

* The data on the first four compounds were obtained by BAGDASARYAN [115], using polymerization initiated by photolysis of benzoyl peroxide at 50° C. ε_0 for butadiene was determined by VOLMAN and GRAVAN [116] from the polymerization of butadiene, initiated by photolysis of di-*tert*.-butyl peroxide.

BAGDASARYAN [115] estimated the most reliable values for ε_p from the data in Table 23. Using the experimental ε_0, he determined the most reliable values of ε_p, which are given in column 4 of Table 23.

It follows from the above data that ε_p increases as q diminishes, the effect being quite strongly marked in this instance. Some discrepancies, which lie within the errors of experiment, were observed for methyl methacrylate.

The addition of CH_3 and C_2H_5 to carbon monoxide has not been investigated. However, FALTINGS [117] observed the formation of acetone when a mixture of ethane and carbon monoxide was irradiated in the Schumann region of the ultra-violet at low temperatures.

There is a considerable body of data in the literature on the reverse reaction, i.e. the decomposition $CH_3CO \rightarrow CH_3 + CO$. The formation of CH_3CO in the photolysis of acetone is well established; at normal temperatures, large amounts of diacetyl are formed. It has been shown by FARMER *et al.* [118] that both CH_3 and CH_3CO are formed in the mercury-sensitized photolysis of acetone (the quartz reaction vessel was directly connected to the ion source of a mass spectrograph). ε for the decomposition $CH_3CO \rightarrow CH_3 + CO$ is given values ranging from 10–20 kcal by different workers. STEACIE [10] analysed the experimental data, and concluded that the most reliable value is 18 kcal.

Q_{CH_3-CO} may be determined from the following cycle:

$$CH_3 + CH_3CHO \rightarrow CH_4 + CH_3CO + q_1$$

$$CH_3CO \rightarrow CH_3 + CO + Q$$

$$CH_4 + CO \rightarrow CH_3CHO + q_2$$

whence it follows that $q_1 + Q + q_2 = 0$.

From tabulated data [34] on ΔH for CH_4, CO, and CH_3CHO, q_2 is found to be -5 kcal. Q_{C-H} for —CHO groups is not known exactly. SZWARC [40] gives it as 85 kcal, but he considers this value to be doubtful. Q_{CH_3-H} is 101 kcal. Hence we have $q_1 = 101 - 85 = 16$ kcal, so that $Q = -q_1 - q_2 = -11$ kcal.

ε_0 is then given by $\varepsilon_0 = \varepsilon - |Q| = 18 - 11 = 7$ kcal. So the reverse reaction combination of CH_3 with CO, will evolve 11 kcal, ε being 7 kcal; the latter value is close to those given above for polymerizations.

The results cannot be considered as of any great significance, since we have good reason to suspect the accuracy of the experimental ε and also Q_{C-H} at 85 kcal for aldehyde groups (some workers give a much lower value).*

Atomic hydrogen appears to combine very slowly with carbon monoxide. For example, hydrogen atoms generated in a discharge do not react appreciably with CO. Addition of H at C=C double bonds occurs much more readily than does combination of H and CO. This indicates that ε for the latter reaction is markedly greater. If $\varepsilon_0 \simeq 2$ kcal for C=C bonds, then ε_0 is undoubtedly considerably greater for CO.

Additions at carbonyl groups RC=O have not been adequately investigated. The literature bears practically no results on gas-phase reactions of this general type involving H or Cl atoms, CH_3 or C_2H_5, etc. However, some investigations into the reverse reactions —decomposition of alkoxy radicals such as

$$\underset{\overset{|}{O\cdot}}{\overset{\overset{R}{|}}{R-C-R}} \rightarrow R + \underset{\overset{||}{O}}{R-C-R}$$

---

* SZWARC [151] and PRITCHARD [119] have recently published papers on pyrolysis of acetone in the presence of toluene, giving $Q_{CH_3CO-CH_3} = 71$–72 kcal. This permits us to calculate the heat of $CH_3CO \rightarrow CH_3 + CO$ as being 17 kcal and consequently $\varepsilon_0 = 1$ kcal, which differs considerably from our calculated value ($\varepsilon_0 \approx 7$ kcal). Thus the point for $q = 17$ kcal and $\varepsilon_0 = 1$ kcal on Fig. 5 falls considerably below the straight line.

have appeared recently. $(CH_3)_3C\dot{O}$, obtained by decomposition of di-*tert.*-butyl peroxide, $(CH_3)_3COOC(CH_3)_3$, reacts in two ways in the presence of ethylene-imine, $(CH_2)_2NH$ [120]:

(1) Decomposition, $(CH_3)_3C\dot{O} \rightarrow CH_3 + CH_3COCH_3 + q$ giving acetone and CH_3;

(2) Hydrogen transfer, $(CH_3)_3C\dot{O} + (CH_2)_2NH \rightarrow (CH_3)_3COH + (CH_2)_2\dot{N}$. The stable product is *tert.*-butyl alcohol.

Despite the ease with which hydrogen may be abstracted from the NH group, decomposition always predominates. Only at high imine concentrations is the rate of alcohol formation comparable with the rate of decomposition.

VOLMAN and GRAVEN [116] have determined ε for the decomposition of *tert.*-butoxy into acetone and CH_3, from the polymerization of butadiene as initiated by photolysis of di-*tert.*-butyl peroxide. ε was found to be $11 \cdot 2 \pm 2$ kcal, i.e. less than the value found by VOLMAN and BRINTON [120] by the previous method (17 ± 3 kcal). The latter value seems unreliable, since it was assumed that the reactions:

$$CH_3 + (CH_2)_2NH \rightarrow CH_4 + (CH_2)_2N$$

and

$$(CH_3)_3CO + (CH_2)_2NH \rightarrow (CH_3)_3COH + (CH_2)_2N$$

have the same activation energy.

We take $\varepsilon = 11$ kcal for (1). q was calculated by GRAY using data on ε and ΔH for organic nitrites and nitrates, as being -3 kcal. Then since $\varepsilon_0 = \varepsilon - q$, $\varepsilon_0 = 8$ kcal. Since the reverse reaction will be the addition of CH_3 to the $C{=}O$: bond, we have $q = 3$ kcal and $\varepsilon_0 = 8$ kcal.

$$CH_3 + CH_3COCH_3 \rightarrow CH_3{-}\overset{\displaystyle CH_3}{\underset{\displaystyle O\cdot}{C}}{-}CH_3$$

for the decomposition $C_2H_5O \rightarrow CH_3 + CH_2O$, is given [121] as about 20 kcal. $Q_{CH_2-CH_3}$ has been calculated (GRAY [50]) to be 13 kcal, so $\varepsilon_0 = 20 - 13 = 7$ kcal. The addition of CH_3 to $C{=}O$ in CH_2O has $q = 13$ kcal; ε_0 is 7 kcal.

Assuming the above values reliable, ε is evidently fairly large for addition of CH_3 to $RC{=}O$ bonds. This is due to the low q-values. From the data above one may suppose that the ease of addition at multiple bonds is due to the readiness of π-bond rupture. The Q-values of σ-bonds are usually substantially greater; reactions involving multiple bonds are often strongly exothermic. It was shown in the section on substitutions that for radical reactions, the greater q, the lower ε_0. Experiment indicates a similar relation

($\varepsilon_0 = A - |q|$) in addition (see Fig. 5 and Table 24). In many cases, however, there seems to be a considerable deviation from this relation, as can be seen from the polymerization data (see Section 11).

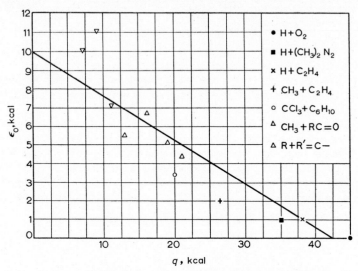

Fig. 5. Relation between ε_0 and q for addition reactions

The values of q and ε given for the addition of CH_3 at C=O bonds are very inaccurate, so a large ε coinciding with a low q is unreliable. The absence of reliable and varied experimental data implies that A and α are of low accuracy, but Fig. 5 shows that the

Table 24. *Heats of reaction and activation energies for some elementary addition reactions*

Reaction	q (kcal)	ε (kcal)	Reference
$H + O_2 \rightarrow H\dot{O}_2$	47	0	—
$H + CH_3\!-\!N\!=\!N\!-\!CH_3 \rightarrow CH_3NH\!-\!\dot{N}CH_3$	35	1	[10]
$H + C_2H_4 \rightarrow \dot{C}_2H_5$	38	1–2	[9]
$\dot{C}H_3 + C_2H_4 \rightarrow \dot{C}_3H_7$	25	1–2	[10]
$\dot{C}Cl_3 + PhH \rightarrow \langle\ \rangle\!-\!CCl_3$	20	3·4	[122]
$\dot{C}H_3 + CO \rightarrow CH_3\dot{C}O$	11 ?	7 ?	[10]
$\dot{C}H_3 + CH_2O \rightarrow C_2H_5\dot{O}$	13	7	[121]
$\dot{C}H_3 + (CH_3)_2CO \rightarrow (CH_3)_2\dot{C}O$	3	8	[116]

values of A and α are not widely different from that for substitution reactions.

The activity relationships of radicals and molecules have been established from detailed investigation of polymerization and copolymerization reactions. It appears that the theoretical aspects of radical and molecular activities in substitution reactions given above are also valid for this case. The corresponding theory was developed by BAGDASARYAN [115]. The greater the free-electron conjugation in a radical, i.e. the greater the extent of electron coupling to interatomic bonds, the lower will be the free-radical activity, and the higher will be the monomer activity. Corresponding to radical series, in which the radicals are arranged in order of increasing activity, there will thus be series of molecules, in which the molecules are arranged in order of diminishing activity. However this is not always the case, especially in copolymerization reactions, which can be explained by the polar effect (see Section 11).

8. RADICAL DECOMPOSITION AND THE ENERGIES OF π-BONDS

Q_π for π-bond formation may be determined from the thermochemistry of alkyl radicals and their halogen derivatives; the value so obtained is for an olefinic $C{=}C$ bond. Knowing Q_{C-H} for the first C—H bond in C_2H_6 (98 kcal) $\Delta H_{C_2H_5}$ is easily found: it is $+ 26$ kcal. $\Delta H_{C_2H_4}$ is known from the tables, as is also ΔH_H, for atomic hydrogen. Using these values, q in the reaction $C_2H_5 \rightarrow C_2H_4 + H + q$ may be found: $26 = 12{\cdot}5 + 51{\cdot}9 - q$ whence $q \simeq 38$ kcal.

Supposing that Q_{C-H} in C_2H_6 is similar to that in C_2H_5, Q_π can be evaluated; $98 - Q_\pi = 38$ or $Q_\pi = 98 - 38 = 60$ kcal. An analogous calculation on $C_3H_7 \rightarrow C_3H_6 + H$ gives $Q_\pi = 54$ kcal.

Q_π can also be derived from $C_3H_7 \rightarrow C_2H_4 + CH_3 + Q$ (1) using thermochemical data for the decomposition $C_3H_8 \rightarrow CH_3 + C_2H_5 - q$. ΔH is known for C_3H_8, CH_3, and C_2H_5. It follows that Q_{C-C} in C_3H_8 will be $q = - 24{\cdot}8 - 32 - 26 = - 83$ kcal (published data [40] give $- 82$ kcal). Q in (1) can now be computed. $\Delta H_{C_3H_7}$ is known from $C_3H_8 \rightarrow C_3H_7 + H - 95$ kcal. $\Delta H_{C_3H_7} = 95 - 24{\cdot}8 - 51{\cdot}9 = 18$ kcal. From the tables [34] $\Delta H_{C_2H_4} = + 12{\cdot}5$ kcal and $\Delta H_{CH_3} = + 32$ kcal. Then $Q = 18 - 12{\cdot}5 - 32 = - 26$ kcal. Q in (1) is equal to the difference between Q_{C-C} in C_3H_7 and Q_π. Assuming that Q_{C-C} in C_3H_7 is equal to that in C_3H_8 (83 kcal), we have $83 - Q_\pi = 26$, so $Q_\pi = 57$ kcal.

Thus we have obtained Q_π by three independent routes. In the three cases given above, Q_π is found to have virtually the same value, i.e. 57 ± 3 kcal.

C_2H_5 and C_3H_7 are active radicals, in which the electrons (including the valence electrons) may be reckoned as being localized. Naturally, Q_{C-C} and Q_{C-H} in such radicals scarcely differ from those in the corresponding molecules, as there are no unsaturated carbon atoms. This is why Q_π was identical in all cases.

Q_π in halogenated alkyls may be derived similarly from thermochemical data. Approximate values for the heats of (1) and (2) are given [123] as $q_1 = -26$ kcal and $q_2 = -13$ kcal. On the other hand:

(1) $H_2C-CH_2Cl \rightarrow CH_2{=}CH_2 + Cl + q_1$,
(2) $H_2C-CH_2Br \rightarrow CH_2{=}CH_2 + Br + q_2$.

these quantities may also be written as $Q_\pi' - Q_{C-Cl}$ and $Q_\pi'' - Q_{C-Br}$ respectively. We assume that the presence of a $\dot{C}H_2$ group does not influence Q_{C-X} in the CH_2X group substantially. In other words we assume that Q_{C-X} for these radicals is the same as in C_2H_5X. Then noting that Q_{C-Cl} and Q_{C-Br} for molecules are 80 and 65 kcal respectively [40], we have:

$$Q_\pi' = q_1 + Q_{C-Cl} = 54 \text{ kcal}$$
$$Q_\pi'' = q_2 + Q_{C-Br} = 52 \text{ kcal}$$

The values are somewhat lower than those given previously: this is due to the halogen atoms increasing the degree of free electron conjugation as compared with C_2H_5, this effect contributing to the increase in Q_{C-Cl} in the radical as against its value in $C_2H_4Cl_2$.

We must now pause to consider some paradoxical results, obtained by BYWATER and STEACIE [124] on the mercury-sensitized decomposition of hydrocarbons. STEACIE showed that the rate constant for $n\text{-}C_3H_7 \rightarrow CH_3 + C_2H_4$ (1) was $k_1 = 10^8 \exp(-19,000/RT)$ sec^{-1}. The pre-exponential factor, at 10^8, is incredibly low relative to the usual value for decompositions (10^{13}). (STEACIE found a normal pre-exponential factor [$k_2 = 10^{13} \exp(-40,000/RT)$ sec^{-1}] for $n\text{-}C_3H_7 \rightarrow C_3H_6 + H$.) Such a small pre-exponential factor is theoretically quite inexplicable. It is not difficult to demonstrate that STEACIE's results are inaccurate, however. Actually, thermochemical data and Q_{C-H} in CH_4 and C_3H_8 indicate that (1) is endothermic (26 kcal) (see above). So ε must be greater than 26 kcal, since $\varepsilon = \varepsilon_0 + Q$. STEACIE found $\varepsilon = 19$ kcal, on the other hand; this is clearly impossible. Later, STEACIE [72] gave in his monograph some thermochemical calculations on (1) above. It was shown that (1) was endothermic (23 kcal for $n\text{-}C_3H_7$, and 26 kcal for $iso\text{-}C_3H_7$). Consequently, the activation energies published previously [124, 125], namely 19–20 kcal, must be incorrect.

STEACIE and MANDELCORN also showed by photolysis of acetone in the presence of C_3H_4, that ε_0 for the addition of CH_3 to ethylene was comparatively high (7 kcal). The usual value previously assumed was 2–3 kcal.

The error in ε is actually due to the amount of C_3H_4 produced being used to determine the rate constant for the decomposition of C_3H_7. The mercury-sensitized cracking reactions are themselves complex, and only by using assumptions which are clearly untrue was STEACIE able to relate the rate of ethylene formation with the rate of the initial step in the decomposition. Clearly, 10^8 as a pre-exponential factor is characteristic not of the elementary decomposition but of the complex overall process.

The rate constant for $C_3H_7 \rightarrow C_3H_6 + H$ as found by STEACIE is not affected by the argument, since this is endothermic (38 kcal), and the activation energy given (about 40 kcal) is quite acceptable; it gives $\varepsilon_0 \simeq 2$ kcal, in agreement with the value found from $H + C_3H_6 \rightarrow C_3H_7$. All alkyl radical decompositions should evidently be taken as having pre-exponential factors of 10^{13}, and low values of ε_0.

9. RADICAL ISOMERIZATIONS

We come now to the third class of radical reactions—isomerizations. We must first consider the angle between the direction of radical approach, and the strength of the bond under attack, since this has a marked effect on the ease of reaction. Very rough quantum-mechanical calculations show that the most advantageous angle of attack occurs when the bond axis and the direction of free valency approach lie in the same straight line, in the case of σ-bonds. If the atom A attacks a diatomic molecule BC, the probability of reaction is greatest when the three atoms lie in the same straight line. It is difficult to estimate the activation energy for approach perpendicular to the bond-axis; rough quantum-mechanical estimates indicate a very large increase, the value being approximately doubled (see Appendix II). Unfortunately experiment has not yet decided the question. The π-orbitals are perpendicular to the bond-axis, and perpendicular approach is then naturally the most favourable.

The direction of approach is not very important in addition or substitution, since only collisions along the most favourable directions are effective. The fact that not all possible collisions are equally effective is accounted for by the steric factor. But the direction of approach is of considerable importance in radical isomerizations.

Isomerizations will be taken as reactions internal to the radical, in which the free valency attacks some other bond in the same radical.

For example,

$$H-\underset{\underset{H}{|}}{\overset{\overset{H}{|}}{C}}-\underset{\underset{H}{|}}{\overset{\overset{H}{|}}{C}}-\underset{\underset{H}{|}}{\overset{}{C}}-H \rightarrow H-\underset{\underset{H}{|}}{\overset{}{C}}-\underset{\underset{H}{|}}{\overset{\overset{H}{|}}{C}}-\underset{\underset{H}{|}}{\overset{\overset{H}{|}}{C}}-H$$

Such reactions occur by transfer of an atom (in this case H) and by free valency transfer (active centre migration). They are thus distinct from the decompositions considered above (type (2′)):

(a) $H_3C-CH-CH_3 \rightarrow H + H_2C = CH-CH_3$ or

(b) $H_2C-CH_2-CH_3 \rightarrow H_2C = CH_2 + CH_3$

In these the free electron acts upon an electron in a σ-bond (C—H in (a), C—C in (b)) causing its transfer, and form a new π-bond. The pre-existing σ-bond is thus broken. Electron transfer is not here accompanied by positional transfer of an atom. Breakage of σ-bonds leads to radical decomposition. The free valency electron also causes the transfer of an electron from a σ-type C—H bond in the isomerization above. However, when an atom is transferred simultaneously one σ-bond is ruptured at the same instant as another is formed, just as in substitution. The difference between transfer and isomerization reactions is simply that in transfer the radical abstracts an atom from another molecule, while in isomerization it merely abstracts an atom from another part of itself.

The following features distinguish the kinetics of isomerizations:

(1) Isomerizations are unimolecular, while transfer reactions are bimolecular. Rates of isomerization take the form:

$$w_{is} = 10^{12} \exp\left(-\varepsilon_1/RT\right) [R]$$

while the rate of a substitution has the form:

$$w_{sub} = 10^{-10} \exp\left(-\varepsilon_2/RT\right) [R][M]$$

where [R] is the radical concentration, and [M] is the molecular concentration. At atmospheric pressure, $[M] \simeq 10^{19}$, so

$$w_{is}/w_{sub} = 10^4 \exp\left[-(\varepsilon_1 - \varepsilon_2)/RT\right]$$

If ε_1 and ε_2 are identical, then isomerization is 10^4 times more rapid than substitution.

(2) Since the angle of attack is bound to be other than zero in isomerization, $\varepsilon_1 - \varepsilon_2 = \Delta\varepsilon$ will, in all probability, be positive. At high temperatures, when the effect of $\exp\left(-\Delta\varepsilon/RT\right)$ is small, isomerization will predominate over transfer, since the pre-exponential factors favour isomerization. At low temperatures the relationship will probably be reversed if $\Delta\varepsilon$ is positive.

Soviet workers have recently examined the question whether

isomerization is a general property of free radicals [126].* Some phenomena in the oxidation of hydrocarbons can only be explained by isomerization.

The routes by which the various products (alcohols, aldehydes, unsaturated hydrocarbons, etc.) were formed, and the complexity of the products, could only be explained by free-radical isomerization. This may be illustrated by the following very simple example.

FOK and NALBANDYAN [128–130] showed that in the mercury-sensitized photo-oxidations of CH_4, C_2H_6, and C_3H_8 at low temperatures, the only products were peroxides, formed in the chain reaction:

(1) $CH_3 + O_2 \rightarrow CH_3OO$

(2) $CH_3OO + CH_4 \rightarrow CH_3OOH + CH_3$

or in the general case:

(1') $R + O_2 \rightarrow RO_2$

(2') $RO_2 + RH \rightarrow ROOH + R$

But above 100° C aldehydes were formed as well as peroxides. The available kinetic data show that under these conditions aldehydes do not result from secondary hydroperoxide reactions, but are formed separately. At still higher temperatures the primary product was almost entirely aldehyde. These results may clearly be explained by the peroxide radical decomposing to aldehyde and OH at the higher temperatures, before it has time to react as in (2):

$$CH_3O\dot{O} \rightarrow CH_2O + \dot{O}H$$

This decomposition can only be explained by an isomerization:

$$
\begin{array}{ccc}
H_3C & & H_2{-}\dot{C} \\
| & \rightarrow & | \\
\dot{O}{-}O & & HO{-}O
\end{array}
$$

followed by decomposition of the latter to aldehyde and OH. The OH reacts with CH_4, to give CH_3 and H_2O (transfer reaction).

Due to the very high ε for isomerization, as compared with transfer, the aldehyde is found as the main product only at the highest temperatures. Many such reactions, assigned to different schemes by various workers, cannot be put into the same form without

---

* In 1936, GLAZEBROOK and PEARSON [127] investigated the photolysis of di-*iso*propyl ketone, trapping the radicals with metallic mercury. After treating the product with HgI_2, they obtained, much to their surprise, n-C_3H_7HgI. The authors presumed that the primary decomposition-product was *iso*-C_3H_7, and that hydrogen migration, to give n-C_3H_7, occurs at the instant of combination with the mercury, since they were unable to observe any isomerization in the absence of the metal.

assuming radical isomerization phenomena. For instance, the proposed scheme for the decomposition of ethylene oxide contains the radical C_2H_3O [131]. In order to explain the reaction product composition C_2H_3O must be supposed to decompose to CH_3 and CO. This is difficult to understand unless the radical is assumed to isomerize first:

$$CH_2\!-\!\overset{\displaystyle O}{\overset{\displaystyle \triangle}{}}\!\dot{C}H \rightarrow \overset{\displaystyle O}{\underset{\displaystyle H_2\ H}{\dot{C}\!-\!C}} \rightarrow \overset{\displaystyle O}{\underset{\displaystyle H_3}{C\!-\!\dot{C}}} \rightarrow CH_3 + CO$$

This is the principal step in the chain pyrolysis of ethylene oxide proposed by LOSSING and INGOLD [131]. The ethylene oxide was decomposed at low concentrations in helium, analysis being mass-spectrometric. Over the range 800–1000° C, $p_{He} = 15$ mm, $p_{C_2H_4O} = 9{\cdot}24 - 28 \times 10^{-3}$ mm and the contact time was 8×10^{-4} sec.

Apart from the stable compounds CH_4, CO (and small amounts of C_2H_6 and CH_2CO), a large $[CH_3]$ was demonstrated. CH_2 was not observed. $[CH_3]$ and $[CH_4]$ were close to $[CO]$. The carbon balance was struck at 92–99 per cent, and the oxygen balance at 100 per cent.

The occurrence of alkyl radical isomerization even at room temperature also follows from the experiments of VOEVODSKII and MARDALEISHVILI [132] on the exchange of deuterium with $CH_2CH(CH_3)_2$, $CH_2CH_2CH_3$ and $cyclo$-C_6H_{11}. They have found that radical recombination products in $H + D_2 +$ olefin mixtures are extensively deuterated (up to 50 per cent). Such an amount of deuterium cannot be explained from the consecutive mechanism

(1) $R + D_2 \rightarrow RD + D$
(2) $RD + D \rightarrow HD + R'D$
(3) $R'D + D \rightarrow R'D_2 + D*$

* Contrary to VOEVODSKII and his co-workers, WHITTLE and STEACIE [134] have shown that CH_3 and C_2H_5 do not exchange extensively with D_2 when produced by photolysis of the corresponding ketones, azo-derivatives, or mercury dialkyls, only monodeutero derivatives being formed. FOK and CHERNYSHEVA have shown that CH_3D is obtained from photochemically generated CH_3, not only at the high temperatures and pressures STEACIE used (100–400° C and 100 mm Hg), but also at room temperatures and 0·5 mm Hg; i.e. under the same conditions as in discharge tubes. The discrepancy between STEACIE's and VOEVODSKII's data cannot be explained, unless we assume (with VOEVODSKII) that it is due to differences in the methods of producing the radicals. In any case it was shown in these experiments that exchange between radical and molecular deuterium actually takes place under certain conditions, the rate of exchange being very high. Though lack of extensive exchange cannot be considered as proving that free radicals are absent, the occurrence of polydeuterated products in amounts that cannot be accounted for by consecutive substitution can apparently be considered as evidence of free valency formation.

since it was shown that the saturated molecules do not react with D_2 under these conditions [133]. Thus it is assumed that the polydeuterated compound is formed only after all the H atoms in C_nH_{2n+1} have been exchanged for D prior to it being saturated.

Free valancies in alkyl radicals can only assist exchange in their vicinity.

The extensive exchange in *cyclo*-C_6H_{11} and $(CH_3)_2CH\ CH_2$ proves that the free valency can be transferred from one site to another in these reactions.

The same authors [133] also showed that *n*-C_3H_7 exchanges more than two hydrogen atoms with O atoms; they supposed that H atoms could be transferred between the terminal groups—a form of isomerization. Since C_2H_5 only exchanges two hydrogen atoms, it may be deduced that hydrogen transfer between neighbouring carbon atoms in the α-position is unlikely. In *n*-C_3H_7, transfer occurs between two carbon atoms joined via a third carbon atom, like in C_4H_9; consequently, extensive deuteration takes place. From steric considerations the transfer to the neighbouring β-position is easier.

The carbon chain in propane, it should be remembered, is not straight:

$$\text{HCH} \overset{\overset{\displaystyle H_2}{\diagup C \diagdown}}{} \text{CH}$$

accordingly, hydrogen transfer from the terminal group is more favoured (as regards the angle of attack) than that from the central carbon atom. Transfer is easiest between the CH_3 groups, exactly as in *iso*-C_4H_9.

In those cases where isomerization at the β-position is hindered (e.g. in the system $H + (CH_3)_2C{=}C(CH_3)_2 + D_2$), extensive exchange is not observed, since isomerization at the β-position cannot occur in the radical obtained by addition of a hydrogen atom, on account of its marked endothermicity (10–12 kcal).

$$\begin{array}{ccc} CH_3 & & CH_3 \\ \diagdown & & \diagup \\ & CH{-}\dot{C} & \\ \diagup & & \diagdown \\ CH_3 & & CH_3 \end{array}$$

Free valency transfer in alkyl radicals would be quite similar to isomerization in oxygenated radicals.

NESMEYANOV *et al.* [157–9] have investigated the isomerization of neutral aliphatic radicals in solution

$$CCl_3\dot{C}\overset{X}{-}CH_2Y \rightarrow \dot{C}Cl_2C\overset{X}{\underset{Cl}{-}}CH_2Y$$

$$\qquad\quad A \qquad\qquad\qquad B$$

where

$$X = H, \quad H, \quad H, \quad CH_3, \quad CH_3, \quad Cl, \quad Cl, \quad Br$$
$$Y = Br, \quad Cl, \quad CCl_3, \quad Br, \quad Cl, \quad Br, \quad Cl, \quad Br.$$

The type A radicals were obtained by chain reaction with hydrogen bromide, the benzoyl peroxide catalyzed addition of CCl_3Br and Br_2 to compounds such as $CCl_3CX = CH_2$ being used under mild conditions in CCl_4 at 50–60°C. If no isomerization was involved the hydrogen bromide reaction should have been

$$CCl_3CX{=}CH_2 + HBr \xrightarrow{Bz_2O_2} CCl_3CXHCH_2Br \qquad (1)$$

In no case studied (X = H,CH$_3$Cl) was a type 1 compound formed but instead ones of types 2, 3 and 4

$$CCl_3CX{=}CH_2 + HBr \xrightarrow{Bz_2O_2} \begin{cases} HCCl_2CXClCH_2Br & (2) \\ CCl_2 = CXCH_2Br & (3) \ (II) \\ HCCl_2CXClCH_2Cl & (4) \end{cases}$$

Their formation can be explained by assuming the A radical (CCl_3CXCH_2Br) to isomerize to the B ($CCl_2CXClCH_2Br$), which produces $HCCl_2CXClCH_2Br$ with HBr and regenerates a Br atom. The mechanisms were thus assumed to be similar to the peroxide-catalyzed additions of hydrogen halides to olefins the A and A′ radicals isomerizing to radicals B and B′ at stages (c) and (f):

$$Bz_2O_2 \quad C_6H_5$$

(a) $C_6H_5 + HBr \rightarrow C_6H_6 + Br$

(b) $CCl_3CX{=}CH_2 + Br \rightarrow CCl_3CXCH_2Br$
          A

(c) $CCl_3CXCH_2Br \xrightarrow{isomerization} CCl_2CXClCH_2Br$
      A   B

(d) $CCl_2CXClCH_2Br + HBr \rightarrow HCCl_2CXClCH_2Br + Br$ (III)
                                            (2)

(e) $CCl_3CXCH_2Br + CCl_3CX{=}CH_2 \rightarrow CCl_2$
                                             (3)
                    $={=}CXCH_2Br + CCl_3CXCH_2Cl$
                                              A′

(f) $CCl_2CXCH_2Cl \xrightarrow{isomerization} CCl_2CXClCH_2Cl$
          A′   B′

(g) $CCl_2CXClCH_2Cl + HBr \rightarrow HCCl_2CXClCH_2Cl + Br$

Compounds 2, 3 and 4 were isolated in the pure state, and their structures were determined by conventional procedures. When

1,1,1-trichloropropene reacted with bromine [157–9] under the same conditions the normal addition products 5 and 6 (resulting from isomerization) were produced,

$$CCl_3CH{=}CH_2 + Br_2 \xrightarrow{Bz_2O_2} \begin{cases} CCl_3CHBrCH_2Br & (5) \\ BrCCl_2CHClCH_2Br & (6) \end{cases} \quad (IV)$$

(5) might have been formed by the electrophilic addition of bromine at the double bond; the A radicals may also possibly have reacted with bromine both with and without isomerization

$$CCl_3CHCH_2Br \xrightarrow{\text{isomerization}} CCl_2CHClCH_2Br \xrightarrow{Br_2}$$

$$A \searrow Br_2$$

$$BrCCl_2CHClCH_2Br + Br \quad (V)$$

$$\searrow CCl_3CHBrCH_2Br + Br$$

(5) and (6) were also produced by photoreaction between 1,1,1-trichloropropene and bromine, whereas in the dark and with no peroxide the only product was (5). In all cases the radical intermediate isomerized so homolytic isomerization in solution (isomeric conversion by a radical chain mechanism) has occurred, (the numerous molecular rearrangements in solution hitherto studied were heterolytic). NESMEYANOV *et al.* [157–9] have discovered a case of radical (or molecular) chain isomerization; 1,1,1-trichloro-2-bromopropene isomerizes completely to 1,1,2-trichloro-3-bromopropene-1 after an induction period of 1 to 2 days at room temperature.

$$CCl_3CBr{=}CH_2 \xrightarrow{h\nu} CCl_2 = CClCH_2Br$$
$$(7) \hspace{4.5cm} (8)$$

Ultraviolet light initiates this isomerization, and small amounts of hydroquinone or dimethylaniline inhibit it; the mechanism seems to be rather similar to that for the chloro-radicals above, the scheme proposed being

$$C_3Cl_3BrH_2 \xrightarrow{h\nu} Br + C_3Cl_3H_2$$
$$CCl_3CBr{=}CH_2 + Br \rightarrow CCl_3CBrCH_2Br$$
$$CCl_3CBrCH_2Br \xrightarrow{\text{isomerization}} CCl_2CBrClCH_2Br \quad (VI)$$
$$CCl_2CBrClCH_2Br + CCl_3CBr{=}CH_2$$
$$\rightarrow CCl_2C{=}ClCH_2Br + CCl_3CBrCH_2Br$$
$$(9)$$

10. TRANSFER REACTIONS

It only remains to add a few words on transfer reactions in order to complete our survey of different types of free radical reaction.

Essentially, the reactions considered above were transfer reactions, in which the radical saturates its own valency by abstracting an atom from a molecule; we have not touched upon reactions in which some fairly complex radical may be abstracted.

The following are examples of such reactions:

(1) $\dot{H} + CH_3CH_2CH_3 \rightarrow CH_4 + \dot{C}_2H_5,$

(2) $\dot{C}H_3 + CH_3CH_2CH_3 \rightarrow C_2H_6 + \dot{C}_2H_5,$

(3) $\dot{C}H + CH_3\!-\!\underset{\|}{\underset{O}{C}}\!-\!\underset{\|}{\underset{O}{C}}\!-\!CH_3 \rightarrow CH_3\!-\!\underset{\|}{\underset{O}{C}}\!-\!CH_3 + CH_3\dot{C}O,$

(4) $H + PhCH_3 \rightarrow PhH + \dot{C}H_3.$

The simplest assumption would be that these involve attack on C—C σ-bonds, approach being perpendicular to the bond-axis. However, this is not plausible since such a mode of attack is accompanied by special difficulties.

$$\dot{H} + H\!-\!\overset{H}{\underset{H}{C}}\!-\!CH_2CH_3 \rightarrow CH_4 + \dot{C}_2H_5$$

End-wise attack (as in type (1)) is rendered difficult by the repulsion of the CH_3 group H atoms, since a Walden inversion must occur upon reaction. This would be expected to involve a high activation energy (14–16 kcal), in agreement with experiment. Thus OGG and POLANYI [135] showed that ε for exchange between atomic iodine and iso-BuI in which a Walden inversion takes place, was 14 kcal.

$$I + \overset{R_1}{\underset{R_3}{\overset{\diagup}{C}}}\!\!-\!I \rightarrow I\!-\!\overset{R_1}{\underset{R_3}{\overset{\diagup}{C}}} + I$$

The exchange between ionic bromine and bromomethanes, investigated with radioactive Br [136], showed activation energies varying between 16 and 26 kcal. Reactions of this type are to be expected in relatively few cases, except at high temperatures.

There are reasons for believing that reactions of types (3) and (4), involving molecules with double bonds, take place in two steps: (a) addition of the radical at the double bond; (b) decomposition of the resulting radical with C—C bond rupture. Combination of atomic hydrogen with cyanogen may occur in just such a fashion:

$$H + N{\equiv}C{-}C{\equiv}N \rightarrow \overset{H}{\dot{N}}{=}C{-}C{\equiv}N \rightarrow \overset{H}{N}{\equiv}C + \dot{C}N$$

(3) and (4) are probably analogous; for (3) we then have:

$$\dot{C}H_3 + CH_3{-}\underset{\underset{O}{\|}}{C}{-}\underset{\underset{O}{\|}}{C}{-}CH_3 \rightarrow CH_3{-}\underset{\underset{\cdot O}{|}}{\overset{\overset{CH_3}{|}}{C}}{-}\underset{\underset{O}{\|}}{C}{-}CH_3 \rightarrow CH_3\underset{\underset{O}{\|}}{\overset{\overset{CH_3}{|}}{C}} + \dot{C}{-}CH_3$$

ε was found to be 5–6 kcal by BLACET and BELL [137] from the photolysis of diacetyl. The above hypothesis as to the mechanisms of similar reactions was first proposed by DARWENT [138], at the Faraday Society Discussion in 1952.

11. POLAR FACTORS IN ORGANIC REACTIONS

It is commonly acknowledged in organic chemistry that the directions and rates of organic reactions are determined by the electron-density distributions in molecules. In electrophilic reactions the points of highest density react most readily—or of lowest density in the nucleophilic case. The rates are largest when the reacting groups are most positive and negative.

This purely electrostatic treatment of reactivity is not in theory justified, i.e. the electron-densities in the reactants do not completely determine the rate. It is still very difficult to test this theory by experiment since the exact density distributions are unknown for most molecules. The densities are often assumed quite arbitrarily which frequently results in unfounded conclusions as to the causes of reactions.

The electronic theory of organic chemistry developed from empirical rules applicable to heterolytic additions, lyses, substitutions etc., in particular relating to aromatic substitution.

But we should remember that the reaction heats of the elementary steps depend on the reactant and product molecular structures (electron-densities in particular) and hence the introduction of polar groups naturally alters heats of reaction.

The empirical reactivity rules may be explainable by activation energy changes dependent on reaction heat changes, as in radical reactions.

Unfortunately, the heats of elementary reactions between ions and molecules are mostly unknown. So we can consider the empirical laws only qualitatively.

Let us consider the elementary addition of X^+ (e.g. NO_2^+) to an aromatic* containing a substituent Y:

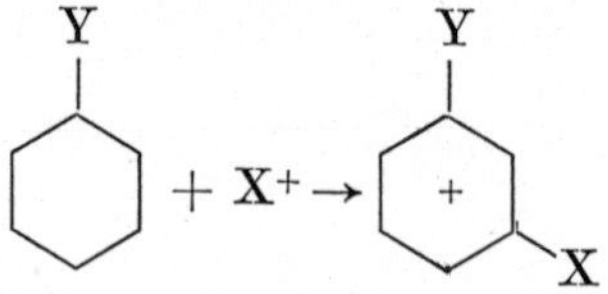

If Y is electronegative (e.g. Cl) electron transfer to the C—X bond must be impeded relative to benzene itself. In fact, no matter what bond is formed (σ-type C—X bond or π-type complex) it will be weaker, i.e. the energy liberated by bond-formation will be less, the more the electrons are drawn off by Y. If, as in radical reactions, the activation energy rises as the heat of reaction decreases, the polar group must reduce the rate, as is found.*

This argument is somewhat analogous to that for radical reactions above. Thus the inertness of benzyl relative to CH_3 we explain by the new bond formed in $C_6H_5CH_2 + RH \rightarrow C_6H_5CH_3 + R$ having, roughly speaking, to extract an electron conjugated to the phenyl, this latter here acting as "negative" substituent. This reduces the energy liberated and increases the activation energy.

Thus in both heterolytic and radical reactions the rate drop is caused by the electron transfer being endothermic. The arguments from energy involved in POLANYI's rule here agree with those from the electronic theory, which relate the rate reduction to the decreased electron-density, although the reasons given are essentially different.

The above arguments would appear to be confirmed by HAMMETT's rule [140, 141]. This rule has been verified for many heterolytic reactions on side-chains attached to benzene nuclei containing ortho- and para-substituents, the rule being

$$\log \frac{k_i}{k_0} = \rho\sigma$$

k_i and k_0 are the rate constants for the substituted and unsubstituted compounds respectively, σ a constant related only to the substituent, and ρ a constant for the particular class of reactions.

When the entropy factors are equal this implies that the activation energy changes for various side-chain reactions are proportional to

---

* MELANDER [139] has shown from isotope effects that the rate-determining step in electrophilic substitution is the addition, at least in nitration.

one another for any given polar substituent. Since ρ for each reaction series is the same if the pre-exponential factors are equal

$$\frac{1}{\sigma_i} \log \frac{k_i}{k_0} = \frac{1}{\sigma_j} \log \frac{k_j}{k_0}$$

Since

$$\log \frac{k_i}{k_0} = \frac{(E_0 - E_i)}{2 \cdot 3 RT}$$

$$E_0 - E_i = \Delta E_i = \frac{\sigma_i}{\sigma_j} (E_0 - E_j) = \frac{\sigma_i}{\sigma_j} \Delta E_j *$$

On the other hand we can anticipate that the heats of the elementary stages will change in proportion when polar substituents are introduced. These reactions involve side-chain bond formation or breakage, e.g. alkali hydrolyses of esters have rate-limiting steps involving OH^- combining with the side-chain CO groups.

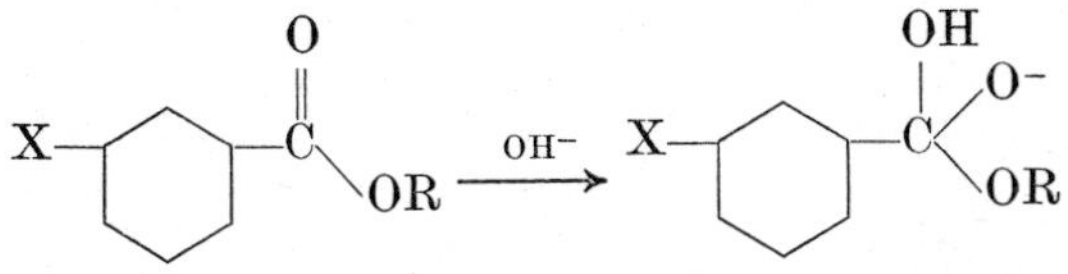

The simplest example is the dissociation of a substituted benzoic acid

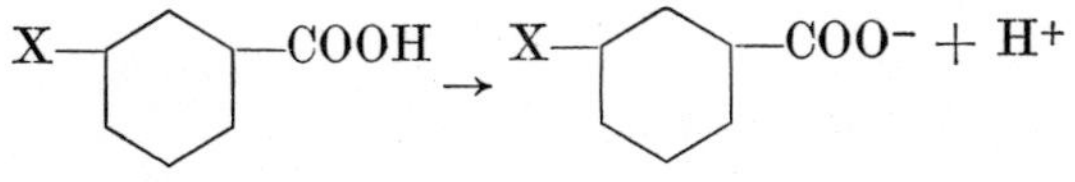

The energy liberated here depends on the bond types and the various active groups present. Since the substances compared differ only in the substituent the bond-energy differences are due to the substituent. The magnitude of the effect will depend on the side-chain length. The further the bond from the ring, the less the effect. To a first approximation it can be represented as γX, where the substituent determines X and the side-chain position γ. If Q_0' to the parent compound for one substituent the bond-energy becomes $Q_0' - \gamma_1 X_1$, for another, $Q_0' - \gamma_1 X_2$, and the difference $\gamma_1(X_1 - X_2)$. For another reaction we thus have $Q_0'' - \gamma_2 X_1$ and $Q_0'' - \gamma_2 X_2$, and the difference $\gamma_2(X_1 - X_2)$. Thus the differences in heats of reaction between the two series of reactions, being determined by the bond-energies, are proportional with a proportionality constant $\gamma_1 \gamma_2$.

* The same relation is obtained if the logs of the pre-exponential factors are linearly related to the activation energies, as is frequently found, particularly in liquid-phase reactions.

6

This is particularly confirmed by HAMMETT's rule also covering the equilibrium constants of certain reactions (in particular σ is defined as $\log K_i/K_0$, where the K's are the dissociation constants for the respective benzoic acids) i.e. the heats of reaction are proportional.

Thus the observed activation energy changes due to polar substituents are proportionate to the heats of the elementary reaction steps. The changes are proportional to one another. As $\Delta E_i = -\beta\Delta q_i$, $E_i = A - \beta q_i{}^*$ i.e. heterolytic reactions give a relation analogous to POLANYI's rule.

Thus polar effects influence reaction rates via heats of reaction. This appears in a qualitative fashion quite often. After all, the polarity of a group is often judged by its effect on acid or base strength, i.e. purely energetically. But a quantitative relation is very often not found. HAMMETT's rule remains unfulfilled even for *ortho*-derivatives, as well as for most aliphatics. This is because steric effects also occur on polar substitution and the entropy terms are not equal. This is particularly clearly seen in *ortho*-derivatives of benzene when the substituent is very close to the reaction site, HAMMETT's rule not being obeyed [140]. The steric effects affect both entropy and activation energy. The effects can sometimes be allowed for more or less directly and hence steric effects differentiated from polar ones. TAFT [142] has done this for certain reactions. The rate constant changes due to purely polar effects appear here to follow HAMMETT's rule. This implies that the above $q - E$ relation for polar substituents applies widely in chemistry.

In radical reactions polarity often operates quite differently from in heterolytic ones. The above rule for heterolytic benzene substitutions does not apply to radical reactions on aromatics. Homolytic substitution occurs roughly equally at all benzene ring positions. A clear directive influence being absent is often taken as evidence for the radical character of the reaction. Thus it has been shown [143] that in homolytic replacement of H by phenyl in aromatics (fluoro-, chloro-, bromo-, nitro-benzene, etc.) a mixture of isomeric diphenyls with the *o*-form predominating ($\sim$ 60 per cent) is formed. Table 25 gives the isomer proportions in certain phenylations.

The data of Table 25 differ considerably from those for heterolytic reactions (nitration, sulphonation, alkylation). In fact 93 per cent *m*-dinitrobenzene is formed on nitrating nitrobenzene, while on phenylating this compound the *m*-isomer is the least abundant. Sulphonation and alkylation also mainly give the *p*-isomer with minute amounts of the *m*-derivative. Latterly HEY *et al.* [144] have

---

* The minus sign implies that similar changes in equilibrium and rate constants imply opposed changes in activation energy and heat of reaction.

Table 25. Isomer contents from phenylation

Compound	Isomer Contents, %		
	o	*m*	*p*
C_6H_5F . . .	54	31	15
C_6H_5Cl . . .	63	23	14
C_6H_5Br . .	49	33	18
$C_6H_5NO_2$ . .	57	10	33

determined the isomer proportions on phenylating several alkyl-
benzenes. Here (see Table 26) the isomer proportions differ from
those found in nitration (heterolytic).

Table 26. Isomer contents from nitration and phenylation

		$C_6H_5CH_3$	$C_6H_5C_2H_5$	$iso\text{-}C_3H_7C_6H_5$	$tert.\text{-}C_7MgC_6H_5$
Nitration	*o*	57	55	30	11·8
	m	3	0	7·7	8·7
	p	40	45	62·3	79·5
Phenylation	*o*	66·5	53	31	24
	m	19·2	28	42	49
	p	14·3	19	27	27

This difference between heterolytic and radical reactions is
natural. In heterolytic substitution the heteropolar substituent
can easily donate or accept electrons, thereby becoming charged.
The heat of reaction for an electropositive substituent (e.g. NH_2)
can thereby increase because the ionization potential of the hetero-
atom is much lower than that of carbon. Hence we get the reaction

From this concept we can explain certain orientation rules for
benzene qualitatively. The *ortho–para* directing action in electrophilic substitution exerted by groups such as NH_2, OH, etc., is
because the hetero-atom can only be charged when addition occurs

at these points, as above. No such structure is possible in the *meta*-position.

When the radical R combines a new radical is formed:

If A loses an electron only a fresh radical can be formed.

The energy absorption in such a transfer is generally zero, or in any case much less than in heterolytic substitution. So the nature of the substituent only influences radical reactions slightly. SZWARC's data for Q_{C-Br} in various substituted bromobenzenes and benzyl bromides [74, 145] confirm this, as do PRITCHARD's [119] data on Q_{C-C} in compounds with C—H replaced by C—F. Tables 8, 27 and 28 show that the various polar substituents only affect Q_{C-Br} slightly.

Table 27. Q_{C-Br} for some substituted benzyl bromides [145]

Substituent	Q kcal	Substituent	Q kcal
o-Cl	0·9	*m*-Me	0·0
m-Cl	0·1	*p*-Me	1·4
p-Cl	0·4	*m*-NO$_2$	2·1
m-Br	0·3	*p*-NO$_2$	1·1
p-Br	0·3	*m*-CN	1·4
o-Me	− 2·0	*p*-CN	0·7

In spite of the above, activation energy changes may not always be due to q alone. It is very likely that the electron-density distribution also affects A in $E = A - \alpha q$ to some extent. Although there is no clear experimental evidence for this a number of factors point to it.

Firstly, the presence of a charge sometimes undoubtedly reduces

Table 28. C—C *bond-energies* [119]

Compound	Q kcal
$CH_3N = NCH_3$ . .	4·6
$CF_3N = NCF_3$ . .	48·5
$CH_3CO\ CH_3$ . .	70·9
$CF_3CO\ CF_3$ . .	67·8

the activation energy. Thus simple positive ions react with molecules with very low activation energies when the heats of reaction are close to 0. This implies $A = 0$ for these reactions. [44, 45, 146, 147].

(1) $NH_3^+ + C_3H_6 \rightarrow C_3H_7^+ + NH_2$ $\qquad + 2$ kcal
(2) $C_3H_6^+ + C_2H_6 \rightarrow C_3H_7^+ + C_2H_5$ $\qquad + 2$ kcal
(3) $H_2S^+ + H_2O \rightarrow H_3O^+ + HS$ $\qquad + 3$ kcal
(4) $CH_3^+ + H_2O \rightarrow H_3O^+ + CH_2$ $\qquad 0 \pm 4$ kcal

ε is also much reduced in halogen atom reactions, A being much lower. Thus when Cl atoms react with CH_4 ε is 3·9 kcal, whereas CF_3 and CH_3 have $\varepsilon = 10$–12 kcal when reacting with CH_4 [148], while ε_0 for the CF_3 reaction is about 2 kcal less than for CH_3. The heats of reaction are almost the same in all cases.

RAZUVAEV *et al.* [149] have shown that polar substituents in acyl peroxides raise the stabilities of the radicals formed on decomposition (this is somewhat contrary to SZWARC's data*). Thus the nitrobenzoyl radicals produced from *p*- or *m*-nitrobenzoyl peroxide are more stable against decomposition with the elimination of CO_2 than unsubstituted benzoyl radicals.

Polar effects are also observed in certain liquid-phase reactions. Work on the radical-initiated chlorinations and brominations of *m*- and *p*-substituted toluenes and chlorinations of substituted *iso*-butanes showed that polar substituents affect the reaction rate— positive ones being accelerators and negative ones retardants. HAMMETT's rule covers the rate ratios for substituted and unsubstituted toluene. In bromination $\rho = 1$·05, in chlorination 1·55. Remembering the usual bromination chain mechanism:

(1) $Br + C_6H_5CH_3 \xrightarrow{k_1} C_6H_5CH_2 + HBr$
(2) $C_6H_5CH_2 + Br_2 \xrightarrow{k_2} C_6H_5CH_2Br + Br$

* SZWARC's data relate to high temperatures where changes in ε of 1·2 kcal lie within the error of experiment. But at low temperatures such a difference is important. The conflict, which also appears in the papers quoted below may be due to this fact.

and assuming the chains are not too short we find that in mixtures of substituted and unsubstituted toluenes the rate-constant ratios will be k_i'/k_1, where k_i' are for (1) for substituted and unsubstituted toluenes respectively. Also Q_{C-H}, which determines the differences in heats of reaction in (1) on introducing polar substituents, is almost independent of the substituent. So we here have a polar effect which only alters the rate (i.e. ε) and not q. The equilibrium constants for (1) should thus not obey HAMMETT's rule, unlike what is found with heterolytic reactions. The sole deduction from this is that, contrary to SZWARC's data for high temperatures, Q can be changed by a polar substituent by several kcal, which has a large effect on the rates of low-temperature liquid-phase reactions (-60 to $\sim +100°C$).

Data confirming this have recently been obtained. Thus SZWARC [151] studied the decompositions of polar-substituted tetrazanes to free radicals in acetone at -60 to $-10°C$:

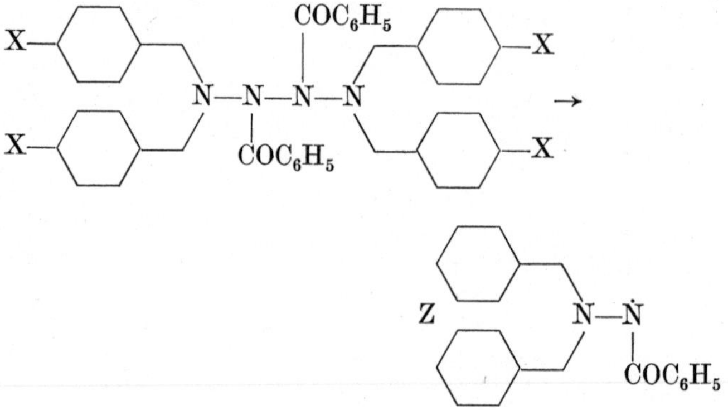

HAMMETT's rule, $\log (K/K_0) = \rho\sigma$ was obeyed, while the q-values being here the Q_{N-N}, were linearly related to σ: $Q = 3\cdot2\sigma + 8\cdot9$ (1'). Since σ can vary by several units between substituents (here $-0\cdot7$ to $+0\cdot9$) Q_{N-N} depends very strongly on the substituent.

The rates of dissociation and ε's for the tetrazanes were also measured. Using these and the q-values the rates and ε's for the reverse dimerization were computed. The equilibrium constant changes also followed HAMMETT's, and ε was linearly related to σ

$$\varepsilon = -2\cdot0\sigma + 7\cdot1 \qquad (2)$$

This implies that POLANYI's rule must be obeyed. In fact the data give

$$\varepsilon = 12\cdot6 - 0\cdot62\,q$$

[(1) and (2) imply this].

Thus this clearly demonstrates HAMMETT's and POLANYI's laws to be connected. Whereas the connexion was previously established indirectly, here where the rupture of a single bond is involved the relation follows directly from experiment plus certain theoretical considerations.

12. POLAR FACTORS IN POLYMERIZATION*

Four chain propagation reactions can occur on copolymerizing two monomers:

(1) $\sim \dot{A} + A \xrightarrow{kAA} \sim A\dot{A}$

(2) $\sim \dot{A} + B \xrightarrow{kAB} \sim A\dot{B}$

(3) $\sim \dot{B} + B \xrightarrow{kBB} \sim B\dot{B}$

(4) $\sim \dot{B} + A \xrightarrow{kBA} \sim B\dot{A}$.

A and B are the monomers, $\sim \dot{A}$ and $\sim \dot{B}$ being polymeric free radicals having $\dot{A}$ or $\dot{B}$ as terminal groups. The copolymerization constants

$$r_1 = \frac{k\dot{A}A}{k\dot{A}B} \quad \text{and} \quad r_2 = \frac{k\dot{B}B}{k\dot{B}A} \dagger$$

can be computed from the composition of the copolymer. The constants indicate how much faster a given terminal group combines with a similar monomer molecule than with a foreign one.

We have already remarked that in radical reactions q and ε vary in opposite directions, while the rate-constants and q's vary in the same sense at constant steric factor.

The difference in the q's for (1) and (2), and correspondingly for (4) and (3) equals the energy difference between $A \to \sim \dot{A}$ and $B \to \sim \dot{B}$ and if $k_{\dot{A}B} > k_{\dot{A}A}$ then $k_{\dot{B}B} > k_{\dot{B}A}$. Hence $r_1 < 1 < r_2$ (or conversely if $k_{\dot{A}B} < k_{\dot{A}A}$).

* PRAVEDNIKOV drew our attention to the role of polar factors in such reactions.

† r_1 and r_2 are determined by experiment [152] by solving

$$\frac{d[A]}{d[B]} = \frac{[A]}{[B]} \cdot \frac{r_1[A] + [B]}{r_2[B] + [A]}$$

graphically, this being derived on the assumption of steady-state copolymerization with fairly long chains. At low percentage conversions the experimental $\frac{\Delta[A]}{\Delta[B]}$ is equated to $\frac{d[A]}{d[B]}$. By taking two cases where [A]/[B] is different we get two equations for r_1 and r_2.

Let B be the more reactive. Hence $\dot{B}$ is inactive. In isolation A and B polymerize quite rapidly. Depending on the reactivity differences of the monomers different types of copolymerization will occur.

(1) B is much more reactive than A. Then $k_{\dot{A}A} \ll k_{\dot{A}B}$ and $k_{\dot{B}B} \gg k_{\dot{B}A}$, i.e. $r_1 \ll 1 \ll r_2$. The addition of a minute amount of B to A retards the polymerization sharply. This is because $\dot{A}$ derived from the low-activity A is very active and reacts very readily with B.

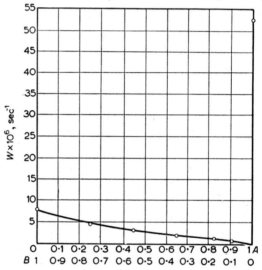

Fig. 6. Relation of the rate of concurrent polymerization in vinyl chloride (A) plus vinylidene chloride to the initial mixture composition

But the $\dot{B}$ so formed is so inactive that it cannot react with the inactive A. As [B] is so low, $\dot{B}$ reacts with it only at a minute rate. So polymerization practically ceases. Increasing [B] raises the polymerization rate, approaching the rate for B alone as limit. Then the polymer obtained contains B alone. A scarcely reacts, i.e. no copolymer is formed. This effect occurs with vinyl acetate (A) and styrene (B). B is much more active than A since styrene is conjugated whereas vinyl acetate is not. Experimentally $r_1 = 0.02$ and $r_2 = 55$ [153]. Fig. 6 shows the rate of this copolymerization as a function of the mixture composition. The deep minimum occurs at very low styrene concentrations.

(2) A and B are about equally reactive. Suppose $r_1 \lesssim 1 \lesssim r_2$. Then adding B to A causes only a slight drop in rate. Further increase in [B] causes the rate to rise. A copolymer is then formed. This occurs for instance with styrene + butadiene [154] ($r_1 = 0.78$

and $r_2 = 1{\cdot}39$), methylmethacrylate + methyl α-chloroacrylate [155] ($r_1 = 0{\cdot}3$ and $r_2 = 1{\cdot}2$), and vinyl chloride + vinylidene chloride [153] ($r_1 = 0{\cdot}2$, $r_2 = 4{\cdot}5$). Fig. 7 shows the last of these.

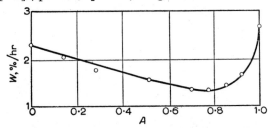

Fig. 7. Relation of the rate of concurrent polymerization in vinyl acetate (A) plus styrene (B) to the initial mixture composition

For many compounds copolymerization follows either (1) or (2), i.e. the radical activity laws are fulfilled. But quite a number of copolymerizations are known where one monomer predominates in the copolymer when this should not occur according to the above arguments. Then $k_{\dot{A}B}$ and $k_{\dot{B}A}$ are abnormally high and r_1 and r_2 are both less than one. This is contrary to the assumed radical

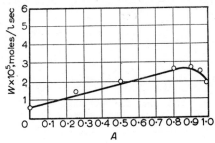

Fig. 8. Relation of the rate of polymerization in vinylidene (A) plus styrene to the initial mixture composition

activities, since A and B will react preferentially with "foreign" radicals, no matter what their activities. This is mostly found when the reactants have polar groups of opposite signs. Thus when vinyl cyanide (A), containing an electron-acceptor group, is copolymerized with styrene (B) [153] it is found that $r_1 = 0{\cdot}03$ and $r_2 = 0{\cdot}36$. Then (see Fig. 8) the rate of concurrent polymerization has a maximum which is greater than that for either monomer alone. This is seen particularly clearly with methylmethacrylate + styrene containing various polar substituents in the benzene ring [156] (see Table 29). r_1 rises gradually on passing from the most electropositive group ($N(CH_3)_2$) to the most electronegative (CN).

Table 29. *Copolymerization of methylmethacrylate
with substituted styrenes at* 60°C

Substituted styrene	r_2	r_1
p-Dimethylaminostryene .	0·205	0·11
p-Methoxystyrene . .	0·29	0·32
p-Styrene . . .	0·46	0·52
p-Chlorostyrene . .	0·415	0·89
p-Bromostyrene . .	0·395	1·10
Styrene-p-nitrile . .	0·22	1·41

This type of copolymerization can be explained in two ways: either ε is much less than it should be, i.e. if the heat of reaction determined the rate, or the presence of polar groups anomalously increases the heat of cross-combination. In considering the various factors which influence q we assumed the free electron could only be conjugated to the given monomer residue and neglected the possibility of conjugation to adjacent residues in the polymer.

The latter can be important in cross-reaction and is absent in separate polymerizations. The heats of the reactions between $\dot{B}$ and A and $\dot{A}$ and B may therefore be increased.

The above arguments certainly demand experimental verification. For this purpose we must find some way of determining the heats of $\dot{A} + B \rightarrow$ and $\dot{B} + A \rightarrow$ directly.

Certain information is available from the heat of copolymerization. If this were less than that for the separate polymerizations we could speak of a purely polar effect (the polar substituent operating only on ε). In the contrary case the second point of view (anomalous increase in q) would appear correct.

REFERENCES

1. E. T. BUTLER and M. POLANYI. *Trans. Faraday Soc.* **39**, 19 (1943).
2. M. LADACKI and M. SZWARC. *J. Chem. Phys.* **20**, 1814 (1952); M. SZWARC and D. WILLIAMS. *J. Chem. Phys.* **20**, 1171 (1952).
3. E. W. R. STEACIE, A. F. TROTMAN-DICKENSON and J. R. BIRCHARD. *J. Chem. Phys.* **19**, 162 (1951).
4. E. W. R. STEACIE and A. F. TROTMAN-DICKENSON. *J. Chem. Phys.* **19**, 169 (1951).
5. E. W. R. STEACIE and W. R. TROST. *J. Chem. Phys.* **16**, 361 (1948); E. W. R. STEACIE and R. E. REBBERT. *J. Chem. Phys.* **21**, 1723 (1953).
6. M. R. BERLIE and D. J. LE ROY. *Disc. Faraday Soc.* **14**, 50 (1953).
7. B. DE B. DARWENT and R. ROBERTS. *Disc. Faraday Soc.* **14**, 55 (1953).
8. A. D. STEPUKHOVICH. *Usp. Khim.* **25**, 263 (1956).
9. H. W. MELVILLE and J. C. ROBB. *Proc. Roy. Soc.* A **202**, 181 (1950).

10. E. W. R. STEACIE. *Atomic and Free Radical Reactions.* New York 1946.
11. E. W. R. STEACIE. *Can. J. Res.* **15B**, 264 (1937); A. FARKAS and H. W. MELVILLE. *Proc. Roy. Soc.* A **157**, 625 (1936).
12. W. R. TROST, B. DE B. DARWENT and E. W. R. STEACIE. *J. Chem. Phys.* **16**, 353 (1948).
13. H. J. SCHUMACHER. *Chemische Gasreaktionen,* pp. 352, 379. Leipzig 1938.
14. A. FARKAS and L. FARKAS. *Proc. Roy. Soc.* A **152**, 124 (1935).
15. L. I. AVRAMENKO and R. V. LORENTSO. *Dokl. Akad. Nauk SSSR* **67**, 867 (1949). English translation: *Can. Nat. Res. Coun.* TT-117 (1950).
16. L. I. AVRAMENKO and R. V. LORENTSO. *Dokl. Akad. Nauk SSSR* **69**, 205 (1949). English translation: *Can. Nat. Res. Coun.* TT-156 (1950).
17. L. I. AVRAMENKO and R. V. LORENTSO. *Zh. Fiz. Khim.* **24**, 207 (1950).
18. F. A. RAAL and E. W. R. STEACIE. *J. Chem. Phys.* **20**, 578 (1952).
19. P. B. AYSCOUGH and E. W. R. STEACIE. *Canad. J. Chem.* **34**, 103 (1956).
20. P. AUSLOOS and E. W. R. STEACIE. *Canad. J. Chem.* **33**, 31 (1955).
21. L. B. ARNOLD and G. B. KISTIAKOWSKY. *J. Chem. Phys.* **1**, 166 (1933).
22. G. B. KISTIAKOWSKY and E. R. VAN ARTSDALEN. *J. Chem. Phys.* **12**, 469 (1944).
23. V. N. KONDRATIEV. *Usp. Khim.* **8**, 195 (1939).
24. H. v. HARTEL, N. MEER and M. POLANYI. *Z. phys. Chem.* **19**, 139 (1932).
25. V. N. KONDRATIEV and M. S. ZISKIN. *Zh. Èks. Teor. Fiz.* **6**, 1083 (1936).
26. W. V. SMITH. *J. Chem. Phys.* **11**, 110 (1943).
27. R. G. W. NORRISH and G. PORTER. *Nature, Lond.* **164**, 658 (1949).
28. G. PORTER. *Proc. Roy. Soc.* A **200**, 284 (1950).
29. R. G. W. NORRISH and B. A. THRUSH. *Quart. Rev. Chem. Soc., Lond.* **10**, 149 (1956).
30. G. PORTER and F. J. WRIGHT. *Disc. Faraday Soc.* **14**, 23 (1953).
31. M. I. CHRISTIE, A. J. HARRISON, R. G. W. NORRISH and G. PORTER. *Proc. Roy. Soc.* A **231**, 446 (1955).
32. *Nat. Bur. Stand. Circular* 500 (1952).
33. M. SZWARC and A. H. SEHON. *J. Chem. Phys.* **19**, 656 (1951).
34. V. V. KOBOROV and A. V. FROST. *Free Energy of Organic Compounds.* Moscow 1949. (In Russian.)
35. H. C. ANDERSEN, G. B. KISTIAKOWSKY and E. R. VAN ARTSDALEN. *J. Chem. Phys.* **10**, 305 (1942).
36. H. C. ANDERSEN and E. R. VAN ARTSDALEN. *J. Chem. Phys.* **12**, 479 (1944).
37. E. I. HORMATS and E. R. VAN ARTSDALEN. *J. Chem. Phys.* **19**, 778 (1951).
38. H. HAGSTRUM. *Rev. Mod. Phys.* **23**, 185 (1951).
39. D. P. STEVENSON, *J. Chem. Phys.* **10**, 291 (1942); D. P. STEVENSON and J. A. HIPPLE. *J. Amer. Chem. Soc.* **64**, 2766 (1942).
40. M. SZWARC. *Chem. Rev.* **47**, 75 (1950).
41. F. O. RICE and M. D. DOOLEY. *J. Amer. Chem. Soc.* **56**, 2747 (1934).
42. V. L. TALROSE and E. L. FRANKEVITCH. *Dokl. Akad. Nauk SSSR* **111**, 376 (1956).
43. J. FRANCK and G. HERTZ. *Ber. Dtsch. phys. Ges.* **16**, 457 (1914).
44. V. N. KONDRATIEV and N. N. SEMENOV. *Z. Phys.* **22**, 1 (1924).
45. V. L. TALROSE and A. K. LIUBIMOVA. *Dokl. Akad. Nauk* **86**, 909 (1952).
46. E. L. FRANKEVITCH and V. L. TALROSE. *Izv. Akad. Nauk SSSR, Otd. Khim. Nauk.* In press.
47. V. N. KONDRATIEV. *Usp. Khim.* **26**, (1952).
48. A. H. SEHON. *J. Amer. Chem. Soc.* **74**, 4722 (1952).
49. J. B. FARMER, I. H. S. HENDERSON, F. P. LOSSING and D. G. H. MARSDEN. *J. Chem. Phys.* **24**, 348 (1956).
50. P. GRAY. *Fifth Symposium on Combustion,* p. 535. Reinold, N.Y., 1955.

51. M. Szwarc and J. W. Taylor. *J. Chem. Phys.* **23,** 2310 (1955).
52. M. Szwarc and J. W. Taylor. *J. Chem. Phys.* **22,** 270 (1954).
53. C. H. Leigh and M. Szwarc. *J. Chem. Phys.* **20,** 844 (1952).
54. A. F. Trotman-Dickenson. *Gas Kinetics.* London, 1955.
55. M. Szwarc and A. H. Sehon. *J. Chem. Phys.* **18,** 1685 (1950).
56. K. Ziegler and L. Ewald. *Liebig's Ann.* **473,** 163 (1929).
57. C. H. Leigh and M. Szwarc. *J. Chem. Phys.* **20,** 403 (1952).
58. M. Szwarc. *J. Chem. Phys.* **17,** 431 (1949).
59. C. H. Leigh and M. Szwarc. *J. Chem. Phys.* **20,** 407 (1952).
60. M. Szwarc and J. W. Taylor. *Trans. Faraday Soc.* **47,** 1293 (1951).
61. M. Szwarc, B. N. Ghosh and A. H. Sehon. *J. Chem. Phys.* **18,** 1142 (1950).
62. F. P. Lossing, K. U. Ingold and I. H. S. Henderson. *J. Chem. Phys.* **22,** 1489 (1954).
63. M. Szwarc. *Proc. Roy. Soc.* A **198,** 285 (1949).
64. M. Szwarc. *Proc. Roy. Soc.* A **198,** 267 (1949).
65. J. Murawski, J. S. Roberts and M. Szwarc. *J. Chem. Phys.* **19,** 698 (1951).
66. M. Ladacki, C. H. Leigh and M. Szwarc. *Proc. Roy. Soc.* A **214,** 273 (1952).
67. M. Szwarc and M. Ladacki. *J. Chem. Phys.* **20,** 1814 (1952).
68. M. Szwarc and D. Williams. *J. Chem. Phys.* **20,** 1171 (1952).
69. D. P. Stevenson. *Trans. Faraday Soc.* **49,** 867 (1953).
70. A. Langer, J. A. Hipple and D. P. Stevenson. *J. Chem. Phys.* **22,** 1836 (1954).
71. J. L. Franklin and J. E. Lumpkin. *J. Amer. Chem. Soc.* **74,** 1023 (1952).
72. E. W. R. Steacie. *Atomic and Free Radical Reactions.* Reinhold, N.Y., 1954.
73. J. B. Farmer and F. P. Lossing. *Can. J. Chem.* **33,** 861 (1956).
74. M. Szwarc and D. Williams. *Proc. Roy. Soc.* A **219,** 353 (1953).
75. A. A. Zilberman-Granovskaya and E. A. Shugam. *Zh. Fiz. Khim.* **14** 1004 (1940).
76. K. Hartley, H. O. Pritchard and H. A. Skinner. *Trans. Faraday Soc.* **47,** 254 (1951).
77. T. L. Cottrell. *The Strengths of Chemical Bonds.* London 1954. Russian translation: Moscow 1956.
78. G. Herzberg. *Spectra of Diatomic Molecules.* 2nd Ed. 1950. Russian translation of 1st edition: Moscow 1949.
79. A. G. Gaydon. *Dissociation Energies and Spectra of Diatomic Molecules.* 1st Ed. 1947. Russian translation: Moscow 1949.
80. L. I. Avramenko and V. N. Kondratiev. *Acta phys. Chim. URSS* **7,** 567 (1928).
81. P. Brix and G. Herzberg. *J. Chem. Phys.* **21,** 2240 (1953),
82. R. Edse. *Third Symposium on Combustion,* p. 611. Baltimore, 1949.
83. J. P. Toennis and E. F. Greene. *J. Chem. Phys.* **26,** 655 (1957).
84. H. Wise. *Phys. Rev.* **92,** 532 (1953).
85. G. S. Pierre and J. Chipman. *J. Amer. Chem. Soc.* **76,** 4787 (1954).
86. A. G. Gaydon. *Dissociation Energies and Spectra of Diatomic Molecules.* 2nd Ed. London, 1953.
87. S. N. Foner and R. L. Hudson. *J. Chem. Phys.* **23,** 1364 (1955).
88. A. P. Altshuller. *J. Chem. Phys.* **22,** 1947 (1954).
89. E. D. Coon. *Proc. N. Dakota Acad. Sci.* **7,** 46 (1953).
90. K. Wieland. *Helv. Chim. Acta.* **24,** 1285 (1941).
91. K. K. Kelly. *Bull. U.S. Bur. Min.* No. 383 (1935).
92. J. G. Winans and M. P. Hertz. *Z. Phys.* **135,** 406 (1953).
93. B. G. Gowenlock, J. C. Polanyi and E. Warhurst. *Proc. Roy. Soc.* A **219,** 270 (1953).

94. F. P. Lossing, K. U. Ingold and I. H. S. Henderson. *J. Chem. Phys.* **22,** 1489 (1954).

95. C. O. Pritchard, H. O. Pritchard, H. I. Shiff and A. F. Trotman-Dickenson. *Chem. and Ind. (Rev.)* 896 (1955).

96. B. S. Rabinowitch and J. F. Reed. *J. Chem. Phys.* **22,** 2092 (1954).

97. F. W. Kirkbride and F. G. Davidson. *Nature, Lond.* **174,** 79 (1954).

98. V. H. Dibeler, R. M. Reese and F. L. Mohler. *J. Chem. Phys.* **20,** 761 (1952).

99. V. H. Dibeler, R. M. Reese and F. L. Mohler. *J. Res. Nat. Bur. Stand.* **57,** 113 (1956).

100. M. G. Evans and M. Polanyi. *Trans. Faraday Soc.* **34,** 11 (1938).

101. Kh. S. Bagdasaryan. *Zh. Fiz. Khim.* **23,** 1375 (1949).

102. N. N. Tikhomirova and V. V. Voevodskii. *Dokl. Akad. Nauk SSR* **79,** 993 (1951). English translation: *Can. Nat. Res. Coun.* TT-260 (1951).

103. G. A. Razuvaev and Yu. A. Oldekop. *Zh. Obshch. Khim.* **19,**736 (1949). English translation: *Can. Nat. Res. Coun.* TT-132 (1950); G. A. Razuvaev and Yu. A. Oldekop. *Zh. Obshch. Khim.* **19,** 1483 (1949).

104. G. A. Razuvaev and Yu. A. Oldekop. *Zh. Obshch. Khim.* **20,** 181 (1950).

105. G. A. Razuvaev, Yu. A. Oldekop and N. S. Vyazankin. *Zh. Obshch. Khim.* **21,** 1283 (1951).

106. S. N. Foner and R. L. Hudson. *J. Chem. Phys.* **21,** 1608 (1953).

107. J. W. Linett and A. J. Poe. *Trans. Faraday Soc.* **47,** 1033 (1951); A. D. Walsh. *J. Chem. Soc.* 2296 (1953).

108. C. N. Hinshelwood, C. F. Cullis and M. F. R. Mulcahy. *Proc. Roy. Soc.* A **196,** 160 (1949).

109. V. V. Voevodskii. *Dokl. Akad. Nauk SSSR* **79,** 455 (1951).

110. J. L. Franklin. *J. Chem. Phys.* **21,** 2029 (1953).

111. J. L. Franklin. *Industr. Engng. Chem.* **41,** 1070 (1949).

112. H. J. Schumacher, H. Schmitz and A. Jager. *Z. Phys. Chem.* B **51,** 281 (1942).

113. C. T. Mortimer, H. O. Pritchard and H. A. Skinner. *Trans. Faraday Soc.* **48,** 220 (1952).

114. W. A. Waters. *The Chemistry of Free Radicals.* Oxford 1946. Russian translation: Moscow 1948.

115. Kh. S. Bagdasaryan. *Zh. Fiz. Khim.* **27,** 542 (1953).

116. D. H. Volman and W. M. Graven. *J. Amer. Chem. Soc.* **75,** 3111 (1953).

117. K. Faltings. *Ber. Dtsch. Chem. Ges.* **72,** 1207 (1939).

118. J. B. Farmer, F. P. Lossing, D. G. H. Marsden and E. W. R. Steacie. *J. Chem. Phys.* **23,** 1169 (1955).

119. H. O. Pritchard and D. Clark. *J. Chem. Soc.* 2136 (1957).

120. D. H. Volman and R. K. Brinton. *J. Chem. Phys.* **20,** 25 (1952).

121. J. A. Gray. *J. Chem. Soc.* 3150 (1952).

122. H. W. Melville, J. C. Robb and R. C. Tutton. *Disc. Faraday Soc.* **14,** 150 (1953).

123. N. N. Semenov. *Usp. Khim.* **21,** 641 (1952).

124. S. Bywater and E. W. R. Steacie. *J. Chem. Phys.* **19,** 319 (1951).

125. R. W. Durham, G. R. Martin and H. C. Sutton. *Nature, Lond.* **164,** 1052 (1949).

126. N. N. Semenov. *Usp. Khim.* **20,** 673 (1951).

127. H. H. Glazebrook and T. G. Pearson. *J. Chem. Soc.* 1777 (1936).

128. N. V. Fok. *Candidate's Dissertation.* Inst. Khim. Fiz., Moscow 1951.

129. N. V. Fok, A. B. Nalbandyan. *Dokl. Akad. Nauk SSSR* **89,** 125 (1953).

130. N. V. Fok and A. B. Nalbandyan. *Dokl. Akad. Nauk SSSR* **86,** 589 (1952). English translation: *Nat. Res. Coun.* TT-396 (1952).

131. F. P. LOSSING, K. U. INGOLD and A. W. TICKNER.   *Disc. Faraday Soc.*
     14, 34 (1953).
132. V. V. VOEVODSKII, G. K. LAVROVSKAYA and R. E. MARDALEISHVILI.
     Symposium on Chemical Kinetics, Catalysis and Reactivity, p. 40. Aca-
     demy of Sciences, Moscow 1956.
133. V. V. VOEVODSKII, G. K. LAVROVSKAYA and R. E. MARDALEISHVILI.
     Dokl. Akad. Nauk SSSR **81**, 215 (1951). English translation: *Nat. Res.
     Coun.* TT-358 (1952).
134. E. WHITTLE and E. W. R. STEACIE.   *J. Chem. Phys.* **21**, 993 (1953).
135. R. A. OGG and M. POLANYI.   *Trans. Faraday Soc.* **31**, 482 (1935).
136. M. B. NEIMAN, B. A. KUZNETSOV and YU. M. SHAPOVALOV.   *Dokl. Akad.
     Nauk SSSR* **92**, 611 (1953).
137. F. E. BLACET and W. E. BELL.   *Disc. Faraday Soc.* **14**, 70 (1953).
138. B. DE B. DARWENT.   *Disc. Faraday Soc.* **14**, 129 (1953).
139. L. MELANDER.   *Nature, Lond.* **163**, 599 (1949).
140. L. P. HAMMETT.   *Physical Organic Chemistry.* McGraw-Hill, 1940.
141. H. H. JAFFE.   *Chem. Rev.* **53**, 191 (1953).
142. R. W. TAFT.   *J. Amer. Chem. Soc.* **74**, 2729, 3121 (1952).
143. D. H. HEY and G. H. WILLIAMS.   *Disc. Faraday Soc.* **14**, 216 (1953).
144. D. H. HEY, B. W. PENGILLY and G. H. WILLIAMS.   *J. Chem. Soc.* 1463
     (1956).
145. M. SZWARC, C. H. LEIGH and A. H. SEHON.   *J. Chem. Phys.* **19**, 657 (1951).
146. V. L. TALROSE.   *Candidate's Dissertation.* Moscow 1952.
147. D. P. STEVENSON and D. O. SHISSLER.   *J. Chem. Phys.* **23**, 1353 (1955);
     D. O. SHISSLER and D. P. STEVENSON.   *J. Chem. Phys.* **24**, 926 (1956);
     S. H. FIELD, J. L. FRANKLIN and S. W. LAMP.   *J. Amer. Chem. Soc.* **78**,
     5697 (1956).
148. G. O. PRITCHARD, H. O. PRITCHARD, H. I. SCHIFF and A. F. TROTMAN-
     DICKENSON.   *Trans. Faraday Soc.* **52**, 849 (1956).
149. G. A. RAZUVAEV, YU. A. OLDEKOP and V. N. LATYAEVA.   *Zh. Obshch.
     Khim.* **26**, 1110 (1956); G. A. RAZUVAEV and YU. A. OLDEKOP. *Zh.
     Obshch. Khim.* **27**, 196 (1957).
150. E. C. KOOYMAN, R. VAN HELDEN and A. F. BICKEL.   *Koninkl. Nederl.
     Akad. Wetensch.* B **56**, 75 (1953); R. VAN HELDEN and E. C. KOOYMAN.
     Rec. Trav. Chim. Pays-Bas **73**, 269 (1954).
151. M. SZWARC and W. K. WILMARTH   *J. Amer. Chem. Soc.* **77**, 4543, 4551
     (1955).
152. A. D. ABKIN.   *Dissertation.* Moscow 1951; T. ALFREY, JR., J. BOHRER and
     H. MARK.   *Copolymerization.* 1952. Russian translation: Moscow 1953.
153. A. D. ABKIN.   *Symposium on Chemical Kinetics, Catalysis and Reactivity.*
     p. 338. Academy of Sciences, Moscow 1955.
154. L. B. SOKOLOV and A. D. ABKIN.   *Zh. Fiz. Khim.* In press.
155. T. ALFREY, J. BOHRER, H. HAAS and C. J. LEWIS.   *J. Polymer. Sci.* **5**, 719
     (1950).
156. C. WALLING, E. BRIGGS, K. WOLFSTIRN and F. MAYO.   *J. Amer. Chem.
     Soc.* **70**, 1573 (1948).
157. A. N. NESMEYANOV, R. KH. FREIDLINA and L. I. ZAKHARKIN.   *Dokl.
     Akad. Nauk SSSR* **81**, 199 (1951); *Usp. Khim.* **25**, 665 (1956); *Quart.
     Rev. Chem. Soc., Lond.* **10**, 330 (1956).
158. A. N. NESMEYANOV, R. KH. FREIDLINA and V. N. KOST.   *Dokl. Akad.
     Nauk SSSR* **113**, 828 (1957); *Tetrahedron* **1**, 241 (1957).
159. R. KH. FREIDLINA, A. B. BELYAVSKY and A. N. NESMEYANOV.   *Izv.
     Akad. Nauk SSSR, Otd. Khim. Nauk* (1958). In press.

Chapter 2

ALTERNATIVE UNIVALENT FREE-RADICAL REACTIONS

1. THE OCCURRENCE OF ALTERNATIVE RADICAL REACTIONS

The first problem in the analysis of reaction kinetics is that of the origin of the various products, i.e. of the reaction pathways. The formation of various products in chain reactions is determined primarily by the bond at which the radical reaction most readily occurs. Farmer [1], for example, has shown that peroxides are formed by oxidation of unsaturated hydrocarbons with molecular oxygen, and that the OOH group is located α to the double bond. Hydrocarbons are oxidized by the following chain mechanism at low temperatures:

(1) $R + O_2 \rightarrow ROO$,

(2) $RO_2 + RH \rightarrow ROOH + R$, etc.

RO_2 abstracts hydrogen from RH in (2); naturally, the hydrogen atom is the most weakly bound one. We have already shown above that considerably less energy is needed to remove an α-hydrogen (for the CH_3 group of C_3H_6, $Q_{C-H} = 77$ kcal, while CH_3 in C_3H_8 has $Q_{C-H} = 95$ kcal; CH_2 in C_3H_6 demands 102–104 kcal).

If allowance is made for the variation of ε_0 with q, we have a natural explanation for the actual course of the reaction.

Peracids such as $CH_3\!-\!\overset{\overset{\textstyle O}{\|}}{C}\!-\!OOH$, rather than peroxides such as $HOO\!-\!CH_2\!-\!C\!\overset{\displaystyle O}{\underset{\displaystyle H}{\diagdown}}$, are formed when aldehydes are oxidized. The chain reaction here also occurs as above; moreover, the peroxide radical will abstract hydrogen from the CHO group, but not from the CH_3 groups (90–95 kcal). *Iso*-peroxides are usually produced by low-temperature oxidation of alkanes for the same reason, since the abstraction of H from a CH_2 group is somewhat easier (4–5 kcal) than from a CH_3 group.

We may take the work of Ivanov et al. [2–4] on the liquid-phase photo-oxidation of hydrocarbons to hydroperoxides by molecular oxygen as an example. His results show that if the hydrocarbon in question has a tertiary C—H bond, then only this will be attacked. For example, the oxidation of *sec.*-butyl benzene [3] gives a hydroperoxide of the following structure:

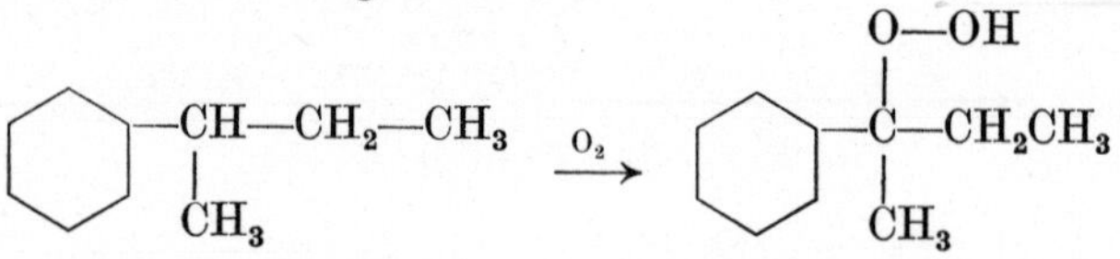

Oxidation of 2,7-dimethyl octane gave 2,7-dimethyl octyl hydroperoxide: [4]

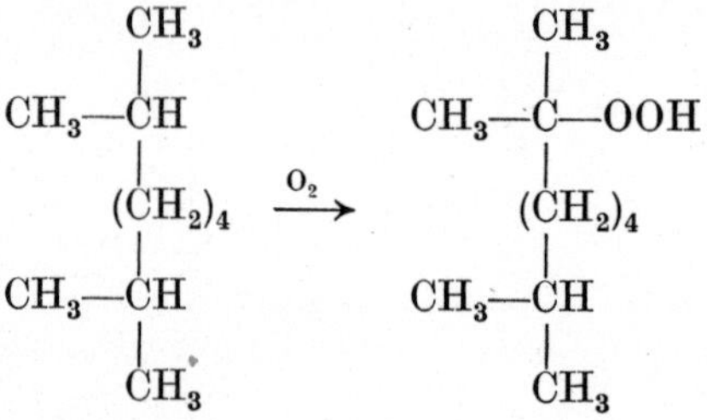

A secondary C—H bond (usually a CH_2 group) is attacked in the absence of a tertiary CH, α to a benzene nucleus. Thus, oxidation of *n*-butyl benzene gave peroxides of the following structure, according to IVANOV *et al.*: [3]

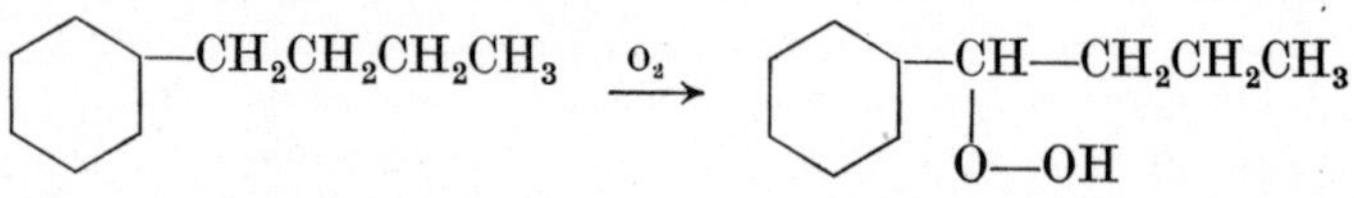

Halogenated alkanes (chloro- and bromo-derivatives) decompose to hydrogen halides and olefins, e.g. $C_2H_5Br \rightarrow C_2H_4 + HBr$. [5] Iodides, like bromides, would give hydrogen iodide and olefin, but such an elimination is rare. The vast majority of iodides decompose to iodine, olefin, and alkane, the overall reaction being:

$$2C_3H_7I \rightarrow C_3H_8 + C_3H_6 + I_2$$

The alternative reaction which yields HI, $C_3H_7I \rightarrow HI + C_3H_6$, is equivalent to the elementary reactions:

(1) $I + C_3H_7I \rightarrow HI + C_3H_6I - q_1$

(2) $I + C_3H_7I \rightarrow I_2 + C_3H_6 - q_1'$.

Q_{H-I} in HI is $\leqslant 70$ kcal. $Q_{C_3H_7-H}$ is 95 kcal. The error in assuming that Q_{C-H} in *n*—PrI is 90 kcal is not large. Then $q_1 \approx 90 - 70 = 20$ kcal. q_1' is the difference between Q_{C-I} in PrI (50 kcal) and Q_{I-I} in I_2 (35·5 kcal), so $q_1' = 50 - 35·5 = 14·5$ kcal.

It is clear that (2) will be the more favoured for n—PrI, since q_1' is 5·5 kcal less than q_1; (2) will therefore be more rapid. Hence, the majority of iodides give iodine, and not HI.

The situation is reversed in the chlorides and bromides. $Br + C_3H_7Br \rightarrow HBr + C_3H_6Br$ (a) absorbs about 5 kcal, since Q_{C-H} is ~ 90 kcal, while Q_{H-Br} is 85 kcal. At the same time, $Br + C_3H_7Br \rightarrow C_3H_7 + Br_2$ (b) is endothermic; the difference between Q_{C-Br} (62–65 kcal) and Q_{Br-Br} (45 kcal) being 17–20 kcal. Thus the bromides give HBr, since (a) is much more rapid than (b). The same applies to chlorides.

Dichloro derivatives usually give olefin + HCl, the over-all reaction being such as:

$$CH_2Cl—CH_2Cl \rightarrow HCl + CHCl = CH_2$$

while the di-iodo derivatives give I_2 + olefin:

$$CH_2I—CH_2I \rightarrow I_2 + CH_2 = CH_2.$$

The two alternative macroscopic reactions are determined by two alternative elementary ones:

(1) $X + CH_2X — CH_2X \rightarrow X_2 + CH_2 — CH_2X + q$,

(2) $X + CH_2X — CH_2X \rightarrow HX + CHX — CH_2X.$

In the chlorides (1) is endothermic (23 kcal). Q_{Cl-Cl} for the Cl_2 formed in (1) is 57 kcal, while Q_{C-Cl} in $(CH_2Cl)_2$ is probably close to that for CH_3Cl (80 kcal), so $q = 57 - 80 = -23$ kcal. In (2), HCl is formed, liberating 102 kcal, while Q_{C-H} is absorbed; this latter being somewhat lower in $C_2H_4Cl_2$ than in ethane itself due to the influence of chlorine. VOEVODSKII has calculated Q_{C-H} for the halomethanes (see Chapter 1, Column 3 of Table 9) and finds that the transition $CH_4 \rightarrow CH_3Cl$ reduces Q_{C-H} from 101 to 97·4 kcal. If we assume by analogy that Q_{C-H} will be reduced by 3–4 kcal in this case, then it becomes 94 kcal. Thus (2) is exothermic by $102 - 94 = 8$ kcal. $C_2H_4Cl_2$ will consequently give HCl alone.

(1) is endothermic by 14·5 kcal in di-iodo derivatives, such as $(CH_2I)_2$, but (2) is endothermic by 20 kcal. (1) will therefore be more rapid than (2), and the di-iodo derivatives will thus mainly give I_2.

The photolysis of mercury diphenyl in $CHCl_3$ was studied by RAZUVAEV and OLDEKOP [6]: the phenyl radical could react in two possible ways; it may either abstract hydrogen from $CHCl_3$ (giving benzene), or chlorine (giving chlorobenzene). Benzene was always the sole product. This evidently implies that benzene formation liberates the more energy. Approximate calculation shows that the heat liberated by benzene formation is 3–5 kcal greater than for chlorobenzene. At the low temperatures used, a difference of 3–5 kcal means that hydrogen will mainly be abstracted.

C_6H_5Hg is formed from the mercury diphenyl as well as phenyl. This abstracts chlorine (not hydrogen) and forms C_6H_5HgCl, since this is considerably more stable than the hypothetical C_6H_5HgH. RAZUVAEV and PETUKHOV [7] have shown that PhHgCl undergoes no further change even upon prolonged irradiation.

Thus methods are available for calculating the main routes of many reactions, since the q-values of radical reactions are determined by the Q-values of bonds, and the activation energies are given by the relation between ε_0 and q.

In this connexion, it is interesting to consider addition of XH (where X may be a halogen or HS), to olefins. Reactions catalysed by light, or by peroxides, take place contrary to Markovnikov's rule. X combines with the atom possessing the largest number of hydrogen atoms. Reactions thus catalysed by light or peroxides occur as follows:

(1) $CH_3—CH = CH_2 + Br \rightarrow CH_3—\dot{C}H—CH_2Br + 13$ kcal,

(2) $CH_3—\dot{C}H—CH_2Br + HBr \rightarrow CH_3CH_2CH_2Br + Br + 5$ kcal.

$Q_{C—Br}$ for Br attachment to CH_2 is also a few kcal greater than $Q_{C—Br}$ for attachment to CH. There are no direct data on the Q-values, but the combination $H + C_3H_6 \rightarrow n$-C_3H_7 yields 5–6 kcal more than that giving iso-C_3H_7. The same may be supposed to apply to bromine, which may consequently be expected to combine contrary to Markovnikov's rule. In the absence of peroxides or in the dark the reaction is probably ionic and C_3H_6 is attacked at the CH_2 group by H^+, a normal C—H bond being formed and the charge being transformed to the neighbouring carbon atom, giving C^+. The carbonium ion reacts with Br^-, giving iso-PrBr according to Markovnikov's rule. This explanation is certainly only hypothetical, but it seems feasible.

A mixed product is always formed at higher temperatures, part being formed in accordance with Markovnikov's rule, and part contrary to it.

2. THE INFLUENCE OF TEMPERATURE AND PRESSURE ON ALTERNATIVE RADICAL REACTIONS

The rules of organic chemistry mostly apply to low-temperature reactions ($T \gg 100°C$). At these temperatures a $\Delta\varepsilon$ of 2–3 kcal largely determines the preferred route. The ratio of rates will be about $\exp(-2000/RT) = (w_2/w_1)$; this will be exactly true, if the steric factors are equal. At 373°K, w_2/w_1 is 7×10^{-2}, i.e. 93 per cent of the product will be formed by the first route, and only 7 per cent by the second. If $\varepsilon_2 - \varepsilon_1 = 3$ kcal, then the first route, for practical purposes, is the only one.

At higher temperatures a $\Delta\varepsilon$ of this magnitude is not decisive. At $700°K$, $\Delta\varepsilon = 2$ kcal, and equal pre-exponential factors, $w_2/w_1 = \exp(-2000/RT) \simeq 0.25$, i.e. 25 per cent of the product is obtained via the second route.

Changes of a preferred path with temperature, when different reactions are possible, will now be considered. Numerous cases are known where a system can undergo two different bimolecular reactions, one of which has a low ε, but also a low f, while the other has a high ε, together with a high f. At low temperatures, the first reaction will mainly occur; at higher temperatures both reactions are important; and finally at the very highest temperatures reaction will be almost exclusively by the second route. An example may be found in the chlorination of unsaturated compounds.

RUST and VAUGHAN [8] showed that, in the chlorination of olefins, and in ethylene in particular, formation of dichloroethanes as the main product was appreciably rapid at $235°C$. At $250–350°C$, two reactions took place; as the temperature rose addition declined in importance, and the relative yield of substitution (giving vinyl chloride) increased. At about $400°C$ the product was practically all vinyl chloride.

Olefins chlorinate chainwise as follows:

I. By addition:

(1) $Cl + C_2H_4 \rightarrow \dot{C}_2H_4Cl$,

(2) $\dot{C}_2H_4Cl + Cl_2 \rightarrow C_2H_4Cl_2 + Cl$, etc.

II. By substitution:

(1a) $Cl + C_2H_4 \rightarrow C_2H_3 + HCl$,

(2a) $\dot{C}_2H_3 + Cl_2 \rightarrow C_2H_3Cl + Cl$, etc.

(1) is exothermic (26 kcal), and ε_0 is about 1–2 kcal. The steric factor is small, as in all additions (10^{-3}–10^{-4}). On the other hand (1a) has $q \simeq 0$, and a high ε. There is no direct evidence on ε, but the activation energy for $Cl + CH_4 = CH_3 + HCl$, is 6.2 kcal overall [9]. We may anticipate that ε will be fairly large for ethylene. The steric factor for (1a) is taken as 0.1–1. It is thus clear why substitution becomes dominant at high temperatures.

The simultaneity of (1) and (1a) is demonstrated by there being both vinyl chloride and dichloroethanes in the product. At $308°C$, dichloroethanes constitute 65 per cent of the product, while vinyl chloride is about 20 per cent. At 346°C about 53 per cent is vinyl chloride, and 20 per cent dichloroethanes.

The simultaneous reactions are frequently found to be a unimolecular process in parallel with a bimolecular one. Peroxides and aldehydes are formed simultaneously in the oxidation of hydrocarbons, for instance.

FOK and NALBANDYAN [10–12] studied the mercury-sensitized photo-oxidation of C_3H_8 at 25–300°C. The excited mercury atoms collide with propane molecules and abstract hydrogen atoms, giving both n- and iso-C_3H_7. These are transformed to peroxide radicals by combination with oxygen, and the former then abstract hydrogen atoms from further alkane molecules, forming hydroperoxide, regenerating the propyl radicals and propagating the chain:

(1) CH_2—CH_2—$\dot{C}H_2$ + O_2 → CH_3—CH_2—CH_2
$$\underset{\cdot O—O}{\big|}$$

(2) CH_3—CH_2—CH_2 + C_3H_8 → CH_3—CH_2—CH_2OOH + $\dot{C}_3H_7$
$$\underset{\cdot O—O}{\big|}$$

and so on.

The iso-propyl chain:

(1') CH_3—$\dot{C}H$—CH_3 + O_2 → CH_3—CH—CH_3
$$\underset{O—O\cdot}{\big|}$$

(2') CH_3—CH—CH_3 + C_3H_8 → CH_3—CH—CH_3 + $\dot{C}_3H_7$
$$\underset{O—O\cdot}{\big|} \qquad\qquad \underset{OOH}{\big|}$$

Thus both n- and iso-C_3H_7OOH may be obtained. At room temperature the principal oxidation product from propane is C_3H_7OOH, according to FOK and NALBANYAN [12]; aldehydes and other substances could not be detected.

$Q_{C—H}$ for the CH_2 group in C_3H_7 is 5 kcal less than for the CH_3 group. So (2) and (2') should give iso-C_3H_7. Both are exothermic and the q-value difference (5 kcal) leads to $\Delta\varepsilon = 1·25$ kcal. This implies that the amount of iso-C_3H-OOH formed should be 8 times greater than the amount of n-C_3H_7OOH, at room temperature. FOK and NALBANDYAN [12] could only detect the iso-propyl derivative, within the errors of analysis, with short contact times (10 sec) at room temperature. At ~ 100°C, the primary product contained aldehydes as well as peroxides. At $T > 300$°C, peroxides were not found, only aldehydes and their oxidation products (CO and CO_2).

FOK and NALBANDYAN [12] and POROIKOVA showed that in the

photo-oxidation of propane in the presence of ammonia the aldehydes are not produced by hydroperoxide decomposition. They have given a kinetic plot for the accumulation of peroxides and aldehydes in early reaction stages. POROIKOVA's results (Fig. 28) for 120 and 220°C are given. The way the peroxide and aldehyde yields depend on the contact time show that they are formed by parallel routes. If the aldehydes were formed directly from peroxides the aldehyde accumulation rate at times near zero should be zero and the accumulation curve would have an S-shape. This is not so (Fig. 9) and the kinetic curves have a characteristic parallel reaction shape. The same should undoubtedly apply to thermal oxidation. A marked increase in peroxide is observed in low-temperature oxidation and there is ample evidence of aldehydes and ketones being formed from peroxides. Thus degenerate branching will also involve the peroxide decomposition route (see Vol. 2, Chapter 8).

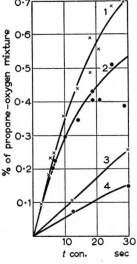

Fig. 9. Relation of the *iso*-propylhydroperoxide and acetaldehyde yields to contact time on oxidizing propane containing ammonia

Total pressure 100 mm Hg
$C_3H_8 : O_2 : NH_3 = 7 : 1 : 2$
x Peroxides
● aldehydes
1 and 2 for 220°C
3 and 4 for 170°C

This is not so in gas-phase hydrocarbon oxidations which usually occur at 300–400°C. It is known to involve very small organic peroxide concentrations. SHTERN has shown [13–15] that the amounts of peroxides found in the oxidations of C_3H_8 and C_3H_6 are very small — $0.3 - 0.4$ per cent of the initial mixture, 70–80 per cent of this being hydrogen peroxide. NORRISH [16] concludes from the oxidation of propane that alkyl hydroperoxides do not form in the reaction zone and that the peroxide observed was hydrogen peroxide. Thus it may be that the aldehydes are not formed from peroxides. It was also shown that acetaldehyde and not peroxide is the branching agent in the oxidations of propylene and propane. SHTERN [15, 17] demonstrated this by stopping the reaction at an intermediate stage and letting the mixture out into a vessel containing mercury, maintained at room temperature.

When the mixture was replaced in the reaction vessel at the initial pressure and temperature the reaction started again after a short induction period, irrespective of the time spent in the other vessel (from 50 sec to 68 hr). No peroxides were observed in the mixture on replacing it in the reaction vessel, as they decompose on prolonged contact with mercury. Thus only aldehydes can act as branching agents, and with propylene and propane the agent was acetaldehyde, as has been shown subsequently. The same method was used later by BATTEN and RIDGE [18] in the oxidation of propylene and *iso*-butane; they also consider that peroxides are not responsible for degenerate branching.

Thus even if peroxides are formed in gas-phase hydrocarbon oxidations their amounts are so small as not to effect the reaction kinetics. Thus, the aldehydes and peroxides are formed by independent parallel routes. This implies that the peroxide radicals must react in two different ways. The first is (2') above, which gives hydroperoxide, the second being peroxide radical decomposition:

$$(3)\ C_3H_7O\dot{O} \Big\langle \begin{array}{l} (3')\ CH_3CHO + CH_3\dot{O} \\ (3'')\ HCHO + C_2H_5\dot{O} \end{array}$$

this giving primary formation of aldehydes. Thus we have here a bimolecular reaction, i.e. (2'), in parallel with a unimolecular one (3).

(3) always involves peroxide radical isomerization, such as:

$$(4)\ \begin{array}{ccc} CH_3-CH-CH_3 & \to & CH_3-\dot{C}H\ CH_3 \\ \quad\ |\quad & & \qquad |\quad\ | \\ \quad O-O- & & \qquad O-O \end{array}$$

In this case the oxygen free valency attacks a C—C bond.* The isomeric radical decomposes into acetaldehyde and a methoxy radical, ε_3 being low. The unimolecular rate-limiting step is isomerization, since this has a substantial activation energy. The bimolecular (2) is exothermic, since Q_{O-H} is always greater than Q_{C-H} ε_2 is certainly not large in this case (usually 5–10 kcal for radical/molecule reactions). Then (2) will have the rate $w_2 = f \times 10^{-10}$ $\exp(-\varepsilon_2/RT)$ [RH][N] where [RH] is the number of alkane molecules in 1 cm³, and [N] is the number of RO₂ radicals in 1 cm³. In this case $f \simeq 0.1$ and $\varepsilon_2 \simeq 7$–10 kcal.

The rate of (3) (isomerization) will be $w_3 = 10^{13} \exp(-\varepsilon_3/RT)$ [N], where $\varepsilon_3 > \varepsilon_2$ or $\varepsilon_3 - \varepsilon_2 > 0$. w_3/w_2 is then equal to the aldehyde : peroxide ratio.

$$\frac{w_3}{w_2} = \frac{10^{13}}{f \cdot 10^{-10}[RH]} \exp\left[\frac{(\varepsilon_2 - \varepsilon_3)}{RT}\right] \simeq \frac{10^{24}}{[RH]} \exp - \Delta\varepsilon/RT$$

$$= \frac{\text{Aldehydes produced}}{\text{Peroxide produced}} \tag{1}$$

* SHTERN *et al.* [13, 14] suggested the possibility of such isomerizations.

$\Delta\varepsilon$ is positive, since ε for isomerization is usually greater than ε for transfer reactions (see Chapter 1, Section 9).

It follows from (1) that the aldehyde content will increase with T, and also as the pressure is reduced. Experimental data [12] indicate that only peroxides are formed at room temperature, but the aldehyde content increases rapidly at 200–300°C, and at 300°C aldehyde constitutes the main product. Suppose $\Delta\varepsilon = 12\cdot5$ kcal, then at 23°C (300°K) and [RH] $\sim 3 \times 10^{18}$

$$\frac{\text{Aldehydes produced}}{\text{Peroxide produced}} \simeq 3 \times 10^5 \exp\left(-12500/600\right) \simeq 3\cdot10^{-4}$$

At 200°C (= 473°K) and [RH] $\sim 2 \times 10^{18}$

$$\frac{\text{Aldehydes produced}}{\text{Peroxide produced}} = 5 \times 10^5 \exp\left(-12500/946\right) \simeq 0\cdot8$$

Assuming that $\Delta\varepsilon = 12\cdot5$ kcal we have found (in agreement with experiment) that the product is 99·97 per cent peroxide and 0·03 per cent aldehyde at 300°K, and that the aldehyde and peroxide contents are almost identical at 200°C. Consequently, $\varepsilon_3 = \varepsilon_2 + \Delta\varepsilon = 20$ kcal. Similar results are given by SERGEEV and SHTERN [19] and by KALINENKO [20] for the bromine-catalysed photo-oxidation of propane. The sole product at low temperatures was $iso\text{-}C_3H_7OOH$.

As another instance of simultaneous bimolecular and unimolecular reactions which result in different products we may take the pyrolysis of propylene.

Propylene does not polymerize at low temperatures. This is a consequence of C_3H_5, which may be produced from propylene, being of very low activity; it cannot combine with propylene at ordinary temperatures. At higher temperatures (300–400°C) propylene polymerizes, but at 700–800°C cracking is observed. KRAUZE *et al.* [21] have shown that propylene polymerizes at 330–430°C at pressures well above normal (90 atm), and PEASE [22] has shown the same for 450–600°C at 1 atm.

Propylene certainly polymerizes via the following chain reaction:

(1) $\dot{C}_3H_5 + C_3H_6 \rightarrow \dot{C}_6H_{11}$ $\left.\right\}$ propagation

(2) $\dot{C}_6H_h + C_3H_6 \rightarrow \dot{C}_9H_{17}$, etc.

(3) $\dot{C}_hH_{2h-1} + C_3H_6 \rightarrow C_hH_{2h} + \dot{C}_3H_5$ chain transfer

(4) $\dot{C}_hH_{2h-1} + \dot{C}_3H_5 \rightarrow C_{h+3}H_{2h+4}$ termination.

E_c is low, about 5–10 kcal, and the steric factor is also low, $\simeq 10^{-4}$, as in all polymerizations. Termination of a particular polymer chain occurs via (3). The chain length is determined by the parallel propagation and chain-rupture reactions. KRAUZE's results show that the polymer molecules contain 4–5 residues. SZWARC [23] proposed the following decomposition scheme for C_3H_6:

(1a) $\dot{C}H_3$—CH=CH_2 → CH_2 = C = CH_2 + H

(2a) H + CH_3—CH=CH_2 → H_2 + C_3H_5.

Another possible atomic hydrogen reaction is:

(2b) H + CH_3CH—CH_2 → $\dot{C}H_3$ + C_2H_4

(3b) $\dot{C}H_3$ + CH_3CH=CH_2 → CH_4 + $\dot{C}_3H_5$.

SZWARC showed that the amounts of CH_4 and C_2H_4 formed were equal, in agreement with this scheme, and that the quantities of hydrogen and allene were approximately equal. Since the quantity of C_2H_4 was somewhat greater than that of allene, the main reaction is via (2b).

We shall see that the allyl radical also plays a part in cracking, just as in polymerization. In polymerization, this radical either combines with C_3H_6, giving C_6H_{11} (1), or else exchanges hydrogen with it (3). In cracking, allyl decomposes to allene + H. The balance between these two reactions will determine the relative amounts of polymerized and cracked products at various temperatures.

The bimolecular:unimolecular rate ratio will be

$$\frac{f \times 10^{-10} \exp\left(-\varepsilon_1/RT\right)[\mathrm{RH}]}{10^{13} \exp\left(-\varepsilon_2/RT\right)}$$

where ε_1 applies to combination of an allyl radical with RH, and ε_2 is the activation energy for allyl radical decomposition. We shall assume $\varepsilon_1 \simeq 10$ kcal; ε_2 is practically equal to that for abstraction of hydrogen from C_3H_5. From the kinetics of allyl decomposition, SZWARC deduces $\varepsilon_2 = 66$ kcal. Assuming $f = 10^{-4}$ and [RH] = 10^{17} (SZWARC used pressures of 6–8 mm Hg [23]), the rates will be equal at 900°C. In fact, the decomposition of propylene is already the main process at 800°C. This discrepancy is apparently due to ε_2 and f being inaccurate.

Pressure also affects the balance of simultaneous reactions. SHTERN showed that increased pressures caused the rate of the bimolecular reaction RO_2 + RH → ROOH + R to increase in the oxidation of propane. The production of peroxide approximately doubled on raising the pressure from 300 to 700 mm Hg.

Another case in point is the oxidation of hydrogen. The effect of pressure is due to the two simultaneous radical reactions

(1) $H + O_2 \rightarrow OH + O - 15$ kcal,

(2) $H + O_2 + M \rightarrow HO_2 + M + \sim 47$ kcal.

(1) has a relatively large activation energy (18 kcal),* so only (2) occurs at relatively low temperatures, since this has $\varepsilon = 0$. Another reaction, $HO_2 + H_2 \rightarrow H_2O_2 + H$, is coupled to (2) and gives hydrogen peroxide. The rate of (1) increases relative to that of (2) as T increases, and at some finite temperature the sole product is H_2O, from the reaction $OH + H_2 \rightarrow H_2O + H$, coupled to (1). If at this high temperature we now increase the pressure (2) again becomes important, and H_2O_2 is again found.

The small ε_0 in (1) found by experiment is also possible from the theoretical point of view. This is because (2) occurs in practice at each ternary collision and has no activation energy. Since M is only needed to remove the excess energy the transient combination of H and O_2 on collision also need not depend on the activation energy being appreciable. The complex formed can decompose to H and O_2 (or to $OH + H$ in this case) without involving a potential barrier, if the energy is high enough (i.e. more than 15 kcal).

3. INTERMEDIARY AND TERMINAL PRODUCTS IN CHAIN REACTIONS

Simultaneous reactions giving different final products are due to there being alternative radical reactions at the pressure and temperature in question. The multiplicity of products formed by oxidation, polymerization and cracking makes it difficult to determine the detailed mechanisms. In such cases the quantities of all stable products are determined; this is a powerful method, and enables one to discover the detailed mechanisms.

The most accurate detailed study of oxidation propane and propylene mechanisms is that of SHTERN *et al.* [13, 14, 15, 17, 24, 25]. Propane–oxygen mixtures were used ($C_3H_8:O_2 = 1:1$ and $2:1$) in the range 280–465°C and at pressures from 280 to 400 mm Hg. The reaction gave aldehydes (HCHO and CH_3CHO), peroxides, methanol, ethanol, acids, propylene, ethylene, methane, hydrogen, carbon monoxide, carbon dioxide and water. Balances were struck for the stable reaction products.

Table 30 gives the kinetic relationships of the substances f formed from $1:1$ $CH_3H_8:O_2$ mixture at 350°C and 282 mm Hg [13, 14].

* According to the latest data $\varepsilon_1 = 15\cdot1 - 15\cdot9$ kcal (see Vol. 2, Chap. 2).

Table 30. *Composition of the reaction mixture in the*
oxidation of propane by oxygen [13]

Time (sec) after mixture entered vessel	Δp (mm Hg)	Content in the mixture (mm Hg)													
		Peroxides	Acids	HCHO	CH_3CHO	CH_3OH	C_3H_6	C_2H_4	CH_4	H_2	CO	CO_2	C_3H_8	O_2	H_2O
57	3	0·24	0·5	1·35	0·5	1·8	6·25	2·8	1·5	0	3·4	0·4	128	137·3	4·5
71·5	10	0·75	0·7	4	1·34	2·3	7·6	3·3	4	2	7·6	1	121	128	12
76·5	17	1·1	0·9	7·65	2·7	5·6	8	3·5	5	4	11	3·8	114	115	20
79·2	22	1·4	1·0	8·65	3·8	6·5	11	4·5	6	5	13	4·5	109	110	24·4
84	30	1·8	1·2	11·5	4·5	8·5	13·7	5·7	9·2	7	20	5·7	99	95·7	34·6
92·5	40	1·6	1·35	11·5	4·5	15·7	15·7	7	11·8	9	35	7·7	87	73·4	54·2
150	60	0·2	1·8	11·5	4·5	25	19	8	12	11	63	13	68	30	93

The water was determined by difference, from the balances for carbon, hydrogen, and oxygen.

The thermal oxidation of hydrocarbons, like photo-oxidation, involves a free radical mechanism. The direct demonstration of free radicals in slow oxidations is very difficult. However, all the known facts taken together leave no doubt as to the presence of free radicals. This is confirmed by introducing free radicals artificially: the action of light, addition of peroxides, of hexaphenyl ethane, and of ions of variable valency; all of which cause the oxidation of hydrocarbons, aldehydes and other organic substances. Most oxidations (particularly those of hydrocarbons) are found to be markedly retarded by traces of certain specific materials.

The chief radicals in the chain oxidation of propane are *n*- and *iso*-C_3H_7, as we have shown above.

Two radical chains occur side by side in the photo-oxidation of propane, giving normal- and *iso*-peroxide radicals, by combination of molecular oxygen with *n*- and *iso*-C_3H_7.

$$CH_3—CH_2—CH_2 \quad \text{and} \quad CH_3—CH—CH_3$$
$$\vert \qquad\qquad\qquad\qquad \vert$$
$$—O—O \qquad\qquad\qquad —O—O$$

As was stated above (page 92) the peroxide radicals decompose practically entirely before they have time to react with propane to form hydroperoxides at $T > 300°C$. In accordance with this, Table 26 shows that, at 380°C, there is only about 1 per cent of peroxide in the first stages, and only 0·1 per cent at the end. SHTERN et al. [13, 14] showed that of the peroxides actually present, 70–80 per cent was hydrogen peroxide, and only 20–30 per cent organic peroxides. Also none of the possible decomposition products of organic peroxides were found—these would be acetone for the iso-C_3H_7OOH, and propionaldehyde for the n-C_3H_7OOH.

The theory proposed by SHTERN [13, 14] for hydrocarbon oxidations is set out below. This is derived from his work on C_3H_8 and C_3H_6. A number of modifications have been introduced by the present author.

We shall first consider the various chain-carrying reactions.

(1) The oxygen atom with the free valency attacks a C—C bond within the radical, giving CH_3—CH—O—O—CH_3 (isomerization, page 93). This then decomposes into CH_3CHO and CH_3O. The first step—isomerization—only has a very small heat value, since a C—C bond is broken and a C—O bond is formed. The second step (decomposition of the isomeric radical) is exothermic, since an O—O bond is broken, absorbing 40–50 kcal, and a C=O bond is formed, liberating about 75 kcal. ε for this step must be quite small. The first step, like all isomerizations, involves a substantial activation energy, which must be ~ 20 kcal. The methoxy radical does not isomerize subsequent to the iso-peroxide radical decomposition,

since the atomic arrangement $H-\overset{\displaystyle H}{\underset{\displaystyle H}{\overset{|}{\underset{|}{C}}}}-\dot{O}$ is very unfavourable to

isomerization. Its decomposition is also unlikely, since this would be strongly endothermic; Q_{C-H} is 95–110 kcal, while the energy liberated by the formation of the second link in C=O is 75 kcal.* RUST et al. [28] have shown that at 195°C methoxy radicals from the decomposition of di-tert.-butyl peroxide give methyl alcohol in 99·8 per cent yield, only 0·2 per cent going to other products by decomposition.

This is why CH_3O almost exclusively abstracts hydrogen from RH giving methanol, and causing the chain to continue, since a radical (in this sense either n- or iso-C_3H_7) is simultaneously produced:

$$CH_3\dot{O} + C_3H_8 \rightarrow CH_3OH + \dot{C}_3H_7$$

This is exothermic, since a propane C—H bond is broken (95 kcal) and an O—H bond is produced. This mode of iso-peroxide radical

---

* Using STEACIE's data on the decomposition of nitrites [26, 27], GRAY has lately calculated ΔH_{CH_3O} and consequently the heat of $CH_3O \rightarrow CH_2O + H$ (25 kcal).

decomposition thus gives acetaldehyde and methanol, and regenerates C_3H_7.

(2) The oxygen free valency may attack a C—H bond in a CH_3 group in the same radical. This is equivalent to the exothermic isomerization:

$$CH_3\text{—}CH\text{—}CH_3 \rightarrow \dot{C}H_2\text{—}CH\text{—}CH_3$$
$$\phantom{CH_3\text{—}}\underset{\text{—O—O}}{|} \phantom{\rightarrow \dot{C}H_2\text{—}}\underset{\text{HO—O}}{|}$$

The resultant radical decomposes into C_3H_6 and HO_2. This would appear to involve the absorption of Q_{C-O}, and liberation of energy equivalent to the second link in an olefinic C=C bond, i.e. it would be endothermic by about 20 kcal. However, allowance has also to be

made for the free-electron conjugation in $\underset{\text{HO—O}}{\overset{\displaystyle CH_2\text{—}CH\text{—}CH_3}{|}}$ being

considerably less than that in HO_2. The activity of HO_2 is small, being at least 15–20 kcal less than that of C_3H_6OOH. Consequently, the decomposition is practically thermoneutral, or perhaps is slightly endothermic. The rate-limiting step is then the isomerization, $C_3H_7OO \rightarrow C_3H_6OOH$, this being exothermic, but with a high activation energy. This second mode of isomerization, which gives propylene (amongst other products) has a rather larger activation energy than does the first, which gave acetaldehyde and methanol. Table 30 shows that much less C_3H_6 than CH_3OH is formed at 350°C. SHTERN and ANTONOVSKII [24] have shown that the relative amount of cracked products increases with temperature.

HO_2 may react in two possible ways. The first gives H_2O_2 and regenerates C_3H_7, to continue the chain: $HO_2 + RH \rightarrow H_2O_2 + R$ (c). At the temperature of the experiment, hydrogen peroxide may decompose, oxidizing the aldehyde in the process [29]. Owing to (c) being endothermic, however, HO_2 may react directly with the aldehyde, giving CO, CO_2 and H_2O by oxidation (molecular oxygen also playing a part), and regenerating C_3H_7.

Thus the initial *iso*-propyl radicals are oxidized to CH_3CHO, CH_3OH, C_3H_6, and oxidation products derived from the aldehyde—CO, CO_2 and H_2O—and C_3H_7 is regenerated in the process, to initiate new chains.

The fate of n-C_3H_7 will now be investigated. Like *iso*-C_3H_7, it combines with oxygen.

$$CH_3\text{—}CH_2\text{—}\dot{C}H_2 + O_2 \rightarrow CH_3\text{—}CH_2\text{—}CH_2$$
$$\phantom{CH_3\text{—}CH_2\text{—}\dot{C}H_2 + O_2 \rightarrow CH_3\text{—}CH_2\text{—}}\underset{\text{—O—O}}{|}$$

giving the n-C_3H_7OO radical; this can also isomerize in two ways, each giving distinct products:

(1) A C—C bond is ruptured, and a C—O bond formed:

$$CH_3—CH_2—CH_2 \rightarrow CH_3—CH_2—O—O—\dot{C}H_2$$
$$\overset{|}{—O—O}$$

The subsequent decomposition of the isomeric radical gives HCHO and C_2H_5O:

$$CH_3—CH_2—O—O—\dot{C}H_2 \rightarrow CH_2O + CH_3CH_2\dot{O}$$

The latter abstracts hydrogen from RH to yield C_2H_5OH. REVZIN [30] has found ethanol in the oxidation of propane, but only at the lower temperatures (285°C); it is not found at 350°C. This is because C_2H_5O can also decompose to CH_2O and methyl:

$$CH_3CH_2\dot{O} \rightarrow \dot{C}H_3 + CH_2O.$$

This reaction is unimolecular and so is more rapid than the bimolecular formation of ethanol.* The methyl radical may react with RH, giving CH_4 and R, or may form CH_3OO with oxygen; this peroxide radical first isomerizes, prior to decomposing into CH_2O and OH (see page 97). When the OH reacts with C_3H_8, water is formed and C_3H_7 regenerated.

(2) The n-propyl derivative may also isomerize thus:

$$CH_3—CH_2—CH_2 \rightarrow \dot{C}H_2—CH_2—CH_2$$
$$\overset{|}{—O—O} \qquad\qquad \overset{|}{HO—O}$$

---

* According to GRAY [27] the heat of $C_2H_5O \rightarrow CH_2O + CH_3$ is 13 kcal and $\varepsilon \approx 20$ kcal. If the activation energy of $C_2H_5O + C_3H_8 \rightarrow C_2H_5OH + C_3H_7$ is 7 kcal and the steric factor 0·1, then the ratio of reaction rates at 285°C in the monomolecular decomposition and substitution of C_2H_5O will be

$$\frac{10^{13}\, e^{-20000/1116}[C_2H_5O]}{10^{-10} \cdot 0\cdot1\, e^{-7000/1116}[C_2H_5O][M]} = \gamma = 3\cdot6$$

$$[M] = 2\cdot7 \cdot 10^{18}\ \text{mol-cm}^3$$

i.e. when C_2H_5O decomposes C_2H_5OH will be formed. $\gamma = 12\cdot3$ at 350°C and decomposition prevails over substitution. If $f = 10^{-3}$, as accepted by STEACIE for substitution reactions [26], then $\gamma = 0\cdot36$ at 285°C, i.e. ethanol should not be formed, which does not agree with experiment.

The latter radical cannot split directly into HO_2 and C_3H_6, and can only decompose:

$$\overset{\cdot}{C}H_2-CH_2-CH_2 \rightarrow CH_2{=}CH_2 + CH_2O + \overset{\cdot}{O}H$$
$$\underset{\displaystyle HO-O}{\vert}$$

This process is mainly an exothermic one.*

In this way $n\text{-}C_3H_7$ gives HCHO, C_2H_4 and water. Upon further oxidation the formaldehyde gives CO or CO_2 and H_2O. All the various branches involved in the oxidation of propane are set out on page 103.

Consistent application of radical theory enables one to predict what the oxidation products of propane will be (only those products are predicted which were actually observed and identified by SHTERN). The theory also affords a natural explanation for the "cracked" products (C_2H_4, C_3H_6) so frequently found in oxidative reactions. It is unlikely that C_3H_7 decomposes directly to C_3H_6 and C_2H_4 at 350°C, since both such processes are strongly endothermic $C_3H_7 \rightarrow C_3H_6 + H - 38$ kcal, and $C_3H_7 \rightarrow C_2H_4 + CH_3 - 25$ kcal. The occurrence of CO, CO_2 and H_2O follows naturally from oxidation of aldehydes. The aldehyde oxidation can also be inferred directly from the experimental data; Table 30 shows that the aldehyde concentrations increase only up to certain limiting values, which remain unchanged thereafter throughout, while the CO, CO_2, and H_2O concentrations increase continuously.

* The formation of propylene and ethylene by peroxide radical decomposition (see equation I, direction (b))

$$
\begin{array}{l}
\text{CH}_3\text{-CH-CH}_3 \\
\quad \underset{\displaystyle \underset{\displaystyle O\cdot}{\vert}}{\overset{\displaystyle \vert}{O}}
\end{array}
\overset{a}{\underset{b}{\diagdown\!\!\!\!\diagup}}
\begin{array}{l}
\underset{\displaystyle O-O}{\overset{\displaystyle \vert\quad\vert}{CH_3-\overset{\cdot}{C}H \quad CH_3}} \rightarrow CH_3CHO + CH_3\overset{\cdot}{O} \\[4mm]
\underset{\displaystyle OOH}{\overset{\displaystyle \vert}{CH_3-CH-\overset{\cdot}{C}H_2}} \rightarrow CH_3-CH = CH_2 + H\overset{\cdot}{O}_2
\end{array}
$$

gives a comparatively simple explanation of the fact that cracking of hydrocarbons in the presence of oxygen proceeds much easier and at temperatures lower than in cracking when oxygen is absent. But SHTERN [17] has shown that this simple scheme encounters certain difficulties in the oxidation of propane due to rapid increase of the cracking : oxidation products ratio with temperature. In other words the activation energy of the radical decomposition which gives cracking products is very high relative to that of the decomposition giving oxidation products (see equation I direction (a)). According to SHTERN the difference in activation energies is ~ 13 cal. But since the decompositions are of the same radical this value could be found experimentally only if the pre-exponential factors for these reactions differ by a factor of 10^5–10^6; and that would be difficult to explain.

The relative concentrations of products from n-C_3H_7 and iso-C_3H_7 run almost parallel, showing that the difference in their heats of formation is small (5 kcal). The corresponding difference in the activation energies is 1·25 kcal, so the rate of formation of iso-C_3H_7 will be exp $(1250/RT)$, times greater than that of n-C_3H_7. At 350°C this is equal to 2·7. This may be checked from the experimental $C_3H_6 : C_2H_4$ ratio. Table 30 indicates that this is 2·2–2·3. However, if we form the ratios (primary CH_2O):(primary CH_3CHO) and (primary CH_2O):(CH_3OH), these being equal, we find that they are about 3,* and also, allowing for the fact that 1 mole of C_3H_8 will give 3 moles of CH_2O, approximately equal amounts of n-C_3H_7 and iso-C_3H_7 are formed. This discrepancy arises from neglect of the steric factors in calculating the ratio theoretically. The probability of production by hydrogen abstraction from C_3H_8 is larger for n-C_3H_7 than for iso-C_3H_7, since there are two methyl groups for n-C_3H_7, while there is only a single methylene group available to form iso-C_3H_7.

TROTMAN-DICKENSON and STEACIE [31] found from CH_3 reactions with various hydrocarbons that the ratio of steric factors in similar cases was 2. The theoretical rate ratio is then 2·72, i.e. 1·35, which agrees approximately with that from the relative concentrations of CH_2O and CH_3OH. The somewhat high value obtained from the C_3H_6 and C_2H_4 contents (2·2–2·3) may possibly be due to formation of some C_3H_6 from n-$C_3H_7O_2$. SHTERN's calculation shows that C_3H_6 is mainly derived from iso-C_3H_7.

The very rapid increase in the yield of cracked products above 420°C found by SHTERN et al. [14, 24] may thus be explained by the possible direct decomposition of both n-C_3H_7 and iso-C_3H_7 to C_3H_6 and C_2H_4 at 400°C.†

This possibility is also evident from the data of BYWATER and STEACIE [32] on the mercury-sensitized photodecomposition of propane, since appreciable amounts of methane were formed even at 400°C.

The propane reaction scheme may be checked by comparing the amount of water formed, in accordance with the various branches, against that calculated from the balances for C, H_2, and O_2; this implies that the amounts of all products must be determined experimentally. It can be demonstrated from the calculated amount of H_2O that the aldehydes are not only oxidized, but must also decompose in part, to account for the hydrogen present.

* The reaction scheme (page 103) shows that the amount of primary CH_3CHO formed (due allowance being made for that which is subsequently oxidized) is equal to the amount of CH_3OH. The concentration of primary CH_2O during the reaction was calculated by SHTERN et al. [14, 15].

† These decompositions are indicated by dotted lines (page 103).

Table 31 gives the H_2O contents during a run at 282 mm Hg and 350°C. The composition of the mixture was $C_3H_8 : O_2 = 1 : 1$.

Table 31. Water-vapour contents, in mm Hg, *during the oxidation of propane by oxygen*

Δp (mm Hg)	t (sec)	H_2O concentration (mm Hg)	
		From balance data	Calculated
10	71·5	12	17·2
17	76·5	20	23·4
22	79·2	24·4	29·4
30	84	34·6	39·4
40	92·5	54·2	57·2
60	150	93	97

The agreement between the two sets of values is quite satisfactory.

Oxidation mechanisms can only be completely explained if the rates of formation (w_1) and removal (w_2) are known for the principal intermediate products. Experimental data usually relate to rates of accumulation, i.e. to w_1-w_2, but it would be interesting to determine w_1 itself, e.g. the rates of aldehyde formation when these products are not subsequently consumed.

SHTERN and POLYAK [15] who studied the kinetic formation of propylene oxidation products were able to strike a balance between initial material consumed and intermediate and end-products accumulating. A chain radical scheme which explained the relationships of the various products, both in nature and amount, could then be proposed. The total amount of aldehydes formed (without allowing for subsequent consumption) can be computed from this scheme. The difference gives the amount consumed, i.e. oxidized to CO, CO_2 and H_2O. The scheme was checked by comparing the calculated and experimental values, of which were found to be in good agreement.

Until recently it has not been possible to determine the rates of production and removal of many intermediary products experimentally. Lately however NEIMAN (Institute of Chemical Physics, Moscow) [33] has developed a kinetic tracer method of investigating complex reactions. In this way, w_1 and w_2, may be determined directly for intermediates. The concentration of some intermediate [B], is defined by

$$\frac{d[B]}{dt} = w_1 - w_2 \qquad (1)$$

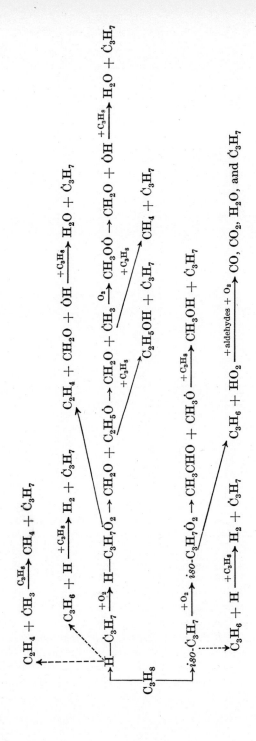

In order to evaluate w_1 and w_2 separately, we require a second equation; this can also be derived by kinetic tracer methods.

If a negligibly small amount of labelled B, B*, is introduced into the system, the specific activity

$$\beta = \frac{[B^*]}{[B]}$$

of B at any future time will be given by

$$\frac{\mathrm{d}\beta}{\mathrm{d}t} = \frac{\mathrm{d}[B^*/B]}{\mathrm{d}t} = \frac{1}{[B]}\frac{\mathrm{d}[B^*]}{\mathrm{d}t} - \frac{\beta}{[B]}\frac{\mathrm{d}[B]}{\mathrm{d}t}$$

Since in any given case no B* is formed, removal being the sole process, $w_1^* = 0$, and $w_2^* = \beta w_2$. Then

$$\frac{\mathrm{d}\beta}{\mathrm{d}t} = -\frac{\beta w_1}{[B]} \qquad (2)$$

(2) allows us to determine the rate of formation of B:

$$w_1 = -[B]\frac{\mathrm{d}(\ln \beta)}{\mathrm{d}t} \qquad (3)$$

The total quantity formed (no account being taken of any removed by subsequent reaction), may be denoted by [B']. [B'] is then given by

$$[B'] = \int_0^t w_1 \mathrm{d}t = \int_\beta^{\beta 0} [B]\mathrm{d}(\ln \beta) \qquad (4)$$

Kinetic tracer methods enable us to compute [B'] directly from experimental data.

NEIMAN et al. [34] used this method to investigate the oxidation of propylene, at $315°C$, $C_3H_6:O_2 = 1:1$, and 243 mm Hg. About 1 per cent of radio-active acetaldehyde was added (2–3 mm). From the variations in β and the total acetaldehyde concentration [B], the amount of acetaldehyde formed [B'] was calculated. The difference between [B'] and [B] gives the amount which is transformed to end-products. Curve 1 in Fig. 10 gives the values calculated from (4), while curve 2 gives the amount of acetaldehyde accumulating. It is clear from Fig. 10 that curve 1 is very similar to curve 3, giving the values calculated by SHTERN and POLYAK [15] from their oxidation scheme.

In order to calculate the rates of formation and removal of the intermediates we need to know the reaction sequences. NEIMAN was able to determine the rate at which some product B was formed from its various possible precursors (one of which (A) should be labelled) and also to follow the secular changes in α and β (the specific activities of A and B), as well as the concentration of B.

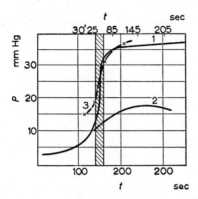

Fig. 10. Formation (1) and accumulation (2) of acetaldehyde in the oxidation of propylene. (3) is the acetaldehyde formed as calculated by SHTERN and POLYAK

Let the rate of formation of B from A be denoted by ω_1, and the rate of formation of B from its other possible precursors be ω_2. Then

$$\frac{d[B]}{dt} = \omega_1 + \omega_2$$

The rate at which the specific activity increases is

$$\frac{d\beta}{dt} = \frac{\omega_1}{[B]}\left(\alpha - \beta \frac{\omega_1 + \omega_2}{\omega_1}\right) \qquad (5)$$

If a small amount of inactive B is added at the start, then $\beta = 0$ at $t = 0$. So β first rises, passes through a maximum, and finally falls in a similar way to α. The value of β at the maximum is determined from $\dfrac{d\beta}{dt} = 0$, i.e. $\left(\alpha - \beta \dfrac{\omega_1 + \omega_2}{\omega_1}\right) = 0$.

Hence

$$\frac{\alpha}{\beta} = \frac{\omega_1 + \omega_2}{\omega_1} \qquad (6)$$

If B is formed only from A, then $\omega_2 = 0$, so $\alpha = \beta$. The curves for α and β then intersect. If $\omega_2 \neq 0$, the curves do not cross, and the value of α/β at the maximum depends on ω_2/ω_1.

Tracer studies were used by NEIMAN et al. [35] to determine whether the CO observed in the oxidation of CH_4 is derived solely from HCHO, or whether any other compound can act as precursor. 0·79 per cent of ^{14}C-formaldehyde and 0·5 per cent CO were added to a mixture containing 33 per cent of methane 66 per cent of air, and 0·1 per cent NO. The experiments were carried out at 670°C. It was found that, at the maximum of the β-curve (see Fig. 11) $\alpha = \beta$, so $\omega_2 = 0$. It follows that the CO is formed in accordance with the over-all reaction:

$$CH_4 \rightarrow HCHO \rightarrow CO$$

Using tracer methods, LUKOVNIKOV and NEIMAN [36] were able to show that the CO_2 formed in the low-temperature oxidation of

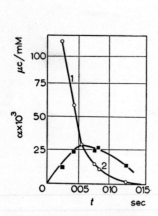

Fig. 11. Specific activities of formaldehyde (1) and CO (2) in oxidizing methane

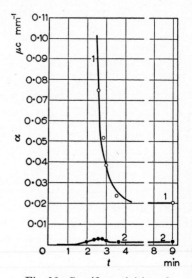

Fig. 12. Specific activities of CO (1) and CO_2 (2) in oxidizing butane

hydrocarbons is not derived in the main from CO, but from other substances, an important source being radical decompositions. In the oxidation of butane, if A═CO and B═CO_2, it was found that, when small amounts of ^{14}CO and of inactive CO_2 were present, that $\beta_{max} \ll \alpha$ (see Fig. 12). Only about 4 per cent of the CO_2 was derived from CO.

Tracer methods also enable one to determine the ratio of rate constants in some cases where different parallel radical reactions take place. An example of this is the work of NEIMAN and SERDYUK on the formation of CO_2 and CO from $CH_3^{14}CHO$. A large number of processes occur in the oxidation of C_3H_6, but this one may be studied in isolation with labelled acetaldehyde. If CO and CO_2 are formed from $CH_3^{14}CO$ in accordance with the scheme

$$CH_3{}^{14}CO \Big\langle \begin{array}{l} \overset{k_1}{\nearrow} CH_3{}^{14}COO_2 \to CH_3O + {}^{14}CO_2 \\ +O_2 \\ \overset{k_2}{\searrow} CH_3 + {}^{14}CO \end{array}$$

then if the total activities of CO and CO_2 are I_{CO} and I_{CO_2}, the ratio of rates of formation of ^{14}CO and of $^{14}CO_2$ (ω_1 and ω_2 respectively), is

$$\frac{\omega_2}{\omega_1} = \frac{k_2}{k_1[O_2]} = \frac{dI_{CO}}{dI_{CO_2}}$$

Oxidation of labelled acetaldehyde alone, as well as oxidation of butane and propylene in the presence of labelled acetaldehyde, showed that $\dfrac{dI_{CO}}{dI_{CO_2}} O_2$ was constant within the limits of error of experiment, although the oxygen concentration changed 10-fold during the oxidation. If it is assumed that $k_2 = 10^{13} \exp(-18000/RT)$, then $k_2 = 2 \cdot 10^{-13} cm^3 \cdot mol^{-1} \cdot sec^{-1}$. At 315°C, k_1 is about 30 times larger than k_2.

This explains the varied relative amounts of CO and CO_2 obtained by different workers in the slow oxidation of hydrocarbons. It is clear that the ratio $CO:CO_2$ must increase as the oxygen pressure diminishes.

The propane oxidation scheme proposed by SHTERN [17] considered above (together with a few additions due to the present author) explains the production of aldehydes, alcohols, hydrocarbons, and other oxidation products in accordance with chain-reaction theory.

BAILEY and NORRISH [37] recently proposed a rather different scheme for the chain oxidation of hexane, according to which the reaction occurs via the following stages:

$$C_6H_{14} \to C_5H_{11}CHO \to C_4H_9CHO \to C_3H_7CHO \to C_2H_5CHO$$
$$\to CH_3CHO \to HCHO$$

The various aldehydes were detected chromatographically. The molecule thus burns from one end like a candle, leading eventually to formaldehyde, which can only arise from the terminal carbon atom. Although other parallel routes were present in NORRISH's scheme, the main route was stepwise destructive oxidation as proposed by POPE et al. [38].

NEIMAN *et al.* [39] investigated the oxidation products from the isotopic *n*-butanes and *n*-pentanes; *n*-butane -1-^{14}C, *n*-butane -2-^{14}C, *n*-pentane -1-^{14}C, -2-^{14}C, and -3-[14]C. HCHO was isolated as the dimedone derivative, and from its activity the probability of its formation from the various carbon atoms in butane and pentane could be calculated. The results are set out in Table 32.

Table 32. *Percentages of formaldehyde formed from the various carbon atoms in different hydrocarbons*

Hydrocarbon	Number of atom in chain					Total
	1	2	3	4	5	
Propane . .	39	22	39	—	—	100
n-Butane .	22	28	28	22	—	100
n-Pentane .	16	26·5	13	26·5	16	100

Table 32 shows that the terminal carbon atoms are not the only source of formaldehyde. In butane and pentane the second carbon atoms are a more important source of formaldehyde than are the terminal carbons. The destructive oxidation theory leads one to expect quite otherwise.

Analogous results have been obtained for acetaldehyde, which may be formed from both the terminal and central carbon atoms. These results cast doubt on the theory of destructive oxidation, and therefore the oxidation scheme set out on page 103 is at present held to be the most correct.

The mechanism of formaldehyde formation postulated in the propane and propylene oxidation schemes [15, 17] was confirmed by the kinetic tracer method. In these schemes HCHO is formed by peroxide radical decomposition, but the methanol formed in hydrocarbon oxidation can possibly also be oxidized to formaldehyde. To verify it SHTERN *et al.* [14] added methanol to the initial $C_3H_8 + O_2$ mixture. It was found that the increase in methanol content at the end actually corresponded to the amount added. In other words the methanol was practically unattacked under these conditions. But the fact that formaldehyde is not formed from alcohol was completely confirmed by NEIMAN and EFREMOV. They carried out a series of propylene oxidations adding a small amount of ^{14}C methanol. The mixture contained 120 mm $CH_3CH=CH_2$ + 120 mm O_2 + 3 mm [14]CH_3OH, at 315°C.

Using the kinetic tracer method they have shown that not more than 5 per cent of formaldehyde is formed by oxidation of methanol. Since no other intermediate products that could give formaldehyde were observed, NEIMAN's results are another proof that formaldehyde is formed from peroxide radicals.

Parallel peroxide radical transformations, i.e. decomposition and reaction with hydrocarbons to form hydroperoxides, would appear to be common to all hydrocarbon oxidations. This also applies to the liquid-phase oxidation of hydrocarbons, but some special features are encountered, due to the very low temperatures (as compared with the gas-phase reactions). The liquid-phase oxidations of saturated hydrocarbons that have been most studied kinetically are those of *n*-decane and *cyclo*hexane [42–45].

The mechanism is currently considered to involve firstly an alkyl radical combination with oxygen, giving the corresponding peroxide radical; the latter then abstracts hydrogen from a hydrocarbon molecule, to give a stable hydroperoxide and an alkyl radical:

$$R + O_2 + RO_2; \; RO_2 + RH \rightarrow ROOH + R.$$

According to this scheme, the peroxide radical reacts in only one way, and the sole primary product is a hydroperoxide. So far, however, this scheme has not been shown decisively to be correct for *n*-alkanes in the range 130–160°C (at which the rate is sufficiently high).

Only very recently have VARTANYAN *et al.* [40] shown by a simple kinetic technique that the *n*-decane oxidation rate at 140°C is at all times practically equal to the intermediate hydroperoxide decomposition rate. Stopping the oxidation at various stages they followed the hydroperoxide decomposition kinetics in nitrogen at the same temperature. The decomposition obeys a first-order law. The product of the first-order rate constant and the hydroperoxide concentration was at all times about equal to the rate of total product formation.

The hydroperoxide was thus shown to be the primary and practically the sole intermediate product. This was confirmed by removing it at some instant and then following the subsequent kinetic behaviour [41]. Alcohol formation was most affected by its removal from the reaction zone, ketone formation less so and acid accumulation not at all. Hence these products are formed in the following sequence:

$$\text{hydrocarbon} \rightarrow \text{hydroperoxide} \begin{smallmatrix} \nearrow \text{alcohol} \searrow \\ \searrow \text{ketone} \nearrow \end{smallmatrix} \text{acid}$$

The principal intermediates are *cyclo*hexyl hydroperoxide, *cyclo*-hexanol, and *cyclo*hexanone. The most important end-product is adipic acid, though this reacts further, e.g. by ester formation or oxidative decarboxylation.

It is very noteworthy that when *cyclo*hexane is oxidized, in addition to *cyclo*hexyl hydroperoxide decomposition products, the same products may be formed directly from the peroxide radical directly under certain conditions. If a glass autoclave is used, much of the product, as with *n*-decane, is produced by hydroperoxide decomposition.

Using radio-active tracers, NEIMAN [33] was able to follow the rates and routes involved in the oxidation of *cyclo*hexanol and *cyclo*hexanone. Since the general kinetics of the removal of these compounds were already known, it was easy to estimate their rates of formation. It was found [46] that oxidation of *cyclo*hexane in a glass reaction vessel at 155°C led to the rate of formation of both *cyclo*hexanol and *cyclo*hexanone being proportional to the hydroperoxide concentration at almost all stages.

Its concentration at the start is much higher than those of alcohol or ketone. We may therefore assume that in a glass vessel the *cyclo*hexanol and *cyclo*hexanone result practically completely from *cyclo*hexyl hydroperoxide decomposition. The mechanism of this decomposition has not been specially studied, but by analogy with other hydroperoxide decompositions it may be represented as follows:

Quite a different result is obtained, however, if the reaction is carried out in a steel vessel.

BEREZIN *et al.* [43] studied *cyclo*hexyl hydroperoxide decomposition in a steel vessel under conditions similar to those used in the oxidation, and found that the decomposition rate was much less than the rates at which the main intermediate products—*cyclo*-hexanol and *cyclo*hexanone—are produced at all times. This can be explained by supposing that in the liquid phase the free peroxide radicals can decompose to the stable intermediate products directly, by-passing the hydroperoxide stage. Then *cyclo*hexanone would be formed via prior peroxide radical isomerization:

$$\text{(ring)}\!\!<^{OO\cdot}_{H} \;\rightarrow\; \text{(ring)}\!\!<^{OOH} \;\rightarrow\; \text{(ring)}\!\!=O + OH$$

The *cyclo*hexanol is supposed to be formed by oxygen transfer between the peroxide radical and *cyclo*hexane.

$$\text{(ring)}\!\!<^{OO\cdot}_{H} + {}^{H}_{H}\!\!>\!C\text{(ring)} \;\rightarrow\; \text{(ring)}\!\!<^{O\cdot}_{H} + {}^{HO}_{H}\!\!>\text{(ring)}$$

The subsequent course of the oxidation is the same for glass and steel reactors and has a number of interesting features. Isotopic tracer methods have shown that the *cyclo*hexanol goes over to *cyclo*hexanone quantitatively.

A number of workers have supposed that the alcohols are difficult to oxidize under these conditions, but this fact disproves their assumption. On the other hand, it is absolutely certain that this reaction involves free radicals. The weakest C—H bond in *cyclo*-hexanol is that adjacent to the OH group, and this, together with the data of BROWN *et al.* [47], enables us to propose the following oxidation scheme for *cyclo*hexanol:

$$\text{(ring)}\!\!<^{OH}_{H} + R \;\rightarrow\; RH + \text{(ring)}\!\!<^{OH}$$

$$\text{(ring)}\!\!<\!OH + O_2 \;\rightarrow\; \text{(ring)}\!\!<^{OH}_{OO\cdot}$$

$$\text{(ring)}\!\!<^{OH}_{OO\cdot} + RH \;\rightarrow\; \text{(ring)}\!\!<^{OH}_{OOH} + R$$

$$\text{(ring)}\!\!<^{OH}_{OOH} \;\rightarrow\; \text{(ring)}\!\!=O + H_2O_2$$

At these temperatures hydrogen peroxide may react further, either being reduced or decomposing.

To describe the reaction completely we must explain the formation of caproic acid as a secondary product in the oxidation of *cyclo*-hexane more exactly [42]. The radical derived from the alcohol tends to isomerize by ring opening, as a number of workers have shown:

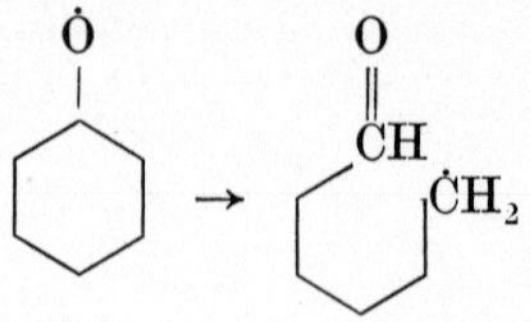

Isomerization of this type is also possible. The isomeric radical abstracts a hydrogen atom to form capraldehyde, which is rapidly oxidized to caproic acid. This route of caproic acid formation is confirmed by the work of MÜLLER and PRITZKOW [48] on the thermal decomposition of *cyclo*hexyl hydroperoxide. A certain amount of caproic acid was found amongst the products.

Caproic acid can also be found in another way by radical isomerization.

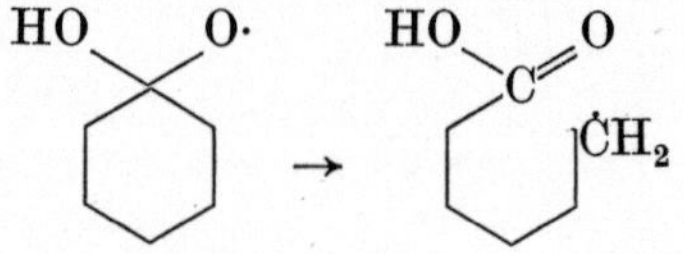

(1)

This isomerization explains why BROWN *et al.* obtained dodecane-1, 12-dicarboxylic acid in good yield when reacting hydroxy*cyclo*-hexylhydroperoxide with ferrous salts; the acid may be formed by isomeric radicals dimerizing [47]:

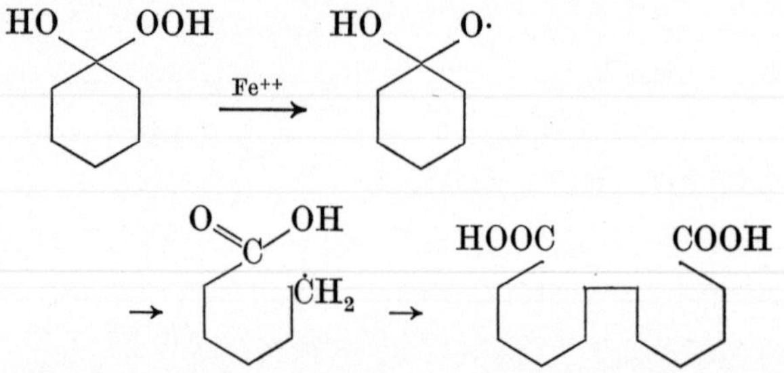

It is very likely that the alcohol oxide radical forms during the oxidation of *cyclo*hexane. The extremely unstable α-hydroxy*cyclo*-hexylhydroperoxide is undoubtedly formed during the oxidation of the *cyclo*hexanol. Most of it decomposes to *cyclo*hexanone and hydrogen peroxide, but a small fraction breaks at the O—O bond, giving the α-oxy*cyclo*hexanol radical. This latter may then rapidly isomerize in two distinct ways: the first being as in (1) above, giving a free radical derived from caproic acid. (This very quickly abstracts hydrogen from some neighbouring molecule to give stable caproic acid.)

A similar mode of isomerization is extraordinarily common in free radicals derived from cyclic alcohols. This explains the formation of methyl-*n*-butyl ketone in the liquid state oxidation of methyl*cyclo*pentane (HAWKINS *et al.* [49]):

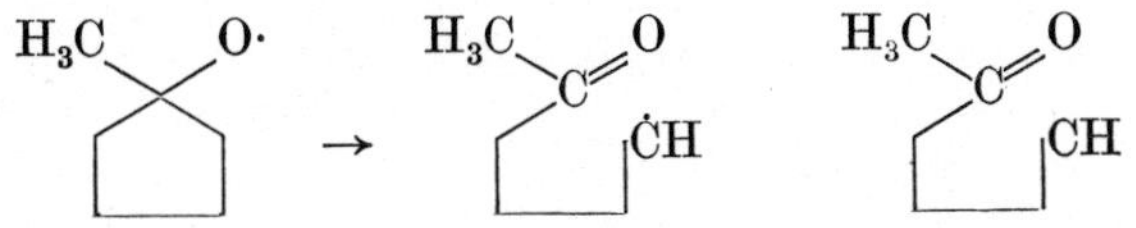

BEREZIN *et al.* demonstrated (by tracer methods) that the acids are only involved in the oxidation process that leads to alcohols (via the formation of esters) to a minor extent, and that over 90 per cent of the esters arose in other ways.

To explain this unexpected result BEREZIN supposes the esters formed (on oxidizing ketones) according to the following scheme; for which there is so far little foundation, since it includes a stage where radical I isomerizes to radical II via oxygen introduction into the carbon chain.

When a chain-carrying radical reacts with a ketone the latter gives a radical. This latter takes up oxygen to form a peroxide radical, which then reacts with the hydrocarbon to give a keto-hydroperoxide

$$R—CH_2—\overset{\underset{\|}{O}}{C}—\overset{\underset{|}{OOH}}{CH}—CH_2—R'$$

The latter breaks at the O—O bond, giving radical I isomerizing to radical II.

$$R_2—CH_2—\overset{\underset{\|}{O}}{C}—\overset{\underset{|}{O\cdot}}{CH}—CH_2—R_1 \rightarrow$$

$$I$$

$$R_2—CH_2—\overset{\underset{\|}{O}}{C}—O—\overset{}{\dot{C}}H—CH_2—R_1 \overset{RH}{\longrightarrow}$$

$$II$$

$$R_2—CH_2—\overset{\underset{\|}{O}}{C}—O—CH_2—CH_2—R_1 + R$$

BEREZIN has proposed a similar type of isomerization to explain the formation of adipic acid in this reaction.

All the stable products detailed in this scheme—ketones, *cyclo*hexyl hydroperoxide, alcohols, and caproic and adipic acids—were separated and identified by BEREZIN [42].

The parallel modes of peroxide radical isomerization, and the other reactions with neighbouring molecules which give hydroperoxide, were demonstrated for liquid heptane by BEREZIN and DENISOV [42] and MAKOLETS [50], at 150°C and 33 atm. IVANOV [2] had earlier found two peroxides in the oxidation of 2, 7-dimethyl octane; namely, the monoperoxide and the α-diperoxide. BEREZIN and MAKOLETS suggest that the β-diperoxide was also formed in their experiments; although it could not be detected directly, its presence could be inferred from the products of its decomposition. The mechanism they proposed (with some minor modifications) is as below. The peroxide radical

$$R-CH-CH_2-CH_2-R$$
$$|$$
$$O-O\cdot$$

may undergo three possible transformations:

(1) Formation of the hydroperoxide:

$$R-CH-CH_2-CH_2-R + RH \rightarrow R-CH-CH_2-CH_2-R + R$$
$$\quad |$$
$$\quad O-O\cdot \qquad\qquad\qquad\qquad\qquad\quad |$$
$$\qquad\qquad\qquad\qquad\qquad\qquad\qquad\qquad OOH$$

(2) Isomerization by transfer of an H atom from the CH_2 group α to the HCOO group, followed by further reactions which yield the α-dihydroperoxide:

$$R-CH-CH_2-CH_2-R \rightarrow R-CH-\dot{C}H-CH_2R \xrightarrow{+O_2}$$
$$\quad |$$
$$\quad O-O\cdot \qquad\qquad\qquad\qquad\quad O-OH$$

$$RCH-CH-CH_2-R \xrightarrow{+RH} R-CH-CH-CH_2-R + R.$$
$$\quad | \quad\;\; |$$
$$\;\; OOH \; O-O\cdot \qquad\qquad\qquad OOH \; OOH$$

(3) Isomerization as above, except that the β—CH_2 group is involved, followed by formation of β-dihydroperoxide:

$$RCH-CH_2-\dot{C}H-R \xrightarrow{+O_2} RCH-CH_2-CH-R \xrightarrow{+RH}$$
$$\quad |$$
$$\quad O-OH \qquad\qquad\qquad OOH \qquad O-O\cdot$$

$$R + R-CH-CH_2-CH-R$$
$$\qquad\quad |\qquad\qquad\quad |$$
$$\qquad\;\; OOH \qquad\qquad OOH$$

The various peroxidized products may then decompose, giving oxidizable products.

The pyrolysis of hydrocarbons ("cracking") gives a wide range of substances. The processes involved are of great importance, due to the economic utilization of mineral oils and natural gases.

In the 1930s RICE and RICE [51] proposed a chain mechanism for reactions of this type, since they had established that free alkyl radicals were involved in the cracking of hydrocarbons. Their scheme was developed and modified by FROST and DINTSES [52].

An example is the cracking of n-butane. The chain carriers are CH_3, n-C_4H_9, iso-C_4H_9 and C_2H_5

$$(1) \quad \dot{C}H_3 + C_4H_{10} \Big\langle \begin{array}{l} CH_4 + \dot{C}H_2CH_2CH_2CH_3 \ (n\text{-butyl}) \\ CH_4 + CH_3\dot{C}HCH_2CH_3 \ (iso\text{-butyl}) \end{array}$$

$$(2) \quad \dot{C}H_2CH_2CH_2CH_3 \rightarrow C_2H_4 + \dot{C}_2H_5$$

$$(3) \quad CH_3\dot{C}HCH_2CH_3 \rightarrow CH_3CH{=}CH_2 + \dot{C}H_3$$

$$(4) \quad \dot{C}H_2CH_3 + C_4H_{10} \Big\langle \begin{array}{l} C_2H_6 + \dot{C}H_2CH_2CH_2CH_3 \\ C_2H_6 + CH_3\dot{C}HCH_2CH_3 \ (iso\text{-butyl}) \end{array}$$

Since both n- and iso-C_4H_9 are formed, and since both may decompose in various ways, a variety of products is to be expected. If the above scheme is correct, then the principal products from butane should be CH_4, C_2H_6, C_2H_4 and C_3H_6, which was confirmed by experiment. If hydrocarbons having the iso-structure are cracked, tertiary radicals will mainly result, and the products will be different. Experimental data on the products from alkane cracking confirm the theoretical predictions.

In order to make the theory quantitative, so that the distribution of products could be predicted, RICE assumed that the probabilities of abstracting primary, secondary, and tertiary hydrogen were in the ratio $1:2:10$ at $600°C$.

More accurate Q_{C-H} values have accumulated since RICE put forward his hypothesis, and these have confirmed the accuracy of RICE's coefficients. It is known, for instance, that the difference between the Q-values for primary and secondary hydrogen is about 5 kcal, and $\Delta\varepsilon$ (calculated from POLANYI's formula) will consequently be $\Delta\varepsilon = 0.25(q_2 - q_1)$, i.e. 1.25 kcal. The ratio of rates at $600°C$ will be:

$$a = \frac{\exp(-\varepsilon_2/RT)}{\exp(-\varepsilon_1/RT)} = \exp[(\varepsilon_1 - \varepsilon_2)/RT] = \exp(\Delta\varepsilon/RT)$$
$$= \exp(1250/1746)$$

where ε_1 and ε_2 are the activation energies for the abstractions. Hence $\log a = 0.31$, or $a \simeq 2$.

A $\Delta\varepsilon$ as small as this implies that at sufficiently high temperatures the relative proportions of the products will change but little with temperature.

RICE was able to predict the relative amounts of products formed from C_3H_8, C_4H_{10}, iso-C_4H_{10}, hexane, 2, 2, 4-trimethyl pentane, etc., using the chain-reaction scheme in conjunction with his hypothetical relative rates of hydrogen abstraction. In all cases the calculated values were in good agreement with experiment. Most data on hydrocarbon cracking obtained in the past 20 years confirm RICE's theory, and the accuracy of his empirical coefficients.

The situation is not so satisfactory in the unsaturated hydrocarbons. The cracking of olefins is characterized by the formation of major quantities of condensed products (dienes, aromatics) which may account for 50 per cent of the starting material. Large amounts of gaseous products also occur; their composition approximates to that from cracking the corresponding alkanes. The mechanism of olefin cracking has not yet been accurately determined. Till now olefin cracking has not been considered as a chain reaction, due to the low activities of radicals of the general type $RCH\!=\!CH\!-\!\dot{C}H\!-\!R'$, which are formed from olefin molecules by hydrogen abstraction. Cracking was supposed to be a simple radical reaction, and the probability of any olefin C—C bond breaking would be fairly constant. The composition of the product could certainly not be calculated from these assumptions.

VOEVODSKII [53] recently showed that olefin pyrolysis is explicable by a chain mechanism. He supposed that the low-activity radicals above could not decompose at the temperatures used ($\sim 600°C$) by rupture of C—C or C—H bonds, and could therefore react with olefin molecules in a manner analogous to that of some chain-transfer processes in polymerization [54]. The reaction assumed in the cracking of butylene, for instance, was:

$$CH_2\!=\!CH\!-\!\dot{C}H\!-\!CH_3 + CH_2\!=\!CH\!-\!CH_2\!-\!CH_3$$
$$\rightarrow CH_2\!=\!CH\!-\!CH\!=\!CH_2 + \dot{C}H_2\!-\!CH_2\!-\!CH_2\!-\!CH_3$$
$$(\text{or } CH_3\!-\!\dot{C}H\!-\!CH_2\!-\!CH_3).$$

A hydrogen atom is transferred to an alkene molecule from the radical, giving a molecule of diene and an alkyl radical. The diene may give rise to complex condensation products of high molecular weight. The alkyl radical will clearly give precisely the same products as in the case of the corresponding alkane (in this case, butane).

1-Butane, for instance, may be supposed to react as follows:

(1) $C_4H_8 \rightarrow CH_2\!=\!CH\!-\!\dot{C}H_2 + \dot{C}H_3$ initiation

(2) $\dot{C}H_3 + C_4H_8 \rightarrow CH_4 + C_4H_7$

(3) $CH_2\!=\!CH\!-\!\dot{C}H\!-\!CH_3 \rightarrow \dot{C}H_3 + C_3H_4$ propagation

(4) $CH_2\!=\!CH\!-\!\dot{C}H\!-\!CH_3 + CH_2\!=\!CH\!-\!CH_2\!-\!CH_3$
$\rightarrow CH_2\!=\!CH\!-\!CH\!=\!CH_2 + \dot{C}H_2\!-\!CH_2\!-\!CH_2\!-\!CH_3$

(5) $\dot{C}H_2\!-\!CH_2\!-\!CH_2\!-\!CH_3 \rightarrow C_2H_4 + \dot{C}H_2\!-\!CH_3$

(6) $\dot{C}H_2\!-\!CH_3 + C_4H_8 \rightarrow C_2H_6 + \dot{C}_4H_7$

(7) $\dot{C}H_2\!-\!CH_3 + C_4H_8 \rightarrow C_2H_4 + \dot{C}_4H_9$

(8) $\dot{C}H_2\!-\!CH_2\!-\!CH_2\!-\!CH_3 \rightarrow CH_3\!-\!\dot{C}H\!-\!CH_2\!-\!CH_3$

(9) $CH_3\!-\!\dot{C}H\!-\!CH_2\!-\!CH_3 \rightarrow CH_3\!-\!CH\!=\!CH_2 + \dot{C}H_3$

(10) $CH_2\!=\!CH\!-\!\dot{C}H\!-\!CH_3 + CH_2\!=\!CH\!-\!CH_2\!-\!CH_3$
$\rightarrow CH_2\!=\!C\!-\!CH\!=\!CH_2 + CH_3\!-\!\dot{C}H\!-\!CH_2\!-\!CH_3$

(11) $2\dot{C}_4H_7 \rightarrow$ termination.

This scheme shows that C_4H_7, formed from 1-butene, may react in three distinct ways:

(1) Decomposition, as in (3), giving allene and CH_3.
(2) Transfer reaction with an alkene molecule, forming a diene and an alkyl radical, as in (4).
(3) Transfer as in (2) above, except that an *iso*-alkyl radical is formed (reaction 10).

The principal gaseous products in the cracking of 1-butene are then CH_4, C_2H_6, C_2H_4, and C_3H_6. These are precisely the products found experimentally.

VOEVODSKII calculated the probable relative rates of the various elementary reactions in the case of 1-pentene, using the gaseous product composition found by ARBUZOV [55]. C_4H_7 may react in three ways, of probabilities α, β, and $\gamma(\alpha + \beta + \gamma) = 1$ for chains of sufficient length. The alkyl radical can react in two ways: it may isomerize (reaction (8)) or it may decompose, as in (5), with a probability δ. C_2H_5 may give C_2H_4 as in 7, or C_2H_6 as in (6), with a probability ϕ. VOEVODSKII derived further equations relating these quantities for 1-pentene, and calculated α, β, γ, α, and ϕ; they were $0\cdot1$, $0\cdot38$, $0\cdot51$, $0\cdot58$, and $0\cdot34$ respectively. The alkyl radical decomposition was the least probable $(\alpha = 0\cdot1)$.

Assuming that all the rate constants for the elementary reactions remained in the same relationship as in 1-pentene, VOEVODSKII calculated the composition of the gaseous fractions in the cracking of 1-butene, 4-methyl-1-pentene and 1-hexene. The agreement between the calculated and experimental values is quite satisfactory, as may be seen from Fig. 13.

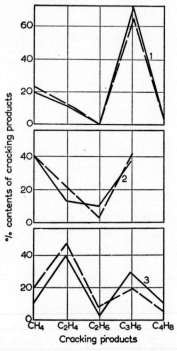

Fig. 13. Full lines: experimental data; dashed lines computed results. 1 and 4: methylpentane; 2: 1-butene; 3: 1-hexene

The possibility of reactions such as

$$CH_2=CH-\dot{C}H-CH_3 + CH_2=CH-CH_2-CH_3$$
$$\rightarrow CH_2=C-CH=CH_2 + \dot{C}H_2-CH_2-CH_2-CH_3$$

does not follow directly from the above concepts.

But if further developments in our ideas occur such a reaction may appear possible. The reaction $CH_2-CH-\dot{C}H-CH_3 \rightarrow CH_2=C=CH-CH_3 + H$ would occasion no objection. However, it is so strongly endothermic that its rate is not sufficiently high at the temperatures employed in cracking. The combination of hydrogen atoms with alkenes to give alkyl radicals has been studied on many occasions. VOEVODSKII's hypothetical reaction merely consists of the two reactions being simultaneous for appropriately disposed radicals and molecules. Since the allyl radical decomposition and the addition of a hydrogen atom to the olefin occur simultaneously, the heat of reaction is only very small, so the activation energy will be low, and the rate will be correspondingly high.

$$CH_2=CH-\dot{C}H-CH_3 + CH_2=CH-CH_2-CH_3$$

$$
\begin{array}{ccc}
& CH_2=C-CH-CH_2 & CH_2=C-CH-CH_2 \\
\rightarrow & H & \rightarrow \qquad + \\
& \dot{C}H_2\cdots CH-CH_2-CH_3 & CH_3-\dot{C}H-CH_2-CH_3
\end{array}
$$

The above chain reactions give a number of different products. However, a large variety of products does not necessarily imply a chain reaction. As a rule the quantities formed correspond with the overall equation, as in simple unimolecular or bimolecular processes. This is why the products may not differ much if a chain-mechanism is involved, or if it is simply a unimolecular or bimolecular process. For example, the chlorination of hydrocarbons in general, and of methane in particular [56], is in accordance with the over-all reaction

$$Cl_2 + CH_4 \rightarrow CH_3Cl + HCl$$

This is a chain reaction, however:

$$Cl + CH_4 \rightarrow CH_3 + HCl + 2 \text{ kcal.}$$
$$CH_3 + Cl_2 \rightarrow CH_3Cl + Cl + 23 \text{ kcal, etc.}$$

The products are CH_3Cl (which may in its turn be further chlorinated) and hydrogen chloride, just as if the reaction were merely a simple bimolecular one. Products from the combination of methyl radicals (C_2H_6) are completely undetectable, owing to the great chain lengths (10^5–10^6).

Although alkyl bromides and chlorides decompose via chains [5], the products are exactly the same as from the unimolecular overall reaction $n\text{-}C_3H_7Br \rightarrow C_3H_6 + HBr$, because the individual chains are of great length and the products due to radical–radical reaction are negligible in amount.

The decomposition of acetaldehyde [57, 58] gives only those products to be expected from the over-all equation $CH_3CHO \rightarrow$

9

$CH_4 + CO$. However, it has been shown recently that a chain mechanism is involved [59, 60]:

$$CH_3CHO \rightarrow CH_3 + HCO,$$

$$CH_3 + CH_3CHO \rightarrow CH_4 + CH_3CO,$$

$$CH_3CO \rightarrow CH_3 + CO \text{ etc.}$$

The small amount of ethane (about 1 per cent of the total) found in the products is formed by methyl radical combination.

In some instances the radical combination products are the same as those from the main reaction. This is so in iodides [5], the overall equation being:

$$2C_2H_5I \rightarrow C_2H_4 + C_2H_6 + I_2$$

The chain-carrying reactions are:

$$I + C_2H_5I \rightarrow I_2 + C_2H_5$$

$$C_2H_5 + C_2H_5I \rightarrow C_2H_6 + C_2H_4I$$

$$C_2H_4I \rightarrow C_2H_4 + I \text{ etc}$$

The following radical–radical reactions occur:

$$I + I \rightarrow I_2$$

$$C_2H_5 + C_2H_5 \rightarrow C_2H_4 + C_2H_6*$$

$$C_2H_5 + I \rightarrow C_2H_5I$$

$$I + C_2H_4I \rightarrow I_2 + C_2H_4$$

The chain gives I_2, C_2H_4 and C_2H_6 which are exactly the same as from the radical–radical reactions.

(4)

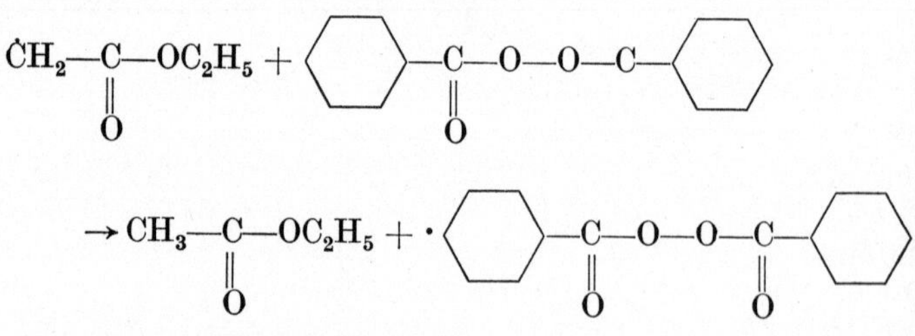

---

* In most cases disproportionation predominates over direct radical combination (which would give butane).

The photo-addition of CCl_3Br to *cyclo*hexene (or other alkenes) in the liquid phase gives only one product; this was studied by MEL-VILLE *et al.* [61]. The following stages are present:

(1) $CCl_3Br \xrightarrow{h\nu} CCl_3 + Br,$

(2) $+ CCl_3 \rightarrow$ $CCl_3,$

(3) $CCl_3 + CCl_3Br \rightarrow$ $CCl_3 + CCl_3$ etc.

The principal end-product is 1-trichloromethyl 2-bromo*cyclo*hexane.

The rate constants and activation energies of (2) and (3) may be calculated from MELVILLE's results. They are given in Table 33 for the addition of CCl_3Br to *cyclo*hexane, vinyl acetate, styrene, α-methylstyrene, and allyl chloride.

Table 33. *Kinetic data for some addition-reactions of* CCl_3Br

	Cyclo-hexene	Vinyl acetate	Styrene	α-Methyl styrene	Allyl chloride
k_2 (30°) (l-mole-sec) .	256	1120	—	—	—
k_3 (30°) (l-mole-sec) .	63·8	2740	$0·2 \times 10^2$	$0·08 \times 10^2$	$0·16 \times 10^2$
a_2 (l-mole-sec) . .	$6·96 \times 10^5$	$2·73 \times 10^7$	—	—	—
a_3 (l-mole-sec) . .	$1·15 \times 10^5$	$9·1 \times 10^7$	12×10^7	$0·3 \times 10^5$	$2·3 \times 10^5$
ε_2 (kcal) . . .	3·4	6·1	—	—	—
ε_3 (kcal) . . .	4·5	7·5	10·0	5·0	5·8

k_2 and k_3 are the rate constants for (2) and (3) respectively, and a_2 and a_3 are the pre-exponential factors, and ε_2 and ε_3 the activation energies, to correspond.

Totally different processes occur if CCl_4, $CHCl_3$, or $CHBr_3$ replace CCl_3Br [40, 41, 42]. These have been investigated at $p > 1$ atm under illumination or in the presence of peroxides. Combination of trichloromethyl with an alkene gives a radical which then undergoes addition at the double bond of another alkene molecule, forming a fresh radical which in turn reacts in the same fashion, and so on:

(1') $CCl_4 + h\nu \rightarrow CCl_3 + Cl,$

(2') $CCl_3 + RCH=CH_2 \rightarrow CHRCH_2CCl_3,$

(3') $CHRCH_2CCl_3 + RCH=CH_2 \rightarrow CHRCH_2CHRCH_2CCl_3$,

(3") $CHRCH_2CHRCH_2Cl_3 + RCH=CH_2$
$$CHRCH_2CHRCH_2CHRCH_2CCl_3 \text{ etc.}$$

The individual chains are terminated by the radical reacting with CCl_4, giving a stable molecule, and regenerating CCl_3:

(4) $(CH_2CH_2)_nCCl_3 + CCl_4 \rightarrow Cl(CH_2CH_2)CCl_3 + CCl_3$.

The polymeric substances produced consist of one molecule of CCl_4 together with several alkene molecules. These polymeric compounds form about 90 per cent of the product with CCl_4, while CBr_4 and CCl_3Br give solely compounds with a molecular ratio of $1:1$.

The formation both of polymers and of compounds with a $1:1$ composition is due to simultaneous reactions of types (3) and (3'). The differences found between the behaviour of CCl_4 and that of CBr_4 or CCl_3Br arise from differences in the C—X bond energies, where X = halogen atom. If Q_{C-X} is relatively small, then (3) occurs $(Q_{CCl_3-Br} = Q_{CBr_2-Br} = 49 \text{ kcal})$. If Q_{C-X} is sufficiently large, as in CCl_4 (68·4 kcal), then chlorine abstraction from CCl_4 is more difficult than is addition at an olefinic double bond; so compounds containing several molecules of alkene to one of CCl_4 (telomers) are formed.

It can also happen that the radicals formed combine or disproportionate at rates comparable to that of chain propagation. The decomposition of benzoyl peroxide, which has been studied by BAGDASARYAN and MILYUTINSKAYA [65] is an example. The first step is decomposition to two benzoate radicals.

(1)

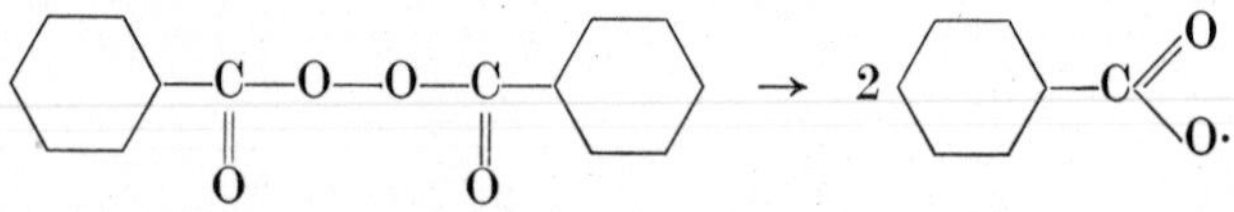

which then give phenyl radicals:

(2)

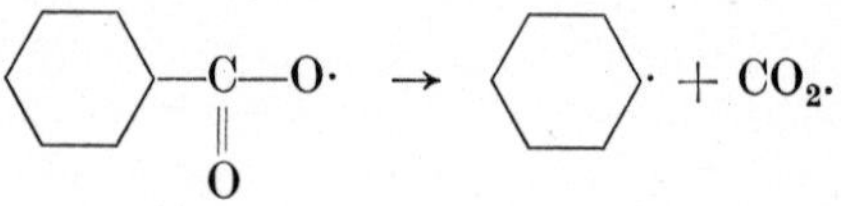

The subsequent reactions depend on the solvent. In aliphatic solvents (hydrocarbons, alcohols, carboxylic acids and esters) the peroxide decomposes. Chain propagation in ethyl acetate is as follows [65]

(3)

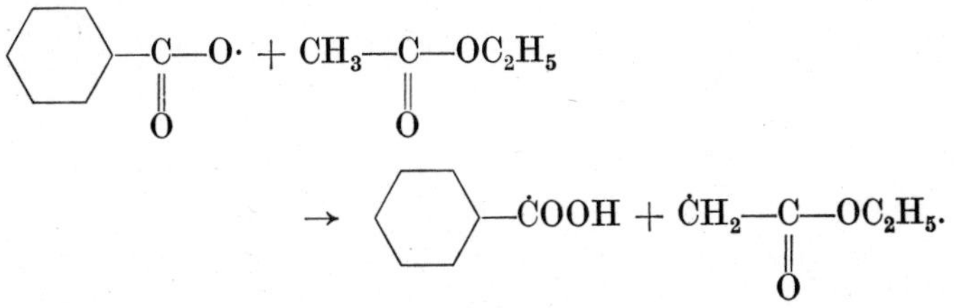

At peroxide concentrations of 0·185 M the chains are 8–9 links long. The product contains benzoic acid (50 per cent yield) and CO_2, indicating partial benzoate radical breakup. At 0·00185 M the chains do not propagate, the rate being the unimolecular breakup one (reaction (1)). The product is again benzoic acid. It probably comes from (3), but here the ethyl acetate radicals mostly combine because the peroxide concentration is so low and do not have time to react as in (4): no chain propagation therefore occurs.

Inhibitors depress the chain reaction. For instance 0·3 mole per cent methylmethacrylate added to the ethyl acetate suppresses the peroxide breakup chain at 0·185 M. Radical addition occurs at the methylmethacrylate double bond.

Benzoyl peroxide breakup goes somewhat differently in aromatic solvents. (1) and (2) are the same as in aliphatic solvents, but the phenyl radical formed, according to WATERS, SZWARC and JAQUISS [66] joins up with an aromatic molecule

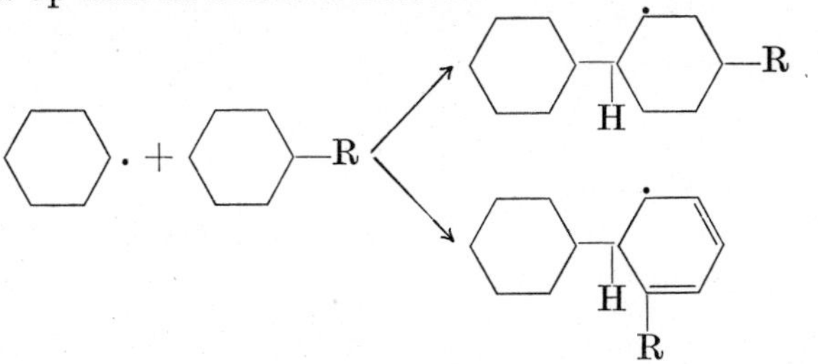

(5)

The resultant radical is inactive, reacting with a benzoate radical

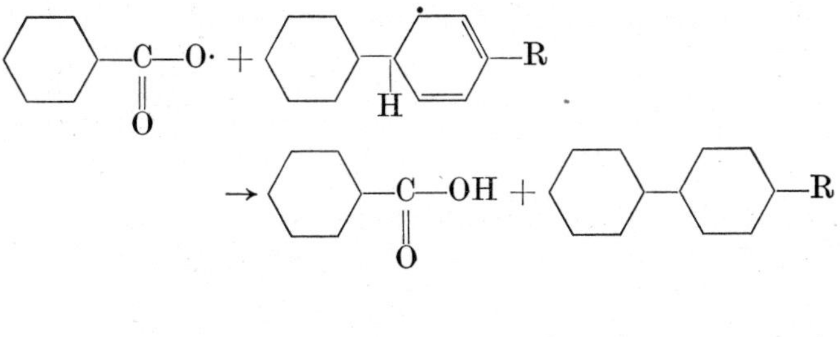

(6)

To demonstrate this mechanism MILYUTINSKAYA and BAGDASARYAN [67] decomposed benzoyl peroxide in partially deuterated benzene. The diphenyl formed showed 45 per cent of the benzene deuterium content, remaining the same when temperature and peroxide concentration were altered. Thus in their opinion most of the diphenyl molecules derive one ring from the peroxide and the other from the benzene. But the partially deuterated diphenyl may result from direct benzoate–phenyl radical reaction, by-passing (5). To eliminate this possibility the benzoic acid would have to be examined, which was not done. BAGDASARYAN and MILYUTINSKAYA did this when studying the decomposition of 4-nitrobenzoyl peroxide in partially deuterated benzene or nitrobenzene. The low-solubility 4-nitrobenzoic acid was here readily separated. The COOH group deuterium content equalled that in the deuterated benzene or nitrobenzene. This result indicates that there is no isotope effect in the solvent-COOH group hydrogen transfer. This is in accordance with the nitrobenzoic acid being formed as in (6), since phenyl radical addition to the benzene ring carbon is independent of whether the carbon carries a hydrogen or deuterium atom. If the reaction were

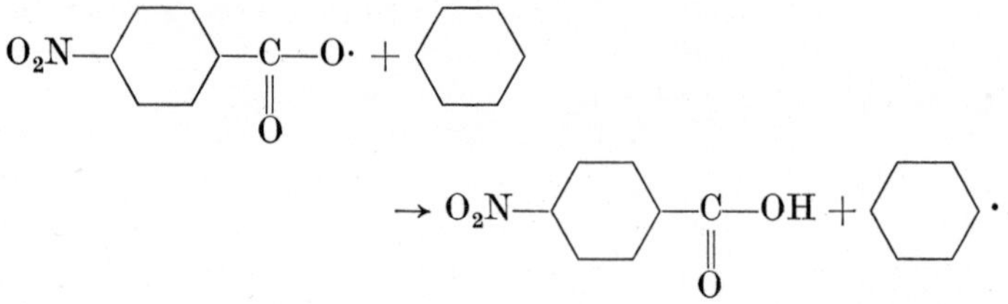

$$O_2N-\bigcirc-\underset{\underset{O}{\|}}{C}-O\cdot \; + \; \bigcirc$$

$$\rightarrow O_2N-\bigcirc-\underset{\underset{O}{\|}}{C}-OH \; + \; \bigcirc\cdot$$

the COOH group deuterium content would be less than the benzene content. Unfortunately the nitrodiphenyl was not recovered in these experiments: this would uniquely decide whether the mechanism involves (5). If toluene is used as solvent the CH_3-group hydrogen mobility results in the following reaction (additional to (5) and (6)) occurring:

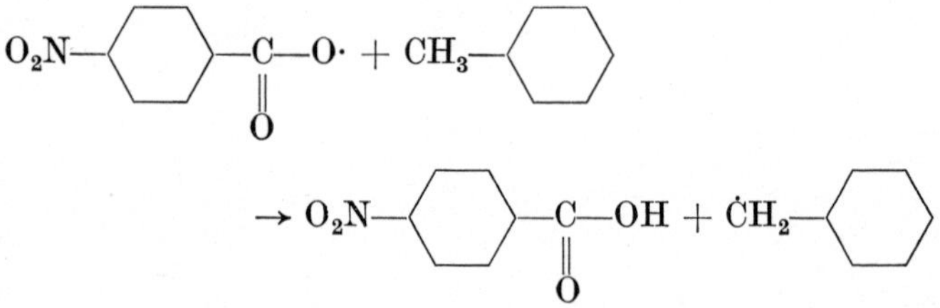

$$O_2N-\bigcirc-\underset{\underset{O}{\|}}{C}-O\cdot \; + \; CH_3-\bigcirc$$

$$\rightarrow O_2N-\bigcirc-\underset{\underset{O}{\|}}{C}-OH \; + \; \dot{C}H_2-\bigcirc \quad (7)$$

as was demonstrated by using CH_3-group deuterated toluene [68]. But a chain reaction cannot develop because the benzyl radicals are inactive, giving dibenzyl, which latter was not analysed. The chain reaction in aromatics is therefore suppressed by the fast reactions (5) and (7) (in toluene) which give inactive radicals. Aromatics are chain inhibitors, like compounds with double bonds.

REFERENCES

1. H. FARMER. *Trans. Faraday Soc.* **42**, 228 (1946).
2. K. I. IVANOV. *Intermediates and Intermediary Reactions in the Auto-oxidation of Hydrocarbons.* Moscow, 1949. (In Russian.)
3. K. I. IVANOV, V. SAVINOVA and V. ZHAKHOVSKAYA. *Dokl. Akad. Nauk SSSR* **59**, 905 (1948).
4. K. I. IVANOV, V. SAVINOVA and V. ZHAKHOVSKAYA. *Dokl. Akad. Nauk SSSR* **59**, 703 (1948).
5. N. N. SEMENOV. *Usp. Khim.* **21**, 641 (1952).
6. G. A. RAZUVAEV and YU. A. OLDEKOP. *Zh. Obshch. Khim.* **19**, 736 (1949). English translation: *Can. Nat. Res. Coun.* TT-132 (1950); *ibid.* **19**, 1483 (1949).
7. G. A. RAZUVAEV and G. G. PETUKHOV. *Zh. Obshch. Khim.* **21**, 646 (1951).
8. F. F. RUST and W. E. VAUGHAN. *J. Org. Chem.* **5**, 472 (1940).
9. M. TAMURA. *Rev. Phys. Chem. Japan* **15**, 86 (1941).
10. N. V. FOK, B. B. BERESLAVSKII, A. B. NALBANDYAN and V. YA. SHTERN. *Dokl. Akad. Nauk SSSR* **67**, 499 (1949). English translation: *Can. Nat. Res. Coun.* TT-119 (1950).
11. N. V. FOK and A. B. NALBANDYAN. *Dokl. Akad. Nauk SSSR* **85**, 1093 (1953). English translation: *Can. Nat. Res. Coun.* TT-380 (1953).
12. N. V. FOK and A. B. NALBANDYAN. *Dokl. Akad. Nauk SSSR* **89**, 125 (1953).
13. V. YA. SHTERN and N. YA. CHERNYAK. *Dokl. Akad. Nauk SSSR* **78**, 91 (1951). English translation: *Can. Nat. Res. Coun.* TT-264 (1952).
14. V. YA. SHTERN, N. YA. CHERNYAK, V. L. ANTONOVSKII and A. F. REVZIN. *Zh. Fiz. Khim.* **28**, 240 (1954).
15. V. YA. SHTERN and S. S. POLYAK. *Zh. Fiz. Khim.* **27**, 341, 631, 950 (1953); *Dokl. Akad. Nauk SSSR* **95**, 1231 (1954).
16. R. G. W. NORRISH and J. H. KNOX. *Proc. Roy. Soc.* A **222**, 151 (1954).
17. V. YA. SHTERN. *Zh. Fiz. Khim.* **28**, 613 (1954).
18. J. J. BATTEN and M. J. RIDGE. *Aust. J. Chem.* **8**, 370 (1955).
19. G. B. SERGEEV and V. YA. SHTERN. *Dokl. Akad. Nauk SSSR* **91**, 1357 (1953).
20. R. A. KALINENKO. *Thesis for Diploma.* Moscow State University, 1952.
21. M. V. KRAUZE, M. S. NEMTSOV and E. A. SOSKINA. *Zh. Obshch. Khim.* **5**, 356 (1935).
22. R. N. PEASE. *J. Amer. Chem. Soc.* **52**, 1158 (1930).
23. M. SZWARC. *J. Chem. Phys.* **17**, 284 (1949).
24. V. YA. SHTERN and V. L. ANTONOVSKII. *Dokl. Akad. Nauk SSSR* **78**, 303 (1951). English translation: *Can. Nat. Res. Coun.* TT-265 (1951).
25. V. YA. SHTERN and S. S. POLYAK. *Zh. Fiz. Khim.* **27**, 341 (1953).
26. E. W. R. STEACIE. *Atomic and Free Radical Reactions.* New York, 1954.
27. P. GRAY. *Fifth Symposium on Combustion*, p. 535. New York 1955.
28. F. F. RUST, F. H. SEUBOLD and W. E. VAUGHAN. *J. Amer. Chem. Soc.* **72**, 338 (1950).
29. E. J. HARRIS. *Trans. Faraday Soc.* **44**, 764 (1948).
30. A. F. REVZIN. *Thesis for Diploma.* Moscow State University, 1951.
31. A. F. TROTMAN-DICKENSON and E. W. R. STEACIE. *J. Chem. Phys.* **19**, 329 (1951).
32. S. BYWATER and E. W. R. STEACIE. *J. Chem. Phys.* **19**, 319 (1951).

33. M. B. NEIMAN. *Zh. Fiz. Khim.* **28,** 1235 (1954).
34. M. B. NEIMAN, V. YA. EFREMOV, N. K. SERDYUK and A. F. LUKOVNIKOV. *Izv. Akad. Nauk SSSR. Otdel. Khim. Nauk* 408 (1956).
35. M. B. NEIMAN, I. N. ANTONOVA, V. N. KUZMIN, R. I. MOSHKINA, A. B. NALBANDYAN and G. I. FEKLISOV. *Izvt. Akad. Nauk SSSR. Otdel. Khim. Nauk* 789 (1955).
36. S. F. LUKOVNIKOV and M. B. NEIMAN. *Zh. Fiz. Khim.* **29,** 1410 (1955).
37. H. C. BAILEY and R. G. W. NORRISH. *Proc. Roy. Soc.* A **212,** 311 (1952).
38. J. C. POPE, E. J. DYKSTRA and G. EDGAR. *J. Amer. Chem. Soc.* **51,** 1875, 2203, 2213 (1929).
39. M. B. NEIMAN, A. F. LUKOVNIKOV and G. I. FEKLISOV. *Symposium on Chemical Kinetics, Catalysis and Reactivity,* p. 184. Academy of Sciences, Moscow 1955.
40. L. S. VARTANYA, Z. K. MAIZUS and N. M. ÉMANUEL. *Zh. Fiz. Khim.* **30,** 856 (1956).
41. L. S. VARTANYAN, Z. K. MAIZUS and N. M. ÉMANUEL. *Zh. Fiz. Khim.* **30,** 862 (1956).
42. I. V. BEREZIN and E. T. DENISOV. *Dokl. Akad. Nauk SSSR* **97,** 273 (1954).
43. I. V. BEREZIN, E. T. DENISOV and N. M. ÉMANUEL. *Symposium on Chemical Kinetics, Catalysis and Reactivity,* p. 273. Academy of Sciences of U.S.S.R., Moscow 1955.
44. *Brit. Pat.* 633354 (1949).
45. A. FARKAS and E. PASSAGLIA. *J. Amer. Chem. Soc.* **72,** 3333 (1950).
46. I. V. BEREZIN, B. G. DZANTIEV, N. F. KAZANSKAYA, L. I. SINOCHKINA and N. I. ÉMANUEL. *Zh. Fiz. Khim.* No. 3 (1957).
47. N. BROWN, M. J. HARTIG, M. J. ROEDEL, A. W. ANDERSON and C. E. SCHWEITZER. *J. Amer. Chem. Soc.* **77,** 1756 (1955).
48. K. A. MÜLLER and W. PRITZKOW. *Chem. Ber.* **89,** 2321 (1956).
49. E. G. E. HAWKINS, E. J. GASSON, A. F. MILLIDGE and D. C. QUINN. *J. Chem. Soc.* 2798 (1950).
50. B. I. MAKOLETS. *Thesis for Diploma.* Moscow State University, 1953.
51. F. O. RICE and K. K. RICE. *The Aliphatic Free Radicals.* Baltimore 1935. Russian translation: Moscow 1937.
52. A. V. FROST. *Usp. Khim.* **8,** 956 (1939); A. I. DINTSES. *Usp. Khim.* **3,** 936 (1934).
53. V. V. VOEVODSKII. *Symposium on Chemical Kinetics, Catalysis and Reactivity.* Academy of Sciences, Moscow 1955.
54. L. SHMERLING. *Symposium on Catalysis in Organic Chemistry,* p. 123. Moscow 1953.
55. YU. A. ARBUZOV. *Scientific Reports of Moscow State University, Organic Chemistry Section* **89,** 7 (1945).
56. N. N. SEMENOV. *Chain Reactions.* Leningrad 1934. (In Russian.) Translated and revised as *Chemical Kinetics and Chain Reactions.* Oxford 1935.
57. V. N. IPATIEFF. *Ber. Dtsch. Chem. Ges.* **35,** 1047 (1902).
58. C. N. HINSHELWOOD and W. K. HUTCHINSON. *Proc. Roy. Soc.* A **111,** 380 (1926).
59. P. D. ZEMANY and M. BURTON. *J. Phys. Chem.* **55,** 949 (1951).
60. L. A. WALL and W. J. MOORE. *J. Phys. Chem.* **55,** 965 (1951).
61. H. W. MELVILLE, J. C. ROBB and R. C. TRUTTON. *Disc. Faraday Soc.* **14,** 150 (1953).
62. M. S. KHARASCH, E. V. JENSEN and W. H. URRY. *J. Amer. Chem. Soc.* **69,** 1100 (1947).
63. R. M. JOYCE, W. E. HANFORD and J. HARMON. *J. Amer. Chem. Soc.* **70,** 2529 (1948).

64. E. C. KOOYMAN and E. FARWNHORST. *Rec. Trav. Chim. Pays-Bas* **70,** 267 (1951).
65. KH. S. BAGDASARYAN and R. I. MILYUTINSKAYA. *Zh. Fiz. Khim.* **27,** 420 (1953).
66. W. A. WATERS. *Trans. Faraday Soc.* **37,** 770 (1941); M. SZWARC and M. T. JAQUISS. *Disc. Faraday Soc.* No. 14, 246 (1953).
67. R. I. MILYUTINSKAYA and KH. S. BAGDASARYAN. *Zh. Fiz. Khim.* In press.
68. R. I. MILYUTINSKAYA and KH. S. BAGDASARYAN. *Zh. Fiz. Khim.* In press.

Chapter **3**

THE REACTIONS OF BIRADICALS

1. THE TRANSITION OF ATOMS TO THE ACTIVE-VALENCE STATE

ATOMS which are typically divalent in the free state, such as O, S, Mg, Ca, or Cd, have an even number of electrons. The ground state in O, S, and Se is a triplet (^3P), i.e. two of the electrons have their spins uncoupled. These atoms are highly reactive, and react with stable compounds just as readily as do atoms of typically univalent elements. ε for $O + H_2 \rightarrow OH + H$ is about 6 kcal, while that for $H^* + H_2 \rightarrow H^*H + H$ is 7 kcal.

Divalent atoms may thus be considered as biradicals —O—; —S—; —Se—. An energy ΔR is required to transform O, S, and Se to the "active-valence" state. This latter term designates the electronic state which would be produced if the bonds joining the atom to a molecule were broken while leaving the electronic state the same as in the intact molecule. Such a state, being unstable, cannot actually exist, and the atom would at once pass over into the condition peculiar to the free state.

Bonds may be conceived as forming in two stages; firstly, the atom goes over to the active-valence state (ΔR absorbed), and the valencies liberated then couple with those of other atoms in the usual way, liberating energy. This conceptual division of bond energies into two parts is quite useful in practice. In oxygen, ΔR is about 14 kcal. This may be deduced from the energies of the "first" and "second" O—H bonds in H_2O being 103 kcal and 117 kcal respectively. The difference, 14 kcal, is ΔR for the oxygen atom.*

It might appear natural to assume that the high chemical activities of the oxygen, sulphur and selenium atoms are due to two electron spins being parallel, and that these two electrons define their biradical properties completely. Unfortunately, this is not the case. The atomic states of Group II metals are singlets, ^1S, i.e. all their electron spins are paired. For this reason ΔR for Group II is greater than for Group VI. The formation (from atoms) of HgCl liberates 23 kcal but

* The excitation energy required is in fact somewhat larger than 14 kcal,

$$\overset{\displaystyle H}{\underset{\displaystyle |}{}}$$

since a certain amount of energy is required to deform the H—O angle from 90° to 104° 40′ because the two H atoms repel one another.

128

addition of the second Cl atom gives $\sim 80 \cdot 5$ kcal, so ΔR for the mercury atom is about 55 kcal. The same combination sequence in Cd and Zn produces energies which are $46 + 104$ kcal, and $50 \cdot 5 + 105$ kcal respectively and so here $\Delta R \sim 50$ kcal. (From KONDRATIEV [1].) None the less, all these atoms are chemically typical biradicals; the ε_0 values when these atoms react with stable molecules are just as low as for univalent or bivalent radicals. The vapour-phase reaction $Zn + Cl_2 \rightarrow ZnCl + Cl$ has $\varepsilon = 8$ kcal, and for $Cd + Cl_2 \rightarrow CdCl + Cl$ ε is $12 \cdot 5$ kcal. q for the Cd reaction is equal to the difference between Q_{Cd-Cl} (51 kcal) and Q_{Cl-Cl} (57 kcal), i.e. -16 kcal. Thus ε_0 is only about $6 \cdot 5$ kcal, since $\varepsilon = \varepsilon_0 + q$.

ΔR for Group II elements is reflected only in reduced q-values, and hence in reduced atomic activities; ε_0 is low, and does not depend on whether the electrons have their spins parallel or antiparallel. Thus Group II atoms may be considered from the chemical point of view as biradicals with low activities, like the univalent radicals HO_2 and $CH=CH-\dot{C}H$. The ground state of the carbon atom is a triplet (^3P), so the atom is in effect divalent; ΔR may be shown to be extremely large, however.

2. REACTIVITY IN THE MOLECULES O_2, S_2 AND Se_2

O_2, S_2 and Se_2 will now be considered. They all have triplet ground states, $^3\Sigma$, so they each have a pair of electrons with parallel spins, and are paramagnetic. They might therefore be considered to be biradicals, e.g. $-O-O-$. However, O_2 does not show the properties of a biradical in its chemical or thermochemical relationships. The strength of the bond formed by the two electrons with parallel spins is actually stronger than that formed by the electrons with antiparallel spins. Q_{O-O} for ordinary $O-O$ bonds (as in peroxides, such as H_2O_2) is about 50 kcal, while $Q_{O=O}$ in O_2 is 118 kcal. Chemically speaking, the oxygen molecule is highly inert. The apparent ease with which O_2 sometimes reacts (as is now well known), is due, not to the molecular activity itself, but to the ease with which the radical chains (via which it reacts) can propagate; i.e. it depends on the properties of atomic oxygen and of the radicals $R-O-O-$. When conditions are unfavourable to chain propagation, O_2 is quite inert. Oxygen may remain in contact with the vapours of phosphorus, phosphine, or silane for days without any sign of reaction under such conditions, but if branched chains can propagate readily, it will react violently even at room temperature.

Oxygen reacts with hydrogen only via a chain mechanism. The direct, purely molecular O_2/H_2 reaction does not occur in practice. E_0 for the direct molecular reaction is about 50 kcal; this is typical of direct reactions between stable molecules, and exceeds ε_0 for radical–molecule reactions by an order of magnitude. The chemical inertness of O_2 is also apparent from its failure to dimerize.*

S_2 and Se_2 resemble one another to a great extent in being biradicals, although their activities are low. Q_{S-S} is about 52 kcal, and $Q_{S=S}$ is 83 kcal [2]. The second bond, formed from electrons with parallel spins, is distinctly weaker than that in O_2. Sulphur is polymeric, as is well known; S_6 and S_8, which have cyclic structures, are found in the vapour. Ordinary bonds connect the atoms in these molecules. Sulphur can also form long polymeric chains (as in polysulphides). No direct data exist on the magnitude of E_0 when S_2 reacts with molecules. However, exothermic reactions occur readily.

The ground state of P_2 is a singlet, $^1\Sigma$, and $Q_{P=P}$ is high (about 116 kcal). P_2 shows the chemical properties of a biradical; it dimerizes to P_4 (P_4 has a tetrahedral structure with ordinary bonds), and 30 kcal is liberated. P_2 is evidently an active molecule, and there are much better grounds for classifying it as a biradical than in the case of O_2, in spite of its spins being coupled in antiparallel pairs.

The chemical and physical features which might be used to classify a particular molecule as a biradical may thus conflict, since the physical criteria (triplet ground state, paramagnetism) do not always coincide with the chemical (absence of an important potential barrier, a tendency to dimerize, and the low strength or absence of a second bond).

3. DIVALENT CARBON

As has been mentioned above, the carbon atom may be considered as a biradical. The result of satisfying its two valencies with hydrogen atoms is to produce CH_2, which so far as chemistry is concerned, behaves as a biradical. (The chemical properties of CH_2 will be dealt with in due course.) It is evident that two further bound valencies are released by saturating the two primary valencies; CH_2 behaves as a typical biradical.

Of the compounds of divalent carbon, CO alone does not behave as a biradical. The considerable increase in $Q_{C=O}$ in CO (256 kcal) as compared with C==O groups in a variety of organic compounds (150–160 kcal) indicates that the carbon s electrons assist in forming the bond in CO.† CO occupies a position amongst the compounds of divalent carbon which is even more remarkable than that of NO amongst univalent free radicals. This is due to the large ΔR (60–80 kcal) for CO; where activated it is a typical biradical. In the reaction $CO + Cl \rightarrow COCl + q_1$, q_1 does not exceed a few kcal,

* The liquid is apparently associated to some extent at low temperatures.
† This is confirmed by SAHNI's calculations (1953).

but about $q_2 \sim 80$ kcal in $COCl + Cl \rightarrow COCl_2 + q_2$. Since Q_{C-Cl} is the same for both bonds in $COCl_2$, the difference $q_2 - q_1$ is of the order of ΔR for CO.

The behaviour of CS, which has a lifetime at room temperature of about 10 sec, according to KONDRATIEV [4], is quite different from that of CO. It shows the typical properties of a biradical, particularly in its tendency to polymerize. Below 100°C CS scarcely reacts with O_2, but the reaction is readily observable above 100°C. CS behaves in fact as a biradical of low activity, intermediate between CH_2 and CO.

Little is known about other compounds of divalent carbon, but the majority of them may be expected to act as biradicals. It is obvious from the examples so far given, that the state of the second carbon electron pair depends strongly on the atoms combining with the first two valencies.

When the two biradicals —S— and —O— combine to SO, the second, more strongly bonded, electron pair in the S atom is activated. Chemically, SO is a typical biradical, and its ground state is a triplet. MARKOVITCH and ÉMANUEL [5] showed that SO dimerizes at low temperatures. SO reacts readily with a variety of molecules, e.g. $O_2 + SO \rightarrow SO_2 + O$.

This process, by which an additional electron pair is sometimes activated, giving the atom typical biradical properties, is found in Groups III, IV, and V of the Periodic Table. However, it is not very common. In most cases the first atoms to combine produce a molecule with saturated valencies, and this then reacts with a characteristic high activation energy.

4. COMPLEX BIRADICALS

Biradicals may be produced from many complex molecules (e.g. hydrocarbons) by abstracting two hydrogen atoms. In practice it is extremely difficult to produce biradicals in this way. However, they are occasionally produced incidentally during a reaction; e.g. in polymerization of pure alkenes, and in diene additions.

Some complex molecules of appropriate structure can be synthesized directly, and are biradicals in their ground states. In 2, 6:2', 6'-tetrachloro 4, 4' di(phenylmethylene)

the chlorine atoms prevent the molecule adopting a quinonoid structure, since the two rings cannot be coplanar. The molecule then possesses two free valencies. Its solutions are deeply coloured, and absorb atmospheric oxygen extremely readily. The solutions are paramagnetic, the susceptibility increasing with temperature, contrary to Curie's law. The apparent molecular paramagnetic susceptibility also increases upon dilution. These facts indicate that in solution the paramagnetic monomer is in equilibrium with dia-magnetic dimer, or with higher polymers. This substance shows all the physical and chemical properties typical of a biradical.

Such compounds must be synthesized in the absence of air and light—an extremely difficult and delicate operation. For this reason, there are very few data in the literature on such biradicals, so only this case will be noted.

The molecular ground states are most often singlets, thermally activated to the biradical state. Obviously, the radical concentra-tion will depend to a very marked extent on the separation between the ground singlet and the lowest biradical state. Allowance must be made for the biradical state contribution whenever this energy difference is small. In Chichibabin's hydrocarbon [6] the activation

$$(C_6H_5)_2C=\!\!\!\!\bigcirc\!\!=\!\!\!\!\bigcirc\!\!=\!\!C(C_6H_5)_2$$

energy is only a few kcal. Even at room temperature about 1 per cent of the molecules will be in the biradical state. Chichibabin's hydro-carbon is well known to be highly reactive; in particular, it rapidly decolourizes in air, with the formation of polymeric peroxides:

$$(C_6H_5)_2C\!\!-\!\!\bigcirc\!\!-\!\!\bigcirc\!\!-\!\!C(C_6H_5)_2(C_6H_5)_2C\!\!-\!\!\bigcirc\!\!-\!\!\bigcirc\!\!-\!\!C(C_6H_5)_2$$
....O—O   O—————O   O—O....

1,4 dimethylene-*cyclo*hexadiene, $H_2C=\!\!\!\!\bigcirc\!\!=\!\!CH_2$ produced by

pyrolysis of *p*-xylene [7], polymerizes readily at room temperature, and also forms the di-iodo derivative with iodine vapour

$$IH_2C\!\!-\!\!\bigcirc\!\!-\!\!CH_2I$$

About 10 kcal is required to activate the diene valencies. Since ε_0 is usually very low when radicals react with iodine atoms, this activa-tion energy, and also that for polymerization, must be approximately equal to the excitation energy, i.e. 10 kcal. The reaction can thus occur at room temperature, since the activation energy is so low.

Molecules with singlet ground states can also give biradicals by absorbing quanta of radiation. The molecule is raised to one of its excited singlet states, but the excited-state lifetime is short (10^{-8}–10^{-9} sec) and the rapid return to the ground state is accompanied either by emission of a quantum of electromagnetic radiation (fluorescence) or by conversion of electronic energy to energy of molecular vibration.

(0) $$A + h\nu \rightarrow A*$$

(1) $$A* \rightarrow A \qquad \text{(rate } k_1A*\text{)}.$$

However, in addition to the usual (singlet) levels, there are also long-lived metastable levels. Some fraction of the molecules in the excited singlet state pass over to the lowest of these levels, part of the electronic energy being internally converted to energy of vibration.

(2) $$A* \rightarrow A^v \qquad \text{(rate } k_2A*\text{)}.$$

Passage from this metastable level to the stable ground state (light being emitted) is also possible:

(3) $$A^v \rightarrow A \qquad \text{(rate } K_3A^v\text{)}.$$

(3) is much slower than (1) and the accompanying emission is called phosphorescence.

TERENIN [8] has shown that the transition involves a spin reversal. The metastable molecules have two electrons with parallel spins; they should therefore behave as biradicals, with two free valencies. The anomalously long lifetime of the lowest triplet state is due to the low probability of the transition to the ground singlet state, accompanied by emission of radiation (phosphorescence).

The measurement of the paramagnetic susceptibility of metastable fluorscein molecules [9] gave a value for the magnetic moment ($2.73 \mu_B$) close to theoretical ($2.83 \mu_B$). This confirms that the metastable molecules have two unpaired electrons.

Phosphorescence measurements on dye solutions have shown that τ for metastable biradical molecules varies from 10^{-2} to 10^{-6} sec at room temperature [10–12]. τ increases with medium viscosity and with drop in temperature. In solvents frozen at liquid nitrogen temperatures τ may be 1–50 sec [13]. Simple compounds also give large τ values. Continuous illumination of solvent glasses can give several per cent of the molecules in the metastable state [14]. Higher values sometimes occur—up to 75 per cent in the case of fluorscein [13].

Metastable molecule concentrations have been determined in solutions at room temperature and the probabilities of excited singlet → triplet transitions calculated. Thus with eosin in glycerine $(2 \times 10^{-4}M)$ $A^v/A^* = 800$. k_1, k_2 and k_3 are 3×10^8, 8×10^5 and $10^3 \sec^{-1}$ respectively.

Flash photolysis is a new technique for producing and studying triplet molecules. High triplet state concentrations can then be produced in liquid and vaporized materials at room temperature as well as in low-temperature glasses. PORTER and WINDSOR [15] have found that anthracene $(10^{-5}M)$ in hexane will give 20 per cent of the molecules in the triplet state. At $2 \times 10^{-6} - 10^3M$ $k_3 \approx 10^4 \sec^{-1}$. This confirms the high probability of $A^* \to A^v$ transitions.

TERENIN [16] first remarked on the important—often decisive—part played in photoreactions by biradical particles. This is partly because high steady concentrations are produced, which exceed those of normal excited molecules by large factors, and partly because they are reactive, not less so than normal excited molecules.

Many experiments on the nature of the photoactive particles have been performed in which the fluorescence quenching effects of additives are compared with the reaction rates. Fluorescence and chemical reaction being concurrent processes, if mostly normal excited molecules react, then fluorescence quenching is *ipso facto* reaction. Hence $\gamma + \phi = $ const., $\gamma + \phi$ being the quantum yields of fluorescence and photoreaction. If the fluorescence is quenched by non-reactants the photoreaction should be retarded. In most cases these ideas are not confirmed, and so it is concluded that fluorescence quenching and photoreaction rate are not linked. The results are, of course, due to the photoactive particles being meta-stable molecules, of which there are many more than excited-singlet ones.

To demonstrate the decisive role of metastable states in complex molecule photoreactions it would be much better to determine the relation between phosphorescence (not fluorescence) and reaction rate. Unfortunately very little has been done on this. Only one semiquantitative investigation in Perrin's laboratory [11] has been reported, in which the glycerine photoreduction of eosin as retarded by KI was compared with the dye fluorescence and phosphorescence quenching. The fluorescence τ was little affected by the KI concentration. The reaction rate and lifetime (from phosphorescence emission) varied much more, the two curves practically coinciding. Thus mostly metastable molecules participate in the photoreaction.

To sum up, we may say that most photoreactions at photon energies less than bond-energies largely depend on metastable molecular electronic states. The states may be metastable for various reasons, one of which is that optical transitions involving multiplicity changes are forbidden. The metastable states are frequently biradical ones. But additional measurements (e.g. magnetic) are always required to determine the nature of the metastable state.

Let us consider a case where metastable states possibly participate in photoreactions. KRASNOVSKII's work [17] on the photoreaction between chlorophyll (as well as bacterial chlorophyll and protochlorophyll) and ascorbic acid (acting as a reducing agent, AH_2) is of interest. The reduced form of chlorophyll, XH, was formed. The chlorophyll takes up either electrons, or hydrogen:

$$X + AH_2 \rightarrow XH + AH$$

If we suppose that X reacts in its biradical state, we have:

(1) $-X- + AH_2 \rightarrow -XH + -AH.$

The biradical reacts with a stable molecule, giving two univalent free radicals.

The correctness of (1) is demonstrated by the following:

(a) XH has the spectral properties of a semi-quinone; the absorption spectrum of XH is displaced considerably towards shorter wavelengths as compared with X;

(b) XH is an extremely reactive substance:

(c) (1) will initiate polymerizations.

Detailed attention will now be given to the production and reactions of the simple biradicals $>CH_2$ and $-O$.

5. PRODUCTION AND REACTIVITY OF $> CH_2$ AND $-O-$

A. The Methylene Biradical $>CH_2$

The ground state of CH_2 is not known at the present time, since its absorption spectrum is not available.

CH_2 may be produced:

(1) By pyrolysis of diazomethane,

(2) By photolysis (using a mercury arc) of diazomethane and ketene.

Investigation of some substituted methylene radicals formed part of the very earliest work on free CH_2. SCHROETER [18] in 1909 showed that the biradical obtained by decomposing phenylbenzoyldiazomethane isomerized to diphenyl ketene:

$$\begin{array}{ccccc} C_6H_5 & & N & & C_6H_5 & & C_6H_5 \\ & \diagdown C \diagup & \| & \rightarrow & \diagdown C = & \rightarrow & \diagdown C = CO \\ C_6H_5CO & & N & & C_6H_5CO & & C_6H_5 \end{array}$$

The biradicals obtained by decomposing diphenyldiazomethane may either combine, or may react with the unchanged compound:

$$2 \ \begin{matrix} C_6H_5 \\ C_6H_5 \end{matrix}\hspace{-4pt}>\hspace{-4pt}C = \ \rightarrow \ \begin{matrix} C_6H_5 \\ C_6H_5 \end{matrix}\hspace{-4pt}>\hspace{-4pt}C = C\hspace{-4pt}<\hspace{-4pt}\begin{matrix} C_6H_5 \\ C_6H_5 \end{matrix}$$

$$\begin{matrix} C_6H_5 \\ C_6H_5 \end{matrix}\hspace{-4pt}>\hspace{-4pt}C = \ + \ \begin{matrix} C_6H_5 \\ C_6H_5 \end{matrix}\hspace{-4pt}>\hspace{-4pt}C\hspace{-2pt}\begin{matrix} N \\ \| \\ N \end{matrix} \ \rightarrow \ \begin{matrix} C_6H_5 \\ C_6H_5 \end{matrix}\hspace{-4pt}>\hspace{-4pt}C = N - N = C\hspace{-4pt}<\hspace{-4pt}\begin{matrix} C_6H_5 \\ C_6H_5 \end{matrix}$$

The products are tetraphenyl ethylene and diphenyl ketazine respectively.

Methylene radicals were first demonstrated by STAUDINGER and KUPFER [19] in 1912, in the decomposition of diazomethane. The diazomethane, mixed with CO, was passed through a heated quartz tube. Ketene was detected in the issuing gas

$$CH_2 + CO \rightarrow CH_2{=}CO$$

It has also been detected with metallic mirrors. PEARSON *et al.* [20], and RICE and GLAZEBROOK [21], found that some active product formed in the pyrolysis of diazomethane could remove mirrors of tellurium, selenium, antimony and arsenic, but could not remove mirrors of zinc, cadmium, lead, and some other metals. When the pyrolytic products acted upon tellurium, telluroformaldehyde (or its polymers) was produced. Selenium gave selenoformaldehyde. Hence diazomethane decomposes to methylene radicals. Tellurium and selenium mirrors were also used to detect the formation of CH_2 in the photolysis of diazomethane and ketene.

The photolysis of ketene $CH_2{=}CO \rightarrow CH_2 + CO$ has a quantum yield of unity. Quanta of energy equivalent to 75–78 kcal are required. The energy required to rupture the $C{=}C$ bond in ketene may be calculated as the difference between $Q_{C=C}$ in ketene (125 kcal) and the energy liberated when $>CO$ goes over to its normal (inactive) state, i.e. $125 - 60 = 65$ kcal. Quanta of energy equivalent to 75–80 kcal are thus quite sufficiently energetic to photolyze ketene.

CH_2 is also formed when atomic sodium reacts with CH_2Cl_2

$$Na + CH_2Cl_2 \rightarrow CH_2Cl + NaCl$$
$$Na + CH_2Cl \rightarrow CH_2 + NaCl$$

The only gaseous product is C_2H_4. If hydrogen is present, methane is formed. CH_2 may also be produced by decomposing CH_4 on hot platinum or carbon filaments. The formation of CH_2 was confirmed by using tellurium or iodine mirrors.

Some reactions of $>CH_2$ will now be considered.

Combination. The main gaseous products formed by photolysis of ketene are C_2H_4 and CO (higher alkenes are formed in small amounts). Since the quantum yield is one, C_2H_4 is produced by dimerization of CH_2.

NORRISH and PORTER [22] found that the rate constant for dimerization of CH_2 was the same as that for CH_3. This clearly indicates that CH_2 is more similar to an active free radical than it is to a molecule such as CO.

The reaction between CH_2 and C_2H_4. The reaction between CH_2 and C_2H_4 has been observed in the photolysis of ketene [22]. The net reaction may be written:

$$2CH_2CO \xrightarrow{h\nu} C_2H_4 + 2CO$$

The pressure increases upon reaction, but as the C_2H_4 content increases, the pressure ceases increasing, and may even fall. The fall is accompanied by formation of methylene polymers of empirical formula $(CH_2)_n$. The polymers arise from the successive reactions

$$C_2H_4 \xrightarrow{CH_2} C_3H_6 \xrightarrow{CH_2} \ldots C_nH_{2n}$$

If C_2H_4 is added before commencing the photolysis, the rate of pressure increase becomes small or zero.

Reaction of CH_2 with H_2. Hydrogen affects the composition of both the gaseous and condensed products from ketene photolysis very markedly. Saturated hydrocarbons are found in both fractions. The condensible product has the empirical formula $C_nH_{(2\cdot3-2\cdot6)n}$. One of the gaseous products is CH_4, produced by

$$CH_2 + H_2 \rightarrow CH_4$$

Reaction of CH_2 with CH_4. If CH_4 is present during the photolysis of ketene, gaseous saturated hydrocarbons (the most important being ethane) are formed. The CH_4 consumed is consistent with the ethane formed:

$$CH_2 + CH_4 \rightarrow C_2H_6$$

ROSENBLUM [23] investigated this reaction; it appears to occur with greater difficulty than that between CH_2 and H_2.

Other reactions of CH_2. CH_2 reacts with diazomethane; this is in accordance with the high quantum yield (of four) for the photolysis of diazomethane, and also with the much shorter lifetime of CH_2 in diazomethane (as compared with ketene). AVRAMENKO and KOLESNIKOVA [24] discovered that CH_2 may be obtained by the action of atomic oxygen on ethylene:

$$O + C_2H_4 \rightarrow CH_2O + CH_2$$

If O_2 was also present, the yield of formaldehyde was substantially increased; this is explained by the CH_2 radicals reacting with O_2:

$$CH_2 + O_2 \rightarrow CH_2O + O$$

B. *The Biradical* —O—

Two methods are available for producing atomic oxygen:

(1) Photolysis of O_2, using the Schumann ultra-violet,

(2) An electrical discharge in O_2 or H_2O.

The part played by atomic oxygen in oxidations is shown by the formation of ozone in the oxidation of CO and, particularly, phosphorus (ozone being very noticeable) and in the oxidation of sulphur vapour, where SO_3 is formed [25]. The oxidation of hydrogen is impossible without atomic oxygen. A number of workers (particularly AVRAMENKO and KOLESNIKOVA [24, 26, 27]) in recent years have studied the reactions of atomic oxygen with a variety of compounds. AVRAMENKO and KOLESNIKOVA have shown that the isolated oxygen atom is exceptionally active, even by comparison with atomic hydrogen.

Non-Russian work has mostly been concerned with pressures in the region of 1 mm Hg, and with high concentrations of atomic oxygen (frequently exceeding that of the hydrocarbon). Under these conditions the reactions are extremely violent, and result in a considerable temperature rise together with extensive oxidation and light emission, the main products being carbon dioxide and water. Any unstable products which might be formed are destroyed at the high temperatures prevailing in the reaction zone. It has been found (at the Institute of Chemical Physics in particular) that these reactions may be carried out under much milder conditions, at pressures of ∼ 10 mm Hg, and at much lower relative concentrations of atomic oxygen. Under these circumstances, the reaction proceeds without considerable heat being produced, and the products include alcohols, aldehydes, acids, and peroxides.

CH_3OH, C_2H_5OH, and CH_3COOH are formed when atomic oxygen reacts with CH_4, C_2H_6, and CH_3CHO respectively. AVRAMENKO and KOLESNIKOVA suppose that these are formed without the intervention of molecular oxygen, and that the oxygen atom is capable of entering the molecule directly at a C—H bond. This hypothesis requires further investigation, since the energy liberated would be large, and it is not clear why the molecule formed does not break either at a C—C or at a C—O bond. These workers also demonstrated that when a hydrocarbon molecule does decompose under these conditions, it breaks at a C—C bond. It is not unlikely that these reactions take place at the walls of the vessel, and are not homogeneous. The mercury-sensitized photodecomposition of N_2O yields oxygen atoms, and the reactions of ethylene and acetaldehyde atomic oxygen produced in this way were studied by CVETANOVIĆ during 1955–56 [28, 29]. CVETANOVIĆ's experiments were carried out at room temperature, and his results do not agree with those of AVRAMENKO; direct combination of oxygen atoms with C_2H_4 and CH_3CHO was not observed. It is probable that the difference is due to wall processes not playing an important part in photosensitized reactions.

6. THE ROLE OF BIRADICALS IN CHAIN REACTIONS

Biradicals play an important part in the kinetics of chain reactions. A new factor is introduced if one step in a univalent free radical chain also produces a biradical. The biradical leads to chain branching, which was discovered by Soviet physicists 20 years ago. For example, in the oxidation of hydrogen the chain-carrying steps are:

(1) $H + O_2 = OH + O$,

(2) $OH + H_2 = H_2O + H$.

(1) gives the biradical $> O$, as well as the univalent radical OH. This biradical will react with H_2:

(3) $O + H_2 = OH + H$,

Fig. 14

thus giving two univalent radicals, which will then react as in (1) and (2), giving two new chains. A completely branched chain is thus formed: a schematic representation of this is given in Fig. 14. The introduction of one primary H or OH radical would be sufficient to cause the major part of the oxygen and hydrogen to react rapidly and completely.

The oxidation of H_2S involves the following steps:

(1) $OH + H_2S = H_2O + HS$,

(2) $HS + O_2 = OH + SO$.

(2) gives the biradical $> SO$, which may then react with molecular oxygen: $SO + O_2 = SO_2 + O$, followed by $O + H_2S = OH + HS$. This produces two additional radicals, OH and HS, which can then start fresh chains. Chain branching thus also occurs here.

In accordance with the rules of valency, when a univalent radical reacts with a stable molecule a fresh radical always results; this is essential to the propagation of univalent radical chains.

A reaction of this type is denoted by $1 \to 1$, which implies that if there is one free valence beforehand, there is also one afterwards. The combination of univalent radicals is symbolized $1 + 1 \to 0$.

Chain initiation is by rupture of some bond or bonds in a stable molecule; this may be denoted by $0 \to 1 + 1$. Branching reactions, whereby one free valency gives a univalent free radical and a biradical (such as $H + O_2 = OH + O$) may be symbolized as $1 \to 1 + 2$. A biradical may react with a molecule to give two univalent radicals, i.e. $2 \to 1 + 1$ ($\dot{Q} + H_2 = \dot{O}H + \dot{H}$). The latter two reactions cause the univalent radical chain to branch. Branching reactions, $1 \to 1 + 2$, are endothermic in most cases; this may explain why they are comparatively rarely observed in kinetic studies. However, the reason why only a few branched-chain reactions are known may be that comparatively few gas-phase reactions have been studied kinetically.

Chain propagation may also occur via biradical alternation, as in univalent radical alternation. For example, such a chain occurs in the vapour-phase oxidation of sulphur at 100–150°C, as was demonstrated at the Institute of Chemical Physics [25]. This reaction is rapid, and light is emitted. It is also characterized by upper and lower limit phenomena, and is undoubtedly a branched chain. The products include some 80 per cent of SO_2 and up to 20 per cent of SO_3. The following steps are probably involved:

$$S_8 = S_7 + \dot{S} \text{ (initiation)}$$
$$\dot{S} + O_2 = \dot{S}O + \dot{Q} \ (2 \to 2 + 2 - \text{branching})$$
$$\dot{Q} + S_8 = \dot{S}O + \dot{S} + S_6 \ (2 \to 2 + 2 - \text{branching})$$

The SO biradicals react with O_2, giving SO_2 and O. The end product is thus SO_2. The chains propagate via two reactions of the type $2 \to 2 + 2$, and are thus chains branched at every point, every step giving two biradicals from one initial biradical. Simultaneously the chain-termination processes $\dot{Q} + O_2 + M \to O_3 + M \ (2 \to 0)$ and $SO_2 + \dot{Q} \to SO_3 \ (2 \to 0)$ also occur. The reaction is soon completely stopped by accumulation of SO_2, unless this is removed by condensation. Unbroken chain propagation cannot otherwise occur.

Another similar biradical chain is the oxidation of CS_2 [30]. This also has two explosion limits. The following chain-carrying reactions have been proposed:

(1) $\dot{Q} + CS_2 = COS + \dot{S} \ (2 \to 2)$

(2) $\dot{S} + O_2 = \dot{S}O + \dot{Q} \ (2 \to 2 + 2)$.

Chain reaction (2) leads to chain-branching, since two biradicals, $\dot{S}O$ and $\dot{Q}$, are formed in it.

Branching of chain reactions was discovered in 1926–29 mainly as the result of work at the Institute of Chemical Physics [31], from the oxidation of phosphorus. The mechanism of this oxidation is still not definitely settled, however. Some possible reactions are [32]:

$$\dot{\mathrm{O}} + \mathrm{P}_4 = \ddot{\mathrm{P}}_4\mathrm{O},$$

$$\ddot{\mathrm{P}}_4\mathrm{O} + \mathrm{O}_2 = \mathrm{P}_4\mathrm{O}_2 + \dot{\mathrm{O}}$$

Branching is by further reactions involving oxidation of $\mathrm{P}_4\mathrm{O}_2$. Chain termination is by collision with the wall at low pressures, and at high pressures by homogenous three-body reaction $\mathrm{O} + \mathrm{O}_2 + \mathrm{M} \to \mathrm{O}_3 + \mathrm{M}$. (Many workers have observed the formation of ozone in the oxidation of phosphorus.) The oxidation of phosphorus may also proceed via

(1) $\ddot{\mathrm{P}} + \mathrm{P}_4 = \dot{\mathrm{P}}\,\mathrm{O} + \ddot{\mathrm{P}} + \mathrm{P}_2\ (2 \to 1 + 3)$

(2) $\ddot{\mathrm{P}} + \mathrm{O}_2 = \dot{\mathrm{P}}\mathrm{O} + \dot{\mathrm{O}}\ (3 \to 2 + 1)$ etc.

Chain branching may occur via $\dot{\mathrm{P}}\mathrm{O} + \mathrm{O}_2 = \dot{\mathrm{P}}\mathrm{O}_3$, followed by $\dot{\mathrm{P}}\mathrm{O}_3 + \mathrm{P}_4 = \mathrm{P}_2\mathrm{O}_3 + \ddot{\mathrm{P}} + \mathrm{P}_2$. These are probably somewhat endothermic, and a process via the triradical $\dot{\mathrm{P}}$———$\dot{\mathrm{P}}$ and atomic oxygen, as below, may also occur:

(1') $\dot{\mathrm{O}} + \mathrm{P}_4 = \dot{\mathrm{P}}\mathrm{O} + \ddot{\mathrm{P}}_3 + 1\ \mathrm{kcal}\ (2 \to 1 + 3)$

(2') $\ddot{\mathrm{P}}_3 + \mathrm{O}_2 = \dot{\mathrm{P}}\mathrm{O} + \dot{\mathrm{O}} + \mathrm{P}_2 + \sim 1\ \mathrm{kcal}\ (3 \to 2 + 1)$.

P_4 has a tetrahedral structure, so three P—P bonds have to be broken to give PO. Since the energy of each bond is 48 kcal, and $Q_{\mathrm{P-O}}$ is ~ 145 kcal, (1') is exothermic by $145 - 144 = 1$ kcal. In (2') a P—P bond is broken, and a P=P bond is formed, the energy of the latter being 116 kcal. The transformation of $\ddot{\mathrm{P}}_3$ to P=P + P thus absorbs 28 kcal, and since the energy available from the formation of PO is about 145 kcal, and $Q_{\mathrm{O=O}}$ is 116 kcal, $q_2 = -1$ kcal.

The main products are $\mathrm{P}_2\mathrm{O}_5$ (as $\mathrm{P}_4\mathrm{O}_{10}$), together with some $\mathrm{P}_2\mathrm{O}_3$ (as $\mathrm{P}_4\mathrm{O}_6$). According to the first set of reactions, the lower oxide of phosphorus first formed is a biradical, and is oxidized to $\mathrm{P}_2\mathrm{O}_5$, which latter, also being a biradical, dimerizes to $\mathrm{P}_4\mathrm{O}_{10}$. According to the second scheme, $\mathrm{P}_2\mathrm{O}_3$ and $\mathrm{P}_2\mathrm{O}_5$ result from

$$\dot{\mathrm{P}}\mathrm{O} + \mathrm{O}_2 \to \dot{\mathrm{P}}\mathrm{O}_3,$$

$$\dot{\mathrm{P}}\mathrm{O}_3 + \mathrm{P}_4 \to \dot{\mathrm{P}}_2\mathrm{O}_3 + \mathrm{P}_3, \qquad 2\mathrm{P}_2\mathrm{O}_3 \to \mathrm{P}_4\mathrm{O}_6$$

$$\dot{\mathrm{P}}_2\mathrm{O}_3 + \mathrm{O}_2 \to \mathrm{P}_2\mathrm{O}_5 \to (\mathrm{P}_4\mathrm{O}_{10}).$$

The formation of lower oxides as intermediate products in the incomplete oxidation of phosphorus by a chain mechanism follows from the experimental finding that P_2O_5 and the lower oxides are present (as a film of the polymers on the walls).

Chain propagation via biradicals or triradicals only occurs when the compounds are such that univalent radical chains are excluded. But long chains can only occur if they are also completely branched.

A univalent radical chain can only be terminated by radical combination, since any reaction of a univalent radical with a stable molecule is bound to regenerate a univalent radical. As the free radical concentrations are very small in most cases, univalent radical chains are usually of great length. On the other hand, collisions of biradicals with parent molecules or intermediate products readily gives stable molecules by loss of the free valencies:

$$\dot{O} + O = O \rightarrow \overset{O}{\underset{O}{|}}\!\!\!\diagdown O \quad \text{or} \quad \dot{O} + SO_2 \rightarrow SO_3 \quad (\text{processes } 2 \rightarrow 0\,)$$

Consequently, biradical chains are easily broken. In cases where univalent radical chains are also possible, the biradical chains are rapidly captured by processes such as $2 \rightarrow 1 + 1$. For instance, the present author at one time proposed a biradical chain for the oxidation of methane [33]; it resembles that proposed by NORRISH and FOORD [34]:

$$\dot{C}H_2 + O_2 \rightarrow CH_2O + \dot{O} \quad (2 \rightarrow 2)$$

$$\dot{O} + CH_4 \rightarrow \dot{C}H_2 + H_2O \quad (2 \rightarrow 2)$$

However, the reactions $\dot{O} + CH_4 \rightarrow OH + CH_3$ $(2 \rightarrow 1 + 1)$ and $\dot{C}H_2 + CH_4 \rightarrow 2CH_3$ $(2 \rightarrow 1 + 1)$ will transform the biradical chain into the longer and more stable univalent radical chain

$$\dot{C}H_3 + O_2 \rightarrow CH_3O\dot{O}$$

$$CH_3O\dot{O} + CH_4 \rightarrow CH_3OOH + \dot{C}H_3$$

or

$$\dot{C}H_3 + O_2 \rightarrow CH_2O + \dot{O}H$$

$$\dot{O}H + CH_4 \rightarrow \dot{C}H_3 + H_2O$$

The biradical chain is thus converted to one involving univalent radicals; one consequence of this is that biradical chains can scarcely occur in any case where univalent chains are possible.

A biradical chain is by no means impossible in the oxidation of

ethylene, however; the following scheme was proposed by AVRA-
MENKO:

$$\dot{C}H_2 + O_2 \rightarrow CH_2O + \dot{O}$$

$$\dot{O} + CH_2{=}CH_2 \rightarrow CH_2O + \dot{C}H_2$$

The univalent chain only propagates with considerable difficulty in
this case, owing to the high C—H bond energy in ethylene:

$$CH_2{=}\dot{C}H + O_2 \rightarrow CH_2{=}CH{-}O{-}\dot{O}$$

$$CH_2{=}CH + CH_2{=}CH_2 \rightarrow CH_2{=}CH + \dot{C}_2H_3$$
$$\quad\ \ |\qquad\qquad\qquad\qquad\qquad |$$
$$\quad\ \ O\qquad\qquad\qquad\qquad\qquad O$$
$$\quad\ \ |\qquad\qquad\qquad\qquad\qquad |$$
$$\quad\ \ \cdot O\qquad\qquad\qquad\qquad\qquad OH$$

It is also quite possible that biradicals may initiate univalent chains.
For instance, the energy required to transform ethylene into the

stable biradical $\overset{|}{C}H_2{-}\overset{|}{C}H_2$ is about 70 kcal.

Biradical hypotheses are directly involved in problems connected
with many important general chemical transformations. The situation as regards univalent radicals is quite clear. If the number of
electrons in the compound is odd, then the particle will always be a
univalent radical as regards its chemical properties (save possibly in
the case of NO); that is, it will dimerize, or polymerize, and its
reactions with a variety of molecules will involve potential barriers
of heights not greater than a few kcal. Physically, such a particle
will have a double ground state, and will be paramagnetic. With
an odd number of electrons the free valency cannot be satisfied
within the molecule.

The situation is much more complicated in biradicals. Like stable
molecules, they also have an even number of electrons. The presence
of two electrons with parallel spins (a physical criterion derived from
optical or magnetic data), does not always correspond with the
particle's chemical activity (as in O_2); and conversely, when all the
electrons are paired the chemical properties may be those appropriate
to a radical—as in P_2, Cd, AlCl, etc.

Thus, biradicals are detected from the chemical behaviour of
the system; i.e. by the relative ease with which the reacting particles
can mobilize two free valencies. Reactions in solution are frequently
complicated by the presence of ions, solvation effects, complexes, etc.,
and it may be quite impossible to distinguish the mechanism of the
reaction between two molecules. As regards gas-phase reactions,
molecules with an even number of electrons may evidently be
divided into two classes. The first group, which comprises the

great majority of such molecules, contains those which react with normal molecules only with considerable difficulty, and which thus involve very high potential barriers of the order of some tens of kilocalories. Such molecules do not form dimers or higher polymers. The second group comprises compounds in which molecular association occurs readily, and which react with characteristically low potential barriers; the number of such compounds is much smaller than that in the first group, and their behaviour is typically that of radicals. Molecules of this type may be termed biradicals, no matter what their spectroscopic or magnetic properties may be. However, apart from a small number of exceptions, the physical and chemical definitions of the biradical state usually lead to the same conclusion.

REFERENCES

1. V. N. KONDRATIEV. *Structure of Atoms and Molecules.* Academy of Sciences, Moscow 1946. (In Russian.)
2. YA. K. SYRKIN and M. E. DYATKINA. *Structure of Molecules and the Chemical Bond.* Moscow 1946. (In Russian.) Translated and revised by M. A. PARTRIDGE and D. O. JORDAN. London, 1950.
3. R. C. SAHNI. *Trans. Faraday Soc.* **49,** 1246 (1953).
4. V. N. KONDRATIEV. *Dokl. Akad. Nauk SSSR* **20,** 551 (1938).
5. V. G. MARKOVITCH and N. M. ÈMANUEL. *Zh. Fiz. Khim.* **21,** 1251 (1947).
6. M. E. DYATKINA and YA. K. SYRKIN. *Izv. Akad. Nauk SSSR, Otdel. Khim. Nauk* 543 (1945).
7. M. SZWARC. *J. Polymer Sci.* **6,** 319 (1951).
8. A. N. TERENIN. *Acta Phys.-Chim. URSS* **18,** 210 (1943); *Zh. Fiz. Khim.* **18,** 1 (1944).
9. G. N. LEWIS and M. CALVIN. *J. Amer. Chem. Soc.* **67,** 1232 (1945).
10. S. I. WAWILOW and W. L. LEWSCHIN. *Z. Phys.* **35,** 920 (1926).
11. S. BOUDIN. *J. Chim. Phys.* **27,** 285 (1930).
12. H. KAUTSKY, A. HIRSCH and W. FLESCH. *Chem. Ber.* **68,** 152 (1935).
13. G. N. LEWIS, D. LIPKIN and T. T. MAGEL. *J. Amer. Chem. Soc.* **63,** 3005 (1941).
14. A. N. TERENIN. *Acta Phys.-Chim. URSS* **12,** 617 (1940); *ibid.* **13,** 1 (1940); *ibid.* **14,** 566 (1941); *Izv. Akad. Nauk SSSR, Otdel. Khim. Nauk* 59 (1940).
15. G. PORTER and M. W. WINDSOR. *Disc. Faraday Soc.* **17,** 178 (1954).
16. A. N. TERENIN. *The Photochemistry of Coloured Compounds and Related Substances.* Moscow–Leningrad 1947. (In Russian.)
17. A. A. KRASNOVSKII. *Dokl. Akad. Nauk SSSR* **60,** 421 (1948); *ibid.* **61,** 91 (1948). English translation: *USAEC (Translation)* No. AEC-tr-2156, pp. 27–29 (April 1956); A. A. KRASNOVSKII, G. P. BRIN and K. K. VOINOVSKAYA. *ibid.* **69,** 393 (1949). English translation: *ibid.,* pp. 34–37; A. A. KRASNOVSKII, G. P. BRIN and K. K. VOINOVSKAYA. *ibid.* **73,** 1239 (1950). English translation: *ibid.,* pp. 42–45; A. A. KRASNOVSKII and K. K. VOINOVSKAYA. *ibid.* **87,** 109 (1952). English translation: *ibid.,* pp. 62–65.
18. G. SCHROETER. *Ber. Dtsch. Chem. Ges.* **42,** 2336 (1909).
19. H. STAUDINGER and O. KUPFER. *Ber. Dtsch. Chem. Ges.* **45,** 500 (1912).
20. T. G. PEARSON, R. H. PURCELL and G. S. SINGH. *J. Chem. Soc.* 409 (1938).
21. F. O. RICE and A. L. GLAZEBROOK. *J. Amer. Chem. Soc.* **56,** 2381 (1934).
22. R. G. W. NORRISH and G. PORTER. *Disc. Faraday Soc.* **2,** 97 (1947).

23. C. ROSENBLUM. *J. Amer. Chem. Soc.* **63**, 3322 (1941).
24. L. I. AVRAMENKO and R. V. KOLESNIKOVA. *Dokl. Akad. Nauk SSSR* **89** 1037 (1953). English translation: *Can. Nat. Res. Coun.* TT-573 (1955).
25. N. N. SEMENOV and G. N. RYABININ. *Zh. Rusk. Fiz. Khim. Obshch. Chast. Fiz.* **60**, 361 (1928).
26. L. I. AVRAMENKO and R. V. KOLESNIKOVA. *Dokl. Akad. Nauk SSSR* **91**, 107 (1953).
27. L. I. AVRAMENKO and R. B. LORENTSO. *Zh. Fiz. Khim.* **26**, 1084 (1952).
28. R. J. CVETANOVIĆ. *J. Chem. Phys.* **23**, 1375 (1955).
29. R. J. CVETANOVIĆ. *Canad. J. Chem.* **34**, 775 (1956).
30. V. G. VORONKOV and N. N. SEMENOV. *Zh. Fiz. Khim.* **13**, 1695 (1939).
31. YU. B. KHARITON and Z. VAITA. *Z. Phys.* **39**, 547 (1926); N. N. SEMENOV. *Zh. Rusk. Fiz.-Khim. Obshch. Chast. Fiz.* **60**, 271 (1928); *ibid.* **58**, 329 (1926); *Z. Phys.* **46**, 109 (1927); *Zh. Fiz. Khim.* **1**, 3 (1930); *Z. Phys. Chem.* **B2**, 161 (1929).
32. N. N. SEMENOV. *Chain Reactions.* Leningrad 1934. (In Russian.) Translated and revised as *Chemical Kinetics and Chain Reactions.* Oxford 1935.
33. N. N. SEMENOV. *Chain Reactions.* Leningrad, 1934. (In Russian.) Translated and revised as *Chemical Kinetics and Chain Reactions.* Oxford 1935.
34. R. G. W. NORRISH and S. G. FOORD. *Proc. Roy. Soc.* A **157**, 503 (1936).

PART II

INITIATION AND TERMINATION OF CHAIN REACTIONS

Chapter 4

MOLECULAR DISSOCIATION AND RADICAL COMBINATION

1. HOMOGENEOUS INITIATION OF CHAINS

THE most difficult part of any chain reaction is the production of the primary free radicals. The most direct way of producing such initial radicals is of course the decomposition of a normal molecule into two free radicals, e.g. a molecule of the primary reactants; this is not by any means the easiest way, however. The bond-dissociation energy Q is given for the bonds of many normal molecules in Tables 6 to 8. For most molecules Q lies between 50 and 100 kcal.

The majority of molecules R_1R_2 decompose by a simple unimolecular process, the rate being given by $w_0 = a \exp(-Q/RT)$ $[R_1R_2]$, where $a \simeq 10^{13}$ sec^{-1}. The simplest molecules decompose bimolecularly, to give atoms, via a two-body collision: e.g.

$$Cl + M \rightarrow Cl + Cl + M - Q$$

where Q is the Cl—Cl bond energy. In this case, $w_0 = b[Cl_2][M] \exp(-Q/RT)$ where $b = f \times 10^{-10}$ cm^3 sec^{-1} (f is the steric factor).

Molecular fragmentation always occurs most readily at the weakest bond. The preferred mode of decomposition of C_2H_6 is thus by C—C bond rupture ($Q = 83$ kcal) to give $2CH_3$, and not the breakage of a C—H bond, to give C_2H_3 and H ($Q = 98$ kcal).

The chain decomposition of C_2H_6 gives C_2H_4 and H_2:

$$C_2H_5 \rightarrow C_2H_4 + H$$
$$H + C_2H_6 \rightarrow H_2 + C_2H_5$$

The chain propagates via C_2H_5 and H, CH_3 not being involved at all. However, any radical, provided only that its activity be sufficient, may initiate a chain reaction. This is why the chain operates via C_2H_5 and H in C_2H_6, although methyl radicals are produced by the primary decomposition of ethane. The C_2H_5 radicals are produced by

$$CH_3 + C_2H_6 \rightarrow CH_4 + C_2H_5$$

146

The initiation of chain reactions by thermal decomposition of molecules is quite a difficult process. Thus any process which facilitates primary radical production for chain initiation is very important. We do not intend to deal with the heterogeneous initiation of chains at this point, although it is a very extensive and important topic, since this forms the subject of Chapter 6; only homogeneous initiation will be considered here.

The first method is the addition of compounds which readily decompose to free atoms or radicals. Examples of such substances are the vapours of sodium, hexaphenyl ethane, iodine, and peroxides:

$$Na_2 \rightarrow 2Na - 17 \cdot 5 \text{ kcal}$$

$$(C_6H_5)_3C\!-\!C(C_6H_5)_3 \rightarrow 2(C_6H_5)_3C - 11 \text{ kcal}$$

$$I_2 + M \rightarrow I + I + M - 35 \text{ kcal}$$

$$(CH_3)_3COOC(CH_3)_3 \rightarrow 2(CH_3)_3CO - 36 \text{ kcal}$$

$$C_2H_5OOH \rightarrow C_2H_5O + OH - (40\text{--}45) \text{ kcal}$$

Dissociation of Na_2 into two atoms takes place so readily that the vapour is almost completely dissociated at 100°C. Thus the addition of sodium vapour to any system is equivalent to the addition of atomic sodium. However, it is very difficult to utilize sodium, owing to its very high reactivity. Reactions between sodium vapour and various organic compounds have been studied in cool dilute flames, in which the sodium vapour and that of the substance under examination react rapidly upon coming into contact at the exits of two concentric tubes; light is often emitted. Only one use of sodium vapour at higher pressures is known. A mixture of hydrogen and chlorine reacts violently on addition of sodium vapour, even at 100°C, while no such reaction occurs below 300°C in the absence of sodium [1]. The mechanism is as follows. An atom of sodium reacts with a molecule of chlorine, to give NaCl + Cl. The chlorine atom then initiates a lengthy chain, as below:

$$Cl + H_2 \rightarrow HCl + H; \quad H + Cl_2 \rightarrow Cl + HCl$$

Some thousand or so molecules of HCl are formed for each sodium atom introduced.

The iodine atom is of low activity, because A—I bonds are relatively weak, and the heats of reaction for iodine atoms are frequently negative:

$$I + C_2H_6 \rightarrow HI + C_2H_5 - 28 \text{ kcal}$$

$$I + CH_3CHO \rightarrow HI + CH_3CO - 15 \text{ kcal}$$

The rates of such reactions are low: thus iodine atoms more commonly recombine than give active radicals by reacting with molecules. Iodine catalysis is only observed at high temperatures, as in the high-temperature pyrolysis of ethers, aldehydes and acetates. Table 34 demonstrates that the activation energies for these reactions are reduced by iodine. (E is the activation energy for the over-all reaction in the absence of iodine, and E' is the same quantity when iodine is present. $\Delta E = E - E'$.)

Table 34. Reduction by iodine of activation energies for decomposition

Compound	E	E'	ΔE
$CH_3OC_2H_5$.	54·5 (2)	38 (3)	11·5
CH_3CHO .	47 (4)	32·5 (5)	14·5
CCl_3CHO .	49 (6)	39 (6)	10
sec.-C_4H_9I .	39·4 (7)	35·2 (7)	4·2

In the pyrolysis of iodides I is one of the chain carrying radicals:

$$I + C_4H_9I \rightarrow I_2 + C_4H_9$$

$$C_4H_9 + C_4H_9I \rightarrow C_4H_{10} + C_4H_8I$$

$$C_4H_8I \rightarrow C_4H_8 + I$$

In the absence of iodine the chains are initiated via $C_4H_9I \rightarrow C_4H_9 + I - 47$ kcal. When I_2 is present, $I_2 \rightarrow I + I - 35$ kcal. In the first case, $[I] \simeq C \exp(-47{,}000/RT)\sqrt{[C_4H_9I]}$ while in the second, $[I] \simeq C' \exp(-35{,}000/RT)\sqrt{[I_2]}$. Thus the difference between E' and E is $(47 - 35)/2 = 6$ kcal, close to the observed value of 4·2 kcal.

It would appear likely that iodine atoms are also involved in some other reactions catalysed by iodine, but a final answer cannot be given at present. For instance, in the decomposition of ethers, the rate is proportional to $[I_2]$, and not to $\sqrt{[I_2]}$, which makes it difficult to explain the iodine catalysis as due to the decomposition of I_2 into atoms. Additional measurements are required in order to settle this question.

At lower temperatures iodine not only does not accelerate the reaction, but may even slow it down, because the radicals present in exothermic chains react readily with I_2 to give $RI + I$, and as a result the active radical R is replaced by the inactive radical I, which tends to combine with another iodine atom at the lower temperatures rather than to react and continue the chain; the chain is thereby broken.

Hexaphenylethane decomposes readily into two triphenylmethyl radicals, even at room temperature. Triphenylmethyl is quite an active radical, and it combines readily with O_2, for instance, forming the fairly active peroxide radical $(C_6H_5)_3COO$—; this latter is capable of initiating long chains, as in the oxidation of olefins.

The chain initiators most widely used are organic peroxides, which decompose to give extremely active radicals. When a hydroperoxide ROOH decomposes, an alkoxy radical and OH are produced, while dialkyl peroxides ROOR give two alkoxy radicals. Peroxides of the

type $\begin{matrix} RCOOCR \\ \| \quad \| \\ O \quad O \end{matrix}$ decompose the most readily; either two radicals

$\begin{matrix} RCO— \\ \| \\ O \end{matrix}$, or $R + CO_2 + \begin{matrix} RCO \\ \| \\ O \end{matrix}$, are formed.

Table 35. O—O bond-dissociation energies for peroxides [8]

Compound	Q (kcal)	Reference
HOOH . . .	78	[9]
HOOH . . .	54	[8]
$C_2H_5OOC_2H_5$ . .	31·7	[8]
$C_3H_7OOC_3H_7$ . .	35	[8]
$(CH_3)_3COOC(CH_3)_3$.	36·4	[8]
$(CH_3)_3COOC(CH_3)_3$.	39	[10]
tert.-$C_5H_{11}OOC_5H_{11}$	37	[11]

The alkyl radicals R can abstract hydrogen from solvent molecules even at 50–100°C; molecules of the corresponding hydrocarbon result. The relatively low O—O bond energies in peroxides are highly favourable to the production of very active radicals. Peroxides have thus become universally employed as initiators for both liquid phase and gaseous reactions—thus peroxides can be used to initiate the addition of hydrogen bromide to olefins in the liquid at 50–100°C, for instance [12]. They initiate the chlorination of aromatic hydrocarbons by sulphuryl chloride; toluene gives benzyl chloride [13]. The chain reaction proceeds thus:

Initiation:

$(C_6H_5COO)_2 \rightarrow \dot{C}_6H_5 + CO_2 + C_6H_5CO\dot{O}$

$\dot{C}_6H_5 + SO_2Cl_2 \rightarrow C_6H_5Cl + \dot{S}_2Cl.$

Propagation:

(1) $\dot{S}O_2Cl \rightarrow SO_2 + Cl$,

(2) $Cl + C_6H_5CH_3 \rightarrow HCl + C_6H_5\dot{C}H_2$,

(3) $C_6H_5\dot{C}H_2 + SO_2Cl_2 \rightarrow C_6H_5CH_2Cl + \dot{S}O_2Cl$, etc.

Peroxides initiate the addition of thiols to olefins [14]. Benzoyl peroxide is used as the source of radicals; these abstract a hydrogen atom from the thiol, and the reaction is then:

$C_6H_5\dot{S} + C_6H_5CH{=}CH_2 \rightarrow C_6H_5\dot{C}H{-}CH_2{-}SC_6H_5$

$C_6H_5\dot{C}HCH_2SC_6H_5 + HSC_6H_5 \rightarrow C_6H_5CH_2CH_2SC_6H_5 + \dot{S}C_6H_5$, etc.

Carboxylation is also brought about when $(COCl)_2$ is used [15]:

Initiation:

$(C_6H_5COO)_2 \rightarrow \dot{C}_6H_5 + CO_2 + \dot{O}COC_6H_5$,

$C_6H_5 + ClCOCOCl \rightarrow C_6H_5Cl + CO + \dot{C}OCl$;

Propagation:

$\dot{C}OCl \rightarrow CO + \dot{C}l$,

$\dot{C}l + RH \rightarrow HCl + \dot{R}$,

$\dot{R} + (COCl)_2 \rightarrow RCOCl + \dot{C}OCl$, etc.

Aldehydes do not give the Cannizarro reaction in the absence of oxygen or peroxides (KHARASCH and FOY [16]). Benzoyl peroxide accelerates this reaction, and a number of workers [17] have supposed that a chain mechanism is involved:

$C_6H_5\dot{C}O + H_2O \rightarrow C_6H_5COOH + H$;

$H + C_6H_5CHO \rightarrow C_6H_5\dot{C}HOH$,

$C_6H_5\dot{C}HOH + C_6H_5CHO \rightarrow C_6H_5CH_2OH + C_6H_5\dot{C}O$.

Benzoyl peroxide decomposes to give C_6H_5, which then initiates the chain via $\dot{C}_6H_5 + C_6H_5CHO \rightarrow C_6H_6 + C_6H_5\dot{C}O$.

RAZUVAEV et al. [18] showed that peroxides catalyse the transformation of mercurous or mercuric salts of organic acids to organo-mercury compounds. Thus mercuric acetate heated alone does not give the acetate of methyl mercury, but if acetyl or benzoyl peroxides are present then the mercuro-organic derivative is formed, together with small amounts of benzoic acid and diphenyl. CO is evolved when mercuric acetate decomposes in this fashion, so the reaction is one involving the decarboxylation of the mercury salts of organic acids:

$$(CH_3COO)_2Hg \xrightarrow{\text{peroxides}} CH_3HgOCOCH_3 + CO_2$$

The yield of mercuro-organic compound is greater than one molecule per molecule of peroxide added, indicating that a chain reaction is involved.

The mechanism by which peroxides catalyse the oxidation of organic compounds is by decomposition to free radicals; these latter abstract hydrogen from the substance (RH) to be oxidized, giving the radical R. The chain reaction

$$\dot{R} + O_2 \rightarrow R\dot{O}_2, \quad R\dot{O}_2 + RH \rightarrow RO_2H + \dot{R}$$

then ensues.

Auto-catalytic oxidation occurs when the primary oxidation products are peroxides; under appropriate conditions, these per-oxides give fresh free radicals, which then initiate new chains, and degenerate branching occurs [19]. Peroxides are widely employed as initiators in polymerization [20].

A great deal of information about chain reactions, and about free radical reaction in general, is derived from photochemical processes. FRANCK [21], TERENIN [22] and KONDRATIEV [23] discovered the photolysis of molecules to atoms of free radicals by light of suffici-ently short wavelength, and gave theoretical explanations. Acetone gives methyl radicals at 2540 Å, and O_2 dissociates at ~ 1800 Å. The number of radicals produced by the light at any instant is determined simply from the number of quanta absorbed. Measure-ment of this number, taken in conjunction with the reaction rate, enables one to deduce the mean chain length V. In alkane chlorina-tion, for instance, the number of links in a single chain may run into thousands or even tens of thousands at room temperature, while when alkenes (e.g. C_2H_4) are chlorinated millions of molecules may react as a result of introducing one primary radical. Chain lengths in the ten thousand range are found in some oxidations, e.g. those of benzaldehyde and sodium sulphite. In other cases the chain lengths are short at room temperature, but increase with temperature. This is the case in aldehyde decompositions, and in the oxidations of CH_4, C_2H_6 and H_2.

If the substance does not absorb at a convenient wavelength (e.g. H_2), then a very small amount of mercury vapour may be added, since this absorbs ultra-violet light of a convenient wave-length. Absorption of mercury resonance radiation gives excited atoms Hg*. Collisions of the second kind between Hg* and molecules cause the latter to dissociate if their dissociation energies are less than the excitation energy of Hg^*. For example, $H_2 + Hg^* \rightarrow Hg + 2H$. The number of radicals produced may be somewhat less than the number of quanta absorbed in this method, however.

2. HOMOGENEOUS RECOMBINATION OF RADICALS

The rate at which a chain-reacting system reacts is determined not only by the rate of chain initiation, but also by the chain length. V is determined by the ratio between the rate of chain propagation and the rate of chain termination. Consequently, chain termination and chain initiation are equally important. The addition of some promoter increases the rate of a chain reaction; and the addition of substances which can terminate chains reduces the reaction rate. In pure compounds, where chain initiators are absent, the reaction is initiated by the parent compound dissociating into free radicals. Conversely, chains in pure compounds are terminated by radical recombination or disproportionation with a consequent loss of free valencies.

The combination of two atoms, or of an atom with a simple diatomic radical such as OH, requires the co-operation of some third body to carry away the energy evolved; in gases, this is by a three-body collision, the third body being a molecule, which stabilizes the newly formed molecule by removing the excess energy, e.g.:

$$Cl + Cl + M \rightarrow Cl_2 + M; \quad H + OH + M \rightarrow H_2O + M$$

Very careful measurements on such processes have shown that the rate of recombination is given by $w = x[Cl]^2[M]$, where $[M]$ is the total number of molecules of all types per cm^3. x depends on the collisional cross-sections of Cl and M, and on the properties of M, which may take up the energy to be removed more or less readily. x may vary between 10^{-32} and 10×10^{-32} cm^6 sec^{-1}. At appreciable pressures more complex radicals combine directly upon collision; even methyl radicals combine at each methyl–methyl collision, the rate being $w_0 = fz \exp(-\varepsilon/RT)[CH_3]^2$ where fz is the pre-exponential factor, which depends on the particle diameter and is usually in the region of 10^{-10}, while the steric factor f is commonly equal to one.

It is also likely that atoms combine bimolecularly with complex radicals $H + C_2H_5 \rightarrow C_2H_6$. Such combination is possible since the excess electronic energy becomes distributed over the numerous molecular vibrational modes, and the molecule is protected from decomposition for a certain length of time. During this brief interval the excited molecule has time to transfer part of the excess energy to some other molecule, and the product is then permanently stable.

Most combinations involving two free radicals do not have high activation energies. It follows that $\varepsilon_0 = O$ in the reverse dissociation, such as $C_2H_6 \rightarrow 2CH_3 - Q$. The dissociation of simple molecules into atoms must also be the reverse of their combination: $Br_2 + M \rightarrow Br + Br + M$. (1) Consequently, these dissociations are not unimolecular, as in complex molecules like C_2H_4, but bimolecular (collision with some particle M). The rate must be given by $fz[Br_2][M] \exp(-Q/RT)$, where $z \simeq 10^{-10}$ and $f < 1$. However, we here encounter a fundamental contradiction which has so far not been resolved; the equilibrium constant is well known, being:

$$K = \frac{[Br]^2}{[Br_2]} \simeq 10^{24} \exp(-Q/RT)$$

(analogous with the formulae for H_2, Cl_2 and I_2). K must be equal to the ratio of the rate constants for combination and dissociation, since at equilibrium

$$k[Br]^2[M] = fz[Br_2][M] \exp(-Q/RT)$$

Hence
$$K = \frac{[Br]^2}{[Br_2]} = \frac{fz \exp(-Q/RT)}{k}$$

But experimental data (see for instance, RABINOWITCH and WOOD [24]) show that when M is A, N_2 and CO_2, k is 0.7×10^{-32}, 1.26×10^{-32} and 3×10^{-32} cm^6 mol.$^{-2}$ sec^{-1} respectively, whereas if M $= Br_2$, then $k = 1.6 \times 10^{-32}$ [20]. The mean value of k may then be taken at about 10^{-32}, and z 10^{-10}, so K must be about $f \times 10^{22} \exp(-Q/RT)$. Consequently, $f \simeq 100$, i.e. $f > 1$, so (1) must occur at a rate of about $10^{-8} \exp(-Q/RT)[Br_2][M]$. It would thus seem that (1) involves cross-sections 100 times greater than the gas-kinetic ones. A similar difficulty is encountered if the equilibria $M + H_2 \rightleftarrows H + H + M$ and $I_2 + M \rightleftarrows 2I + M$ are considered, and it probably also exists in the case of chlorine.

CHRISTIE et al. [25] investigated the recombination of iodine atoms in He, Ne, A, Kr and Xe, using flash photolysis. They found that the constants for three-body collisions were quite similar for these gases, being comparable with those given by RABINOWITCH and WOOD [24]. If M $=$ He, $k = 0.67 \times 10^{-32}$, for M $=$ A, $k = 6.84 \times 10^{-32}$, and for M $=$ Xe, $k = 2.99 \times 10^{-32}$. I_2 was found to be exceptionally effective: $I + I + I_2 \rightarrow 2I_2$ gave $k = 470 \times 10^{-32}$ cm^6 mol.$^{-2}$ sec^{-1}. So this implies cross-sections larger by two orders of magnitude than those for He or A.

RICE [26] proposed two hypotheses to explain the anomalously high cross-sections in these collisions. The first amounts to the assumption that the probability of dissociation upon collision is proportional to the closeness of the molecular vibrational states. At the present time it is difficult to advance any theoretical arguments in support of this. The second concerns the complex formed between I_2 and benzene (the latter acting as the third body), the formation of which precedes dissociation of I_2. The rate-limiting step is the decomposition of the complex, leading to the iodine dissociating. CHRISTIE et al. [25] used the same assumption to explain the exceptionally high recombination constant for I_2. They assumed, in agreement with ROLLEFSON and EYRING [27], that a fairly stable compound I_3 was formed. Such a complex may actually exist, and it would increase the effective recombination constant, thus accounting for the unusually high dissociation constant.

Let us consider the dissociation process assuming a complex I_3 in equilibrium with I and I_2. Formation of I_3 from I and I_2 liberates energy ΔE.

At equilibrium

$$I + I_2 \rightleftarrows I_3$$

and

$$\frac{[I_3]}{[I][I_2]} = K = K_0 \exp(\Delta E/RT)$$

and assuming

$$K_0 = \frac{10^{-10}}{10^{14}} = 10^{-24}$$

we have

$$[I_3] = K_0 \exp(\Delta E/RT)[I][I_2] = 10^{-24} \exp(\Delta E/RT)[I][I_2]$$

Thus the recombination rate (ω_R) determined by

$$(2)\ I_3 + I \rightarrow 2I_2$$

is

$$\omega_R = k_2[I_3][I] = k_2 \times 10^{-24} \exp(\Delta E/RT)[I]^2[I_2]$$

assuming that $k_2 = 10^{-10}$.

Hence

$$\omega_R = 10^{-34} \exp(\Delta E/RT)[I_2][I]^2$$

Assuming that $\Delta E = 6$ kcal at 300°K we get

$$\omega_R = 10^{-30}[I_2][I]^2$$

which is in good agreement with experiment.

The rate of

$$(2')\ 2I_2 \rightarrow I_3 + I - 35 \cdot 5 + \Delta E$$

is consequently given by

$$k_2'[I_2]^2$$

where
$$k_2' = 10^{-10} \exp - \left(\frac{35\cdot5 + \Delta E}{RT}\right)$$
$$= 10^{-10} \exp\left(-35\cdot5/RT\right) \exp \Delta E/RT$$

The equilibrium constant, which is equal to the ratio of dissociation and recombination constants, will have its normal value

$$K_{eq} = \frac{k_2'}{k_2} = \frac{10^{-10} \exp\left(35\cdot5/RT\right) \exp\left(\Delta E/RT\right)}{10^{-34} \exp\left(\Delta E/RT\right)}$$
$$= 10^{24} \exp\left(-35\cdot5/RT\right)$$

Thus the supposed formation of I_3 gives the correct values for the recombination and dissociation constants, which correspond with the equilibrium constant.

It is more difficult to explain the results with the inert gases. RICE [26] assumes that complexes are formed via Van der Waals' forces but that such complexes are less stable, and therefore have less effect. The formation of H_3 is even less likely in the recombination of hydrogen. The discrepancy between the equilibrium constant and the constants for the forward and reverse reactions is still unresolved. Regrettably, the literature contains little discussion on this topic, and the discrepancy appears not to have been noted (save by the present author [28]). SOKOLOV and NIKITIN [49, 50] are at present trying to eliminate this contradiction between the two approaches.

The part played by recombination in chain reactions will now be considered. Chain reactions usually propagate via several free radicals such as R_1 and R_2 (minimum two). Chain termination by radical combination can therefore occur in three ways: (1) $2R_1 \rightarrow (R_1)_2$; (2) $2R_2 \rightarrow (R_2)_2$; (3) $R_1 + R_2 \rightarrow R_1R_2$. The rate constants for these three processes may vary somewhat (theory would indicate only very small changes), depending on the collision cross-sections and steric factors. However, if one of the free radicals is in fact an atom (e.g. R_1), then the rate of (1) will be less than that of (3) (the combination of the atom with a complex radical (R_2)) and also that of (2). In this case, $k[M] \simeq 10^{-32}[M]$ for (1), which at atmospheric pressure is less by the factor 10^3 than the rates due to two-body collisions, since $z = 10^{-10}$ and $[M] \simeq 10^{19}$.

The dominant recombination is determined by the concentrations of R_1 and R_2 developed during the reaction. $[R_1]$ and $[R_2]$ are determined by their reaction rates during chain propagation. If the rate of the reaction in which R_1 takes part is less than that of the reaction involving R_2, then $[R_1]$ will be greater than $[R_2]$. Consequently, on the average, (1) will predominate. But if R_1 is an atom, while R_2 is a complex radical, then the rate constant for (1) will be

10^3 times lower than that for (3), so the latter will predominate, although $[R_1] > [R_2]$.

The combination of two free radicals, as a consequence of which the free valencies are lost, does not exhaust the possible reactions between radicals. Disproportionation is frequently encountered with complex radicals; in this, two radicals, neither of which has a double C—C bond, react to give two molecules, one of which has a double bond. Thus in solution diphenylmethyl ethane gives $(C_6H_5)_2C$—CH_3; at low temperatures this disproportionates as below:

$$(C_6H_5)_2\underset{\underset{CH_3}{|}}{C} + (C_6H_5)_2\ \underset{\underset{CH_3}{|}}{C} \rightarrow (C_6H_5)_2C{=}CH_2 + (C_6H_5)_2CHCH_3$$

with C_2H_5, not only is butane formed by combination, but disproportionation also gives C_2H_4 and C_2H_6 ($\varepsilon_0 \simeq 0$).

Two types of attack are possible when two C_2H_5 radicals collide:

$$(a) \qquad H_3C\overset{\overset{H}{|}}{\underset{\underset{H}{|}}{C}}{\cdot} + \cdot\overset{\overset{H}{|}}{\underset{\underset{H}{|}}{C}}CH_3$$

giving n-butane. There are no steric difficulties in the case of such simple radicals and consequently no activation energy is required;

(b) One C—H bond in a radical is attacked by the free valency on the C atom, the angle of attack being near to zero

$$H_3C\overset{\overset{H}{|}}{\underset{\underset{H}{|}}{C}}{\cdot} + H\overset{\overset{H}{|}}{\underset{\underset{H_2}{|}}{C}}CH_2 \rightarrow H_3C\overset{\overset{H}{|}}{\underset{\underset{H}{|}}{C}}H + CH_2{=}CH_2$$

This reaction liberates ~ 60 kcal and consequently $\varepsilon_0 \approx 0$.

Thermodynamic arguments show that the existence of a process whereby two radicals produce two molecules (ε_0 being zero, or very low—2–3 kcal) implies that the reverse process, by which two radicals are formed from two molecules, must also occur. The negligible activation energy for the exothermic disproportionation implies that the reverse endothermic process $C_2H_4 + C_2H_6 \rightarrow 2C_2H_5 - 57$ kcal also has $\varepsilon_0 = 0$, and that therefore the rate of the back reaction is determined solely by its endothermicity. So chain initiation in pure substances occurs other than by direct dissociation of the parent compounds, e.g. by reaction between two molecules giving two free radicals. Such processes may demand less energy than direct dissociation, and may thus be more favoured as a mode of initiation. This question will be considered further in Sections 3 and 4 of Chapter 7. At this point, we confine ourselves to the remark that the oxidation of a hydrocarbon is much more readily initiated by processes of the type $RH + O_2 \rightarrow R + HO_2$ than by disruption of RH at a C—C or C—H bond.

3. DEPENDENCE OF OVERALL REACTION KINETICS ON CHAIN-TERMINATION MECHANISM

The way the overall reaction rate depends on the reactant concentrations, and on the overall activation energy, will vary with the dominant process in chain termination. A number of examples are given below to illustrate this point.

(A) $H_2 + Cl_2 \rightarrow 2HCl$

Initiation:

(0) $Cl_2 + M \rightarrow Cl + Cl + M$

Propagation:

(1) $H_2 + Cl \rightarrow HCl + H$, $\varepsilon_1 = 6$ kcal

(2) $H + Cl_2 \rightarrow HCl + Cl$, $\varepsilon_2 = 2$ kcal.

In long chains, $w_1 = w_2$, i.e.

$$10^{-10}[H_2][Cl] \exp(-6000/RT) = 10^{-10}[Cl_2][H] \exp(-2000/RT)$$

Hence
$$\frac{[Cl]}{[H]} = \frac{[C_2]}{[H_2]} \exp(4000/RT)$$

so at $\simeq 600°$ K and $[Cl_2] \simeq [H_2]$ we have $[Cl]/[H] \simeq 25$. Consequently, the rate of recombination

(3) $Cl + Cl + M \rightarrow Cl_2 + M$

will be 625 times greater than the rate of

(3') $H + H + M \rightarrow H_2 + M$

and 25 times greater than the rate of

(3'') $Cl + H + M \rightarrow HCl + M$.

This is why we can disregard (3') and (3'') as compared with (3) in practice.

Chlorine atoms are produced at a rate $w_0 = k_0[Cl_2][M]$ in (0) and removed at a rate $w_3 = k_3[M][Cl]^2$ in (3) since they are regenerated in chain propagation. Thus we find $[\text{Cl}] = \sqrt{k_0/k_3}\sqrt{[\text{Cl}_2]}$ so the overall rate w is equal to

$$w_1 + w_2 = 2k_1[\text{Cl}][\text{H}_2] = 2k_1 \sqrt{\frac{k_0}{k_3}} \sqrt{[\text{Cl}_2]}[\text{H}_2].$$

Since $k_0 \sim \exp(-Q/RT)$ where Q is $Q_{\text{Cl}-\text{Cl}}$ (57 kcal), and $k_1 \sim \exp(-\varepsilon_1/RT)$ (here $\varepsilon_1 \simeq 6$ kcal), then the activation energy of the overall reaction, E_C, is $\frac{1}{2}Q + \varepsilon_1 = (57/2) + 6$, i.e. 34·5 kcal. The ratio k_0/k_3 then appears as the equilibrium constant for $\text{Cl}_2 \rightleftharpoons 2\text{Cl}$. This implies that $[\text{Cl}]$ during the chain reaction is the same as at equilibrium in the absence of hydrogen.

If ε_2 had been greater than ε_1 and consequently the principal recombination process had been $(3')$ then the kinetic law would have been different; instead of $w = k'[\text{Cl}_2]^{1/2}[\text{H}_2]$ we would have $w = k'[\text{Cl}_2]^{3/2}$, with $E_C = \varepsilon_2 + Q/2$. If again the dominant process had been $\text{Cl} + \text{H} \rightarrow \text{HCl}$, then we would have had $w = k'[\text{Cl}_2][\text{H}_2]^{1/2}$ and $E_C = \frac{1}{2}(Q + \varepsilon_1 + \varepsilon_2)$.

Let us now reconsider a decomposition, where one of the chain stages is unimolecular:

(B) $\text{C}_2\text{H}_5\text{Br} \rightarrow \text{C}_2\text{H}_4 + \text{HBr}$

Initiation:

(0) $\text{C}_2\text{H}_5\text{Br} \rightarrow \text{C}_2\text{H}_5 + \text{Br} - 65$ kcal

Propagation:

(1) $\text{Br} + \text{C}_2\text{H}_5\text{Br} \rightarrow \text{HBr} + \text{C}_2\text{H}_4\text{Br} - 5$ kcal

(2) $\text{C}_2\text{H}_4\text{Br} \rightarrow \text{C}_2\text{H}_4 + \text{Br} - 13$ kcal.

Three recombination processes are possible:

$(3a)$ $\text{Br} + \text{Br} + \text{M} \rightarrow \text{Br}_2 + \text{M}$,

$(3b)$ $\text{Br} + \text{C}_2\text{H}_4\text{Br} \rightarrow \text{C}_2\text{H}_4\text{Br}_2$,

$(3c)$ $2\text{C}_2\text{H}_4\text{Br} \rightarrow (\text{C}_2\text{H}_4\text{Br})_2$.

The rates of these have been estimated to be: $w_{3a}:w_{3b}:w_{3c} = 10^{-10}:2 \times 10^{-3}:4 \times 10^{-7}$ [22]. Thus $(3b)$ predominates. Neglecting secondary recombinations, the overall rate w is:

$$w = -\frac{d[\text{C}_2\text{H}_5\text{Br}]}{dt} \sqrt{\left(\frac{k_1 k_2 k_0}{k_{3b}}\right)} [\text{C}_2\text{H}_5\text{Br}] \exp\left(\frac{-Q + \varepsilon_1 + \varepsilon_2}{2RT}\right)$$

$$\simeq \sqrt{\left(\frac{10^{-10} \cdot 10^{13} \cdot 10^{13}}{10^{-10}}\right)} \exp\left(\frac{-Q + \varepsilon_1 + \varepsilon_2}{2RT}\right) [\text{C}_2\text{H}_5\text{Br}]$$

$$\simeq 10^{13} \exp\left(\frac{-Q + \varepsilon_1 + \varepsilon_2}{2RT}\right)$$

Hence this complex chain reaction simulates a simple unimolecular law with a characteristic rate constant of 10^{13}. The activation energy is:

$$\left[E_C = Q/2 + \frac{\varepsilon_1 + \varepsilon_2}{2} = \frac{Q}{2} + \frac{q_1 + q_2}{2} + \frac{\varepsilon_{01} + \varepsilon_{02}}{2} \right]$$

where Q is $Q_{C_2H_5-Br}$, $q_1 + q_2 = u$ is the heat absorbed by (B), and $\frac{1}{2}(\varepsilon_{01} + \varepsilon_{02})$ is the mean of the heights of the potential barriers for the two steps.

If (1) went much more slowly than (2), [Br] would be so great that the main recombination reaction would become (3a). The reaction rate would then depend on concentration according to:

$$w = \frac{k[C_2H_5Br]^{3/2}}{[M]^{1/2}}$$

where

$$k = k_1 \sqrt{\frac{k_0}{x}} \simeq 10^{-10} \sqrt{\left(\frac{10^{13}}{10^{-32}} \right)} \exp\left(-\varepsilon_1/RT \right) \exp\left(-Q/2RT \right)$$
$$\simeq 10^{12 \cdot 5} \exp\left(-\varepsilon_1 + \tfrac{1}{2}Q \right)/RT$$

In pure C_2H_5Br vapour, $[M] = [C_2H_5Br]$, so the reaction would appear first-order. However, on mixing with an inert gas, we would be able to distinguish it from true unimolecular reactions. This means that E_C will take the same form as for the reaction between Cl_2 and H_2: $E_C = \frac{1}{2}Q + \varepsilon$. The nature of the termination process clearly influences the overall kinetic law considerably.

In the instance just considered, all the various recombinations lead to products (e.g. Br_2, $C_2H_4Br_2$) distinct from C_2H_5Br. As a consequence, the radical concentrations do not correspond strictly with the thermodynamic equilibrium $C_2H_5Br \rightleftharpoons C_2H_5 + Br$.

4. SPECIAL ASPECTS OF RADICAL GENERATION AND RECOMBINATION IN LIQUIDS

All the principles discussed above for gas-phase reactions apply in the liquid phase, but there are also some features peculiar to liquids, due to the fact that radical pairs if formed may separate only with difficulty, owing to the small diffusion constants, and are thus liable to recombine. The radicals are contained in a cage of surrounding solvent molecules. If they do succeed in separating, then they recombine with extreme difficulty. Molecular dissociation and radical combination have rates different from those in the gas-phase. Since the rates of both are affected, the steady-state concentrations are not materially altered. The dissociation rates being reduced by the solvent, in turn reduce the rate of any minor-component catalysed chain reaction (the solvent being taken as inert). This hypothesis was put forward by FRANCK and RABINOWITCH [30], who used it in their calculations on chain initiation in solution. This hypothesis is only true for solvents inert to the radicals produced by the initiator. If, as is often the case, the radicals can react with the solvent, then the free valence passes over to the solvent. The free valence is then successively transferred between solvent molecules, since this is isothermal, and thus rapidly escapes from the "cage". This raises the rate of chain initiation, but it also accelerates radical combination. The free valency in such a system moves in a similar way to the free radicals in gas-phase reactions, but with the important difference that in a gas the radical itself diffuses, whereas in liquids the free valency moves by successive transfer between solvent molecules.

The calculation of valency transfer rates is made simpler if the solvent is such as to give only the same radicals as are produced by the initiator; e.g. if the initiator is diacetyl peroxide and the solvent acetic acid. The CH_3COO radical is then transmitted unchanged, being continually regenerated in transfer:

$$CH_3COO + CH_3COOH \rightarrow CH_3COOH + CH_3COO$$

The velocity v at which the free valency diffuses may be estimated as follows. The vibrational frequency ν of the radical in the "cage" of solvent molecules is given by $u/(d - \sigma)$, where d is the cage diameter, σ is the molecular diameter, and u is the mean velocity due to thermal agitation. If we assume $d - \sigma \sim 10^{-8}$ cm, $u = 10^4$ cm/sec, then $\nu \simeq 10^{12}$ sec^{-1}.

Assuming that ε_0 for valency transfer is 5 kcal, the time the free valency spends in the cage is $\tau = 1/[10^{12} \exp(-5000/RT)]$. In time τ the free valency is transferred a distance $d \simeq 3 \times 10^{-8}$ cm. The mean speed of free valency diffusion is thus $v = d/\tau = 3 \times 10^{-8} \times 10^{12} \exp(-5000/RT)$. At 400°K, $v = 6 \times 10^{-11} \times 10^{12} = 60$ cm/sec.

This may be compared with gaseous diffusion in which $v = 10^4$ cm/sec; it is thus 160 times lower. But the coefficient of diffusion is 10^4 times smaller in liquids than in gases, so stepwise free-valency transmission is some 60 times more rapid than purely diffusive transfer. Should ε_0 be larger, however, then diffusive transfer may become more rapid than valency transmission. For instance, if $\varepsilon_0 = 10$ kcal then the ratio of velocities will be 10.

The transmission mechanism is likely to be extremely important for free valencies in solids, since diffusion is then completely absent.

5. THE EFFECTS OF INHIBITORS ON THE RATES OF CHAIN REACTIONS

The Reaction Between Hydrogen and Chlorine

In the absence of appropriate additives chain termination is by combination of the chain radicals. If some substance having weak bonds is added, then the chain radicals may start to react with it. Inactive radicals may result, and their rates of reaction with the reactants may be much lower than their rates of mutual combination. Such compounds may thus terminate the active chain prematurely. Inhibitors, as these substances are called, may reduce the rate of reaction enormously, even when present in very small concentrations.

A classic instance is the effect of O_2 on the H_2/Cl_2 photoreaction. In this case one of the active radicals, H, combines with O_2, giving the low-activity radical HO_2,* which is unable to regenerate the active radical H† at ordinary temperatures.

One per cent O_2 has been shown [31] to give rates for $H + Cl_2 \rightarrow HCl + Cl$ and $H + O_2 + M \rightarrow HO_2 + M$ in the ratio of some hundreds at atmospheric pressure. This ratio gives the chain length. In the absence of oxygen, chain termination occurs mostly by combination of chlorine atoms, and the chain length is of the order of several hundred thousand. The rate is reduced 10^3 times by 1 per cent O_2. An appreciable reduction in rate is produced by even as little as 0.01 per cent O_2. NCl_3, even in the minutest amounts, has an even more marked effect. This compound acts via the reaction $NCl_3 + Cl \rightarrow NCl_2 + Cl_2$, which probably occurs at every NCl_3/Cl collision. Q_{N-Cl} is 20 kcal less than Q_{Cl-Cl}, and so the back reaction is exceedingly slow at room temperature.

The much greater effectiveness of NCl_3 relative to O_2 has two causes; firstly, the reaction $NCl_3 + Cl \rightarrow$ does not involve a three-body collision (this alone increases the effectiveness of NCl_3 by 300 times), and secondly, stage 1 in the chain $Cl + H_2 \rightarrow HCl + H$ (1) and $H + Cl_2 \rightarrow HCl + Cl$ (2) (in which atomic chlorine reacts) is by far the slower. Consequently, [Cl] is much larger than [H], and so NCl_3 removes active centres far more effectively than O_2, since the active centres are mostly chlorine atoms. The amounts required to produce any given effect are 10^5 times lower than for O_2. This is why the chain cannot propagate even in the presence of 0.001 per cent NCl_3. The usual methods of producing chlorine give NCl_3 contents of this order. As a consequence, the reaction between hydrogen and chlorine was considered, in the last century, to have a long induction period. On the other hand, carefully purified gases, which contain no NCl_3, show no induction period. The induction period is explained by each quantum absorbed destroying one molecule of NCl_3, and the reaction rate can become normal when all the NCl_3 has been destroyed.

Similar induction periods are often found in reactions with long

* By three-body collision, $H + O_2 + M$.
† $HO_2 + H_2 \rightarrow H_2O_2 + H$ is strongly endothermic ($\varepsilon \simeq 24$ kcal).

chains, since minute amounts of strong inhibitors may be introduced accidentally. The kinetic order will depend on whether termination is by combination of chain radicals, or by reaction with inhibitor. The cases considered above all involved combination of chain radicals. The rate of the H_2/Cl_2 reaction, in the absence of inhibitors, may be put in the form:

$$w = 2k_1 \sqrt{\frac{k_0}{k_3}} [Cl_2]^{1/2}[H_2]$$

i.e. the rate is proportional to the square root of the rate constant for initiation, and inversely proportional to the square root of the rate constant for termination, and the activation energy is $\frac{1}{2}Q + \varepsilon_1$. If the chains are terminated by an inhibitor, such as NCl_3, it may readily be shown that

$$w = 2k_1[H_2][Cl] = 2k_1[H_2] \frac{k_0[Cl_2]}{k'[NCl_3]}$$

The reaction will then simulate a bimolecular process, and $w = k[Cl_2][H_2]$ (instead of $w = k[Cl_2]^{1/2}[H_2]$), the rate being proportional to the rate constant for initiation, and inversely proportional to the rate constant for termination and to the concentration of inhibitor. The activation energy is $Q + \varepsilon_1 - \varepsilon_1'$, where ε_1' is the activation energy of $Cl + NCl_3 \rightarrow Cl_2 + NCl_2$.

Inhibitor Effects in Liquid-phase Reactions

The actions of small amounts of added substances on the reaction rates in liquids are very clearly seen in polymerizations, oxidations of a variety of organic compounds, in the decomposition of H_2O_2, etc. Thus the addition of 1 part in 10^4 of hydroquinone to acrolein completely protects it against oxidation, and makes the industrial production of acrolein possible. Benzaldehyde containing 1 part in 135 of hydroquinone takes a year to absorb as much oxygen as is otherwise taken up in a minute. The importance of inhibitors in stabilizing petrols obtained by cracking, or oils, is well known. The most powerful inhibitors for many oxidations and polymerizations are pyrogallol, hydroquinone, pyrocatechol and resorcinol. The various possible inhibitors act differently in different reactions, however. Thus the agents most effective in stabilizing oils and cracked petrols are diphenylhydrazine, diphenyl, p-aminophenol, naphthylamine, etc., but hydroquinone, though a powerful anti-oxidant for benzaldehyde and Na_2SO_3, has very little effect on the oxidation of oils.

The inhibitor does not alter the oxidation products; it always acts by producing a less active radical, which latter, being unable to react with the compound to be protected (ε is very large), combines with a similar radical without regenerating an active centre.

Antioxidants may act in a double fashion:

(1) In the chain $R + O_2 \rightarrow RO_2$; $RO_2 + RH \rightarrow RO_2H + R$. R may react more easily with the inhibitor AH than with RH, if Q_{A-H} is less than Q_{R-H}. The reactions $RO_2 + AH \rightarrow ROOH + A$, or $R + AH \rightarrow RH + A$ may give radicals so inactive that they cannot react with O_2 or RH. The chain is thereby terminated. Another possibility, which appears to us to be the more common state of affairs, is that A may combine with O_2 to form AO_2; as AO_2 is sufficiently inactive not to react via $AO_2 + RH \rightarrow AOOH + R$, the chain is terminated. The latter mode of inhibition seems likely, since many antioxidants (e.g. pyrogallol) are also readily oxidized: $A + O_2 \rightarrow AO_2$; $AO_2 + AH \rightarrow AOOH + A$.

(2) Many antioxidants readily react with hydroperoxides ROOH to form molecular products. The hydroperoxides are removed, and are thus not available to initiate new chains. Many auto-oxidations have substantial induction periods; slow oxidation occurs during the induction period, and towards the end the rate of oxidation begins to rise; finally it becomes considerable.

The autocatalysis is due to the hydroperoxides formed decomposing to free radicals, and so the rate rises progressively, in proportion to the accumulation of reaction products. Antioxidants, by removing the hydroperoxides, prevent autocatalysis, and maintain the rate at its initial level, which is often inappreciable.

It is common knowledge that various compounds, mainly polyphenols, secondary aromatic amines, quinones and nitro-derivatives, inhibit polymerizations; the actions of polyphenols and amines have long been explained by their reacting with the chain-carrier radicals [17]. But DOLOGOPLOSK et al. [38–40] have shown that the inhibition mechanisms in thermal and initiated polymerizations with such substances are such that if the oxygen effect is completely absent there is no inhibition. They observed no inhibition even with substances such as methyl acrylate and vinyl acetate, which give the most active free radicals, only a slight change in kinetics occurring on adding polyphenols or amines in the absence of oxygen. An induction period was only found if a certain amount of oxygen was present; they suppose that the inhibition found with polyphenols plus oxygen is due to radicals particularly active in hydrogen abstraction being formed, so conditions are more favourable for the phenols and aromatic amines to be oxidized to the corresponding semiquinones, the resulting quinoid products being very effective free radical acceptors. The proposed interpretation explains the inhibiting action in polymerizations shown by small amounts of oxygen. This effect is related to the following reaction sequence:

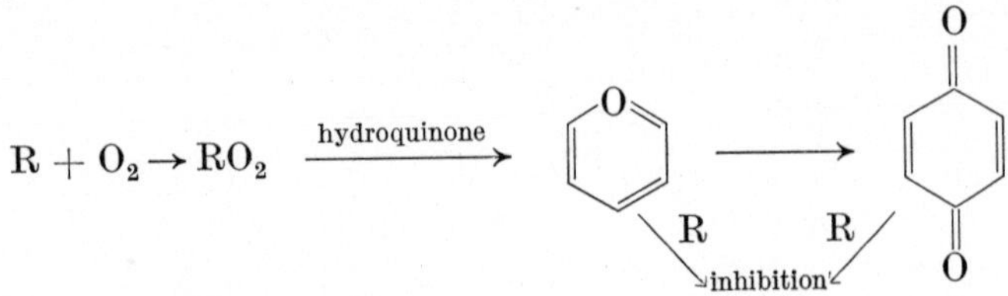

$$R + O_2 \rightarrow RO_2 \xrightarrow{\text{hydroquinone}}$$

where R is a polymer radical.

Hence in systems containing traces of polyphenols or aromatic amines the oxygen produces a polymerization inhibition effect. A similar effect occurs if oxygen is replaced by peroxides (e.g. benzoyl peroxide, cumol hydroperoxide) or heavy metals (Fe, Cu, Mn), the following cycle then occurring

These data imply that the actual inhibitors are the quinoid derivatives, and not the polyphenols or amines themselves; quinones, particularly benzoquinone, inhibit polymerizations without oxygen being present [39–42], the mechanism being that the quinones react with the free polymer radicals to give semiquinone radicals, these latter being too inactive to continue the polymerization chains. In particular, the benzoquinone reaction gives the corresponding hydroquinone ethers [40, 43];

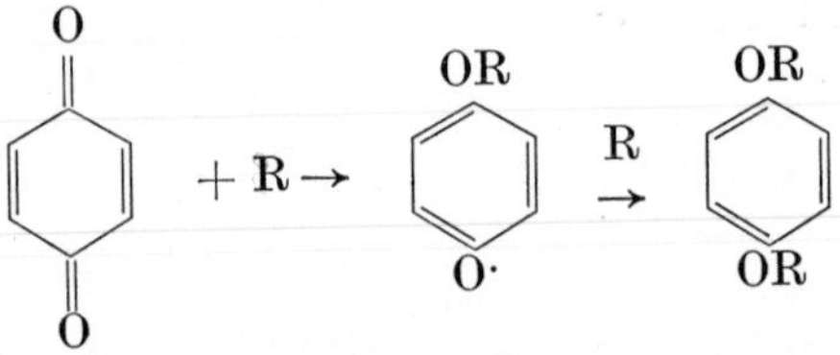

Aromatic nitrocompounds belong to this species of inhibitor; they have been studied several times [44–48]. The inhibition is much enhanced by traces of oxygen [48]. Table 36 illustrates the tendencies of quinones and nitrocompounds to react with free radicals; the yield of CH_4 when CH_3 reacts with a hydrocarbon plus inhibitor is given, the CH_3 source being methyl phenyl triazene which on heating breaks up in solution as below:

$$CH_3-N = N-NHC_6H_5 \rightarrow CH_3 + N_2 + C_6H_5NH$$

The rates at which these materials react with CH_3 parallel their efficiencies as polymerization inhibitors; the inhibiting action is here clearly related to alkylation, and not to hydrogen abstraction from the inhibitor, since no fall in yield of CH_4 should be found in the latter case.

These arguments on the quinoid mechanism cannot be transferred to oxidation processes unchanged; in the latter case the polyphenols and secondary aromatic amines are enormously more effective inhibitors than the quinones.

Table 36 [48]. *Effects of inhibitors on the methane content of the gas from pyrolyzing a* 1 *per cent solution of methyl phenyl triazene*

Inhibitor	Temp. °C	Solvent	Inhibitor: triazene ratio	Gas content, (per cent)
None	125	Ethylbenzene	—	31·0
m-Dinitrobenzene .	125	Ethlybenzene	5:1	21·0
m-Dinitrobenzene .	125	Ethlybenzene	8:1	18·1
2, 4-Dinitrochlorobenzene .	125	Ethylbenzene	8:1	16·7
Trinitrobenzene .	125	Ethylbenzene	1:1	10·0
Trinitrobenzene .	125	Ethylbenzene	5:1	2·5
Naphthoquinone .	100	Cumene	2:1	1·5
Benzoquinone . .	100	Cumene	2:1	0

While the relationship between inhibitor action and reactant structure is well understood for polymerizations (see, for instance, [32]), the relationships are not equally clear in oxidations, and this important problem still awaits solution. All such oxidation inhibitors have weakly bound hydrogen atoms. During the oxidation the peroxide radicals RO_2 abstract hydrogen atoms from inhibitor molecules; in the di- and tri-hydroxy benzenes, the phenolic H is only weakly bound to oxygen. The attachment of H in the NH_2 groups of aniline and other amines is also weak.

We still have to demonstrate that the radical AO_2, as formed from pyrogallol, is so inactive that it is unable to abstract hydrogen from the oxidizable compound, but is capable of abstracting inhibitor hydrogen, to give A. This is necessary because many inhibitors are readily oxidized.

In order to discuss antioxidant action in concrete terms, the following hypothetical scheme is put forward. It is extremely likely that intramolecular rearrangement follows hydrogen abstraction from pyrogallol, giving an *o*-quinoid radical structure, which may then form a peroxide radical with O_2.

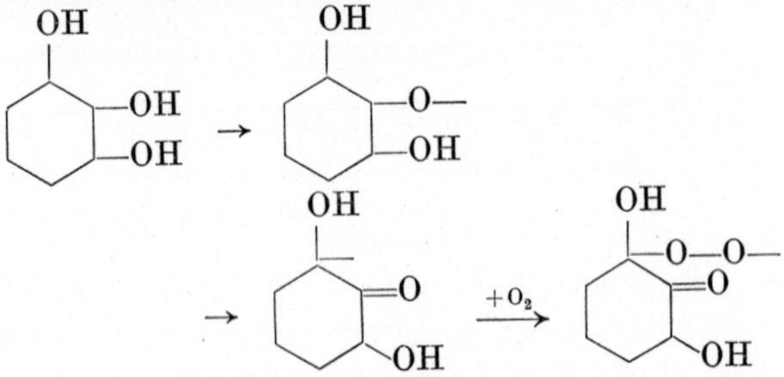

O—O— and —OH groups attached to the same carbon must certainly be an unstable arrangement; and consequently the C—O bond is also weak, relative to the fairly strong O—O bond. The radical is then extremely inactive, which is another reason for the strong retarding action of pyrogallol. The radical is sufficiently active to react when in pure pyrogallol, giving 3-hydroxy 1, 2-*cyclo*-hexadienedione, water and a radical of quinoid type:

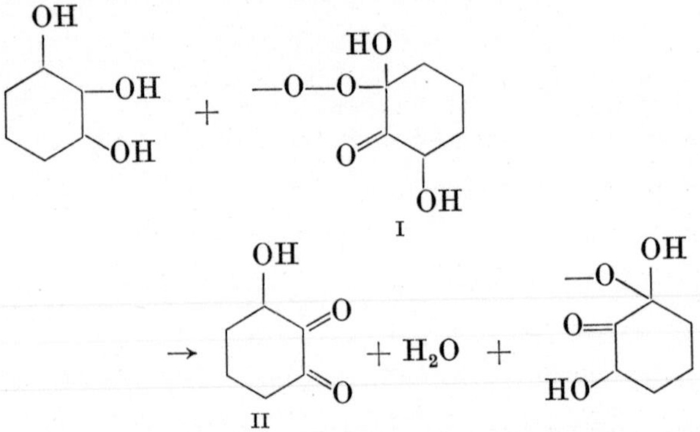

The latter abstracts hydrogen from further pyrogallol, giving the radical with which the cycle started, together with an unstable molecule, which decomposes to water and the dione II above.

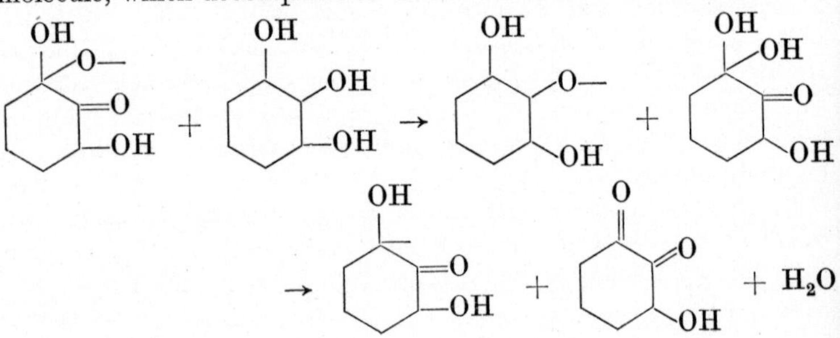

With aniline as retarding agent, the reaction may be as follows (water is also produced):

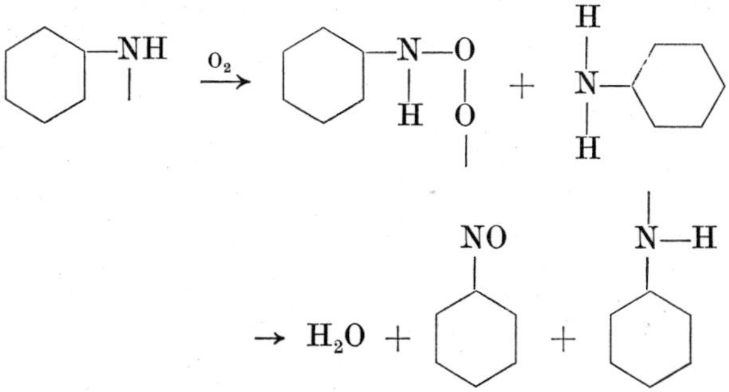

The action of any particular retardant depends not only on the nature of the reactants, but also on the experimental conditions. Large inhibition effects are found under the conditions specified below.

(1) The chain radicals must react more readily with retardant than with one another. Obviously, radical–radical reactions occur more readily at higher rates of initiation. This is why inhibitors very strongly retard reactions with low rates of initiation (typical instances are photoreactions at low light intensities, or low-temperature reactions). Their action is correspondingly weak when the rate of initiation is high, e.g. at high light intensities and high temperatures.

Experiments are usually conducted during intervals bearing some convenient relation to the reaction rate. Consequently reactions with long chains have to be conducted at low rates of initiation (e.g. low light intensities). So retardant effects will be more readily observed in reactions with long chains than in those with short chains.

(2) When chain radicals interact with inhibitors the product radicals must be sufficiently inert to combine with one another in preference to regenerating the chain radicals by reacting with the main reactants. The inhibitor can naturally have no retarding action if this condition is not fulfilled. The greater or lesser ease with which the inhibitor radicals react with the parent compounds depends not only on the properties of the inhibitor, but also on those of the main reactants. If the main bonds reacting have sufficiently low Q-values, then a radical of low activity (an allyl radical, say) may regenerate a chain radical from the main reactant. Consequently, one and the same inhibitor may strongly retard one reaction, while scarcely influencing a second.

12

(3) The retardant bonds may also be of such strength that dissociation into radicals is easier than for the main reactants, so the retardant is also simultaneously an initiator. This is quite frequently the case, since the properties of an inhibitor are such that this is likely to occur. Such substances thus have a double function; they may act as inhibitors under some circumstances, and as accelerators under others, in any given system. These varied actions will depend both on the properties of the reactants and on temperature.

The Actions of I_2, NO, NO_2 and NOCl

Iodine shows just such dual action. I_2 frequently acts as a retardant, due to the weakness of the I—I bond; radicals react readily with I_2 and the resultant iodine atoms are of low activity, being unable to abstract hydrogen from the parent compounds. Consequently, iodine retards polymerizations, oxidations, or chlorinations in the lower temperature ranges. On the other hand, the low Q_{I-I} means that I_2 can easily dissociate into atoms, and these atoms may abstract hydrogen from RH molecules at high temperatures, if the R—H bond is not exceptionally strong. Radical chains are thereby initiated, and the reaction is accelerated.

Iodine catalysis is observed in many high-temperature reactions, as indicated above. For instance, Q_{C-H} is comparatively small (~ 80 kcal) in —CHO groups, and Q_{H-I} is 70 kcal, so the formation of HI from aldehyde + I is only endothermic by 10 kcal. Chain initiation by this route is much more favoured than direct rupture of C—C or C—H bonds in the aldehyde, since these have bond energies of 70 and 80 kcal respectively. This mode of catalysis is also observed in the decompositions of organic compounds.

The dual action of iodine may be observed in the oxidation of methane. At a fairly low temperature (340°C) the addition of 0·3 per cent I_2 increases the induction period from 14 to 135 min, while at a somewhat higher temperature (447°C) 2 per cent I_2 reduces the induction period [33].

NO also shows an analogous dual action; it acts as a latent radical, its activity being very small at low temperatures, since the free electron forms an additional one-electron bond between the atoms. NO combines readily with free radicals; e.g. triphenylmethyl combines instantaneously, giving Ph_3C—NO. NO thus inhibits many chain reactions efficiently, though in some cases it can act as an accelerator. NO catalysis is observed on raising the temperature; the elevated temperature causes the inactive NO to react with other components, and the radicals produced initiate chains: e.g. NO + $CH_3CHO \rightarrow CH_3NO$ + CHO. This reaction generates a free radical more readily than can direct rupture of a C—C or C—H bond. The detailed processes involved are obscure; the possibility that they occur at the walls cannot be excluded.

NO thus acts in some reactions as an inhibitor, and in others as an accelerator. Reactions are known which are inhibited by NO at low concentrations, but are accelerated at high concentrations— instances are the pyrolyses of benzaldehyde, acetaldehyde, dimethyl, and diethyl ethers, and the oxidation of di*iso*propyl ether. Under all circumstances NO acts simultaneously as both a retardant and an accelerator, and only the overall effect is significant [34]. The photolysis of acetaldehyde is retarded by NO at low rates of initiation, while NO acts as an accelerator at somewhat higher temperatures, in the dark.

The catalytic actions of NO and NO_2 are well known. Methane, ethane, ethylene and benzene may be oxidized at lower temperatures, and the intermediates are not destroyed—formaldehyde, acetaldehyde, phenol, alcohols, ketones, etc., all are recoverable. Although the mechanism is not obvious, and has still not been discovered, NO and NO_2 appear to behave as radicals at fairly high temperatures; they produce hydrocarbon radicals from hydrocarbons and thereby start radical chains. NO reduces the induction period usual in hydrocarbon oxidations, and accelerates the reaction when the induction period is over; it also frequently modifies the shapes of the kinetic curves.

A number of authors (particularly TITOV [35]) have supposed that hydrocarbons are nitrated via free hydrocarbon radicals

$$RH + NO_2 \rightarrow R + HNO_2$$

which combine with NO_2 to give nitro-compounds. Oxidation products are formed as well as the nitro-compounds; this is to be expected, since even small amounts of NO_2 can initiate oxidation chains if O_2 is present, by producing free radicals.

NOCl also shows a dual action: because Q_{N-Cl} is small (38 kcal), NOCl readily decomposes to NO + Cl, and the Cl atom can then start a chain reaction. This may well be the reason why CH_4 simultaneously nitrates and chlorinates in mixtures of CH_4, NO_2, and Cl_2 (at suitable temperatures), whereas if either NO_2 or Cl_2 is absent the reactions hardly take place [36.] On the other hand, NOCl can also be an inhibitor since it can react exothermically with Cl atoms: $Cl + NOCl \rightarrow NO + Cl_2 + 19\cdot2$ kcal. The activation energy is about $1\cdot06$ kcal. Traces of NOCl retard the photocombination of CO and Cl_2, for instance; $0\cdot1$ mm Hg of NOCl reduces the rate of phosgene formation by about 30 times [37].

REFERENCES

1. M. POLANYI. *Atomic Reactions*. London 1932; ST. V. BOGDANDY and M. POLANYI. *Z. Phys. Chem.* **B1,** 21 (1928); M. POLANYI and G. SCHAY. *ibid.* **B1,** 30 (1928); H. OOTUKA and G. SCHAY. *ibid.* **B1,** 62 (1928).
2. E. W. R. STEACIE. *J. Chem. Phys.* **1,** 618 (1933).
3. P. A. K. CLUSIUS. *J. Chem. Soc.* 2607 (1930).
4. A. BOYER, M. NICLAUSE and M. LETORT. *J. Chim. Phys.* **49,** 345 (1952).
5. C. N. HINSHELWOOD, K. CLUSIUS and G. HADMAN. *Proc. Roy. Soc.* A**128,** 88 (1930).
6. F. H. VERHOEK and C. N. HINSHELWOOD. *Proc. Roy. Soc.* A**146,** 334 (1934).
7. R. A. OGG and M. POLANYI. *Trans. Faraday Soc.* **31,** 482 (1935).
8. R. E. REBBERT and K. J. LAIDLER. *J. Chem. Phys.* **20,** 574 (1952).
9. T. L. COTTRELL. *The Strengths of Chemical Bonds*. London 1954.
10. E. R. BELL, J. H. PALLY, F. F. RUST, F. H. SENBOLD and W. E. VAUGHAN. *Disc. Faraday Soc.* **10,** 242 (1951).
11. J. MURAWSKI, J. S. ROBERTS and M. SZWARC. *J. Chem. Phys.* **19,** 698 (1951).
12. M. S. KHARASCH and F. R. MAYO. *J. Amer. Chem. Soc.* **55,** 2468, 2521, 2531 (1933).
13. M. S. KHARASCH and H. C. BROWN. *J. Amer. Chem. Soc.* **61,** 2142 (1939); M. S. KHARASCH, H. C. BROWN and T. H. CHAO. *ibid.* **62,** 2393 (1940).
14. M. S. KHARASCH, A. T. READ and P. R. MAYO. *Chem. and Ind. (Rev.)* **57,** 752 (1938).
15. M. S. KHARASCH and H. C. BROWN. *J. Amer. Chem. Soc.* **64,** 329 (1942).
16. M. S. KHARASCH and M. FOY. *J. Amer. Chem. Soc.* **57,** 1510 (1935).
17. W. A. WATERS. *The Chemistry of Free Radicals*. Oxford 1946. Russian translation: Moscow 1948.
18. G. A. RAZUVAEV, YU. A. OLDEKOP and N. A. MAYER. *Zh. Obshch. Khim.* **25,** 697 (1955).
19. K. I. IVANOV and V. K. SAVINOVA. *Izv. Akad. Nauk SSSR, Ser. Khim.* 329 (1938); S. S. MEDVEDEV and A. G. PODYAPOLSKAYA. *Zh. Fiz. Khim.* **13,** 719 (1939); E. J. HARRIS and A. C. EGERTON. *Proc. Roy. Soc.* A**168,** 1 (1938).
20. KH. S. BAGDASARYAN. *Zh. Fiz. Khim.* **27,** 542 (1953); D. H. VOLMAN and W. M. GRAVEN. *J. Amer. Chem. Soc.* **75,** 3111 (1953); S. N. KAMENSKAYA and S. S. MEDVEDEV. *Zh. Fiz. Khim.* **14,** 922 (1940); P. S. SHANTOROVICH and S. S. MEDVEDEV. *ibid.* **23,** 1426 (1949); G. V. TKACHENKO, P. M. KHOMIKOVSKII and S. S. MEDVEDEV. *ibid.* **25,** 823 (1951).
21. J. FRANCK. *Trans. Faraday Soc.* **21,** 536 (1925).
22. A. N. TERENIN. *The Photochemistry of Vapours of Salts*. 1934. (In Russian.)
23. V. N. KONDRATIEV. *Elementary Chemical Processes*. Leningrad 1936. (In Russian.)
24. E. RABINOWITCH and W. C. WOOD. *Trans. Faraday Soc.* **32,** 907 (1936); E. RABINOWITCH and W. C. WOOD. *J. Chem. Phys.* **4,** 897 (1936).
25. M. I. CHRISTIE, A. J. HARRISON, R. G. W. NORRISH and G. PORTER. *Proc. Roy. Soc.* A**231,** 446 (1955).
26. O. K. RICE. *J. Chem. Phys.* **9,** 258 (1941).
27. G. K. ROLLEFSON and H. EYRING. *J. Amer. Chem. Soc.* **54,** 170 (1932).
28. N. N. SEMENOV. *Chain Reactions*. Leningrad 1934. (In Russian.) Translated and revised as *Chemical Kinetics and Chain Reactions*. Oxford 1935.
29. N. N. SEMENOV. *Usp. Khim.* **21,** 641 (1952).
30. J. FRANK and E. RABINOWITCH. *Trans. Faraday Soc.* **30,** 120 (1934).
31. M. BODENSTEIN and W. UNGER. *Z. phys. Chem.* **B11,** 253 (1930).

32. KH. S. BAGDASARYAN. *Zh. Fiz. Khim.* **18,** 294 (1944); Dissertation for doctorate. Karpov Institute of Physical Chemistry (1950).

33. W. A. BONE and R. E. ALLUM. *Proc. Roy. Soc.* A**134,** 578 (1931).

34. V. I. GOLDANSKII. *Usp. Khim.* **15,** 63 (1946).

35. A. I. TITOV. *Zh. Obshch. Khim.* **18,** 465, 473 (1948).

36. A. V. TOPCHIEV and V. P. ALANIYA. *Dokl. Akad. Nauk SSSR* **67,** 297 (1949).

37. F. S. DAINTON. *Trans. Faraday Soc.* **43,** 365 (1947).

38. I. W. BREITENBACH and K. HOREISHY. *Ber. Dtsch. Chem. Ges.* **74,** 1386 (1941).

39. B. A. DOLGOPLOSK and D. S. KOROTKINA. *Trud. VNIISK** 198 (1951).

40. B. A. DOLGOPLOSK and G. A. PARAFNOVA. *Trud. VNIISK** 224 (1951).

41. H. W. MELVILLE and W. F. WATSON. *Trans. Faraday Soc.* **44,** 886 (1948).

42. S. G. COHEN. *J. Amer. Chem. Soc.* **69,** 1057 (1947).

43. A. F. BICKEL and W. A. WATERS. *J. Chem. Soc.* 1764 (1950).

44. S. G. FOORD. *J. Chem. Soc.* 48, 1940.

45. C. T. PRICE, R. W. BELL and E. KREBS. *J. Amer. Chem. Soc.* **64,** 1103 (1942).

46. R. L. FRANCK and C. E. ADAMS. *J. Amer. Chem. Soc.* **68,** 908 (1946).

47. G. SCHULZ. *Makromol. Chem.* **1,** 94 (1947).

48. B. A. DOLGOPLOSK. *Trud. VNIISK** 163 (1953).

49. E. NIKITIN. *Dokl. Akad. Nauk SSSR* **116,** 584 (1957).

50. E. NIKITIN. *Dokl. Akad. Nauk SSSR* **119,** (1958) (in press).

* All-Union Institute of Synthetic Rubber Research.

Chapter 5

IONS OF VARIABLE VALENCY AS CHAIN INITIATORS

1. FORMATION OF RADICALS AND IONIC RADICALS BY ELECTRON TRANSFER

RADICALS may be formed in electrolyte solutions in two ways; firstly, in a manner analogous to that described above, and secondly by ionic reaction, in which a stable molecule gains or loses an electron.* Such electron transfers are possible, due to the presence of high concentrations of charged particles—ions—in electrolytes.

Most ions obey the usual valency relationships, i.e. their electrons have antiparallel spins; typical ions are those of oxy-acids, carboxylic acids, and acids containing no oxygen, e.g. SO_4^{2-}, CH_3COO^-, and Cl^-, as well as H_3O^+, OH^-, and of the majority of metals: Na^+, Ca^{2+}, Al^{3+}, etc. The capture or loss of two electrons by a particle with all valencies satisfied does not produce any free valencies; typical processes of this kind are:

$$SO_3^{2-} - 2e \rightarrow SO_3$$
$$Sn^{4+} + 2e \rightarrow Sn^{2+}$$

p–Quinone   Hydroquinone ion

If such a particle loses or gains one electron, however, a free radical or ionic radical is formed:

$$OH^- - e \rightarrow \dot{O}H$$
$$SO_3^{--} - e \rightarrow \dot{S}O_3^-$$
$$(C_6H_5)_3C^+ + e \rightarrow (C_6H_5)_3\dot{C}$$

Triphenyl carbonium ion   Triphenylmethyl

Hydroquinone ion   Semiquinone ion

---

* Promotion of reaction by ions of variable valency is well known. Copper or iron ions (and particularly mixtures of these) substantially accelerated the oxidation of sulphite by persulphate, as SHILOV and BULYGINA [1] discovered in 1913. The mechanism was not studied in detail, but they considered the catalytic action of these ions as being due to the formation of alternating valency states.

Ions may sometimes have one uncoupled electron, but still show only slight radical properties; this is so with ions of variable valency. Thus Cu^{2+} may be considered as an ionic radical, formed by $Cu^+ - e \rightarrow Cu^{2+}$; $[Cu^{2+}]$ may be very high in solution, but Cu^{2+} gives only very slight evidence of being a radical. Many other ions, such as Cr^{3+}, Mn^{2+}, Fe^{3+}, etc., have uncoupled electrons, but are quite stable in solution.

Electron transfer occurs at the electrodes during electrolytic oxidation or reduction. The cathode donates electrons to the neighbouring particles, whereas the particles give up electrons to the anode. Generally speaking, only one electron is transferred at a time, since the simultaneous transfer of two electrons is much less probable. If the second electron is transferred very easily, then an appreciable amount of products with unsatisfied valencies from the transfer of only one electron never accumulates. On the other hand, if the transfer of the second electron is difficult, or if it cannot in practice be performed, then a free radical or ion radical will be formed. As a rule, radicals which transfer only one electron are those that give stable end-products. The anodic oxidation of SO_3^{2-} gives the ion-radical $\dot{S}O_3^-$; two of these then combine to $S_2O_6^{2-}$ (the anion of dithionic acid), which has all its valencies satisfied. The products from the transfer of single electrons are sometimes of low activity, and may therefore accumulate in considerable quantities. Semiquinones fall in this class—they are formed by incomplete reduction of quinones to dihydroquinones.

The main route by which the quinone (B) is reduced may be symbolized as below:

$$B + e \rightarrow \dot{B}^- \text{ (semiquinone ion-radical)},$$

$$\dot{B}^- + e \rightarrow B^{2-} \text{ (hydroquinone ion)};$$

there are also other possibilities. The reduction of duroquinone in alkaline media at $pH \geqslant 9$ is a concrete example; the quinone is transformed to a free radical [2]:

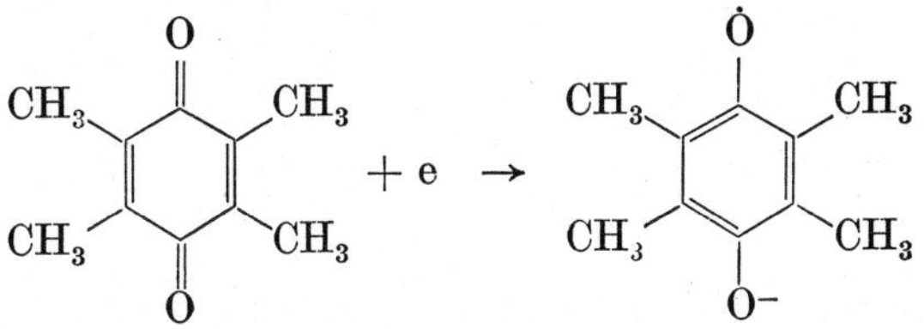

Considerable amounts of semiquinone are formed by reduction of α-ketophenazine and N-methyl α-ketophenazine in acid media [3];

the α-ketophenazine reacts as a conjugated acid, having taken up two protons from the medium:

$$+ 2H^+ \rightleftharpoons$$

The addition of an electron gives a semiquinone ion radical:

$$+ e \rightarrow$$

The formation of semiquinone is indicated by the characteristic colour, which is different from the colours of both the initial compound and the completely reduced product, and by the paramagnetism of the solution. The presence of two stages in the reduction is also indicated by any reducing agent giving not one, but two inflexions in the potentiometric titration curve; the electrons are transferred one by one, and not simultaneously.

Electron transfer can also occur without electrodes, by transfer between particles. A stable particle may transfer an electron to another stable particle, giving two free radicals or radical ions, e.g.:

$$B + SO_3^{2-} \rightarrow \dot{B}^- + \dot{S}O_3^- \qquad (B = \text{a quinone})$$

Ionic radicals derived from metals of variable valency may abstract or donate electrons with stable particles, and thereby form active free radicals or radical ions; e.g. in the reaction of a sulphite with a salt of divalent copper: $SO_3^{2-} + Cu^{2+} \rightarrow \dot{S}O_3^- + Cu^+$. In this case the electron is transferred from SO_3^{2-} to Cu^{2+}, producing the highly active radical SO_3^-; the latter immediately dimerizes to $S_2O_6^{2-}$ [4].

Salts of V^{2+} react with a solution of triphenyl carbinol, $(C_6H_5)_3COH$ to produce the fairly stable radical triphenylmethyl:

$$(C_6H_5)_3C^+ + V^{2+} \rightarrow (C_6H_5)_3\dot{C} + V^{3+}$$

The carbinol solution contains the ion $(C_6H_5)_3C^+$, and this carbonium ion abstracts an electron from V^{2+} [5].

2. THERMODYNAMIC AND KINETIC ASPECTS OF FREE RADICAL FORMATION

Equilibrium may be established between stable molecules or ion-radicals and free radicals, depending on the properties of the substances involved. The equilibrium constant depends as a rule on the energy absorbed by the electron transfer, i.e. on the value of ΔH. If the equilibrium is not complicated by bond rearrangements, then ΔH is determined by the difference between electron affinities of the various particles, and by the difference between the heats of the solvation of the parent particles and final products.

Consider the process $Fe^{3+} + OH^- \rightarrow Fe^{2+} + \dot{O}H$. Electron transfer from OH^- to Fe^{3+} might appear energetically favoured, accompanied as it is by charge neutralization, but in solution it is also accompanied by loss of the difference in solvation energies of Fe^{3+} and Fe^{2+}, and by loss of the OH^- solvation energy (ions being considerably more strongly solvated than uncharged particles, such as molecules and radicals—in addition, energy of solvation increases with ionic charge). The process is consequently strongly endothermic, and $\Delta H = + 44$ kcal.

On the other hand, $Fe^{2+} + H_2O_2 \rightarrow Fe^{3+} + OH + OH^-$ would appear to be energetically unfavourable, since the transfer is from a charged ion to a neutral molecule, and an O—O bond is also ruptured. However, Fe^{3+} is more strongly solvated than Fe^{2+} (due to the increased charge) and the OH^- solvation energy is also available. The process is, in fact, only slightly endothermic, and $\Delta H = 5$ kcal.

The changes in state of solvation result in changes in the state of order amongst the dipoles of neighbouring solvent molecules. Large entropy changes are consequently also associated with these processes. In $Fe^{3+} + OH^- \leftrightarrows Fe^{2+} + \dot{O}H$, the degree of order is sharply reduced in the forward direction, and the entropy thus increases very markedly: $\Delta S = 59$ kcal/mole-deg. At 300°K the free energy change is $\Delta F = \Delta H - T\Delta S = 44 - 18 = 26$ kcal. The degree of order increases sharply in $Fe^{3+} + H_2O_2 \rightarrow Fe^{3+} + OH + OH^-$, and $\Delta S = - 50$ kcal/mole-deg. In this case ΔS determines ΔF, instead of $\Delta H : \Delta H = + 5$ kcal, but $T\Delta S = - 15$ kcal, and so $\Delta F = + 20$ kcal. The values of $\Delta F (= \Delta H - T\Delta S)$, i.e. the free energy changes in similar reactions, are given by URI [6]. The equilibrium constant K may be derived from these data, and hence the equilibrium free radical concentrations, since K is related to the free energy change by the equation $\Delta F = - RT \ln K$; R enters because all data for ΔF are tabulated with equilibrium concentrations expressed in moles/litre. This leads to $K = \exp(-\Delta F/RT) = \exp(\Delta S/R) \exp(-\Delta H/RT)$.

$\Delta F = + 26$ kcal for $Fe^{3+} + OH^- \rightarrow Fe^{2+} + OH$, and thus we have:

$$K = \exp(-\Delta F/RT) = 2 \times 10^{-19} \text{ (at } 300°K)$$

But, on the other hand:

$$K = \frac{[Fe^{2+}][OH]}{[Fe^{3+}][OH^-]}$$

Since $[Fe^{2+}] = [OH]$, $[OH]$ can be readily derived for any solution in which $[Fe^{3+}]$ and $[OH^-]$ are given. Suppose we have a solution which is 0·1 N in alkali, and that 10^{-6} mole of some Fe^{3+} salt is present, then $[OH]$ is

$$\sqrt{(K[Fe^{3+}][OH^-])}$$
$$= \sqrt{(2 \times 10^{-19} \times 10^{-6} \times 6 \times 10^{20} \times 0·1 \times 6 \times 10^{20})}$$
$$= 8·5 \times 10^7 \text{ radicals/cm}^3$$

ΔF is 30 kcal for $Fe^{3+} + H_2O_2 \rightleftharpoons Fe^{2+} + HO_2 + H^+$

Then we have:

$$K = \frac{[Fe^{2+}][HO_2][H^+]}{[H_2O_2][Fe^{3+}]} = 6 \times 10^{20} \exp(-\Delta F/RT)$$
$$= 0·12 \text{ molecule/cm}^3$$

The factor 6×10^{20} is involved in transforming from moles to molecules/cm^3, K having the dimensions of a concentration in this case.

$[HO_2]_{eq}$ in a neutral solution which is 0·1 N in H_2O_2 and contains 10^{-6} mole/l. of Fe^{3+} ions is 10^{10} cm^{-3}; it becomes larger on passing to alkaline solutions, and in 0·1 N alkali (other conditions being the same) $[HO_2]_{eq}$ rises to 10^{13} cm^{-3}. This may be compared with the analogous reaction with copper:

$$Cu^{2+} + H_2O_2 \rightleftharpoons Cu^+ + HO_2 + H^+$$

$$\Delta F_0 = 46 \text{ kcal}$$

$$K = 6 \times 10^{20} \exp(-\Delta F_0/RT) = 3 \times 10^{-13} \text{ cm}^{-3}$$

$[HO_2]$ will be 5×10^5 times lower if $[Cu^{2+}]$ and $[Fe^{3+}]$ are equal. The reaction $Fe^{2+} + H_2O_2 \rightleftharpoons Fe^{3+} + OH + OH^-$ has $\Delta F_0 = 20$ kcal, hence $K = 6 \times 10^{20} \exp(-\Delta F_0/RT) = 1·8 \times 10^6$ cm^{-3}.

In a neutral solution which is 0·1 N in both H_2O_2 and Fe^{2+}, $[OH]$ will be about 10^{16} cm^{-3}. This system is thus a powerful source of OH radicals.

It is obvious from these instances that electron-transfer processes may produce considerable concentrations of free radicals, and are thus capable of initiating chain reactions.

Electron transfer from ions of variable valency to oxidizing or reducing agents is a fast and comparatively easy process. It might appear possible to measure bimolecular rate-constants and determine activation energies and pre-exponential factors for several such reactions. It is somewhat difficult to determine these constants due to secondary processes initiated by the free radicals formed in the main reaction which also consume the parent substances.

For instance

$$H_2O_2 + Fe^{2+} \rightarrow$$

becomes more complicated because the decomposition of hydrogen peroxide is initiated by the free OH formed. Therefore rate constants are usually determined either at very small reagent concentrations or only from the initial parts of the curve, or when certain monomers, such as acrylonitrile, which react with the free radicals to initiate polymerization are present—these impede the reactions between these radicals and the peroxide.

The pre-exponential factors and activation energies for several such reactions are listed in Table 37.

Table 37

Reaction	K, cm³/sec	ε, kcal	Reference
$Fe^{2+} + H_2O_2 \rightarrow Fe^{3+} + OH^- + \dot{O}H$.	$7\cdot3 \times 10^{-13}$	94	[7]
$Fe^{2+} + S_2O_8^{--} \rightarrow Fe^{3+} + \dot{S}O_4^- + SO_4^{--}$.	$1\cdot65 \times 10^{-11}$	121	[8]
$Fe^{2+} + C_6H_5C(CH_3)_2OOH$ . . .	$0\cdot4 \times 10^{-12}$	111	[9]
$Fe^{2+} + C_6H_5C(CH_3)_2OOH*$ . . .	$1\cdot60 \times 10^{-11}$	120	[10]
$Fe^{3+} + OH^- + (C_6H_5)C(CH_3)_2O$ . .	$5\cdot8 \times 10^{-13}$	99·7	[11]
$Fe^{2+} + C_6H_5C(CH_3)_2OOH$ . . .	$8\cdot2 \times 10^{-11}$	104	[12]

* In this case Fe++ is present as a complex with versenatione (ethylene-dinitryltetra-acetate).

3. IONS OF VARIABLE VALENCY AS CHAIN INITIATORS

The oxidation of aqueous sodium sulphite is an auto-oxidation exemplifying the above initiation mechanisms. It is a typical chain reaction. It is very sensitive to light, the quantum yield being about 10^5 [13]. It is also sensitive to the presence of some organic compounds, such as aniline, carbohydrates or glycerol; any of these, if added in small amounts, renders the sulphite solution stable to oxygen [14].

At the present time the chain is believed to propagate as follows [15]:

$$\dot{S}O_3^- + O_2 \rightarrow \dot{S}O_5^-$$

$$\dot{S}O_5^- + SO_3^{2-} \rightarrow SO_5^{2-} + \dot{S}O_3$$

The SO_5^{2-} ion (the anion of Caro's acid) then reacts with SO_3^{2-}

$$SO_5^{2-} + SO_3^{2-} \rightarrow 2SO_4^{2-}$$

The salts of some metals of variable valency accelerate the oxidation, and the oxidation only appears to proceed in the dark if traces of these metals are present [16]. This is clearly a direct consequence of radical-ion production:

$$SO_3^{2-} + Cu^{2+} \rightarrow SO_3^- + Cu^+$$

Another instance is the auto-oxidation of benzaldehyde. This is also a typical chain reaction, being susceptible to light and negative catalysts; the quantum yield is about 10^4[13]. The chain mechanism below has been proposed[15]:

$$C_6H_5\dot{C}\!\!\diagdown_{\!\!O} + O_2 \rightarrow C_6H_5C\!\!\diagup^{\!\!OO-}\!\!\diagdown_{\!\!O}$$

$$C_6H_5C\!\!\diagup^{\!\!OO-}\!\!\diagdown_{\!\!O} + C_6H_5CHO \rightarrow C_6H_5\dot{C}\!\!\diagdown_{\!\!O} + C_6H_5C\!\!\diagup^{\!\!OOH}\!\!\diagdown_{\!\!O}$$

This oxidation is also catalysed by suitable metallic ions, and has been the subject of detailed study for solutions in glacial acetic acid containing cobalt acetate [17]. The equation for the rate takes the form

$$-\frac{d[O_2]}{dt} = k[C_6H_5CHO]^{3/2}[CO(CH_3COO)_2]^{1/2}$$

A relationship of this form indicates that the catalyst initiates the reaction, radicals being generated via:

$$C_6H_5CHO + Co^{3+} \rightarrow Co^{2+} + C_6H_5\dot{C}O + H^+$$

The rate of initiation was investigated by adding a retardant (β-naphthol). The rate of initiation is equal to the rate of inhibitor destruction, the latter being readily determined from the ratio of the inhibitor concentration at the start to the induction period. The process is apparently bimolecular, with a rate $w = k[C_6H_5CHO][K]$, where $[K]$ is the catalyst concentration. The rate-constant for initiation, at 25°C, was found to be 0·018 cm^3 mole^{-1} sec^{-1} = 3×10^{-26} cm^3 molecule^{-1} sec^{-1}.

The reaction of C_6H_5CHO with Co^{3+} must certainly be independent of the oxygen pressure. The kinetics in glacial acetic acid were investigated (in the absence of oxygen) by measuring the amount of Co^{2+} accumulating. The reaction was found to be bimolecular, with a rate-constant of $3 \cdot 5 \times 10^{-26}$ cm³ molecule^{-1} sec^{-1} at 26°C. The agreement between this value and the rate-constant for chain-oxidation initiation in benzaldehyde containing cobalt salts completely confirms the initiation mechanism suggested.

The interaction of Co^{3+} with other organic compounds—such as formic acid, formaldehyde, and the lower alcohols—was investigated in an analogous manner [18]. All these reactions were carried out in strongly acid media, to eliminate interactions between Co^{3+} and OH^-. The relationships observed in their kinetics may be most simply explained by the rates being determined by the interaction of Co^{3+} with an organic molecule:

$$Co^{3+} + CH_3OH \rightarrow Co^{2+} + CH_3\dot{O} + H^+$$

$$Co^{3+} + HCOOH \rightarrow Co^{2+} + HCO\dot{O} + H^+$$

$$Co^{3+} + HCHO \rightarrow Co^{2+} + HC\dot{O} + H^+$$

It would also appear that the mechanism given for catalysis by metals of variable valency plays an important part in the oxidation of hydrocarbons. Thus, cobaltic acetate in glacial acetic acid catalyses the oxidation of olefins [19]. The stearates of cobalt, iron, copper and manganese catalyse the oxidation of liquid alkanes [20] and *cyclo*hexane [21].

A change in catalyst valency was observed when the oxidation was catalysed by managese and cobalt stearates. This is an important proof of the oxidation-reduction mechanisms of catalysed processes.

Catalyst initiation can be accounted for by reactions such as

$$Mn^{2+} + ROOH \rightarrow Mn^{3+} + RO + OH^-$$

$$Mn^{3+} + RCHO \rightarrow RCO + Mn^{3+} + H^+$$

giving additional free radicals and chains. Since the metal ion reacts with intermediate products such reactions can be considered as degenerate branching reactions.

One liquid-phase reaction that has been thoroughly investigated is the decomposition of hydrogen peroxide.

The high quantum yield of the photo-reaction, and the ease with which it is retarded by minute amounts of certain compounds, indicate that a chain mechanism is involved. At the present time the most likely scheme is considered to be that given below.

$$OH + H_2O_2 \rightarrow HO_2 + H_2O$$

$$HO_2 + H_2O \rightarrow H_3O^+ + O_2^-$$

$$O_2^- + H_2O_2 \rightarrow OH^- + OH + O_2$$

The chain may be initiated by either OH or HO_2.

We have already seen that it is possible to obtain high equilibrium concentrations of OH (and especially HO_2) in the presence of ions of variable valency. Fe^{3+} is consequently an active catalyst for the decomposition of H_2O_2. Cu^{2+}, which produces much lower radical concentrations, is much less active. Very high OH concentrations may be developed in systems which contain Fe^{2+} and H_2O_2. Consequently, a mixture containing hydrogen peroxide and Fe^{2+} (Fenton's reagent) is a powerful oxidizing agent. Fenton's reagent is at present known to oxidize in two distinct ways, one via a chain reaction, and the other involving radicals (without chain reaction). In both cases OH abstracts hydrogen, $RH + \dot{O}H \rightarrow \dot{R} + H_2O$. If R is capable of rupturing the O—O bond in H_2O_2, then the chain reaction:

$$\dot{R} + H_2O_2 \rightarrow ROH + \dot{O}H$$

$$\dot{O}H + RH \rightarrow \dot{R} + H_2O$$

can occur. Fenton's reagent oxidizes primary alcohols thus [22]:

$$Fe^{2+} + H_2O_2 \rightarrow OH^- + \dot{O}H + Fe^{3+}$$

$$CH_3CH_2CH + \dot{O}H \rightarrow CH_3\dot{C}HOH + H_2O$$

$$CH_3\dot{C}HOH + H_2O_2 \rightarrow \dot{O}H + CH_3CH(OH)_2 \rightarrow CH_3CHO + H_2O$$

If a chain cannot propagate $\dot{R}$ combines with another $\dot{R}$ or with $\dot{O}H$. The latter occurs when toluene is oxidized by Fenton's reagent [23]:

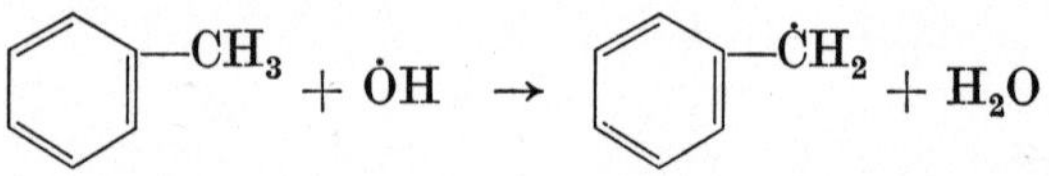

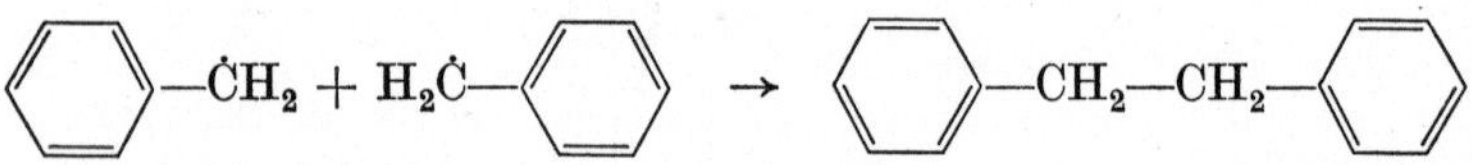

The benzyl radical is of low activity, and is unable to break the O—O bond in H_2O_2, so the benzyl radicals combine to dibenzyl. The chain cannot propagate under these conditions. *m*-Cresol is formed at the same time by OH attack on a ring C—H bond:

$$\text{C}_6\text{H}_4(\text{CH}_3)\text{—H} + \dot{\text{O}}\text{H} \rightarrow \text{C}_6\text{H}_3(\text{CH}_3) + \text{H}_2\text{O}$$

The radical produced (tolyl) is highly active, and attacks the O—O bond in H_2O_2, giving cresol:

$$\text{C}_6\text{H}_3(\text{CH}_3) + \text{H}_2\text{O}_2 \rightarrow \text{C}_6\text{H}_3(\text{CH}_3)(\text{OH}) + \dot{\text{O}}\text{H}$$

However, the chain does not develop, since the probability of OH giving rise to a fresh tolyl radical is very much less than that it will produce benzyl, as previously. The chain is thus in effect broken.

Polymerization is a very common liquid-phase process. If a system containing unsaturated compounds can polymerize, it is an important argument for free radicals being present. In particular, polymerization can be initiated by Fenton's reagent, and many other oxidation–reduction systems are known which can also initiate polymerizations. A system containing persulphate and thiosulphate ions precipitates the polymerization of methacrylamide. The formation of three radicals or ion radicals is possible:

$$S_2O_8{}^{2-} + S_2O_3{}^{2-} \rightarrow SO_4{}^{2-} + \dot{S}O_4{}^- + \dot{S}_2O_3{}^-$$

$$\dot{S}O_4{}^- + S_2O_3{}^{2-} \rightarrow SO_4{}^{2-} + \dot{S}_2O_3$$

$$\dot{S}O_4{}^- + H_2O \rightarrow SO_4{}^{2-} + \dot{O}H + H^+$$

$$\dot{O}H + S_2O_3{}^{2-} \rightarrow OH^- + \dot{S}_2O_3{}^-$$

Any radical may initiate the polymerization:

$$\dot{S}O_4{}^- + M \rightarrow \text{—M—}SO_4{}^-$$

$$\dot{S}_2O_3{}^- + M \rightarrow \text{—M—}S_2O_3{}^-$$

$$\dot{O}H + M \rightarrow \text{—M—}OH$$

where M is a molecule of the monomer [24].

Another system which can also initiate polymerizations is Ti^{3+} and NH_2OH [25]. In this case, initiation is via

$$Ti^{3+} + NH_2OH \rightarrow Ti^{4+} + \dot{N}H_2 + OH^-$$

$$\dot{N}H_2 + M \rightarrow \dot{M}\text{—}NH_2$$

Such methods have found an important application in emulsion polymers[15]. Polymerization occurs in a water emulsion of monomer, the free radicals being in the water, e.g. using Fe^{2+}/H_2O_2 or Fe^{2+}/S_2O_8. At low concentrations the rate of radical destruction in the water is small, and collisions with drops of monomer transfer a free valency to a molecule in the drop. Polymerization then starts in that drop. If the drop is sufficiently small, then the probability of collision with a second radical, i.e. the probability of chain termination, is also small. Thus if the emulsion is sufficiently dilute and the radical concentration in the water is low, polymers of very high molecular weight may be obtained.

REFERENCES

1. N. A. SHILOV and N. M. BULYGINA. *Chem. Z.* **37,** 512 (1913).
2. L. MICHAELIS, M. P. SCHUBERT, R. K. REBER, J. A. KUCK and S. GRANICK. *J. Amer. Chem. Soc.* **60,** 1678 (1938).
3. L. MICHAELIS. *Oxidation-reduction Potentials.* English translation: L. B. Flexner, Philadelphia 1930. (Original in German.) Russian translation: p. 130, Moscow 1936.
4. H. BAUBIGNY. *C.R. Acad. Sci., Paris* **154,** 701 (1912).
5. J. B. CONANT and A. W. SLOAN. *J. Amer. Chem. Soc.* **45,** 2466 (1923).
6. N. URI. *Chem. Rev.* **50,** 375 (1952).
7. W. G. BARB, G. H. BAXENDALE, P. GEORGE and K. R. HARGRAVE. *Trans. Faraday Soc.* **47,** 462 (1951).
8. J. W. L. FORDHAM and H. L. WILLIAMS. *J. Amer. Chem. Soc.* **73,** 4855 (1951).
9. J. W. L. FORDHAM and H. L. WILLIAMS. *J. Amer. Chem. Soc.* **72,** 4465 (1950).
10. J. W. L. FORDHAM and H. L. WILLIAMS. *J. Amer. Chem. Soc.* **73,** 1634 (1951).
11. W. L. REYNOLDS and J. M. KOLTHOFF. *J. Phys. Chem.* **60,** 69 (1956).
12. W. L. REYNOLDS and J. M. KOLTHOFF. *J. Phys. Chem.* **60,** 996 (1956).
13. H. L. J. BÄCKSTRÖM. *Z. phys. Chem.* **B25,** 122 (1934).
14. K. K. JEU and H. N. ALYEA. *J. Amer. Chem. Soc.* **55,** 575 (1933).
15. W. A. WATERS. *The Chemistry of Free Radicals.* Oxford 1946. Russian translation: Moscow 1948.
16. N. N. SEMENOV. *Chain Reactions.* Leningrad 1934. Translated and revised as *Chemical Kinetics and Chain Reactions.* Oxford 1935.
17. C. E. H. BAWN. *Disc. Faraday Soc.* **14,** 181 (1953).
18. C. E. H. BAWN and A. G. WHITE. *J. Chem. Soc.* 339, 343 (1951).
19. C. E. H. BAWN, A. A. PENNINGTON and C. F. H. TIPPER. *Disc. Faraday Soc.* **10,** 282 (1951).
20. J. P. WIBAUT and A. STRANG. *Proc. Acad. Sci. Amst.* **54B,** 102 (1951); J. H. T. BROOK and J. B. MATTHEWS. *Disc. Faraday Soc.* **10,** 298 (1951); D. G. KNORRE, Z. K. MAIZUS and N. M. ÈMANUEL. *Zh. Fiz. Khim.* **29,** 710 (1955).
21. E. T. DENISOV and N. M. ÈMANUEL. *Zh. Fiz. Khim.* **30,** No. 10 (1956).
22. J. H. MERZ and W. A. WATERS. *J. Chem. Soc.* 15 (1949).
23. J. H. MERZ and W. A. WATERS. *J. Chem. Soc.* 2427 (1949).
24. D. DUNN. *Trans. Faraday Soc.* **42,** 190 (1946).
25. P. DAVIES, M. G. EVANS and W. C. E. HIGGINSON. *J. Chem. Soc.* 2563 (1951).

Chapter 6

WALL INITIATION AND RETARDATION OF CHAIN REACTIONS

1. GENERATION AND REMOVAL OF FREE RADICALS AT THE VESSEL WALLS [1]

THE walls of a vessel may take up free atoms or radicals, terminating chains if the reaction is a volume one. Chain termination at the wall was discovered and investigated mainly by Soviet workers; it was first proposed to explain why the lower explosion limit for phosphorus vapour depends on the dimensions of the vessel [2]. It was further found that the tendency of chains to terminate on the walls depended very strongly on their nature and state.

TRIFONOV [3] first studied the heterogeneous retardation of homogenous reactions, and established that chlorine atoms were absorbed by the walls during the photocombination of chlorine and hydrogen. The reaction rate depended on the diameter, when initiation was by a narrow beam of light passing along the axis of a long cylindrical vessel; it increased with the diameter, i.e. as the distance between the axis and the wall increased. TRIFONOV used two vessels of diameters 14 mm and 27 mm. A narrow parallel beam of light, of diameter 3–5 mm, was projected along the axis. The light produced the same number of primary Cl atoms in both vessels. If the chain lengths had been determined by homogeneous recombination of chlorine atoms, or by homogeneous reaction with some retardant, they would have been identical in both vessels, and the rates of HCl formation would have been the same. TRIFONOV found, though, that the reaction was more rapid in the 27 mm vessel at 30 mm Hg, the rate being proportional to d^2 (d = diameter). This must imply that the chain length is d_2^2/d_1^2 times greater in the larger vessel. This can only be explained if the chains terminate on the walls, since the larger the vessel, the longer the chlorine atoms diffuse before striking the wall and being adsorbed. As diffusion times are proportional to d^2, the rate of HCl production will be proportional to d^2.

Homogeneous recombination and other chain-terminating processes become more important as the pressure increases, since the atomic chlorine and impurity concentrations increase with pressure. The rate increases less and less rapidly with d as the pressure is raised, until at $p = 100$ mm Hg the difference between the rates vanishes, evidently because all chains terminate homogeneously. An analogous effect would be found on considerably increasing d; in two vessels having a very large d ratio the ratio of rates is no longer proportional to d^2 even at $p = 36$ mm Hg, much lower pressures being required before proportionality again obtains. This is due to the diffusion time at any particular pressure increasing with d. TRIFONOV's experiments and SOROKIN's theoretical investigations verified the assumption that chain termination could occur at the wall. Wall absorption of a chlorine atom causes it to combine with another chlorine atom, either already present on the wall, or derived subsequently from the gas. The chlorine molecule then desorbs from the wall, and the site is ready to take up another chlorine atom. This particular process will now be investigated in more detail.

Suppose we have a glass vessel, containing pure chlorine; depending on the exact temperature and pressure used, there will be some equilibrium concentration of chlorine atoms present, determined by the relative rates of the forward and back reactions in $Cl_2 + M \rightleftharpoons Cl + Cl + M$. The equilibrium constant defines [Cl]:

$$K_e = [Cl]^2/[Cl_2]$$

As we have shown above, the vessel walls adsorb chlorine atoms at a definite rate. According to the principle of detailed balancing, at equilibrium there must be not only a process of removal, but also a reverse process of formation. Thus separate equilibria for wall processes must be established:

(0) $Cl_2 + M \rightarrow Cl + Cl + M$; $\quad k_0[Cl_2] = a[Cl]^2$

The wall process may be symbolized:

(1) $Cl + wall \rightarrow (Cl)$; $\quad$ (2) $Cl + (Cl) \rightarrow Cl_2$,

free atoms being lost; and the reverse process (production of free atoms by the wall):

(3) $Cl_2 \rightarrow (Cl) + Cl$; $\quad$ (4) $(Cl) \rightarrow Cl$.

It follows from thermodynamic considerations that the equilibrium concentrations of chlorine atoms from these two sources must be equal, i.e. the wall does not influence the extent of chlorine dissociation in the gas (principle of detailed balancing).

If $[Cl]_{gas}$ is raised above the equilibrium value artificially (e.g. by illumination) then although the wall produces chlorine atoms at the same rate, the rates of the heterogeneous processes (1) and (2) increase considerably, in proportion to $[Cl]_{gas}$, and thus tend to reduce the concentration excess. But if a substance such as NCl_3 is added, which rapidly removes chlorine atoms, and reduces $[Cl]_{gas}$ below the equilibrium value, then the rates of (1) and (2) fall, and the role of the wall is reversed; it becomes a net producer of chlorine atoms, and tends to raise $[Cl]_{gas}$ above the value it would otherwise have. In both cases the wall tends to bring $[Cl]_{gas}$ back to equilibrium.

The rates of the heterogeneous processes are usually greater than those for the corresponding homogeneous ones, because the two atoms are produced simultaneously in the gas, Q_{Cl-Cl} being absorbed in one step (57 kcal), while the heterogeneous processes occur in two stages: first one chlorine atom is liberated (reaction (3)), and $(57 - Q)$ kcal is absorbed (Q is the energy liberated by adsorption of Cl), followed by release of the second atom (reaction (4)), which requires Q kcal; both energies are less than 57 kcal. The presence of two stages, each requiring less energy than for the direct decomposition, gives a substantial increase in the overall rate.

The surface does not affect the thermodynamic equilibrium, but although [Cl] is unchanged, the walls cause the equilibrium to be established far more rapidly. It can fairly easily be shown that the time required to attain 50 per cent $[Cl]_{eq}$ at 600°K is 1·5 min if only homogeneous processes are involved. When H_2 and Cl_2 react, the steady-state [Cl] is the same as in the absence of H_2. The rate of HCl formation is $w = [Cl][H_2]$. Data on the H_2/Cl_2 reaction show that the equilibrium $Cl_2 \rightleftharpoons 2Cl$, and thus the stationary rate of HCl formation, is established in less than 1 sec. This must be due to wall effect. The adsorption of Cl atoms by the wall, which is firmly established, must imply that the wall can also generate atoms.

When $Cl_2 \rightleftharpoons 2Cl$ reaches equilibrium, the walls do not affect $[Cl]_{gas}$, and thus do not alter the rate at which pure H_2 and Cl_2 react. If the H_2/Cl_2 mixture also contains some substance which readily initiates or terminates chains, then the walls may still influence the steady reaction rate by reducing the action of initiators, and by tending to reduce $[Cl]_{gas}$ to its equilibrium value. MARKEVICH [4] demonstrated the production of atoms at the wall by direct experiment, from the temperature distribution in a vessel in which H_2 and Cl_2 were reacting, in the range 260–360°C. The temperature distribution was exactly the same with pure gases as that calculable from the rate being uniform throughout the vessel, all the heat liberated being lost via the walls. If an inhibitor (oxygen) was added, then all the heat was evolved in a narrow zone near the walls. This zone became thinner the higher $[O_2]$. The elementary chain-carrying reactions were concentrated near the walls, since the Cl atoms are mostly generated there; the chains encounter oxygen molecules after only getting a short distance from the wall, and so the reaction could not propagate to the central region.

CHAIKIN [5] (Laboratory of Kinetics, Moscow State University), also demonstrated, by differential calorimetry, that chains were generated and terminated at surfaces in the thermal H_2/Cl_2 reaction. In this case any change in the ratio of surface to volume (S/V) was without effect on the rate. CHAIKIN showed that increasing S/V 8 times only altered the rate by 10 per cent ($T = 286°C$, $[H_2] = [Cl_2]$, $p = 115$ mm Hg). O_2 terminated the chains in the gas by reacting with Cl atoms. If chain initiation was homogeneous, then any change in S/V would still not affect the rate. Additional experiments showed that the rate was increased 6 times by an 8·5-fold increase in S/V with O_2 present, however ($H_2:Cl_2:O_2 = 1:1:0·15$); this confirms surface generation of chains.

The above facts, together with the thermodynamic considerations, indicate that the wall–gas contact is a potent source of free radicals. POLYAKOV [6] first proposed a homogeneous–heterogeneous catalysis mechanism to explain a number of known facts about the generation of oxidation chains at surfaces. KOVALSKII and BOGOYAVLENSKAYA [7] investigated the reduction of SO_2 by CO, which only occurs if a catalyst (usually bauxite) is present, but they considered that it took place homogeneously. Having first developed and applied a method for the differential calorimetry of volumes and surfaces, KOVALSKII demonstrated that at least 96 per cent of the heat was produced in the gas, and not at the surface. Consequently, the bauxite does not act like the usual heterogeneous catalysts, in which the reaction is a surface one. Some active material is produced on the bauxite surface, which then starts a chain reaction. Many instances are known where not merely the surface treatment, but even poor control of some inappreciable surface layer may affect rates of reactions by factors between ten and a hundred, particularly in oxidations. Alkyl chlorides decompose homogeneously, via a number of successive reactions, as in oxidations, and the rates are quite different in clean vessels [8]. Reproducible results were only obtained after repeated experiments with alkyl bromides [9]. No wall effect has been observed with alkyl iodides, however. The rate of free radical production and of chain termination varies very greatly with the nature of the surface layers.

The probability of the surface adsorbing a free atom or radical varies from 0 to 1, for different radicals and solid surfaces. Experimentally determined values range from 10^{-5} to 1 [10–13]. The probability has also been shown to increase with temperature, the activation energy being usually from 4 to 12 kcal [10, 14]. The adsorption is thus chemical, giving a coordination-type bond, or even a pure valence bond, between the radical and the particles in the wall. In many cases the radical actually reacts with the wall, and is not merely sorbed. MoO_3 becomes blue under the action of atoms of oxygen and hydrogen, mirrors of antimony and other metals are removed by alkyl radicals (with the formation of metallo-organic compounds), etc. One may thus suppose the sorption of atoms and free radicals to be accompanied by bonding to the adsorbent molecules via valence- or coordination-type bonds.

2. THE METHOD OF DIFFERENTIAL CALORIMETRY

The method of differential calorimetry, first developed by KOVALSKII [7], enables one to decide to what extents the reaction occurs in the volume and on the surface in many cases; this is important to our understanding of reaction mechanisms.

This method involves comparing temperatures measured within the reaction vessel with those calculated from the rate and heat

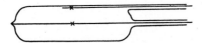

Fig. 15. Reaction vessel

yield of reaction assuming some mode of heat liberation. Differential thermo-couples are used to make the measurements, one junction being at the centre of the vessel and the other at the wall (Fig. 15). The couples are insulated with fine capillaries of the reaction vessel material. The temperature difference ΔT is proportional to the heat of reaction and in this respect measures the reaction rate.

These data, together with normal pressure or reagent concentration measurements, throw fresh light on reaction kinetics. But ΔT depends on the mode of heat liberation and vessel geometry. If the heat is liberated uniformly throughout the vessel, i.e. the reaction is purely homogeneous, then with a cylindrical vessel and steady conditions we have

$$\Delta T_1 = \frac{q_1}{4\pi\lambda} \tag{1}$$

where λ is the thermal conductivity of the reaction mixture and q_1 is the amount of heat liberated per unit time in unit volume.

If the heat is liberated purely heterogeneously, i.e. only at the surfaces (and thus also at the surface of the central capillary) we then have for a cylindrical vessel

$$\Delta T_2 = \frac{q_2}{4\pi\lambda} \frac{2r}{R+r} \ln{(R/r)} \tag{2}$$

where r is the radius of the central capillary, R that of the vessel and q_2 means the same as q_1, except that the heat is only liberated at the surface. If the rate is measured independently and q is known we can easily calculate ΔT from (1) and (2). The reaction type can easily be determined by comparing the computed and experimental values.

(1) or (2) are only applicable to purely homogeneous or heterogeneous reactions. If the reaction is of mixed type the total ΔT will be the sum of ΔT_1 and ΔT_2.

$$\Delta T = \Delta T_1 + \Delta T_2 = \frac{q_1}{4\pi\lambda} + \frac{q_2}{4\pi\lambda} \frac{2r}{R + r} \ln (R/r) \qquad (3)$$

where $q = q_1 + q_2$ is the total heat liberated per unit time per unit length of reaction vessel.

(2) and (3) imply that the heterogeneous component depends on the ratio of radii of reaction vessel and central capillary. So by altering one of these we can change ΔT, which is of value in processes involving stages of both types. When catalysts are studied they can be present as thin coatings on central capillary or reaction vessel.

In the purely heterogeneous case $\Delta T = 0$, all heat being liberated at the walls of the vessel. If a purely homogeneous reaction occurs under these conditions (1) is applicable. If both occur the observed rise will be less than ΔT_1, being

$$0 \leqslant \Delta T_{\text{exp}} \leqslant \Delta T_1 \qquad (4)$$

In the second case (catalysts only on the central capillary) we have, for a purely heterogeneous process

$$\Delta T_3 = \frac{q_3}{4\pi\lambda} 2 \ln (R/r) \qquad (5)$$

A purely homogeneous process is then described by (1). In the mixed case

$$\Delta T_1 \leqslant \Delta T_{\text{exp}} \leqslant \Delta T_3 \qquad (6)$$

The reliability of data obtained by KOVALSKII's method when the catalyst is deposited on the central capillary may be illustrated as follows. Taking the reaction vessel and capillary diameters as 30 and 0·5 mm respectively, at equal rates for purely heterogeneous and homogeneous processes we have

$$\Delta T_3/\Delta T_2 = 2 \ln (R/r) = 8·2$$

Figure 16 shows this, as the temperature distribution in the vessel in the purely homogeneous case (curve 1) and the purely heterogeneous case (reaction on central capillary—curve 2). Differences as large as this would give reliable information on the heat production in the vessel.

Using this method KOVALSKII and BOGOYAVLENSKAYA [7], MARKEVICH [4] and CHAIKIN [5] have found that several reactions (reduction of SO_2, H_2/Cl_2 thermal reaction, thermal addition of

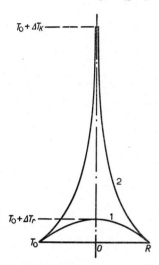

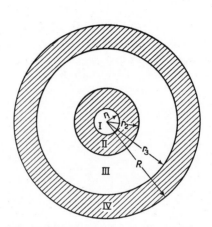

Fig. 16. Radial temperature distribution. T_0 is the oven temperature. 1 is for the homogeneous reaction. 2 is for the heterogeneous reaction on the central capillary

Fig. 17. Homogeneous reactions surface-located. R and r, are the radii of the reaction vessel and central capillary. r_2 and r_3 are the radii of the reaction zone edges

chlorine to ethylene) are homogeneous with wall chain initiation (or catalyst initiation in the SO_2 case).

If an inhibitor is added to the mixture ($Cl_2 + H_2$, or $Cl_2 + C_2H_4$) which gives volume chain termination (oxygen) the reaction is localized at the surface (see Fig. 17). When enough O_2 is present the reaction zone width drops from 11 mm (no O_2) to 1 mm.

KOVALSKII has also shown that when CO is oxidized on Al_2O_3 (catalyst attached to the vessel wall) there is no temperature rise, i.e. as would be expected the reaction is heterogeneous.

KOVALSKII's method has thus been used to detect a class of homogeneous–heterogeneous reactions.

MAIZUS et al. [15] have used KOVALSKII's method in the HBr-catalysed oxidation of propane and have detected the initial fast initiating stage. POLYAKOV et al. [16] have observed some similar interesting effects. They showed that there were two maxima on the curve when methane was oxidized with oxides of nitrogen present. Normal kinetic measurements using pressure recording during the reaction are insufficient to elucidate the complex initial stage of the process.

KOVALSKII's method is also applicable to laminar gas flows. Using the decomposition of ozone MARKEVICH [17] has shown that when Reynolds number is small (up to 100–150) the relationships established for static conditions remain true under flow ones.

3. FREE VALENCIES IN THE WALLS

The designation of the process as chemisorption in the instances of H and Cl has not so far been explained in concrete terms. An attempt will now be made to deal in some detail with chain initiation and termination at the walls. For the sake of clarity, we shall assume the walls composed of ZnO. The ZnO bonds are not so polar as in NaCl, but to simplify the discussion (while not detracting in any way from its value) we will suppose the ZnO crystal composed of Zn^{2+} and O^{2-}. We suppose the ions arranged in a single layer on the surface for simplicity:

$$Zn^{2+}\ O^{2-}\ Zn^{2+}\ O^{2-}$$
$$O^{2-}\ Zn^{2+}\ O^{2-}\ Zn^{2+}$$
$$Zn^{2+}\ O^{2-}\ Zn^{2+}\ O^{2-} \tag{2}$$

and this will be represented by $Zn^{2+}\ O^{2-}$ for brevity. Thermal excitation or light absorption may cause an electron to pass from O^{2-} to Zn^{2+}, giving two ion radicals $\dot{O}^-$ and $\dot{Z}n^+$. This process is endothermic, the energy absorbed being U. Electron exchange between ions enables the free valencies to propagate through the crystal: $\dot{O}^- + O^{2-} \rightarrow O^{2-} + \dot{O}^-$; $\dot{Z}n^+ + Zn^{2+} \rightarrow \dot{Z}n^{2+} + Zn^+$. The original ions $\dot{Z}n^+\ \dot{O}^-$ thus migrate rapidly. After a sufficient time the ions encounter one another again, and the reverse exothermic process may occur: $\dot{O}^- + \dot{Z}n^+ \rightarrow O^{2-} + Zn^{2+}$. The electron returns to the initial stable state, and U is liberated. Thus crystal surfaces always have some free valencies, due to thermal agitation. The surface concentration of such free valencies is defined by the equilibrium $O^{2-} + Zn^{2+} \rightleftharpoons \dot{O}^- + \dot{Z}n^+ - U$.

This picture is somewhat naive, since such processes strictly form part of semiconductor theory, where the problem is considered quantum-mechanically (band theory of semiconductors, see [18–21] for instance). According to this theory, the lattice excitation is described more correctly as an electron transfer from the bound zones to the conduction band, leaving behind a "hole", i.e. a state lacking one electron. The electrical conductivity of a semiconductor is determined by the motions both of the electrons in the conduction band and of the "holes" (which latter correspond to the motion of positive charges), under an applied electric field. The electrons in the conduction band and the holes are not considered as being localized on any particular ions, but as constituting a continuum throughout the whole crystal. If some atom or molecule approaches the crystal surface, however, an ion will interact with it, and either an electron or a hole will become localized on that ion as a result; the ion is thus transformed to $\dot{Z}n^+$ (or $\dot{O}^-$) with a probability $N\sigma$, where σ is the area occupied by one ion, and N is the number of electrons or holes per cm^3.

The chemical-type mechanism given above, with the ion radicals $\dot{Z}n^+$ and $\dot{O}^-$ in a sense is the result of some particle interacting with the ions at the crystal surface; in practice, the result is identical with that from a quantum-mechanical treatment, and so its use is permissible. In both treatments excitation of one electron gives two surface free valencies.*

The energy required to produce two surface free valencies is considerably less than that to dissociate molecules of the starting material into free radicals in the gas phase, as we shall presently proceed to demonstrate. We may expect that this will result in the surface having an important influence on the gas-phase processes.

In order better to explain the catalytic mechanism at the walls, (i.e. the production of free valencies), we shall use a very simple example. It is scarcely to be doubted that if the walls were coated with atoms of some active metal (sodium, say) which were not chemically bound to the wall, then upon collision with a molecule such as Cl_2 impinging from the gas phase the reaction

$$Na + Cl_2 \rightarrow NaCl + Cl \qquad (3)$$

would occur, in a manner analogous to that of Na and Cl_2 in the gas phase. $[Cl]_{gas}$ would then be higher than the equilibrium value, exactly as in the photodecomposition of chlorine. AVRAMENKO et al. [22] have assumed that, when ethyl chloride reacts with a sodium-lead alloy, a process of this type gives tetraethyl lead:

$$C_2H_5Cl + (Na) \rightarrow C_2H_5 + NaCl \qquad (4)$$

The ethyl radical then combines with the lead, giving a metallo-organic compound.

* VOLKENSHTEIN [19–21] has developed a theory of adsorption and catalysis from the band theory of solids. SEMENOV and VOEVODSKII have developed the concept of wall generation of free radicals, and expressed corresponding ideas about catalysis, starting from the simplified concepts given above.

In a precisely analogous fashion a chlorine molecule may collide with some spot on the surface where a free valency is located, and react as below:

$$V + Cl_2 \rightarrow VCl + Cl + q_1 \tag{5}$$

A chlorine atom is thereby returned to the gas phase. ε_0 for (5) is in all probability quite small, as in all radical reactions. This is one reason why radicals can be produced easily at surfaces.

The mechanism symbolized by (5) may be considered as being the following. Cl_2 collides with an ion radical $\dot{Z}n^+O^{2-}$, giving a compound with the surface $Cl^-Zn^{2+}O^{2-}$, the other chlorine atom being returned to the gas, the energy absorbed being equal to the difference between the energy Q_{V-Cl} of the $Cl^- Zn^{2+}$ bond and $Q_{Cl-Cl} : q_1 = Q_{V-Cl} - Q_{Cl-Cl}$. The surface free valency may be said to have disappeared, and to have been replaced by that of the chlorine atom.

The surface compound $\begin{matrix} Cl^- \\ | \\ Zn^{2+}O^{2-} \end{matrix}$ (or $\begin{matrix} Cl \\ | \\ Zn^+O^{2-} \end{matrix}$ if the bond should be homopolar) will be represented by VCl. The non-excited lattice elements will be denoted by V_2 ($= Zn^{2+}O^{2-}$). The excitation $Zn^{2+}O^{2-} \rightarrow Zn^+O^-$ is then:

$$V_2 \rightarrow 2V - U$$

When a chlorine atom collides with a site where there is no free valency, the surface chain-terminating reaction

$$V_2 + Cl \rightarrow VCl + V + q_2 \tag{6}$$

may occur: Cl is then chemisorbed, and a surface free valence is produced.* In order to form a picture of the process, we may suppose that Cl causes the transfer of one electron from O^{2-} as it approaches the surface, and the complex $\begin{matrix} Cl \\ Zn^{2+}\dot{O}- \end{matrix}$ $\left(\text{or } \begin{matrix} Cl \\ Zn^+\dot{O}- \end{matrix} \right)$ is formed, depending on whether a heteropolar or homopolar bond is energetically the more favoured. q_2 is given by $q_2 = Q_{V-Cl} - U$, where U is the excitation energy of the crystal lattice, as above.

When equilibrium is attained, then the reverse reactions in (5) and (6) must occur. The reactions $V + Cl \rightarrow VCl$ (the combination of a free atom and a free valency) and $VCl \rightarrow V + Cl$ (dissociation of VCl

---

* This may possibly occur in two stages: (a) the chlorine atom collides with the surface, and is bound by relatively weak forces; a one-electron bond may be formed, liberating a few kilocalories (according to VOLKENSHTEIN); (b) the chlorine atom may either escape from this weakly bound state, or form VCl by surmounting the potential barrier, and thus be truly chemisorbed.

into an atom and a free valency) must be possible. At equilibrium we then have four forward and four reverse reactions:

$$Cl_2 + V \rightleftharpoons Cl + VCl + q_1 \tag{5}$$

with
$$q_1 = Q_{V-Cl} - Q_{Cl-Cl} \tag{6}$$

$$Cl + V_2 \rightleftharpoons VCl + V + q_2$$

with
$$q_2 = Q_{V-Cl} - U$$

$$V + Cl \rightleftharpoons VCl + Q_{V-Cl}$$

$$V + V \rightleftharpoons V_2 + U$$

From these equations it is not difficult to derive the relation between [Cl] and the surface concentrations [V], [VCl] and [V_2] on the assumption that their sum is constant, i.e. that all sites are occupied either by V, VCl or V_2. [VCl] is defined by:

$$\frac{[VCl]}{[V_2]^{1/2}[Cl_2]^{1/2}} = C \exp\left[\frac{-\frac{1}{2}(U + Q_{Cl-Cl}) + Q_{V-Cl}}{RT}\right]$$

The constant C includes the S/V ratio for the vessel.

This expression shows that the concentration of chemisorbed chlorine atoms, [VCl], will be higher if the V—Cl bond is stronger. If the bond is very strong, Q_{V-Cl} is considerably greater than U and Q_{Cl-Cl} and [VCl] will be so great that the whole surface will be covered by a chemisorbed layer. In such a case (5) will be exothermic, and will take place very readily. This will mean that the surface will be rapidly covered by [VCl], and that [V] will be very small. It then becomes impossible to maintain the generation of free chlorine atoms. If, on the other hand, Q_{V-Cl} becomes much less than Q_{Cl-Cl}, [VCl] will be low. The walls will remain clean, but (5) will be strongly endothermic, and the steady-state value of [Cl] will again be low, since the rate of generation will be low. Thus for any given value of U (less than Q_{Cl-Cl}) the rate of production of chlorine atoms will be maximal at some value of Q_{V-Cl} less than Q_{Cl-Cl} (but not too small by comparison with Q_{Cl-Cl}). Consequently, not every type of wall will be an effective producer of free radicals. In practice, though, since the various parts of any surface are not identical, different areas will have different values of Q_{V-Cl}, and the surface activity will thus be defined (for any given U) by the relative proportion of surface which has the optimum Q_{V-Cl}.[*]

---

[*] The above account neglects the entropy changes associated with these surface effects. Thus, if chlorine atoms formed in the gas are absorbed by the wall, a substantial reduction in entropy occurs; this renders the chemisorbed state much less probable, and [VCl]$_{eq}$ is consequently reduced.

4. RADICAL PRODUCTION AT ACTIVE SURFACES

If there is to be an intensive production of radicals at any surface, the most essential requirement is that the surface should have a comparatively low U. The condition for vigorous generation of chlorine atoms by the wall is $U < Q_{Cl-Cl}$. If on the other hand $U > Q_{Cl-Cl}$, homogeneous dissociation will be more favoured.

U if fairly small for crystals such as $Zn^{2+}O^{2-}$, (a typical semi-conductor), being about 1–2 eV, i.e. 20–50 kcal. This relates to the general body of the crystal, but U may be even lower at the surface. It may be shown from semiconductor theory that [V] is given by $C \exp(-U/2RT)$, where $C \simeq 10^{13}$ cm^{-2} [19, 21]. Since some 10^{13} particles are present per cm^2, the fraction occupied by free valencies is $\alpha = 10^{-2} \exp(-U/2RT)$. If q_1 in (5) is -10 kcal then, supposing that $\varepsilon_0 \simeq 0$, and that the number of collisions on 1 cm^2/sec at atmospheric pressure is $v/4$, $[Cl_2] \simeq 10^4 \times 10^{19} = 10^{23}$; then the number of Cl atoms produced per second by 1 cm^2 is

$$J = 10^{23} \times 10^{-2} \exp(-U/2RT) \exp(-10,000/RT)$$
$$= 10^{21} \exp\left[-(\tfrac{1}{2}U + 10,000)/RT\right]$$

If $U \approx 1$ eV $= 23$ kcal, and $T = 600°$K, then

$$J = 10^{21} \exp(-21,000/1200) \simeq 10^{13 \cdot 5}$$

MARKEVICH's data [4] give 10^{11} for glass walls [1]. The rate at which Cl atoms are produced per cm^3 by $Cl_2 + M \rightarrow Cl + Cl + M - 57$ kcal is not greater than 10^7/sec. S/V is usually about 1 (for a cylinder of internal diameter 3 cm, $S/V = 4/3$). Under the above conditions, the rate at which the walls generate chlorine atoms is 3×10^4 times as great as that in the gas. If U had been taken as 1·5 eV, then the rates would have been in the 300 : 1 at atmospheric pressure, and the wall rate would be 100 times lower than at $U = 1$ eV.

If $q_1 = 0$, and if $\varepsilon = 3$ kcal in (5), then the wall rate at $U = 1·5$ eV will be 10^5 times greater than that in the gas, i.e. it will increase by a factor of 300. At $\varepsilon = 3$ kcal and $U = 2$ eV the surface will produce Cl atoms at a rate of the same order as that in the gas. This latter result is not surprising, since under these conditions the difference between Q_{Cl-Cl} (57 kcal) and Q_{V-V} (46 kcal) is not great.

It is not necessarily true, however, that materials with very high U cannot produce chlorine atoms. In fact, the structure is not absolutely regular in real crystal, and various kinds of defects (e.g. vacant lattice sites) are present, such as missing O^{2-} ions at some positions. U may be much reduced as compared with its value in an ideal crystal in the neighbourhood of such a defect. This means that each such defect is a free valency. In our approximate picture, the absence of one O^{2-} ion renders the neighbouring ions singly charged. Clearly, such defects may migrate throughout the crystal and surface free valencies may thus be found. Such surfaces will then act as sources of chlorine atoms. Geometrical conditions permitting, it is probable that the defects will be filled by tightly bound chlorine atoms during the reaction. However, the chlorine atoms will tend to migrate into the crystal, due to internal defects, or wall porosity, and this will free the surface to continue the action until the whole crystal mass is saturated with chlorine. Such a "defective" wall may continue to act as a source of chlorine atoms for a long time, even at low temperatures, until it becomes completely poisoned.

The problem previously considered concerned chlorination reactions. The wall may be equally effective in producing other free radicals, e.g. by abstracting hydrogen from an alcohol, a hydrocarbon, etc., and may initiate a variety of chain reactions. The passage of radicals into the gas may be more or less rapid, depending on the bond-dissociation energies and heats of chemisorption involved. In hydrocarbons a hydrogen atom may naturally be abstracted by an O^{2-} ion (but not by Zn^{2+}) to form a bond of hydroxyl type:

$$Zn^{2+}O^- + RH \rightarrow Zn^{2+}O^-\text{---}H + R, \text{ or } Zn^{2+}O^2\text{-}H + R$$

the hydrocarbon radical R being then transferred into the gas. Active surfaces are found not only in ZnO, but also in many other dielectrics and semiconductors. Any active surface will act as a source of free radicals to a greater or lesser extent. By an active surface is meant one on a crystal for which U is substantially less than Q for a molecule $\rightarrow$ radical transition or else for which U may be high but which contains a sufficiently large number of defects.

5. HETEROGENEOUS PRODUCTION OF RADICALS WHEN GASEOUS ADMIXTURES ARE PRESENT

Even if the walls do not affect the reactants directly, they may still substantially assist initiation by impurities. For example, hydroperoxides (bond energy 45–50 kcal) may not dissociate sufficiently rapidly in the gas, and may thus be removed without giving free radicals. They may produce free radicals readily at the wall: $V + ROOH \rightarrow VOOH + R$.

The promotion of hydrocarbon reactions by traces of oxygen may be explained by some analogous mechanism. O_2 may be supposed to react with the surface: $V + O_2 \rightarrow VOO\text{---}$; the surface then acts as a strong peroxide radical, $VOO\text{---}$. If hydrocarbons are present this radical may react, giving VOOH and R.

The catalytic action of oxygen in the pyrolyses of organic compounds is recorded in the literature. Small amounts of oxygen usually increase the rate of decomposition, but only within certain limits. The rate becomes concentration-independent at high O_2 concentrations. The effect of small amounts of oxygen may be explained by its influence on heterogeneous chain initiation. Furthermore, direct experiment shows that on filling the vessel with oxygen, followed by pumping-out, the rate at which *tert.*-butyl chloride decomposes is increased, while the admission of oxygen with the butyl chloride is without effect. Poltorak also demonstrated [23] that oxygen catalysis in the cracking of propane depends very greatly on the state of the walls and the treatment they have received. Thus the initial rate in propane containing 2 per cent of oxygen was 4 times greater in a vessel treated with hydrogen fluoride than in one having walls covered with a film of carbide.

The retarding action of some compounds on hydrocarbon transformations (e.g. of NO on cracking) is also characterized by saturation. This has an important bearing on the assumption that they act heterogeneously. The explanation usually given for saturation is that there are two possible reaction mechanisms —by chain reaction, and in the molecular way—but in our opinion this is in general unlikely.

The action of NO is apparently connected with its radical properties: by occupying all the active sites it prevents chains starting at the walls. Conversely, in the presence of oxygen NO will catalyse the reaction. As was shown by POLTORAK [23], NO reacts with oxygen under these conditions, and this gives a heterogeneous production of radicals. If the walls are treated with MoO_3, which readily donates an oxygen atom, then the retarding action of NO is abolished.

Some cases of "after-effect" in systems subsequent to extensive chain initiation also belong to the class of heterogeneous initiations. KALINENKO [24] showed that, in the low-temperature oxidation of propane, catalysed by Br and light, the reaction continued at a comparable rate for some tens of minutes when the light had been cut off, although the dark reaction did not occur in practice under these conditions. This effect was shown by direct measurement to be due to Br atoms on the walls. Using flow methods it was found that the walls remained active for 2–3 hr in the dark.

Surface effects are likewise responsible for chlorine catalysis in the oxidation of propane under flow conditions. ÉMANUEL [25] found that the rate was enhanced for a long time after cutting off the chlorine, even in the dark. These effects may be explained as due to halogen atoms penetrating fairly deeply into the walls. This naturally alters the rate of chain generation at the walls, since the surface properties are altered. Above all, the effect arises from changes in the energy-level distribution; surface free valencies are produced more readily, and the rates of gas reactions are raised.

6. HETEROGENEOUS MOLECULAR REACTIONS GIVING FREE RADICALS

It was concluded from the discussion of wall effects in the reaction between pure chlorine and hydrogen that the wall does not influence the equilibrium $Cl_2 \rightleftharpoons 2Cl$, and thus the reaction rate. This rule applies in general, if no irreversible changes occur at the walls or in the gas in the stages leading to the terminal products. If the chemisorption is irreversible, it may lead to $[Cl]_{gas}$ being greater than the equilibrium value. But if it is not reversible, then once the whole wall has become covered it ceases to exert any further influence.

It was also shown that the wall accelerates the reverse process if the gas contains some impurity which removes Cl atoms irreversibly (e.g. oxygen). Even in the pure gases the non-reversible process $H + Cl \rightarrow HCl$ terminates chains, as does the reversible process $Cl + Cl \rightarrow Cl_2$. On account of the low steady state $[H]$ in this reaction, the rate of the non-reversible reaction is low. Although this only accounts for a small part of the chlorine atoms removed, it nevertheless reduces $[Cl]$ below the equilibrium value, and the wall thus has a slight accelerating effect even in the pure gases.

The treatment given for the Cl–wall interaction may not be quite complete if H_2 is present. Another reaction which can also occur is $H_2 + Cl_2 \rightarrow HCl + H + Cl - 58$ kcal. Since this is so strongly endothermic, it can play no real part in the gas reaction, but at the walls (supposed once more to consist of $Zn^{2+}O^{2-}$) it may absorb much less energy, on account of the energy Q liberated by adsorption of the H atom:

$$Zn^{2+}O^{2-} + H_2 + Cl_2 \rightarrow Zn^+O^- + H + HCl + Cl - U + Q_{O-H} -$$
$$- 58 \text{ kcal (7)}$$

The chlorine atom is returned to the gas, and $\dot{Z}n^+$ is formed in the surface. The O—H bond binding the chemisorbed H atom to the surface is certainly weaker than ordinary O—H bonds in alcohols (100–110 kcal); but Q_{O-H} may still be quite considerable, perhaps as large as 60 kcal. If $U = 40$ kcal, then $Q = Q_{O-H} - U = 20$ kcal, and the process giving Zn^+ and Cl^- will only be endothermic by $58-20 = 38$ kcal. The rate of such a process can thus be fairly large, although it will evidently be lower than that of (5). However, (7) may be the preferred one, being related to the irreversible formation of HCl, whereas (5) reverses. This will cause $[Cl]_{gas}$ to be greater than the gas equilibrium value, and also causes [V] to be greater than corresponds to the equilibrium $V_2 \rightleftharpoons 2V$.

The above hypothesis that non-equilibrium processes cause free radical generation at the walls, either from the starting materials or from the intermediate products, is of some value, since such processes are present in many reactions (see also [1]).

7. APPLICATION OF THE ABOVE CONCEPTS TO HETEROGENEOUS CATALYSIS

As was demonstrated above (Chapter 5), solutions containing ions of variable valency may produce free radicals, and thereby initiate free radical reactions in the solute.

The surfaces of metals and semiconductors may similarly initiate free radical reactions to a greater or lesser extent, since such surfaces may readily produce free valencies,

Initiations at semiconductor surfaces occur via

(1) $A_2 + V \rightarrow AV + A$.

A molecule A_2 from the gas phase collides with the surface at a point where there is a free valency, and a free radical is formed. The number of free valencies per cm^2 is given by $n = C \exp(-U/2RT)$ where $C = 10^{13}$ cm^{-2}.

If $T = 600°K$ and $U = 23$ kcal, then $n \simeq 10^9$. Then the fraction of surface occupied by free valencies is $10^9/10^{15} = 10^{-6}$. The free valency concentrations in dielectrics and semiconductors are comparatively small.

It is not essential that A should return immediately to the gas phase. It may remain bound by weak bonds, e.g. the one-electron bonds proposed by VOLKENSHTEIN [26]. If this bond energy is small (substantially less than 10 kcal), then the bound atom (A), will be freed after a certain interval:

(A) $\rightarrow A - q$.

(A) may also react on release from the bound state:

(2) $(A) + AV \rightarrow A_2 + V$

or (3) $(A) + V_2 \rightarrow AV + V$.

Not every atom formed in (1) will therefore be returned as such to the gas phase. At equilibrium the converse processes will also happen, and thus the detailed nature of the reactions will not materially affect the volume concentration of atoms.

The assumptions just made must be considerably revised if some other gas B_2 is present which can take part in the various reactions and also react non-reversibly with A:

(1') $B_2 + V \rightarrow BV + (B)$,

(2') $(B) + BV \rightarrow B_2 + V$,

(3') $(B) + V_2 \rightarrow BV + V$.

(A) may be transported across the surface, and react with BV, or (B) may react with AV:

(4) $(A) + B \rightarrow AB + V$,

(4') $(B) + AV \rightarrow AB + V$.

(4) and (4') are non-reversible under these conditions, in so far as they give terminal products. They reduce the concentrations of (A) and (B), and consequently reduce the amounts of A and B transferred to the bulk phase, but a heterogeneous reaction is still going on at the crystal surface.

If the gases are also "physically" absorbed on the surface, as (A_2) and (B_2), then reactions of the standard chain type may occur along the surface:

(5) $(A) + (B_2) \rightarrow AB + (B)$,

(5') $(B) + (A_2) \rightarrow AB + (A)$, etc.

provided that reactions of types (3) and (3') do not terminate the chains. Nevertheless the system (1), (1'), (3), (3'), (4), (4'), may constitute a self-sustaining chain reaction, in which wall free valencies are one active type of chain centre. Chains of this type are terminated by one of the following free valency combination processes:

(6) $(A) + (A) \rightarrow A_2$,

(6') $(B) + (B) \rightarrow B_2$,

(7) $(A) + (B) \rightarrow AB$,

(8) $V + V \rightarrow V_2$.

The interrelations of the two types of chain are worth noting. Termination of normal chains (reactions (3) and (3')) gives centres active for the second type of chain, since free valencies V are formed.

If the bonds A—V and B—V are very strong, (3) and (3') are more rapid than (4) and (4'), so chemisorbed particles AV and BV are formed in preference to terminal products such as AB. This will continue until almost the whole surface is covered by chemisorbed atoms. In a short while the free portion will become so small that (1) and (1') will be very slow, and the catalytic action of the surface will approach vanishing point.

Conversely, if the bonds A—V and B—V are very weak, then the heat values of (1) and (1') will also be small, since $q_1 = Q_{A-V} - Q_{A-A}$ and $q_1' = Q_{B-V} - Q_{B-B}$, where Q_{A-V} and Q_{B-V} are the energies of the bonds A—V and B—V. Since Q_{A-A} may be fairly large q_1 and q_1' may be negative, and the activation energies of (1) and (1') will be extremely large, their rates small and the catalytic activity low.

Thus for any pair of values of Q_{A-A} and Q_{B-B} the surface must have some quite definite values of Q_{A-V} and Q_{B-V}, which may be neither too large nor too small, if its catalytic activity is to be optimal.

Small amounts of certain specific substances added to semiconductors frequently change the conductivities. This is due to the heteroatoms being always either electron donors or electron acceptors, thus producing more electrons or holes (i.e. a number of free valencies) respectively. In the latter case U would be reduced. Other lattice defects, e.g. missing atoms at various sites, have a similar effect. The action of promoters could be explained in this way, as also the differences between different catalyst preparations.

The number of free valencies per unit area of crystal surface is determined by the bulk properties since the free valencies can migrate.

The view that catalysis takes place via radicals was recently developed by VOLKENSHTEIN [27], who first proposed a number of hypotheses on this topic, and also by SEMENOV and VOEVODSKII [28]. Latterly ROGINSKII has demonstrated that heterogeneous processes are difficult to explain without supposing that radicals and surface chains are involved in catalysis.

The concepts previously developed will now be applied to catalysis by metals. The electrons in metals are not localized, no particular electron being assigned to any given atom. The energy levels of the electron-cloud are extremely closely spaced, and the filled levels are directly contiguous with the unfilled levels. Consequently some electrons readily undergo thermal excitation to vacant levels, and this is responsible for the high electrical conductivity of metals. Since an uncoupled electron in the free state may be excited to the higher vacant levels, the metal is similar to a polyvalent free radical. This is also responsible for the ease with which the metal surface and adsorbed molecules react, in a manner similar to free radicals and molecules: $Na + Cl_2 \rightarrow NaCl + Cl$.

The interactions between the electrons in metals are extremely strong, and comparable with those between the electrons and the ions, giving high heats of sublimation and work-functions for metals. A metallic surface resembles a radical of fairly low activity, and the energy required to excite an electron to the active-valence state is extremely large. The active-valence state is here one in which the electron is in effect localized near a particular atom. This excitation involves breaking the conjugation with all the other electrons in the metal. Metal surfaces are in this sense like the weak radicals allyl or NO, where the interaction of the free electron with the other electrons and the atomic cores (i.e. the conjugation) is strong.

Unlike semiconductor surfaces, metallic surfaces act as though completely covered with free valencies. This results in (1) being greatly accelerated:

$$(1) \quad A_2 + V \rightarrow AV + A.$$

The second difference from semiconductors is that (3) does not occur with metals, since all the atoms in the metal are in principle free radicals. The concept of V_2 is also not involved, since it applies to surfaces having no free valencies. The process $A + V \rightarrow AV$ (2″) is extremely rare in semiconductors, since [V] is extremely small, but becomes the exclusive one here; like all radical combinations, it is always exothermic, and the activation energy, if appreciable at all, is very small. Hence the radical A produced by (1) is in practice at once taken up by the metal surface; which is equivalent to the chemisorption of A_2 in two stages:

$$(1) \quad A_2 + V \rightarrow AV + A$$

and (2) $A + V \rightarrow AV.$

the net reaction being $A_2 + 2V \rightarrow 2AV.$

When some other gas B_2 is introduced, both A_2 and B_2 will be chemisorbed as above, and virtually no reaction can occur, since $A + BV \rightarrow AB + V$ and $B + AV \rightarrow AB + V$ cannot commence. However, as [AV] and [BV] increase, a state will eventually be reached where A is formed directly beside a site BV; and in order to react with V as in (2″) the atom must diffuse a certain distance to find a free site. The diffusion time τ will increase as the proportion of the surface taken up by occupied sites increases. During the time τ (4) and (4′) may occur, and if the fraction covered is sufficiently large, catalytic action can take place.

As with semiconductors, if Q_{A-V} and Q_{B-V} are too great, reaction will be impeded, since practically the whole surface will be covered by occupied sites, and virtually no free sites will remain at which (1) $(A_2 + V \rightarrow AV + A)$ can occur. On the other hand, if the bonds are too weak the catalysed reaction will be unable to proceed, since q_1 will be reduced (if Q_{A-V} is low, q_1 may be negative). This implies

that ε for (1) will be greatly increased. Thus in metals conditions are the most favourable for some intermediate Q_{A-V}, exactly as in semiconductors. The presence of "physical" adsorption may cause propagation of chains, as with semiconductors: $(A) + (B_2) \rightarrow AB + (B)$; $(B) + (A_2) \rightarrow AB + (A)$, etc.

Lattice defects such as peaks, foreign atoms and vacant sites will have an important influence on the rate of reaction, since all such defects affect L, the energy of the non-localized electrons. The q-values of all the various processes may also be affected, particularly via Q_{A-V}. The heats of chemisorption and the activation energies will not be constant at all points on the surface. Reaction will occur preferentially on those parts having most favourable values of Q_{A-V} and Q_{B-V}.

All the ideas so far discussed can only constitute a first approximation to the real state of affairs; but they probably form a suitable basis for a theory capable of explaining some types of catalytic processes. In particular, since only elementary reactions have been considered, and no account has been taken of the regularities of overall reactions, some phenomena (e.g. modification effects) cannot be explained.

Radical catalysis was illustrated above in the transfer reaction $A_2 + B_2 \rightarrow 2AB$. Additions are of greater practical interest, the hydrogenation of ethylene being one of the simplest of these. Radical-catalysed additions do not differ essentially in mechanism from substitutions. There are some special features, all the same. In substitution, A_2 gave AV upon reacting with V (A being chemisorbed), and a second atom A very weakly bound to the surface, having properties usually associated with free radicals. Compounds with double bonds react with free valencies to give free radicals, but one end of such a free radical is firmly bound to the surface by a chemical bond: $C_2H_4 + V \rightarrow VCH_2$—$CH_2$—. Radicals thus chemisorbed may react in a variety of ways.

First mode: the radical reacts with V_2: VCH_2—CH_2— $+ V_2 \rightarrow VCH_2CH_2V + V$, giving a strongly chemisorbed ethylene molecule.

Second mode: the chemisorbed radical reacts with a hydrogen molecule, either impinging on the surface or else already bound by physical adsorption: VCH_2CH_2— $+ H_2 \rightarrow VCH_2CH_3 + H$. A radical CH_2CH_3 bound to V in the same way as an atom is formed. The H atom also produced either attacks the C—V bond holding the radical at once, liberating the surface free valency and forming C_2H_6.

(9) $H + CH_2CH_3V \rightarrow CH_3CH_3 + V$,

or else reacts with the surface

$$H + V_2 \rightarrow VH + V$$

This regenerates the surface free valency as well as giving a chemisorbed hydrogen atom. The surface will eventually become covered with chemisorbed particles: hydrogen atoms, ethyl radicals and ethylene molecules. But the more surface thus occupied, the more readily (9) and $H + VCH_2CH_2V \rightarrow VCH_2CH_3 + V$ will take place. In addition, the greater the fraction of surface occupied, the more rapidly

$$VCH_2CH_2 + HV \rightarrow VCH_2CH_3 + V$$

will give ethyl radicals. The totality of such processes will lead to a quasi-steady state being established, and the ethylene will hydrogenate at some definite rate.

Under certain conditions, VCH_2CH_2— can react with ethylene molecules, dimers or trimers being formed.

Processes of this type commonly occur simultaneously with the main hydrogenation, and sometimes lead to the catalyst being poisoned. If the hydrocarbons are complex, the radical first formed probably defines the subsequent processes of isomerization, polymerization, and cyclization that can take place.

The following hypothetical scheme for hydrocarbon formation from CO and H_2 will repay study, as illustrating the principles set out above.

Catalytic syntheses, by which complex molecules are built up from simple ones, cannot be explained simply by adsorption forces acting on the particles of the starting materials. Organic chemists have frequently concluded that such reactions must involve free radical mechanisms. ZELINSKII and SHUIKIN [29] explained a number of organic reactions by the surface formation of the biradical CH_2. EIDUS and ZELINSKII [30] used this to explain the synthesis of hydrocarbons from CO and H_2. SEMENOV and VOEVODSKII demonstrated that the reaction scheme proposed by ZELINSKII and EIDUS could be derived without assuming high concentrations of CH_2 by supposing that the reactions involved univalent radicals, in which the free valencies could migrate. According to SEMENOV and VOEVODSKII, only one end need be attached to the surface when the formation was from simple gaseous molecules, the opposite end accumulating new links.

The following hypothetical scheme gives complex products from carbon monoxide and hydrogen:

(1) $V + CO \rightarrow VC{=}O$
    $\qquad\qquad\qquad\quad |$

(2) $VC{=}O + H_2 \rightarrow VC{=}O + H.$
    $\;\;|\qquad\qquad\qquad\;\; |$
    $\qquad\qquad\qquad\quad H$

The hydrogen atom derived from (2) either reacts directly with $VC=O$
$|$
H , to give a radical derived from methanol:

$$(3) \quad VC{=}O + H \quad \rightarrow \quad VC{-}OH$$
$$\quad\quad\;\; | \quad\quad\quad\quad\quad\quad\quad |$$
$$\quad\quad\;\; H \quad\quad\quad\quad\quad\quad\quad H$$

or else reacts with the surface, being chemisorbed and producing a surface free valency:

$$(3') \quad H + V_2 \rightarrow HV + V.$$

The radical in (3) reacts with H_2:

$$\quad\quad\quad\quad\quad\quad\quad\quad\quad\quad\quad H$$
$$\quad\quad\quad | \quad\quad\quad\quad\quad\quad\quad\quad |$$
$$(4) \quad VC{-}OH + H_2 \quad \rightarrow \quad VC{-}OH + H.$$
$$\quad\quad\quad | \quad\quad\quad\quad\quad\quad\quad\quad |$$
$$\quad\quad\quad H \quad\quad\quad\quad\quad\quad\quad\quad H$$

The atom then either attacks the C—O bond, giving H_2O and $VC{-}$ (with H above and H below):

$$\quad\quad\quad H \quad\quad\quad\quad\quad\quad\quad\quad H$$
$$\quad\quad\quad | \quad\quad\quad\quad\quad\quad\quad\quad |$$
$$(5) \quad VC{-}OH + H \quad \rightarrow \quad H_2O + VC{-}$$
$$\quad\quad\quad | \quad\quad\quad\quad\quad\quad\quad\quad\quad |$$
$$\quad\quad\quad H \quad\quad\quad\quad\quad\quad\quad\quad\quad H$$

or else attacks the V—C bond, giving one of the terminal products—methanol—frequently found in these syntheses:

$$\quad\quad\quad\quad\; H$$
$$\quad\quad\quad\quad\; |$$
$$(5') \quad H + VC{-}OH \quad \rightarrow \quad CH_3OH + V.$$
$$\quad\quad\quad\quad\; |$$
$$\quad\quad\quad\quad\; H$$

H
$|$
$VC{-}$ reacts in turn with CO:
$|$
H

$$\quad\quad\quad H \quad\quad\quad\quad\quad\quad H$$
$$\quad\quad\quad | \quad\quad\quad\quad\quad\quad |\quad |$$
$$(6) \quad VC{-} + CO \quad \rightarrow \quad V{-}C{-}C{=}O.$$
$$\quad\quad\quad | \quad\quad\quad\quad\quad\quad\quad |$$
$$\quad\quad\quad H \quad\quad\quad\quad\quad\quad\quad H$$

Alternation of (2), (3), (4), (5) and (6), will cause the carbon chain to grow, the hydrocarbon radical $V(CH_2)_n$— being formed. This radical will react with H_2 to give $V(CH_2)_{n-1}$—CH_3 + H. The latter atom will attack the V—C bond, forming an alkane, $CH_3(CH_2)_{n-2}CH_3$ and freeing the surface valency. Collateral reactions such as (5′) will give higher alcohols.

The hydrogen atom captured by the surface in (3′) produces a site HV, so the whole surface will tend to become covered with chemisorbed hydrogen atoms and radicals derived from alcohols

$$\begin{matrix} & H \\ & | \\ \text{(such as } V\dot{C} & —OH). \\ & | \\ & H \end{matrix}$$

But when the fraction of surface covered be-

comes sufficiently large, the rate of (3′) will be reduced, while the hydrogen atoms will tend mainly to react as in (3), (5) and (5′). In addition, when [VH] is sufficiently large, the radicals formed in (3), (5) and (6) will react with VH as well as with H_2; this will free surface valencies, and some steady rate is attained.

8. HETEROGENEOUS CATALYSIS IN BIOLOGY

A great variety of chemical reactions in living organisms occur at the surfaces of highly specialized catalysts (enzymes). All enzymes so far studied chemically are either pure proteins, or proteins complexed with non-protein prosthetic groups. Biocatalysis is therefore essentially heterogeneous catalysis at protein molecule surfaces. Consider, for instance, tissue respiration processes, which form the main energy source. The net reaction is that hydrogen is transferred from a substrate to atmospheric oxygen, water being formed; but many distinct steps are involved before the potential energy is entirely released. Some of these steps are hydrogen transfers between components of the main oxidation pathway, others are electron transfers. It was long ago concluded that these reactions can occur in cells without direct contact between the reacting molecules; we should also remember that the energy produced does not appear as heat but is used to drive endothermic reactions, e.g. the production of the ATP required for muscular contraction. The efficiency of this transfer is very high, perhaps as much as 85 per cent. If the energy transfer was direct at least six reacting molecules would have to collide simultaneously, two of these being high-polymer ones. These data, together with some from photosynthesis and muscular contraction, force us to assume that energy migrates in biological systems.

In 1941 SZENT-GYÖRGYI [31] proposed an electronic energy

migration mechanism, drawing an analogy between proteins and metals. However, simple calculations and data on the electrical conductivities of protein films and on protein fluorescence spectra showed that the conduction bands in protein structures, if existing at all, must lie at least 3–4 eV above the valence bands and must therefore be empty at the temperatures found in organisms. Other energy migrations mechanisms so far proposed are purely hypothetical.

In 1954 COMMONER et al. [32] observed relatively high unpaired electron concentrations of 10^{-6}–10^{-8} M in freeze-dried animal and plant tissues by EPR methods; subsequently BLYUMENFEL'D [33] has shown that these unpaired electrons do not belong to simple free radicals or ions of variable valency, but to the enzyme proteins themselves, but are present only while enzymatic processes are occurring. The lack of hyperfine splitting and the narrowness of the EPR spectra indicate that the unpaired electrons are very much delocalized in the protein structure. It is supposed that conduction channels run along hydrogen bond chains transverse to the main polypeptide chains (see diagram).

During enzyme catalysis the substrate forms a temporary complex with the enzyme (or with its prosthetic group, in some cases), and acts as an impurity with inherent electron levels lying near the conduction or valence bands of the protein. Unlike in ordinary semi-conductors, these bands are here very narrow (a few tenths of an electron-volt), so the complex can be considered as an impurity semi-conductor of n- or p-type. An electron which enters the conduction band cannot transfer to the completely filled valence band and so will migrate along the hydrogen bond chains until it falls into the acceptor trap formed by the complex. Hence redox reactions can be effected at a distance, no direct molecular contact being involved. The endothermic reactions may be supposed coupled to conduction bands containing excess unpaired electron concentrations produced by exothermic processes.

BLYUMENFEL'D and KALMANSON's work [34, 35] on the EPR spectra of free radicals formed by γ-irradiation in aminoacids, peptides, and native and denatured proteins has shown that the unpaired electrons can be delocalized in the protein structure, and that this effect is closely related to the regular hydrogen bond network being preserved. Very recently COMMONER [36], using model oxidative enzyme processes, has observed two types of EPR spectrum from simple intermediate products of semi-quinone type and a single signal from complex molecules, of semi-conductor type. These data are the first direct evidence for the role of semi-conducting properties in heterogeneous catalyses in biological systems. It is very likely that similar methods would also be highly productive if applied to normal surface catalytic reactions.

REFERENCES

1. V. V. VOEVODSKII. *Dokl. Akad. Nauk SSSR* **90**, 815 (1953).
2. YU. B. KHARITON and Z. VALTA. *Z. Phys.* **39**, 547 (1926); N. N. SEMENOV. *Zh. Rusk. Fiz.-Khim. Obshch. Chast Fiz.* **58**, 329 (1926); N. N. SEMENOV. *Chain Reactions.* Leningrad 1934. (In Russian.) Translated and revised as *Chemical Kinetics and Chain Reactions.* Oxford 1935.
3. A. TRIFONOV. *Z. phys. Chem.* **B3**, 195 (1929).
4. A. M. MARKEVICH. *Zh. Fiz. Khim.* **22**, 941 (1948).
5. A. M. CHAIKIN. Candidate's dissertation, Moscow State University (1955).
6. M. V. POLYAKOV. *Usp. Khim.* **17**, 351 (1948).
7. A. A. KOVALSKII and M. L. BOGOYAVLENSKAYA. *Zh. Fiz. Khim.* **20**, 1325 (1946).
8. D. H. R. BARTON and K. E. HOWLETT. *J. Chem. Soc.* 155 (1949).
9. A. MACCOLL and P. J. THOMAS. *J. Chem. Phys.* **19**, 977 (1951).
10. G. K. LAVROVSKAYA and V. V. VOEVODSKII. *Zh. Fiz. Khim.* **25**, 1050 (1951).
11. G. K. LAVROVSKAYA and V. V. VOEVODSKII. *Zh. Fiz. Khim.* **26**, 1164 (1952).
12. A. B. NALBANDYAN and S. M. SHUBINA. *Zh. Fiz. Khim.* **20**, 1249 (1946).
13. A. E. BIRON and A. B. NALBANDYAN. *Acta phys.-Chim. URSS* **6**, 43 (1937).
14. L. I. AVRAMENKO. *Zh. Fiz. Khim.* **23**, 790 (1949). English translation: *Can. Nat. Res. Coun.* TT-123 (1950).
15. Z. K. MAIZUS, A. M. MARKEVICH and N. M. ÈMANUEL. *Dokl. Akad. Nauk SSSR* **89**, 1049 (1953).
16. V. I. URIZKO and M. V. POLYAKOV. *Dokl. Akaá. Nauk SSSR* **95**, 1293 (1954).
17. A. M. MARKEVICH. *Zh. Fiz. Khim.* **30**, 735 (1956).
18. F. F. VOLKENSHTEIN. *Electrical Conductivity of Semiconductors.* Gostekhizdat 1947. (In Russian.)
19. F. F. VOLKENSHTEIN. *Zh. Fiz. Khim.* **27**, 159 (1953).
20. F. F. VOLKENSHTEIN. *Zh. Fiz. Khim.* **27**, 167 (1953).
21. F. F. VOLKENSHTEIN. *Zh. Fiz. Khim.* **26**, 1462 (1952).
22. L. I. AVRAMENKO, M. I. GERBER, M. B. NEIMAN and V. A. SHUSHUNOV. *Zh. Fiz. Khim.* **20**, 1347 (1946).
23. V. A. POLTORAK and V. V. VOEVODSKII. *Dokl. Akad. Nauk SSSR* **91**, 589 (1953).
24. R. A. KALINENKO. Thesis for Diploma. Moscow State University (1952).
25. N. M. ÈMANUEL and K. E. KRUGLYAKOVA. *Izv. Akad. Nauk SSSR. Otdel. Khim. Nauk* **1**, 18 (1957).
26. F. F. VOLKENSHTEIN. *Zh. Fiz. Khim.* **21**, 1317 (1947); *ibid.* **26**, 1462 (1952).

27. F. F. VOLKENSHTEIN. *Zh. Fiz. Khim.* **27**, 159, 167 (1953); *Usp. Fiz. Nauk* **50**, 253 (1953).
28. V. V. VOEODSKII, F. F. VOLKENSHTEIN and N. N. SEMENOV. *Symposium on Chemical Kinetics, Catalysis and Reactivity*, p. 423. Academy of Sciences of USSR, 1955.
29. N. D. ZELINSKII and N. I. SHUIKIN. *Dokl. Akad. Nauk SSSR* **3**, 255 (1934).
30. YA. T. EIDUS and N. D. ZELINSKII. *Izv. Akad. Nauk SSSR, Otdel. Khim. Nauk* 289 (1940); 190 (1942).
31. A. SZENT-GYÖRGYI. *Science* **93**, 609 (1941).
32. B. COMMONER, J. TOWNSEND and G. PAKE. *Nature, Lond.* **174**, 689 (1954).
33. L. A. BLYUMENFEL'D. *Izv. Akad. Nauk SSSR; ser. biol.* 285 (1957).
34. L. A. BLYUMENFEL'D and A. E. KALMANSON. *Biofizika* **2**, 552 (1957).
35. L. A. BLYUMENFEL'D and A. E. KALMANSON. *Dokl. Akad. Nauk SSSR* **117**, 72 (1957).
36. D. COMMONER. *Free radicals in biological systems.* Symposium Programme. Symposium on the Formation and Stabilization of Free Radicals. September, 1957.

PART III

KINETICS OF CHAIN REACTIONS

Chapter 7

CHAIN REACTIONS COMPETING WITH REACTIONS BETWEEN SATURATED MOLECULES

SIMPLE unimolecular or bimolecular reactions and chain reactions always occur simultaneously in every chemical system. The question is how their rates compare. In some cases the rate of a simple direct reaction may be so high relative to that of a chain reaction that the latter can be neglected, and vice versa. In other cases the rates of both do not appreciably differ. The rate of a simple direct reaction is that of separate molecular acts and consequently does not depend on the experimental conditions other than temperature and mixture concentration, whereas the chain reaction rate depends to a great extent on the experimental conditions, on small amounts of additives, on the admixture of inert gases, and so on. This occurs because many different factors influence chain initiation and termination. Therefore by changing the conditions we can also alter the balance between simple and chain reactions. For instance, ethyl bromide decomposes directly mainly to molecular products, but a very small amount of Br_2 (dissociating into atoms and favouring chain initiation) changes the reaction mechanism, initiating chain decomposition.

All the structurally possible chain reactions occur simultaneously in every chemical system, and not merely one such. The rates of these chain reactions usually differ greatly, one being as a rule predominant and determining the overall rate and the contents of intermediate and end-products. But sometimes another reaction may become predominant under different conditions, e.g. at a different temperature, and thus give other products. Intermediate zones are then observed where the various chain rates are similar and consequently many different products are formed. This will be illustrated further.

1. ENERGY DEPENDENCE OF CHAIN REACTIONS AND MOLECULAR REACTIONS

Both biradicals and normal molecules have even numbers of valence electrons, but their properties are quite different.

Thirty years ago, before the chain theory was proposed, the role of free radicals in chemical changes explained and current views on ionic processes were developed, almost all reactions were considered as being between stable molecules (both in gases and in liquids). Hence transfer reactions, such as $H_2 + I_2 \rightarrow 2HI$, $CH_3I + HI \rightarrow CH_4 + I_2$, decompositions, like $CH_3CHO \rightarrow CH_4 + CO$ and $C_2H_5Br \rightarrow C_2H_4 + HBr$, the cracking of hydrocarbons, and additions, e.g. $H_2 + C_2H_4 \rightarrow C_2H_6$. $I_2 + C_2H_4 \rightarrow C_2H_4I_2$ and $RH + O_2 \rightarrow RO_2H$, were all considered as reactions between stable molecules. The majority of gas phase reactions involve substantial activation energies, since the potential barrier height is about 30–50 kcal. This is greater than for free radical reactions by almost an order of magnitude, and the activation energy E, as well as the potential barrier height E_0, bear no relation to q. A few examples will be given to illustrate this.

Table 38. *Activation energies and heats of reaction for some molecular reactions*

Reaction	q (kcal)	E (kcal)	E_0 (kcal)	Reference
(1) $H_2 + I_2 \rightarrow 2HI$	+ 2	40	40	[1]
(2) $CH_3I + HI \rightarrow CH_4 + I_2$	+ 14	33	33	[1]
(3) $H_2 + C_2H_4 \rightarrow C_2H_6$	+ 32·5	43	43	[1]
(4) $C_2H_5Br \rightarrow C_2H_4 + HBr$	− 18	50	32	[2]
(5) $C_2H_5Cl \rightarrow C_2H_4 + HCl$	− 15	59	44	[2]
(6) $CH_3CHO \rightarrow CH_4 + CO$	+ 5·5	47	47	[3]
(7) $CH_3OCH_3 \rightarrow CH_4 + HCHO$	0	58	58	[1]
(8) $(CH_2)_2O \rightarrow CH_4 + CO$	+ 32	42	42	[43]

There is evidently no relation between E_0 and $|q|$: E_0 varies from 30 kcal even up to 60 kcal, quite independently of $|q|$.

Many of the E-values given above are likely to be too low, since a considerable part of the reactions proceed via free radical chains.

Every molecular reaction occurs via some transition state; energy is absorbed in forming this transition state, this energy being the activation energy for molecular decomposition. For endothermic reactions $E = E_0 + q'$, while for exothermic reactions $E = E_0$ (E_0 is the potential barrier height, and q' is the heat of reaction).

The relation $\varepsilon_0 = A - \alpha|q|$ was given for free radical reactions in Chapter 1, the changes in A being small as between one radical reaction and another; A is usually about 11 kcal, and α is close to 0·25. By virtue of the existence of this equation, we were able to presume that ε_0 was a function of the difference between the energies of the bonds formed and broken, to a first approximation. It is likely that an analogous equation exists for molecular decomposition: $E_0 = A' - \alpha'|q'|$; this also being approximate. q' is of the same order as in radical reactions—in most cases $q' > 20$–30 kcal. A' must therefore be several times greater than A. Even if the variations in $\Delta A'/A'$ are the same for varied molecular structures as $\Delta A/A$ for various radicals, then the variations in reaction rate will be much greater for molecular elimination reactions than for radical decompositions, since the rate changes will be defined by $\exp(\Delta A'/RT)$ and $\exp(\Delta A/RT)$ respectively. This implies that any change in A' has a much more marked effect on the molecular reaction rate than the corresponding change in A does on radical reactions and that changes in q' are very unimportant. The large changes in A' are due to at least two bonds being involved in activated complex formation, whereas only one is involved in radicals. The energy required to form the activated complex depends extraordinarily strongly on the geometrical relations of the reacting groups, and even a single change in the mutual spacing leads to a large change in A'. The ease with which the activated complex is formed depends more or less on the rigidities and bond energies, (and not merely on the difference between the bond energies, which defines q') of the initial and final molecules. Moreover, E_0 depends not only on the properties of the initial molecular bonds, but also on those of the product bonds. Thus E_0 depends very strongly on the structures of the initial and final molecules. The quantum-mechanical value for E_0 is extremely unreliable and to determine the activation energies of molecular reactions a very great deal of experimental data is required. To analyse the experimental data rigorously we should have to verify that the measured activation energy was the activation energy for the elementary act of primary molecular decomposition, and not the activation energy of the overall process, which may involve a chain-mechanism at some stage. While the way radical reaction theory will develop is clearly established only the first steps have yet been taken in the theory of molecular reactions.

What is the inertness of molecules due to? We might think that, as all the chemical forces in a molecule are satisfied, it would be relatively stable, and that it would therefore react only with difficulty, even though the net result is to produce yet more stable compounds. It is necessary to excite the atoms in the molecule very vigorously, before upsetting their relative stability, and so very high activation energies are required. Free radicals act directly upon the molecules, since some valencies are uncoupled. In general, quantum-mechanical calculations using LONDON's approximations lead to activation energies in the region of some tens of kcal, in molecular reactions such as $AB + CD \rightarrow AC + BD$ (see Appendix II). LONDON's equations give a substantially lower value if free radicals are involved.

The results quoted apply to attack along the axis of a σ-bond, $A + B - C \rightarrow A - B + C$, where A, B and C lie in the same straight line. If A approaches at right-angles to the B—C bond, then LONDON's method gives a much larger height for the potential barrier, which may only be lower by a factor 2 than that for a reaction between two molecules

$$
\begin{array}{cc}
\text{A—B} \\
\text{C—D}
\end{array}
\rightarrow
\begin{array}{cc}
\text{A} \\
| \\
\text{C}
\end{array}
+
\begin{array}{cc}
\text{B} \\
| \\
\text{D}
\end{array}
$$

Although it is not directly stated at any point, the quantum-mechanical consideration of the relative inertness of molecules as compared with free radicals involves the arrangement of the particles at the instant of attack. A free radical or an atom can attack a molecule from the most favourable direction, and the activated complex thus formed has a linear configuration $A \cdots B \cdots C$. The geometrical arrangement is generally not favourable when two molecules react directly, since the reacting centres form a trapezium in the activated complex (or, in the most general case, an irregular quadrilateral):

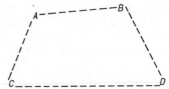

If AB and CD collide to form a linear arrangement, which is the one most favoured from the point of view of activation energy, $A \cdots B \cdots D \cdots C$, then the reaction evidently cannot give AC and BD as products directly since the arrangement would lead to BD and two radicals, A and C:

$$AB + DC \rightarrow A \cdots B \cdots D \cdots C \rightarrow A + BD + C$$

This process would involve a low potential barrier, but the energy liberated would be less than in $AB + CD \rightarrow AC + BD$, by Q_{A-C} (the bond-dissociation energy for AC), so it would be strongly endothermic. For example, if $H_2 + Cl_2 \rightarrow 2HCl$ evolves 44 kcal, then $H_2 + Cl_2 \rightarrow HCl + H + Cl$ absorbs $102 - 44 = 58$ kcal. The activation energy for the latter will be very large, even if E_0 is small (5–10 kcal), and so it will be of low probability.

Thus if a direct molecular reaction, which gives molecular products, is favoured by energetic considerations, E_0 is high; and conversely, if E_0 is low, the change is improbable because of the energy demanded. In both cases E will be high. Free radical reactions of the type $A + BC \rightarrow AB + C$ are not usually strongly endothermic, since one bond is broken, but another is formed. This circumstance, taken in conjunction with the low potential barriers (the angles of attack being favourable), makes radical reactions extremely probable ones. Consequently, in most instances a chain mechanism is more favourable than direct molecular reaction; this applies frequently to homogeneous thermal reactions as well as to photochemical or catalysed ones.

2. THE RELATIVE RATES OF DIRECT MOLECULAR AND CHAIN REACTIONS

The direct reaction $AB + CD \rightarrow AC + BD$ has a rate $w_0 = k[AB][CD]$, where k is the bimolecular rate constant, approximately equal to $10^{-10} \exp(-E/RT)$. Consider the chain reaction:

(1) $A + CD \rightarrow AC + D$,

(2) $D + AB \rightarrow A + BD$, etc.

If the radicals A are generated by artificial means, e.g. photochemically, the chain propagates at a rate:

$$w_C = k_1[A][CD] = k_2[D][AB] \simeq 10^{-10} \exp(-\varepsilon_1/RT)[A][CD]$$

where ε_1 relates to the rate-limiting step. Thus the ratio of rates is:

$$\gamma = \frac{w_D}{w_C} = \frac{[AB]}{[A]} \exp\left(-\frac{E - \varepsilon_1}{RT}\right)$$

[A] is defined by the fact that the number of radicals produced by photolysis of AB per sec, J, must be equal to the number removed per sec (e.g. by combination). The rate of self-combination is of course $k_3[A]^2$, so $J = k_3[A]^2$, and hence:

$$[A] = \sqrt{(J/k_3)}$$

It follows that:

$$\gamma = \frac{w_D}{w_C} \frac{[AB]}{\sqrt{(J/k_3)}} \exp\left(\frac{E - \varepsilon_1}{RT}\right) \tag{1}$$

where

$$w_C \simeq 10^{-10} \exp(-\varepsilon_1/RT)[A][CD]$$

$$w_D \simeq 10^{-10} \exp(-E/RT)[AB][CD]$$

At atmospheric pressure $[AB] \simeq 10^{19}$.

If the radicals A combine at each A—A collision, then $k_3 \simeq 10^{-10}$. If A is an atom, three-body collisions are required, and $k_3 \simeq 10^{-32}[M]$ where [M] is the total number of separate particles per cm^3. At $p \simeq$ 1 atm, $[M] \simeq 10^{19}$ and $k_3 \simeq 10^{-13}$. Since k appears under the root sign in (1), γ will differ by a factor of 30 in the two cases.

If we suppose that $k_3 \simeq 10^{-10}$, and $[AB] \simeq 10^{19}$, we find

$$\gamma = \frac{10^{14}}{\sqrt{J}} \exp\left(-\frac{E - \varepsilon_1}{RT}\right)$$

E is of considerable magnitude for molecules, e.g. 40 kcal. In radical reactions ε_1 is small, say 5 kcal. Thus

$$\gamma = \frac{10^{14}}{\sqrt{J}} \exp\left(-\frac{35}{RT}\right)$$

If the system is strongly illuminated $J \simeq 10^{15}$, whereas if the light is weak, $J \simeq 10^{12}$. Assume $J \simeq 10^{12}$, then $\gamma = 10^8 \exp(-35/RT)$ so that at 600°K $\gamma \simeq 10^{-5}$, and at 400°K $\gamma \simeq 10^{-11}$. It is clear that the direct reaction is quite negligible under these conditions, and that only the chain mechanism occurs.

The above comparison of photochemical chain and direct reactions is of little significance, due to the high light intensity used. A more interesting case arises when there is no artificial source of free radicals. The radicals then originate by thermal dissociation of AB, and $J = 10^{13} \exp(-Q/RT)[AB]$ (here J indicates the number of radicals generated thermally per cm^3) and at atmospheric pressure $J = 10^{32} \exp(-Q/RT)$, where Q is the energy required to dissociate AB into radicals. Then we have

$$[A] = \sqrt{\left\{\frac{10^{13} \exp(-Q/RT)[AB]}{10^{-10}}\right\}} \simeq 10^{21} \exp\left(\frac{-Q}{2RT}\right)$$

The chain rate then becomes

$$w_C = 10^{11} \exp\left(-\frac{\tfrac{1}{2}Q + \varepsilon_1}{RT}\right)[CD]$$

and the rate of the direct reaction is

$$w_D = 10^9 \exp(-E/RT)[CD]$$

According to (1),

$$\gamma = \frac{w_D}{w_C} = \frac{[AB]}{\sqrt{(J/k_3)}} \exp\left(-\frac{E - \varepsilon_1}{RT}\right)$$

$$= \frac{10^{19} \exp[-(E - \varepsilon_1)/RT]}{\sqrt{[10^{32} \exp(-Q/RT)/10^{-10}]}}$$

$$= 10^{-2} \exp\left(-\frac{E - \varepsilon_1 - \tfrac{1}{2}Q}{RT}\right)$$

$$= 10^{-[2 + (E - \varepsilon_1 - \tfrac{1}{2}Q)/4 \cdot 6T]}$$

In H_2/Cl_2 reaction the chain propagates via $Cl + H_2 \rightarrow HCl + H$; $H + Cl_2 \rightarrow HCl + Cl$, and recombination occurs via three-body collisions $Cl + Cl + M \rightarrow Cl_2 + M$, while Cl_2 dissociates bimolecularly, $Cl_2 + M \rightarrow Cl + Cl + M$. Hence we have

$$k_3 = 10^{-32}[M] \text{ and } J = 10^{-10}[Cl_2][M] \exp(-Q/RT)$$

Since $[Cl_2] \backsimeq 10^{19}$ at 1 atm,

$$\gamma = \frac{w_D}{w_C} = \frac{10^{19} \exp[-(E - \varepsilon_1)/RT]}{\sqrt{\{(10^{-10} \times 10^{19}[M] \exp[-Q/RT])/10^{-32}[M]\}}}$$

$$\simeq 10^{-1} \exp\left(-\frac{E - \varepsilon_1 - \frac{1}{2}Q}{RT}\right)$$

Thus if $E - \varepsilon_1 - \frac{1}{2}Q > 0$, the chain always predominates, since $\gamma < 0.1$, and consequently w_D is never more than 10 per cent of w_C. If $E - \varepsilon_1 - \frac{1}{2}Q < 0$, the direct reaction can predominate. $H_2 + I_2 \rightarrow 2HI$ is bimolecular, the activation energy being 40 kcal. $I + H_2 \rightarrow HI + H$ is strongly endothermic, since Q_{H-I} is 70 kcal, while Q_{H-H} is 103 kcal. The reaction is then endothermic (33 kcal) ε_0 is very small, so we may take $\varepsilon_1 = 33$ kcal. Q_{I-I} is 35·5 kcal, so $E - \varepsilon_1 - \frac{1}{2}Q = 40 - 33 - 17·8 = -10·8$ kcal. Since at 700°K, $\gamma \simeq 2 \times 10^2$, i.e. w_C is 200 times less than w_D.

$H_2 + Cl_2$ and $H_2 + Br_2$ are known to react by chain mechanisms. E is not known for the direct reactions, but since it is virtually independent of the heat yields, and the Cl—Cl and Br—Br bonds are strong by comparison with the I—I bond, we may anticipate that $E > 40$ kcal. Let us suppose that $E = 40$ kcal in both cases. ε_1 for $Cl + H_2 \rightarrow HCl + H$ is 6 kcal, $q = 1$ kcal and $Q_{Cl-Cl} = 57$ kcal. From these values it follows that $E - \varepsilon_1 - \frac{1}{2}Q = 40 - 6 - 28·5 = 5·5$ kcal, so $\gamma \simeq 0.1 \exp(-55,000/RT)$ so at 600°K (at which temperature the rate is measureable) $= 10^{-3}$. Thus w_D must be 1000 times less than w_C.

In the Br_2/H_2 reaction, $Br + H_2 \rightarrow HBr + H$, $q = -16$ kcal, $\varepsilon_1 \simeq 17$ kcal, and $Q \simeq 46$ kcal. Then $E - \varepsilon_1 - \frac{1}{2}Q = 40 - 17 - 23 = 0$. Hence $\gamma = w_D/w_C = 0.1$, so w_D is 10 times less than w_C. E is probably substantially greater than 40 kcal, and therefore $w_C/w_D \gg 10$. Experimentally, only chain reactions can be observed in H_2/Cl_2 and H_2/Br_2 mixtures.

The discussion of hydrogen halide formation was simplified, firstly, because a lower limit could be set for E in the direct reactions, and secondly, because both steps in the chains are bimolecular transfer reactions. The pre-exponential factor does not vary much in these, so the rate limiting step is the one with the largest ε.

15

E is not known in most cases, but the overall activation energy E_C may be known from experiment; if $E_C = \varepsilon_1 + \frac{1}{2}Q$, where Q is the energy demanded by the initiating step, and ε_1 is the activation energy of the slowest stage, there are good grounds for believing the reaction to be a radical chain. If the primary radicals are atoms produced by dissociation of one reactant, then Q is a bond-dissociation energy, and is known in a fair number of cases. ε_1 may be obtainable from photochemical data, or by using a discharge as a source of atoms. Data are lacking on ε_1 for most reactions, unfortunately. If both chain steps are exothermic $\varepsilon_1 = \varepsilon_{01}$ (ε_{01} is normally less than 11 kcal) then if we have:

$$E_D > \tfrac{1}{2}Q \text{ and } E_D - \tfrac{1}{2}Q = \varepsilon_{01} < 11 \text{ kcal} \tag{2}$$

a chain may reasonably be supposed. ε_{10} may be estimated if q is known for the least endothermic stage: $\varepsilon_{01} = 11 - 0.25\,q$ (see Chapter 1). When one chain step is endothermic, $\varepsilon_1 = \varepsilon_{01} + q$ (the heat of reaction being $-q$). In this case, the chain mechanism may predominate, if

$$E_D > \tfrac{1}{2}Q + q \tag{3}$$

and
$$E_D - (\tfrac{1}{2} + q) = \varepsilon_{01} < 11 \text{ kcal} \tag{4}$$

Some instances where these formulae are useful will now be considered.

Exchange Between H_2 *and* D_2 [1]

$H_2 + D_2 \rightarrow 2HD$ occurs homogeneously above 600°C. The experimental activation energy is about 57 kcal. The following chain is possible:

(0) $H_2 + M \rightarrow 2H - 103$ kcal,   (initiation)

(1) $H + D_2 \rightarrow HD + D - 1$ kcal, $\left.\vphantom{\begin{matrix}a\\b\end{matrix}}\right\}$

(2) $D + H_2 \rightarrow HD + H + 0.7$ kcal, $\Big/$ (propagation)

(3) $D + D + M \rightarrow D_2 + M$.   (termination).

This mechanism will have an activation energy

$$E_C = 103/2 + 1 + \varepsilon_{01} = 52.5 + \varepsilon_{01}$$

Since one chain step is endothermic, we may use (3) above:

$$E_D = 57 > \tfrac{1}{2}Q + 1 = 52.5 \text{ kcal}$$

and $E_D - \tfrac{1}{2}Q - q_1 = 57 - 51.5 - 1 = 4.5 < 11$ kcal

The result indicates that the system very probably reacts by a chain mechanism. The activation energy for $H + D_2 \rightarrow HD + D$ has been found by direct experiment to be 6·5 kcal (reference [1], page 269). Consequently, $\varepsilon_{01} = 5·5$ kcal, and $E_C = 52·5 + 5·5 = 58$ kcal; this latter is in agreement with the experimental value 57 kcal, within the errors involved. Thus the reaction mainly occurs by a chain mechanism.

Reaction Between Methyl Iodide and Hydrogen Iodide

$$CH_3I + HI \rightarrow CH_4 + I_2 + 14 \text{ kcal}$$

The following chain is possible:

(0) $CH_3I \rightarrow CH_3 + I - 52$ kcal, (initiation)

(1) $I + CH_3I \rightarrow CH_3 + I_2 - 18$ kcal, $\Bigg\}$

(2) $CH_3 + HI \rightarrow CH_4 + I + 32$ kcal, (propagation)

(3) $I + I + M \rightarrow I_2 + M + 35$ kcal. (termination).

The activation energy for propagation is:

$$E_C = \tfrac{1}{2}Q + q_1 + \varepsilon_{01} = 26 + 18 + \varepsilon_{01} = 44 + \varepsilon_{01}$$

The experimental E_D is 33 kcal (5). (3) above may be applied here:

$$E_D = 33 > \tfrac{1}{2}Q + q = 44$$

Evidently (3) is not complied with in this case, and this chain scarcely occurs in practice. Another mode of initiation is possible, however, in which CH_3I does not dissociate directly into CH_3 and I ($Q_{CH_3-I} = 52$ kcal) but reacts bimolecularly with HI; $CH_3I + HI \rightarrow CH_4 + 2I - 21$ kcal.

It will be shown in the next section that there is good reason to believe that processes in which molecules give two free radicals involve potential barriers as low as, or lower than, those found in radical/molecule reactions. Then if we assume that $Q = 21 + \varepsilon_{00}$, and the same mechanism for propagation and termination, we obtain the following expression for E_C

$$E_C = 21/2 + 18 + \varepsilon_{01} + \tfrac{1}{2}\varepsilon_{00} = 28·5 + \varepsilon_{01} + \tfrac{1}{2}\varepsilon_{00}$$

Applying (3):

$$E_D = 33 > \tfrac{1}{2}Q + q_1 = 28·5 \text{ kcal}$$

and $\quad E_D - \tfrac{1}{2}Q - q_1 = 33 - 28·5 = 4·5 < 11$ kcal

(3) and (4) thus apply, and so this reaction quite probably occurs either partially or entirely by the chain mechanism.

The Formation of Nitric Oxide

$N_2 + O_2 \rightarrow 2NO - 44$ kcal occurs at $\sim 1000°C$. The following chain is possible:

(0) $O_2 + M \rightarrow O + O + M - 117$ kcal,   (initiation)

(1) $O + N_2 \rightarrow NO + N + 75$ kcal, $\left.\begin{array}{c} \\ \\ \end{array}\right\}$
(2) $N + O_2 \rightarrow NO + O + 31$ kcal, $\qquad$ (propagation)

(3) $O + O + M \rightarrow O_2 + M + 117$ kcal.   (termination).

E_D is given as 129 kcal by ZELDOVICH *et al.* [6] from experimental data. At the high temperatures involved, E_D cannot be determined with an accuracy greater than 10 kcal. The above scheme implies:

$$E_C = \tfrac{1}{2}Q + q_1 + \varepsilon_{01} = 59 + 75 + \varepsilon_{01} = 134 + \varepsilon_{01}$$

The reverse of (1) is strongly exothermic (75 kcal), and so ε_{01} is probably very low. Then we have $E_C = 134$ kcal, i.e. slightly greater than that found experimentally. In this case E_D is quite likely to be inaccurate, and so we assume the chain mechanism. This assumption is in agreement with the experimental data, since ZELDOVICH *et al.* found that the rate is proportional to $[N_2][O_2]^{1/2}$, as in the chain mechanism, and not to $[N_2][O_2]$, as it would be for a direct bimolecular reaction.

The above simple relationships dealing with competition between chain and molecular reactions only apply when the elementary chain stages are solely bimolecular, such as transfer reactions between radicals and molecules.

The pre-exponential factors differ little for such reactions. If the chains involve reactions other than transfer or substitution, such as additions, then steric factor changes must be allowed for as well as changes in ε in order to define the rate-limiting step. It was shown in Chapter 1 that additions of atoms or radicals at double bonds were slower than transfer (substitution) reactions, since the steric factors are comparatively small. The most difficult (rate-limiting) elementary reaction may thus be an addition at a double bond, although its activation energy may be lower than any of the others. The hydrogenation of ethylene will now be considered as an instance of this.

Hydrogenation of Ethylene

$$C_2H_4 + H_2 \rightarrow C_2H_6 + 33 \text{ kcal [7]}$$

The elementary chain steps are the following:

(1) $C_2H_4 + H \rightarrow C_2H_5 + 38$ kcal,
(2) $C_2H_5 + H_2 \rightarrow C_2H_6 + H - 5$ kcal.

ε is known to be small (about 2 kcal) in (1). As (2) is endothermic, its activation energy is larger—various workers give values ranging from 11 to 14 kcal [8]. We assume $\varepsilon_2 = 13$ kcal. If the steric factors are the same for both, then (2) will be the slower, and k_1/k_2 will be exp $(\varepsilon_2 - \varepsilon_1/RT)$. At the temperatures at which ethylene hydrogenates reasonably rapidly (about 800°K), k_1/k_2 is about 10^3. If the steric factors are different, then $k_1/k_2 = (f_1/f_2)$ exp $(\varepsilon_2 - \varepsilon_1/RT)$.

There are reasons for supposing the steric factors for reactions such as (1) 10^3–10^4 times smaller than for transfer reactions, like (2). If this is so, $k_1/k_2 = 10^{-3} \times 10^3$, i.e. 1. Under such circumstances, both steps occur at the same rate, so $[C_2H_5]$ and $[H]$ are equal, and the main mode of chain termination will be combination of the different radicals involved:

(3) $C_2H_5 + H \rightarrow C_2H_6.$*

Chain initiation by parent compound dissociation is difficult, since:

$$H_2 \rightarrow 2H - 103 \text{ kcal}$$

and

$$C_2H_6 \rightarrow C_2H_5 + H - 97 \text{ kcal}$$

are so strongly endothermic. We may therefore suspect that the main free radical source is:

$$H_2 + CH_2{=}CH_2 \rightarrow H + CH_2CH_3 - 65 \text{ kcal}$$

Consider the following chain hydrogenation of ethylene:

(0) $H_2 + C_2H_4 \rightarrow H + C_2H_5 - 65$ kcal,   (initiation)

(1) $H + C_2H_4 \rightarrow C_2H_5 + 38$ kcal, $\left.\begin{array}{c} \\ \\ \end{array}\right\}$ (propagation)

(2) $C_2H_5 + H_2 \rightarrow C_2H_6 + H - 5$ kcal,

(3) $C_2H_5 + H \rightarrow C_2H_6.$ (termination).

The activation energies for (0), (1) and (2) are:

$$\varepsilon_0 = Q_0 + \varepsilon_{00} = 65 + \varepsilon_{00}, \ \varepsilon_1 \simeq 2 \text{ kcal}, \ \varepsilon_2 \simeq 13 \text{ kcal}$$

The ratio of steric factors f_1/f_2 is taken to be 10^3. The kinetic equations give

$$w = \sqrt{\left(\frac{k_0 k_1 k_2}{k_3}\right)} [H_2][C_2H_4]$$

---

* $H + H + M \rightarrow H_2 + M$ is slower, since it is a three-body collision. The disproportionation $C_2H_5 + C_2H_5 \rightarrow C_2H_4 + C_2H_6$ is slower than (3) because the mean velocity of hydrogen atoms is very high, and possibly because some steric factor is also involved.

The chain mechanism evidently follows the simple bimolecular law found experimentally. Making the following assumptions:

$$k_0 = 10^{-10} \exp\left[-(65 + \varepsilon_{00})/RT\right]$$
$$k_1 = f_1 \times 10^{-10} \exp\left(-2/RT\right)$$
$$k_2 = f_2 \times 10^{-10} \exp\left(-13/RT\right)$$

and $\quad\quad k_3 = 10^{-10}$

we find that

$$w = \sqrt{(f_1 f_2)}\, 10^{-10} \exp\left(-\frac{65 + 20 + 13 + \varepsilon_{00}}{2RT}\right)[H_2][C_2H_4]$$

Assuming that $f_1/f_2 = 10^3$, and supposing $f_1 \simeq 1$, we get

$$w = 3 \times 10^{-12} \exp\left(\frac{-40 + \tfrac{1}{2}\varepsilon_{00}}{RT}\right)[H_2][C_2H_4]$$

ε_{00} can hardly exceed 2–3 kcal. Consequently

$$w = 3 \times 10^{-12} \exp\left(-41\cdot5/RT\right)[H_2][C_2H_4]$$

The experimental relation [7] is

$$w = 10^{-11} \exp\left(-43\cdot15/RT\right)[H_2][C_2H_4]$$

Thus the theoretical and experimental results are in exceedingly good agreement. The proposed chain mechanism for hydrogenation of ethylene is confirmed by ethane decomposing to ethylene and hydrogen via a chain mechanism, which has been demonstrated by various direct experiments.

Chlorination of Ethylene

$$C_2H_4 + Cl_2 \rightarrow C_2H_4Cl_2 + 43\cdot6 \text{ kcal}$$

The reaction is initiated photochemically $Cl_2 \xrightarrow{h\nu} 2Cl$. The following elementary reactions are generally agreed:

(1) $Cl + C_2H_4 \rightarrow C_2H_4Cl + 25$ kcal,*

(2) $C_2H_4Cl + Cl_2 \rightarrow C_2H_4Cl_2 + Cl + 17\cdot6$ kcal.

SCHMITZ et al. [9] found that the quantum yield was 3×10^6 at room temperature. The temperature coefficient was very small, at $1\cdot09/10°C$, ε for the slower stage being about $1\cdot5$ kcal. The chains are of great length at room temperature since ε is very low.

* The heat of reaction was calculated indirectly and is thus not of very high accuracy.

The photoreaction is strongly impeded by small amounts of oxygen, but the O_2 is not destroyed, so some unstable compound must be formed, such as ClO_2 or $C_2H_4ClO_2$, which subsequently decomposes without liberating Cl. ClO_2 is known to decompose to molecular chlorine and oxygen: $2ClO_2 \rightarrow Cl_2 + 2O_2$.

The thermal chlorination of ethylene may take place in two ways: directly, $Cl_2 + C_2H_4 \rightarrow C_2H_4Cl_2$, or by a chain mechanism, via preliminary formation of chlorine atoms, as in (1) and (2). The main product at 200–250°C, is dichloroethane, and substitution products are absent in practice (see Chapter 2, page 87). Oxygen also impedes the thermal reaction strongly.

CHAIKIN (Moscow State University) has recently investigated the chlorination of ethylene in detail [10]. Chlorination was carried out at 227°C and 200 mm Hg. CHAIKIN found that the initial rate was related to the oxygen content by the formula:

$$w = w_0 + \frac{a}{b + c[O_2]}$$

This was in very good agreement with all the experimental data. The ratio $b:c$ is such that, even at 2·5 per cent O_2, $c[O_2]$ was some 10 times greater than b. w_0 is defined as the limiting rate in the presence of oxygen, and is extremely small. When oxygen is absent, $w_0/w \simeq 0.01$. The law followed by $w - w_0$ clearly indicates a chain mechanism. The rate of the direct molecular reaction cannot exceed w_0, i.e. if it occurs at all, w_D must be 100 times less than w_C. The molecular reaction in all probability occurs at the surface of the vessel, since its rate depends on the product (dichloroethane) concentration.

CHAIKIN determined the detailed distribution of the reaction by differential calorimetry [10]. It was similar to that for the H_2/Cl_2 reaction (page 186, Chapter 6), the chains originating at the surfaces. Kinetic data on the relation of the normal and retarded reaction rates to S/V showed that, as in the H_2/Cl_2 reaction, the chains were generated and terminated on the surface if oxygen was absent, whereas they were generated on the surface and terminated in the gas when oxygen was present. The activation energy was 17 kcal, and this must imply that the chains only start at the surface, since the initiation reaction in the gas, $Cl_2 + M \rightarrow 2Cl + M - 57$ kcal, would involve a much larger activation energy.

Chain initiation on the walls would also explain why many results are not reproducible, since they would be affected by uncontrollable changes in the condition of the walls. Thus RUST and VAUGHAN's [12] conclusion that small amounts of oxygen not only do not retard the chlorination of ethylene at higher temperatures, but even accelerate it, may be explained by wall effects.

The catalytic action of small amounts of oxygen was also observed by POLTORAK and VOEVODSKII [13] in the cracking of propane and by BARTON [13] in the pyrolysis of some chlorinated hydrocarbons (1, 2-dichloroethane, 1, 1, 2-trichloroethane and 1, 1, 2, 2-tetrachloroethane).

CHAIKIN found that the reaction products had a strong negative catalytic action, and that this was independent of $[O_2]$. (The initial rate was of second order in p, but as the reaction proceeded the order of the reaction increased, tending to a fifth-power dependence on p.) The self-retardation resembles that observed in the cracking of hydrocarbons. The nature of this effect is at present uncertain, and the problem requires detailed investigation.

Detailed investigation of all the various kinetic relationships gives the equation:

$$w - w_0 = \frac{a[Cl_2][C_2H_4]}{b + c(O_2)}$$

where $b = b_0 + \Delta x$, Δx being the amount of starting material reacted, or the amount of products formed. Precisely this equation may be derived from the following scheme:

(0) $Cl_2 \xrightarrow[\text{at wall}]{k_0} 2Cl,$ (initiation)

(1) $Cl + C_2H_4 \xrightarrow{k_1} C_2H_4Cl,$

(2) $C_2H_4Cl + Cl_2 \xrightarrow{k_2} C_2H_4Cl_2 + Cl,$ (propagation)

(3) $Cl + \text{some product of the reaction} \xrightarrow{k_3},$

(4) $Cl \xrightarrow[k_4]{\text{at wall}},$ (termination)

(5) $Cl + O_2 \xrightarrow{k_5} ClO_2.$

$$w = \frac{2k_0k_1[Cl_2][C_2H_4]}{k_3[\text{prod.}] + k_4 + k_5[O_2]}$$

Thus the gas-phase combination of ethylene with chlorine involves a chain mechanism, the direct molecular combination being unobservable in practice.*

Decomposition reactions will now be considered. Chain decompositions normally involve two or three elementary reactions, one being usually a unimolecular radical decomposition, and another often a bimolecular substitution or transfer. As there is a substantial difference between the pre-exponential factors for these two types of

---

* The chlorination of ethylene in the liquid state happens at much lower temperatures. The mechanism has not yet been investigated.

elementary reaction, it is impossible to decide which is the rate-limiting step from the activation energies alone.

Decomposition of Acetaldehyde

$$CH_3C{\overset{O}{\underset{H}{\diagup}}} \rightarrow CH_4 + CO + 5\,kcal$$

The simple unimolecular decomposition competes with the chain detailed below:

(0) $CH_3C{\overset{O}{\underset{H}{\diagup}}} \rightarrow CH_3 + HCO - 72\,kcal,$ (initiation)

(1) $CH_3 + CH_3CHO \rightarrow CH_4 + CH_3CO + 17\,kcal,$ } (propaga-
(2) $CH_3CO \rightarrow CH_3 + CO - 12\,kcal.*$ tion).

The rate of (1) is:

$$w_1 = k_1[CH_3][CH_3CHO] = f_1 10^{-10} \exp{(-\varepsilon_{01}/RT)}[CH_3][CH_3CHO]$$

The rate of (2) is similarly:

$$w_2 = k_2[CH_3CO] = 10^{13} \exp{\left(-\frac{|q_2| + \varepsilon_{02}}{RT}\right)}[CH_3CO]$$

If conditions are steady and the chains are sufficiently long $w_1 = w_2$ hence:

$$\frac{[CH_3]}{[CH_3CO]} = \frac{10^{13} \exp{[-(|q_2| + \varepsilon_{02})/RT]}}{f \times 10^{-10} \exp{(\varepsilon_{01}/RT)}[CH_3CHO]}$$

$$= \frac{10^{23}}{f_1[CH_3CHO]} \cdot \exp{\left(-\frac{|q_2| + \varepsilon_{02} - \varepsilon_{01}}{RT}\right)}$$

Since $|q_2| = 12\,kcal$, and ε_{01} and ε_{02} are given to a first approximation by $\varepsilon_{01} = 11 - (0\cdot25 \times 17) = 7$ and $\varepsilon_{02} = 11 - (0\cdot25 \times 12) = 8,$ then $\varepsilon_2 = \varepsilon_{02} + |q_2| = 8 + 12 = 20\,kcal,$ and $|q_2| + \varepsilon_{02} - \varepsilon_{01} = 13\,kcal.$
Thus

$$\frac{[CH_3]}{[CH_3CO]} = \frac{10^{23}}{f_1[CH_3CHO]} \exp{\left(-\frac{13}{RT}\right)}$$

---

* SzWARC [14] considers that ΔH for CH_3CO is $10\cdot8\,kcal$. Then $Q_{CH_3-CO} = 16\,kcal$, and $Q_{CH_3CO-H} = 80\,kcal$. If this is so, then $q_1 = 21\,kcal$. The value we have assumed for Q_{CH_3-CO} ($12\,kcal$) leads to $Q_{CH_3CO-H} \sim 85\,kcal$; this value was earlier adopted by SzWARC [15].

at $T \simeq 800°K$ this implies that

$$\frac{[CH_3]}{[CH_3CO]} = \frac{10^{23}}{f_1[CH_3CHO]} 10^{-3.5}$$

At $p \simeq 1$ atm $[CH_3CHO] \simeq 10^{19}$, so

$$\frac{[CH_3]}{[CH_3CO]} \simeq \frac{3}{f}$$

We may observe from this result that although ε_2 is 20 kcal (unimolecular reaction), and ε_{01} is only 7 kcal (bimolecular reaction), (1) is in fact the slower.

Even if $f_1 = 1$, $[CH_3] > [CH_3CO]$. Since $f \simeq 0 \cdot 1$ normally, $[CH_3]$ is roughly 30 times as great as $[CH_3CO]$, and so the chains are mainly terminated by combination of methyl radicals:

(3) $CH_3 + CH_3 \rightarrow C_2H_6$.

When the kinetic equations are applied to the above scheme, we find

$$k_3[CH_3]^2 = k_0[CH_3CHO]$$

or

$$[CH_3] = \sqrt{(k_0[CH_3CHO]/k_3)}$$

The overall rate is

$$w = w_1 = k_1(k_0/k_3)^{1/2}[CH_3CHO]^{3/2}$$

The chain activation energy is $E_C = (72/2) + 7 = 43$ kcal. The experimental value (for $p \simeq 1$ atm) is about 48 kcal, and w is proportional to $[CH_3CHO]^{3/2}$ [3]. The discrepancy of 5 kcal in E_C is probably due to errors in E, Q and ε_{01}. Direct photochemical determination gives ε_{01} as 10 kcal [9], i.e. 3 kcal greater than assumed here. Applying this correction, the calculated E_C is increased to 46 kcal, which practically coincides with the experimental 48 kcal. The general chain character of the reaction is confirmed by many direct experiments (inhibition by NO [10], by propylene [17], acceleration by oxygen and by diacetyl [3], and by di-*tert*.-butyl peroxide [18]).

The Decomposition of Dimethyl Ether [19]

$$CH_3-O-CH_3 \rightarrow CH_2O + CH_4 \rightarrow CO + H_2 + CH_4, q \text{ overall} \simeq 0$$

A possible chain mechanism is:

(0) $CH_3OCH_3 \rightarrow CH_3O + CH_3 - Q$,   (initiation)

(1) $CH_3 + CH_3OCH_3 \rightarrow CH_4 + CH_2OCH_3 + |q_1|$,

(2) $CH_2OCH_3 \rightarrow CH_2O + CH_3 - |q_2|$.   } (propagation).

Since the overall reaction is thermally neutral, $|q_1| = |q_2| = |q|$. If $q \simeq 12$ kcal, $[CH_3]/[CH_3OCH_3]$ will be the same as for acetaldehyde, i.e. $3/f_1$. q would appear to be greater than 12 kcal in this case, and $[CH_3]/[CH_2OCH_3] \simeq 1$. Consequently all modes of radical combination will be equally likely. This approximates to chain termination being dominated by the combination of different radicals:

(3) $CH_3 + CH_2OCH_3 \rightarrow CH_2O + C_2H_6$ or $CH_3CH_2OCH_3$.

The kinetic equations give the overall rate as:

$$w = \sqrt{\left(\frac{k_0 k_1 k_2}{k_3}\right)} [CH_3OCH_3]$$

i.e. the chain reaction gives the simple unimolecular law found from experiment.

The unimolecular constant

$$k = \sqrt{\left(\frac{k_0 k_1 k_2}{k_2}\right)} \simeq \sqrt{\left(\frac{10^{13} \cdot 10^{-10} \cdot 10^{13}}{10^{-10}}\right)} \exp\left(\frac{Q + |q_2| + \varepsilon_{01} + \varepsilon_{02}}{2RT}\right)$$

then $k = 10^{13} \exp(-E_C/2RT)$, where $E_C = \frac{1}{2}Q + \frac{1}{2}(\varepsilon_{01} + \varepsilon_{02} + |q_2|)$. k is found to be $1 \cdot 5 \times 10^{13} \exp(-58/RT)$ by experiment [12]. Using the thermochemical data given by GRAY [20], we may calculate Q in (0). The ΔH's for the ether, and for CH_3 and CH_2OCH_3 are $-45 \cdot 6$, $-0 \cdot 5$ and $31 \cdot 5$ kcal respectively. Hence $-45 \cdot 6 = -0 \cdot 5 + 31 \cdot 5 - Q$, so $Q_{C-O} = 76 \cdot 6$ kcal. ε_{01} may be calculated from $\varepsilon_0 = 11 \cdot 5 - 0 \cdot 25 |q|$ (see Chapter 1). If $q = 12$ kcal, then $\varepsilon_{01} = 8 \cdot 5$ kcal. The calculated ε_{02} was 7 kcal (see Chapter 1). Hence

$$E_C = 58 = Q/2 + \frac{\varepsilon_{01} + \varepsilon_{02} + |q_2|}{2}$$

$$= 38 \cdot 3 \frac{8 \cdot 5 + 7}{2} + \frac{q_2}{2} \approx 46 + \frac{q}{2}$$

q_2 should apparently not be more than 14–16 kcal. Thus the experimental E is probably too high (by ~ 4 kcal), as in the previous case. Since the calculated E_C is lower than the experimental one, it is a convincing proof of the chain mechanism. It would seem that E, Q, ε_{01} and ε_{02} were not very accurately determined.

The reaction is thus extremely likely to be of chain type; this is also indicated by strong NO inhibition.

Decomposition of Di-iodoethane

$$C_2H_4I_2 \rightarrow C_2H_4 + I_2 - 11 \text{ kcal}$$

The chain scheme proposed is:

(0) $C_2H_4I_2 \rightarrow C_2H_4I + I - 48$ kcal,   (initiation)

(1) $I + C_2H_4I_2 \rightarrow I_2 + C_2H_4I - 11$ kcal,
(2) $C_2H_4I \rightarrow C_2H_4 + I \pm 0$ kcal, } (propagation)

(3) $I + I + M \rightarrow I_2 + M + 35 \cdot 5$ kcal.   (termination).

The rate-limiting step is evidently (1), which is endothermic. The activation energy of (1) is

$$\varepsilon_1 = \varepsilon_{01} + |q| \simeq \varepsilon_{01} + 11 \text{ kcal}$$

ε_{01} is normally very small for reactions involving iodine atoms. In this instance ε_1 is known from photochemical measurements to be about 12 kcal [13]. Hence $E_C \simeq 24 + 12 = 36$ kcal $(Q = 47 - 48$ kcal). The experimental value is $36 \cdot 6$ kcal [21].

If I_2 is present the primary decomposition $I_2 \rightarrow 2I$ requires $35 \cdot 5$ kcal. In this case, $E_C \simeq 17 \cdot 8 + 12 \simeq 30$ kcal, compared with the experimental value of $30 \cdot 2$ kcal. It is obvious that this is a chain reaction.

ARNOLD and KISTIAKOWSKY [21] concluded that the chain reaction only occurred when iodine was used as a catalyst. If iodine was absent, the iodide decomposed directly to C_2H_4 and I_2. We consider [2] this view incorrect, for the reasons given below.

(1) The activation energies, calculated on the assumption that both reactions involve chains, are in agreement with experiment for both the catalysed and the uncatalysed reactions.

(2) BUTLER and POLANYI have shown [22] that alkyl iodides decompose entirely to alkyl radicals and iodine atoms when mixed with nitrogen and passed through a heated tube.

(3) KISTIAKOWSKY's data may all be explained on the assumption that the reactions occur via a chain mechanism, with two different modes of initiation:

(a) $C_2H_4I_2 \rightarrow C_2H_4I + I$

and (b) $I_2 + M \rightarrow I + I + M$.

The kinetic equations for the above chain scheme give the initial rate to be

$$w = 2k_1 \sqrt{\left(\frac{k_0[C_2H_4I_2]}{k_3} \right)} [C_2H_4I_2]$$

Since k_3 is the rate constant for recombination of iodine atoms (via three-body collisions, $I + I + M \rightarrow I_2 + M$), $k_3 = x[M]$, where $x \simeq 10^{-32}$, and [M] is the initial concentration of $C_2H_4I_2$, then

$$k_1 = 10^{-10} \exp(-12/RT), \quad k_0 = 10^{12} \exp(-48/RT)$$
$$w = 10^{12 \cdot 8} \exp(-38/RT)[C_2H_4I_2]$$

The experimental result [13] was

$$w = 10^{13} \exp\left(-\,36 \cdot 6/RT\right)[C_2H_4I_2]$$

Thus the chain reaction simulates a unimolecular law, and the theoretical and experimental rates are in agreement.

An analogous calculation may be made for the iodine-catalysed reaction. Here the chains are initiated by dissociation of iodine

(0) $I_2 + M \rightarrow I + I + M - 35 \cdot 5$ kcal.

$k_0 = 10^{13} \exp\left(-\,35 \cdot 5/RT\right)$. The rate of the iodine-catalysed reaction is

$$w^* = 2k_1 \sqrt{K} \sqrt{[I_2]} \cdot [C_2H_4I]$$

where K is the equilibrium constant of $I_2 \rightleftharpoons 2I$; it is given approximately by

$$K \simeq 10^{24} \exp\left(-\,35 \cdot 5/RT\right)$$

From this we may derive:

$$w^* = 2 \times 10^{-10} \times 10^{12} \sqrt{(I_2)} \exp\left(-\,29 \cdot 75/RT\right)[C_2H_4I_2]$$

$$= 200 \sqrt{[I_2]} \exp\left(-\,29 \cdot 75/RT\right)[C_2H_4I_2]$$

The experimental equation is:

$$w^* = 80 \sqrt{[I_2]} \exp\left(-\,30 \cdot 2/RT\right)[C_2H_4I_2]$$

The theoretical and experimental activation energies agree within the observational errors. The pre-exponential factors differ by a factor $2 \cdot 5$. The reaction actually occurs via a chain mechanism, but the chains are not long (~ 10 cycles).

Decomposition of sec.-*Butyl Iodide*

Overall reaction: $2C_4H_9I \rightarrow C_4H_8 + C_4H_{10} + I_2$. Chain scheme:

(0) $C_4H_9I \rightarrow C_4H_9 + I - Q_{C-I}$,   (initiation)

(1) $C_4H_9 + C_4H_9I \leftarrow C_4H_{10} + C_4H_8I$,

(2) $C_4H_8I \rightarrow C_4H_8 + I$,   (propagation)

(3) $I + C_4H_9I \rightarrow I_2 + C_4H_9 - 11 \cdot 5$ kcal†,

(4) $I + I + M \rightarrow I_2 + M + 35 \cdot 5$ kcal.   (termination).

Q_{C-I} in $n-C_4H_9I$ is known to be 49 kcal. In *tert.*-C_4H_9I Q_{C-I} is 45 kcal [22]. We cannot make a large error, therefore, if we take Q_{C-I} in *sec.*-C_4H_9I as being 47 kcal. The calculated chain activation

† This is the rate-limiting step.

energy is $E_C = \frac{1}{2}Q_{C-I} + \varepsilon_3 : \varepsilon_3 = q_3 + \varepsilon_{03}$ where q_3 is the heat absorbed in (3); in this the C—I bond is broken, and the I—I bond is formed, so $q_3 = Q_{C-I} - 35 \cdot 5$ kcal. Hence $E_C = \frac{3}{2}Q_{C-I} - 35 \cdot 5 + \varepsilon_{03}$. If $Q_{C-I} = 47$ kcal then $E_C = 35 + \varepsilon_{03}$. The decomposition is accelerated by molecular iodine, since the chains are more readily initiated. If I_2 is sufficiently high this is the sole mode of initiation. The calculated activation energy for the catalysed chain decomposition of *sec.*-BuI is

$$E_C{}^* = \tfrac{1}{2}Q + \varepsilon_3 = (35 \cdot 5/2) + Q_{C-I} - 35 \cdot 5 + \varepsilon_{03}$$
$$= 17 \cdot 75 + 11 \cdot 5 + \varepsilon_{03} = 29 \cdot 25 + \varepsilon_{03}$$

The experimental $E_C{}^*$ is $35 \cdot 2$ kcal [23]. Then $\varepsilon_{03} = 35 \cdot 2 - 29 \cdot 5 \simeq 6$ kcal. By comparison, E_C (uncatalysed reaction) assuming ε_{03} the same in both cases, is:

$$E_C = 35 + \varepsilon_{03} = 35 + 6 = 41 \text{ kcal}$$

The experimental value is $39 \cdot 4$ kcal [23], which agrees with theory within the limits of experimental error, and thus confirms that the uncatalysed mechanism is also a chain.

As was indicated above, the initial phase of the uncatalysed reaction is quasi-unimolecular. w^* is proportional to $\sqrt{[I_2]}$ and $[C_4H_9I]$, in agreement with the empirical relationship. The calculated pre-exponential factors of both reactions (catalysed and uncatalysed) are 20 times greater than the experimental ones, which may be explained by a steric factor of $0 \cdot 05$ in (3).

3. ALKYL BROMIDE DECOMPOSITION

Some most interesting features of the competition between direct and chain reactions are found in the decompositions of C_2H_5Br, n-C_3H_7Br, and iso-C_3H_7Br. The role of structure in parallel reactions is seen with particular clarity in this instance, and it may serve as an illustration.

The reverse reaction (addition of HBr to olefins), involves a chain (see Chapter 2, 1, page 86), if the system is illuminated or peroxides are present, addition occurring contrary to Markovnikov's [24] rule. In the absence of initiators addition is in accordance with Markovnikov's rule if carried out in the liquid phase at low temperatures (as regards 90 per cent of the products [25]). As MARKOVNIKOV himself anticipated [26] the proportion of the product formed contrary to Markovnikov's rule increases with temperature.

It follows that alkyl bromides at 300°C must also decompose via chain reactions under the influence of initiators:

(1) $\text{Br} + C_nH_{2n+1}Br \rightarrow \text{HBr} + C_nH_{2n}Br - q_1$ (~ 5 kcal),

(2) $C_nH_{2n}Br \rightarrow C_nH_{2n} + \text{Br} - q_2$ (~ 13 kcal).

Suppose $q_1 + q_2 = U$, then U is the energy absorbed in the overall reaction. U has been found to be approximately 18 kcal in the simplest alkyl bromides [27, 28]. The mode of termination was analysed by the present author in 1952 [2], and the dominant mode was concluded to be cross-reaction of two different radicals.

(3) $Br + C_nH_{2n}Br \rightarrow$ molecular products.

If the reaction is purely thermal (initiators absent) chains are only initiated by molecular decomposition:

(0) $C_nH_{2n+1}Br \rightarrow C_nH_{2n+1} + Br - Q_{C-Br}$.

Q_{C-Br} is 65 kcal for C_2H_5Br. We take $Q_{C-Br} \simeq 59$ kcal for iso-C_3H_7Br, and $\simeq 62$ kcal for n-C_3H_7Br. The kinetic equations then readily give the chain rate to be:

$$w_C = \sqrt{\left(\frac{k_0 k_1 k_2}{k_3}\right)} \exp\left(-\frac{Q + u + \varepsilon_{01} + \varepsilon_{02}}{2RT}\right) [C_nH_{2n+1}Br]$$

Assuming that the pre-exponential factors for the various elementary reactions are 10^{-10} (bimolecular, k_1 and k_3), and 10^{13} (unimolecular, k_0 and k_2), this then becomes

$$w_C = 10^{13} \exp\left(-\frac{Q + u + \varepsilon_{01} + \varepsilon_{02}}{2RT}\right) [C_nH_{2n+1}Br]$$

For C_2H_5Br

$$\frac{Q + u + \varepsilon_{01} + \varepsilon_{02}}{2} = \frac{65 + 18\cdot3}{2} + \frac{\varepsilon_{01} + \varepsilon_{02}}{2} = 41\cdot65 + \frac{\varepsilon_{01} + \varepsilon_{02}}{2}$$

Experiment gives [2] $w = 10^{13} \exp(-50/RT)$; this agrees with theory if we assume $(\varepsilon_{01} + \varepsilon_{02})/2 = 8\cdot35$ kcal, as is quite reasonable.

The experimental E_C is $47\cdot8$ kcal for iso-C_3H_7Br [29]. The theoretical $E_C = 38\cdot5 + (\varepsilon_{01} + \varepsilon_{02})/2$ agrees with experiment if we suppose $(\varepsilon_{01} + \varepsilon_{02})/2 = 8\cdot5$ kcal. The activation energies for reactions in which only simple unimolecular mechanisms are involved such as those above, had formerly not been determined. Strangely enough, it was supposed that it would be approximately the same as the activation energy E_C estimated for the chain mechanism, which agreed with the experimental value. This led us to conclude that the alkyl bromides decomposed in the same fashion as the iodides, i.e. via a chain mechanism. The mean chain length so calculated was found to be very great (10^4–10^5), while the chain length in the iodides was very much smaller (3–30). Four years have passed since the article in *Uspekhi Khimii* was written. The experimental data on bromides were very scanty in 1951. Latterly the scope of the problem has been accurately defined by workers at Moscow State University (Department of Chemical Kinetics) and abroad as a result of various approaches to the question.

SZWARC in particular [30] has shown that the bromides decompose differently from the iodides, and that C_2H_5Br decomposes more readily into C_2H_4 and HBr than into C_2H_5 and Br. This must mean that the activation energy for unimolecular decomposition is considerably less than 65 kcal, and possibly ~ 50 kcal. BLADES and MURPHY [31] examined the decompositions of ethyl bromide, n-propyl bromide, and iso-propyl bromide, using a rapid-flow toluene carrier method, the toluene being intended to impede chain propagation. All three bromides were found to decompose unimolecularly, the activation energies being 52·3, 50·7 and 47·7 kcal respectively. The careful experiments of SERGEEV and KAPRALOVA on n-propyl and iso-propyl bromides under static conditions showed that the activation energy for $n\text{-}C_3H_7Br$ was 42 kcal, whereas for $iso\text{-}C_3H_7Br$ it was the same as under dynamic conditions (about 47 kcal) [32]. Evidently the flow method gives the primary unimolecular activation energy in both bromides. The fact that the same activation energy is found for the iso-compound by both methods is probably to be interpreted as implying that the process is unimolecular in both cases. The 10 kcal reduction as between the flow and static experiments with $n\text{-}C_3H_7Br$ indicates that a chain reaction is occurring in the static case. $n\text{-}C_3H_7Br$ and $iso\text{-}C_3H_7Br$ have different orders of reaction in static conditions: $iso\text{-}C_3H_7Br$ is of first order in $[C_3H_7Br]$, while $n\text{-}C_3H_7Br$ is of order 3/2.

The decompositions of n- and $iso\text{-}C_3H_7Br$ as influenced by the addition of various compounds have been investigated by SERGEEV [32, 33]. Decomposition of $n\text{-}C_3H_7Br$ was accelerated by Br_2 and O_2, but somewhat retarded by C_3H_6. Propylene inhibition was only observed during the initial stages. Curiously, HBr accelerated the decomposition somewhat, while C_3H_6 and HBr in a 1:1 ratio did not affect the rate.

Propylene did not influence the decomposition of $iso\text{-}C_3H_7Br$, so these isomeric bromides react differently.

To explain the unexpected differences between these two very similar bromides one has to assume the chain mechanism previously [2] proposed incomplete; the possibility of parallel chain and direct decompositions should be re-examined. The reverse reaction (addition of HBr to propylene) as catalysed by peroxides, is known to involve a chain reaction; it always gives the normal configuration (i.e. contrary to Markovnikov's rule). If the gas-phase combination at very high temperatures is analogous (no experimental data are available on this), then it is at once obvious why only $n\text{-}C_3H_7Br$

decomposes chainwise. It is not difficult to demonstrate this conclusion.

Hydrogen is abstracted from $n\text{-}C_3H_7Br$:

(1) $Br + CH_3—CH_2—CH_2Br \rightarrow HBr + CH_3—CH—CH_2Br.$

The hydrogen is taken from the CH_2 group, since this hydrogen is most weakly bound. The resultant radical decomposes to olefin + Br:

(2) $CH_3—CH—CH_2Br \rightarrow CH_3—CH=CH_2 + Br.$

The bromine atom is this regenerated and the chain continues. $CH_3—CBr—CH_3$ is formed in (1) from the *iso*-compound:

(1) $CH_3—CHBr—CH_3 + Br \rightarrow HBr + CH_3—CBr—CH_3.$

This radical cannot decompose to olefin + Br, and can only combine either with another radical of the same type or with an atom of bromine. The chain therefore cannot propagate in $iso\text{-}C_3H_7Br$ and only direct decomposition ($E_D = 47$ kcal) is found to occur. Since the chain can propagate in $n\text{-}C_3H_7Br$, the overall activation energy (42 kcal) is 8·7 kcal lower than for unimolecular decomposition (50·7 kcal).

This is not a satisfactory explanation for the difference between the two bromides, however, since it only gives a qualitative picture. Peroxide- or photo-catalysis of C_3H_6/HBr mixtures is known to give $n\text{-}C_3H_7Br$ at $\sim 273°K$. A larger $iso\text{-}C_3H_7Br : n\text{-}C_3H_7Br$ ratio may be expected as the temperature increases. If this is so, then a reverse chain reaction giving $iso\text{-}C_3H_7Br$ must be possible at high temperatures. Theoretically speaking, this is quite plausible, since $CH_3—$ $\dot{C}Br—CH_3$ can isomerize and then decompose at high temperatures. This isomerization might be either unimolecular or (which is more likely) occur by exchange with $iso\text{-}C_3H_7Br$. $CH_3—CHBr—\dot{C}H_2$, obtained by isomerization, is capable of decomposing. Chain decomposition of $iso\text{-}C_3H_7Br$ is thus possible, as below:

(1) $Br + CH_3—CHBr—CH_3 \rightarrow HBr + CH_3—\dot{C}Br—CH_3 + q_1,$

(1′) $CH_3—\dot{C}Br—CH_3 + CH_3—CHBr—CH_3 \rightarrow CH_3—CHBr—CH_3$
$\qquad\qquad\qquad\qquad\qquad\qquad + CH_3CHBr—\dot{C}H_2 + q_1',$

(2) $CH_3—CHBr—\dot{C}H_2 \rightarrow CH_3—CH=CH_2 + Br + q_2.$

The rate-limiting step is readily shown to be (1′), so $[CH_3\dot{C}BrCH_3]$ will be greatest, and the main chain-termination process will be

(3) $2CH_3\dot{C}BrCH_3 \rightarrow$ molecular products.

Suppose that chains are initiated by decomposition of iso-C_3H_7Br to radicals:

O CH_3—$CHBr$—$CH_3 \rightarrow Br + CH_3$—$\dot{C}H$—$CH_3 - 59$ kcal

Taken in conjunction with the other reactions, this leads to the kinetic law:

$$w_C = k' \sqrt{\left(\frac{k_0}{k_3}[RBr]\right)} [RBr] \qquad (5)$$

i.e. it is of order 3/2 in the iso-propyl bromide concentration.

In order to carry out any further calculations we need to know Q_{C-H} for the various C—H bonds in the two bromides; accurate data are not available. Q_{C-H} is known for the CH_3 and CH_2 groups in C_3H_8: $Q_{CH-H} = 89$ kcal, and $Q_{H_2C-H} = 95$ kcal. We further assume that replacing H by Br reduces Q_{C-H} by about 3 kcal in both cases. Then $Q_{BrC-H} = 86$ kcal, and $Q_{HBrC-H} = 92$ kcal. Q_{H-Br} is 85 kcal, and we take U (the energy absorbed in the overall decomposition of n- or iso-C_3H_7Br) to be 18 kcal (from experimental data).

The following may then be calculated for the chain decomposition of iso-C_3H_7Br: $q_1 = -1$ kcal; $q_1' = -9$ kcal; $q_2 = U - q_1 - q_1'$ $= -18 + 1 + 9 = -8$ kcal.

Another reaction is possible: Br may abstract hydrogen from the CH_3 group. (1) is then replaced by (1a):

(1a) $Br + CH_3$—$CHBr$—$CH_3 \rightarrow HBr + \dot{C}H_2$—$CHBr$—$CH_3 + q_{1a}$,

followed by decomposition of $\dot{C}H_2CHBrCH_3$ to Br and propylene. However, $q_{1a} = -95 + 86 = -9$ kcal, i.e. the ratio between the rates of (1a) and (1) will be $\exp\left(-\dfrac{9}{1\cdot4}\right) \simeq 10^{-3}$ at $T = 700°K$.

(1a) may evidently be neglected.

The activation energy for the chain decomposition of iso-C_3H_7Br may be estimated as follows: $k_0 = 10^{13} \exp(-Q_{C-Br}/RT)$, where $Q_{C-Br} = 59$ kcal for iso-C_3H_7Br; $k_3 \simeq 10^{-10}$; $k_1' = 10^{-10} \exp[-(q_1' + \varepsilon_{01}')/RT]$ where $q_1' = -9$ kcal. Then $E_C = \frac{1}{2}Q + q_1' + \varepsilon_{01} = 29\cdot5 + 9 + \varepsilon_{01}' = 38\cdot5 + \varepsilon_{01}$.

According to the standard formula (Chapter 1, page 27), $\varepsilon_{01} = 11\cdot5 - 0\cdot25|q_1'|$, whence $\varepsilon_{01}' = 9\cdot3$ kcal. So $E_C = 47\cdot8$ kcal, and the rate of decomposition at $[RBr] \simeq 10^{19}$ is

$$w_C = 10^{11} \times 10^{19} \exp(-47\cdot8/RT)$$

Dynamic experiments [23] give the unimolecular decomposition rate as

$$w_0 = 10^{13}[RBr] \exp(-47\cdot7/RT)$$
$$= 10^{13} \times 10^{19} \exp(-47\cdot7/RT)$$

E_C and E_D accidentally coincide, but the pre-exponential factors are different, and $w_D/w_C \simeq 100$, so the direct decomposition occurs 100 times more rapidly than the chain decomposition.

Different relationships are found in $n\text{-}C_3H_7Br$. The chain reaction has two alternative paths, A and B, according as to whether H is abstracted from the CH_2 or the CH_2Br group.

A.

(1) $Br + CH_3CH_2CH_2Br \rightarrow HBr + CH_3\text{—}\dot{C}H\text{—}CH_2Br - 4$ kcal,

The subsequent radical decomposition is rapid:*

(2) $CH_3\text{—}\dot{C}H\text{—}CH_2Br \rightarrow Br + CH_3\text{—}CH{=}CH_2 - 14$ kcal.

The other reaction also occurs simultaneously:

B.

(1a) $Br + CH_3CH_2\text{—}CH_2Br \rightarrow HBr + CH_3\text{—}CH_2\text{—}\dot{C}HBr -$
$$- 7 \text{ kcal.}$$

The radical thus obtained cannot decompose, and can only either recombine or propagate the chain:

(1′) $CH_3\text{—}CH_2\text{—}\dot{C}HBr + CH_3CH_2CH_2Br$
$$\rightarrow CH_3CH_2CH_2Br + CH_3\text{—}CH\text{—}CH_2Br + 3 \text{ kcal.}$$

(2) $CH_3 + \dot{C}H\text{—}CH_2Br \rightarrow CH_3CH{=}CH + Br - 14$ kcal.

Since (1a) is very endothermic, it will be about 10 times less rapid than (1), but it should be taken into account, since it gives the inactive radical $CH_3CH_2\dot{C}HBr$, which terminates the chain:

(3) $2CH_3CH_2\dot{C}HBr \rightarrow$ products of low activity.

The kinetic law, analogous to (5), derived from the above scheme is:

$$w_C = 10k_1' \Big/ \sqrt{\left(\frac{k_0}{k_3}[RBr]\right)} [RBr]\dagger$$

The activation energy will not be the same, since q' and Q_{C-Br} are different, the latter being about 62 kcal: $E_C = \frac{1}{2}Q_{C-Br} + \varepsilon_1'$.

---

* It is rapid in spite of being strongly endothermic, because it is unimolecular and therefore has a large pre-exponential factor.

† The data of AGIUS and MACCOLL [34], which have been verified by KAPRALOVA and SERGEEV, imply an order of 3/2 in [RBr]. AGIUS and MACCOLL explain this (incorrectly) as being due to chain termination by combination of bromine atoms. Their scheme may readily be shown to give an initial rate proportional to [RBr], and not to $[RBr]^{3/2}$ as found by experiment.

$\varepsilon_1' = q' + \varepsilon_{01} = 9 + 9 \cdot 3 = 18 \cdot 3$ kcal for $iso\text{-}C_3H_7Br$, while $(1')$ is exothermic in $n\text{-}C_3H_7Br$, and $\varepsilon_1' = 11 \cdot 5 - 0 \cdot 25|q| \simeq 10 \cdot 5$ kcal. Then $E_C = 31 + 10 \cdot 5 = 41 \cdot 5$ kcal. At $[RBr] \simeq 10^{19}$, we find (in agreement with experiment)

$$w_C = 10^{12} \times 10^{19} \exp\left(-41 \cdot 5/RT\right)$$

During the past year MACCOLL *et al.* [35–40] have published data on the pyrolysis of a number of organic bromides: $n\text{-}C_3H_7Br$, $iso\text{-}C_3H_7Br$, allyl bromide, etc. Their kinetic analysis agrees precisely with ours. The possibility that bromine might give two distinct radicals from the bromide was considered; the first being an active chain-carrying radical, and the second of low activity. According to MACCOLL, the inactive radical in the case of $n\text{-}C_3H_7Br$ is

$$\dot{C}H_2CH_2CH_2Br,$$

but it seems more likely that it is $CH_3CH_2\dot{C}HBr$, since Q_{C-H} for the CH_2Br group is 5 kcal less than for the CH_3 group.

MACCOLL also proposes that chain termination occurs by the inactive radical combining with bromine. A termination mechanism of this type is quite probable: the scheme proposed implies an order of $3/2$:

$(3')$　$Br + CH_3CH_2\dot{C}HBr \rightarrow$ products.

$$w_C = \sqrt{\left(\frac{k_0 k_1'}{k_3' k_{1a}}\right)}$$

The activation energy will be $E_C = \varepsilon_1 + \frac{1}{2}(Q_0 + \varepsilon_{01} - \varepsilon_{1a})$. ε_1 and ε_{1a} are determined from the standard formula (14·5 and 16·7 kcal respectively) $\varepsilon_{01}' = 11 \cdot 5 - (0 \cdot 25 \times 3) = 10 \cdot 75$ kcal. Hence $E_C = 14 \cdot 5 + (63 + 10 \cdot 75 - 16 \cdot 7)/2 \sim 42$ kcal, which is in good agreement with experiment. This means that $n\text{-}C_3H_7Br$ decomposes unimolecularly at a rate $w_D = 10^{13} \exp\left(-50 \cdot 7/RT\right)[RBr]$ [31]. Hence $w_C/w_D = 0 \cdot 1 \exp\left(+9/RT\right)$, so $w_C/w_D = 60$ at $700°K$. Thus the chain reaction is some 60 times more rapid than the direct decomposition in $n\text{-}C_3H_7Br$.

The decomposition of $n\text{-}C_3H_7Br$ in toluene [31] or *cyclo*hexane [41] cannot be considered as a simple molecular reaction, with no secondary complications, e.g. short chains. If we take (1) as correct and calculate the rates which should be observed at the temperatures used by SERGEEV (conditions static) e.g. $406°C$, we find that the molecular and chain rates are about equal at ~ 16 mm Hg. Since the unimolecular direct reaction is of the first order, while the chain reaction is of the order $3/2$, then some deviation from the $3/2$ law should be observable at $406°C$, but this is not the case.

If E_D is raised from 50·7 to 54 kcal, then $w_D/w_C \sim 0·1$, and the observed relation would be complied with. The extent to which the 3/2 law is obeyed is illustrated by Fig. 18. Fig. 19 contains the data of Fig. 18 replotted using w_0/P_0 and $\sqrt{P_0}$ as axes. If the reactions are simultaneous, $w_0 = k_1 P_0^{3/2} + k_2 P_0$, or $w_0/P_0 = k_1 \sqrt{P_0} + k_2$,

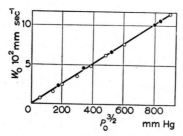

Fig. 18. Initial rate of decomposition in n-C_3H_7Br as a function of initial pressure to the power 3/2 at 403°C

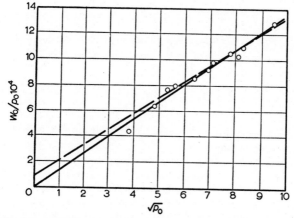

Fig. 19. Relation between chain and molecular decomposition

where k_1 is the constant for the chain reaction and k_2 for the molecular. The intercept on the axis of w_0/P_0 must give k_2.

The points are evidently such that the intercept cannot be greater than 1, i.e. $k_2 = 1·0 \times 10^{-4}$ sec^{-1}. This is much lower than the constant in (1), where $k' = 10^{13} \exp(-50·7 = 1·352) = 10^{-3}$ sec^{-1} at 403°C. Since the experimental k_2 is 10^{-4} sec^{-1}, E_D must be 54 kcal. This is the least possible value E_D can have, and in that case the chain length may be greater than 60.

When C_2H_5Br decomposes in a vessel that has been used for many previous static experiments, it does so unimolecularly, since the walls are covered with a thin layer of polymeric products. By analysis of experimental data I have found that the decomposition of C_2H_5Br has an activation energy of 49–50 kcal; this has been confirmed by SERGEEV and KAPRALOVA's data. The chain reaction has two elementary steps, as we supposed:

(1) $Br + C_2H_5Br \rightarrow HBr + C_2H_4Br$,

(2) $C_2H_4Br \rightarrow C_2H_4 + Br$.

(1) can be shown to occur in two distinct ways:

(1) $Br + CH_3\text{—}CH_2Br \rightarrow HBr + \dot{C}H_2\text{—}CH_2Br - 5$ kcal.

the radical then decomposing in (2):

(2) $\dot{C}H_2CH_2Br \rightarrow C_2H_4 + Br - 18$ kcal.

These two reactions carry the chain readily. Another mode is possible:

(1a) $Br + CH_3\text{—}CH_2Br \rightarrow HBr + CH_3\text{—}\dot{C}HBr - 2$ kcal.

(assuming $Q_{C\text{—}H}$ is greater by 3 kcal for CH_3 than for $CHBr$). The radical cannot decompose and liberate bromine, and can only either recombine or react as in (1'):

(1') $CH_3\dot{C}HBr + CH_3\text{—}CH_2Br \rightarrow CH_3CH_2Br + \dot{C}H_2\text{—}CH_2Br$
$$- 3 \text{ kcal.}$$

The radical formed in (1') is capable of decomposing as in (2). Since (1) is more endothermic than (1') the chain mainly propagates via (1a), (1') and (2). Ethyl bromide occupies a position intermediate between the propyl bromides as far as the relative balance between chain and molecular modes is concerned. The heat of (1') for iso-C_3H_7Br is $- 9$ kcal, while for n-C_3H_7Br it is $+ 3$ kcal, and for C_2H_5Br it is $- 3$ kcal. Taking ε_0 as being 1–2 kcal for ethyl bromide, and $Q_{C\text{—}Br}$ as 65 kcal, E_C is found to be 44·5 kcal, which is some 5–6 kcal less than E_D (unimolecular decomposition). At 700°K this difference between the energies implies that the chain reaction is 34 times more rapid. The pre-exponential factor in the chain reaction rate constant is some 100 times less than that for the unimolecular reaction, at pressures near atmospheric. So the unimolecular rate at pressures near $p = 1$ atm exceeds that of the chain reaction by several times.*

Any factor which tends to make the initial free radical production easier (by reducing the energy required to produce the first bromine

* At $p \sim 0·1$ atm the chain rate is some tens of times lower.

atoms) will evidently tend to make a chain reaction dominant: added bromine has precisely this effect. This is probably also the reason why the state of the container wall, or oxygen and other substances, so strongly accelerate decomposition.

SERGEEV [42] has investigated the decompositions of all the isomeric butyl monobromides. Table 39 gives SERGEEV's main data for the propyl and butyl bromides.

Out of the four butyl bromides, two (n- and iso-C_4H_9Br) decompose inherently by chain mechanisms. This was shown by all the usual effects—catalytic action of bromine and oxygen, retarding action of propylene and cyclohexane, poor reproducibility and 3/2 order of reaction. The secondary and tertiary bromides had first-order decompositions, and the rates were apparently unaffected by bromine and propylene. iso-C_4H_9Br gave the clearest indications of chain-

$$\begin{array}{c} CH_3 \\ \diagdown \\ \diagup \\ CH_3 \end{array} CH - CH_2Br$$

decomposition: this would naturally be expected, since bromine will mainly abstract hydrogen from the tertiary carbon, $(CH_3)_2\dot{C}$—$CHBr$ being formed; the latter readily goes over iso-butylene and atomic bromine, and the chain propagates. As in n-C_3H_7Br, the probability of obtaining the hydrogen from the CH_2Br group is lower, and the result would be the same.

The activation energy for iso-BuBr may be somewhat less than for n-C_3H_7Br, since $Q_{C—Br}$ for iso-C_4H_9Br is probably somewhat less for n-C_3H_7Br. The observed activation energy (30 kcal) is extremely small, though, and can only be explained by chain initiation at the walls; this would also explain the poor reproducibility.

Although n-C_4H_9Br is similar in structure to n-C_3H_7Br, it is possible to obtain two different inactive radicals from n-C_4H_9Br, by abstracting hydrogen from the CH_2 and CH_2Br groups respectively. The same relationship is found by kinetic analysis as in n-C_3H_7Br. An unexplained discrepancy is that the activation energy is 6 kcal greater than for n-C_3H_7Br. This may possibly be due to the increased probability of producing inactive radicals, however.

The CHBr hydrogen atom is most readily removed from sec.-butyl bromide; this gives an inactive radical which cannot decompose directly. An active radical is formed by abstracting from the CH_2 group, though this is energetically more difficult, since $Q_{C—H}$ for the CHBr group is 5 kcal less than for the CH_2 group. As in iso-C_3H_7Br, chain reaction is still possible, but it is much slower than molecular elimination. The ratio of rates will not be so great with sec.-C_4H_9Br as with iso-C_4H_9Br, however, since the active radical is

Table 39. Decomposition of bromides

No.	Compound and conditions	E (kcal)	k	Action of additional materials	Mode of reaction	(Data of MACCOLL [41]—decomposition in presence of excess *cyclohexane*)
1	n-C_3H_7Br $p = 10$–100 mm Hg $T = 347$–$397°C$	42	$1.21T^{1/2} \exp(-42/RT)$ $(cm^3/mol)^{1/2}sec^{-1}$	O_2, Br_2 accelerate; HBr accelerates weakly; C_3H_6 retards somewhat	Chain	$8 \times 10^{12} \exp(-50.7/RT) sec^{-1}$
2	iso-C_3H_7Br $p = 10$–150 mm Hg $T = 347$–$497°C$	47	$5.5 \times 10^{12} \exp(-47/RT) sec^{-1}$	C_3H_6—no action	Molecular	$4.2 \times 10^{13} \exp(-17.8/RT) sec^{-1}$
3	n-C_4H_9Br $p = 20$–150 mm Hg $T = 340$–$460°C$	48	$0.6 \times 10^8 T^{1/2} \exp(-48/RT)$ $(cm^3/mol)^{1/2} sec^{-1}$	Br_2 accelerates; C_3H_6 retards somewhat	Chain	$1.5 \times 10^{13} \exp(-50.9/RT) sec^{-1}$
4	iso-C_4H_9Br $p = 10$–150 mm Hg $T = 300$–$390°C$	30	$0.58 \times 10^{-3} T^{1/2} \exp(-30/RT)$ $(cm^3/mol)^{1/2} sec^{-1}$	Br_2 accelerates; C_3H_6 retards somewhat *reproducibility poor*	Chain	$1.12 \times 10^{13} \exp(-50.4/RT) sec^{-1}$
5	sec.-C_4H_9Br $p = 10$–200 mm Hg $T = 330$–$400°C$	45.5	$1.1 \times 10^{13} \exp(-45.5/RT) sec^{-1}$	C_3H_6—no action	Molecular	$4.25 \times 10^{12} \exp(-42.2/RT) sec^{-1}$
6	$tert$.-C_4H_9Br $p = 10$–150 mm Hg $T = 265$–$825°C$	41	$1.7 \times 10^{13} \exp(41/RT) sec^{-1}$	C_3H_6—no action	Molecular?	$10^{14} \exp(-42.2/RT) sec^{-1}$

obtained by attack on the CH_2 group, which makes less demands on the energy. The activation energy reduction on going from iso-C_3H_7Br to $sec.$-C_4H_9Br (47 kcal to 45·5 kcal) is probably connected with reduced Q_{C-H} (see this Chapter, Section 3).

When hydrogen is abstracted from $tert.$-C_4H_9Br the radical formed can always decompose readily into olefin + Br. Chain termination here occurs by combination of the active radical with Br, and the reaction is consequently of the first order. The activation energy calculated from the elementary reactions is 42 kcal, which agrees well with the experimental value (41 kcal). All the data might appear to point to its being a chain reaction, but a number of facts cannot be reconciled with this. Thus, the rate is not affected by bromine, which may be considered as indicating unimolecularity. This is not entirely compatible with the low activation energy, as Q_{C-H} is high for the CH_3 groups, as in $sec.$-C_4H_9Br and iso-C_3H_7Br. Although all the above facts indicate that iso-C_3H_7Br and $sec.$-C_4H_9Br decompose unimolecularly, all the bromides (including these two) show self-inhibition, the reaction finally stopping almost completely. SERGEEV [33] showed that this did not mean that thermodynamic equilibrium was reached (as MACCOLL and THOMAS suppose [29]) since it occurs far from the equilibrium concentrations. SERGEEV carried out experiments on n-C_3H_7Br until the pressure changes ceased, which seemed to indicate equilibrium. The mixture compositions corresponding to this state were then calculated and artificial mixtures made. When these artificial mixtures were introduced into the reactor at 400°C a reaction, characterized by a pressure change, took place. Consequently, cessation of reaction in the first case is not due to attainment of equilibrium.

Self-inhibition phenomena at stages far from completion are characteristic of chain reactions, even if the principal products do not retard the reaction—a particular instance being hydrocarbon cracking. This is impossible in unimolecular reactions. If iso-C_3H_7Br and $sec.$-C_4H_9Br were to give the same result as n-C_3H_7Br (as is very probable, since inhibition effects are similar for all bromides) then the presumed molecular character of their decompositions would have to be reviewed.

These experiments give a first qualitative relation between reaction mechanism and structure of reactants.

4. ALKYL CHLORIDE DECOMPOSITION

The decompositions of alkyl chlorides to HCl and olefin (chloro-olefins being produced from polychlorides) differ markedly in the way the state of the walls influences the rate.

The rate in a fresh quartz vessel exceeds that found in the same vessel when it has been used for a hundred-odd experiments, by a factor of some dozens. Evidently some unsaturated carbon compounds are formed in very minute quantities in addition to the main products from chloride decomposition, and these deposit a very thin layer on the surfaces. This layer is not removed on evacuation, and remains there from one experiment to another. After some dozens of experiments the surface layer becomes quite appreciable, being of a dark grey colour. The rate falls as the layer grows, some limiting stable value, subsequently unchanged, being attained after around 100 experiments.

Most workers (BARTON, HOWLETT, WILLIAMS, etc.) have restricted their main investigations of chloride pyrolysis to such stabilized vessels. All chlorides have been shown to have first-order decompositions, the rate-constant remaining the same up to 30–50 per cent transformation. The constant is somewhat reduced on increasing the percentage transformation. Increase of S/V alters the rate little.

It has further been shown that alkyl chlorides behave differently under these stabilized conditions: they can be divided into two groups. The first comprises those showing propylene [43] n-hexane [43] and acetaldehyde [44] retardation, and oxygen and chlorine catalysis [45]. In some cases, particularly in propylene retardation, an induction period is at first observed, followed by autocatalysis. 1,2 dichloroethane [43], 1,1,1 trichloroethane [46], 1,1,2 trichloroethane [47], 1,1,1,2 tetrachloroethane [48], 1,1,2,2 tetrachloroethane [48] and 1,4 dichlorobutane [47] fall in this group.

BARTON [43, 44, 46], HOWLETT [43, 44] and WILLIAMS [47, 48] suppose that chain decomposition occurs here, e.g. via

(0) $CH_2Cl-CH_2Cl \rightarrow Cl + CH_2-CH_2Cl - Q$,   initiation

(1) $Cl + CH_2Cl-CH_2Cl \rightarrow HCl + CHCl-CH_2Cl + q_1$,
   ($q_1 \sim$ 3–5 kcal)

(2) $CHCl-CH_2Cl \rightarrow Cl + CHCl = CH_2 - q_2$,
   ($q_2 \sim$ 24 kcal)

chain

(3) $Cl + CH_2Cl-CHCl \rightarrow CH_2Cl-CHCl_2$.   termination.

The second group comprises those insensitive to propylene, oxygen, etc. (at least under stabilized conditions). This includes: EtCl [49], 1,1 dichloroethane [49], 1,2 dichloropropane [50], 2-chloropropane [50], n-propyl chloride [51], n-butyl chloride [51] and *iso*butyl chloride [52]. The respective workers suppose they decompose by truly molecular mechanisms, direct to HCl and olefin.

We consider that this hypothesis is supported by some purely chemical arguments. As was noted in relation to bromide decompositions, chain propagation is inhibited if, when atomic chlorine reacts with the chloride, the radical most likely to be formed cannot give an olefin by loss of atomic chlorine. Chain decomposition is then impeded, and so direct production of HCl + olefin becomes predominant. Actually, with EtCl and 1, 1 dichloroethane, in (1) above, the H atom more readily removed is from the chlorinated group, $CHCl-CH_3$ and CCl_2-CH_3 being formed, these not being able to lose Cl.

Conversely, with Group I chlorides, (1) above gives $\dot{C}HCl-CH_2Cl$, $CCl_3-\dot{C}H_2$, $CCl_3-\dot{C}HCl$, $\dot{C}Cl_2-CH_2Cl$ and $\dot{C}Cl_2-CHCl_2$ respectively. Each of these may give Cl + olefin, and the chains may propagate easily.

Most workers who have studied chloride decompositions believe that chain initiation and termination are homogeneous, and that the actions of propylene and other retardants are explained by their terminating chains homogeneously. However, this ignores the very clear and characteristic fact that the rates of decomposition in fresh vessels are quite high for chlorides of both groups. BARTON studied the kinetics in clean vessels quantitatively [45] in a flow apparatus, under conditions where no film deposited on the surface for some time. The reaction was found to be first-order under these conditions, but the constant was considerably greater than in treated vessels. BARTON [45] found the following constants for 1,2 dichloroethane in treated vessels: $k_1 = 6 \cdot 4 \times 10^{10} \exp(-47/RT)$ sec^{-1}, in clean vessels (under flow conditions): $k_1{}^1 = 1 \cdot 6 \times 10^6 \exp(-27 \cdot 1/RT)$ sec^{-1}, so at 362°C, $k_1 = 6 \cdot 4 \times 10^{-6}$, $k_1{}^1 = 8 \cdot 8 \times 10^{-4}$ and at 485°C; $k_1 = 2 \times 10^{-3}$ and $k_1{}^1 = 2 \cdot 8 \times 10^{-2}$. KAPRALOVA's measurements (1954–1955, Institute of Chemical Physics), give $k_1 = 3 \times 10^{11} \exp(-48/RT)$ sec^{-1} and $k_1{}^1 = 10^8 \exp(-32/RT)$ sec^{-1}, which gives, at 480°C, $k_1 = 4 \cdot 8 \times 10^{-3}$ and $k_1{}^1 = 5 \cdot 6 \times 10^{-2}$; at 560°C $k_1 = 9 \cdot 4 \times 10^{-2}$, and $k_1{}^1 = 4 \cdot 5 \times 10^{-1}$.

The rate could also be measured under static conditions in clean vessels. However, it was impossible to get accurate data as the surface deteriorated and the rate fell between one experiment and the next.

Two hypotheses as to the reaction in clean vessels may be proposed:

(1) It is a direct, heterogeneously catalysed one at the walls: it is naturally inhibited when the walls are covered with a sufficiently thick layer of condensed products due to using the vessel:

(2) It is practically entirely a homogeneous chain reaction, but the chains are readily initiated at clean walls.

(1) would give the rate as proportional to the surface area; BARTON [53] noted that, in the flow decomposition of 1,2 dichloroethane at 500°C, the rate increased by 17–19 per cent on doubling the surface area. Hence we may conclude that decompositions in clean vessels are not simple, heterogeneously catalysed reactions.

KAPRALOVA showed directly by differential calorimetry that, in both fresh and treated vessels, 1,2 dichloroethane decomposed homogeneously. In sufficiently large vessels (~ 4 cm) the reaction was observed to be non-uniformly distributed. It occurred in a zone about 1 cm thick attached to the wall.

KAPRALOVA's experiments can scarcely be considered other than direct proof that the reaction is generated at the walls in clean vessels, propagating as a chain in the gas. Termination is mainly at the surface, but partially homogeneous, thus causing the reaction zone found in large vessels.

KAPRALOVA found similar results for treated vessels. The reaction is also homogeneous here: in large vessels (diameter ~ 3 cm) it was localized near the wall, in a zone ~ 1 cm wide. The possibility that the chain decomposition occurs with its initiation and termination being mainly at the walls cannot be ruled out. In the absence of homogeneous termination the chain decomposition of the chloride would be first-order, if termination is determined by wall uptake of ACl radicals (A = an olefin biradical: i.e. with $(CH_2Cl)_2$ A = $CHCl—CH_2$), while wall initiation of chains is via:

$$ClH_2C—CH_2Cl + wall \rightarrow Cl_{ad} + CH_2—CH_2Cl$$

KAPRALOVA's most interesting results were obtained on retardation of 1,2 dichloroethane decomposition by propylene.

As BARTON and HOWLETT showed [43] the addition of propylene reduces the rate by a factor of several times in a treated vessel. For example, KAPRALOVA found that, at 555°C 2·7 per cent C_3H_6 reduced the rate by a factor $\sim 2\cdot7$: addition of 10 per cent C_3H_6 reduced the initial rate by a factor 3, and of 20 per cent C_3H_6, by 3·36 times.

KAPRALOVA first studied the action of propylene on chloride decompositions in clean vessels. It was incomparably greater than that found in treated vessels, e.g. at 430°C 0·5 per cent C_3H_6 reduced the rate by about a factor 20. Such a difference of itself casts doubt on the hypothesis that propylene acts by terminating chains homogeneously. KAPRALOVA showed, by differential calorimetry, that, after the zone had contracted slightly, due to the small amount of propylene added ($\sim 0\cdot01$ per cent), further addition of C_3H_6, up to 0·5 per cent, did not alter the zone width any more. Meanwhile, 0·01 per cent C_3H_6 reduced the rate only by a factor 1·5–2, while 0·5 per cent reduced by a factor 20.* Otherwise put, propylene does

---

* The retardation was considerably greater in the initial phase, e.g. at 4 per cent change the rate was reduced by a factor 50 by 0·5 per cent C_3H_6. As the percentage change increased the retarded reactions became appreciably faster in all cases.

not reduce the rate by shortening the homogeneous chains, i.e. it acts on the surface, not on the gas.

Propylene evidently gradually blocks the wall free valencies by being adsorbed on the surface, thereby reducing the rate of wall initiation of chains. The nature of the limiting retarded reaction occurring when a definite amount of C_3H_6 has been added (further propylene not affecting the rate) cannot be considered as established. It may possibly be of the purely molecular type proposed by HINSHELWOOD [54] for hydrocarbon cracking, completely NO-retarded. This limiting retarded reaction may be a chain one, with equilibrium radical concentrations, just as has been shown for the H_2/Cl_2 reaction (Chapter 6, Section 1).

5. THE CRACKING OF HYDROCARBONS

Alkane cracking has been studied in most detail, particularly for the lower homologues. The initial rate is of first order with respect to the initial pressure at medium pressures (50–500 mm/Hg).*

RICE and HERZFELD [55], as indicated above, sought to explain some aspects of these processes via chain mechanisms, which later received general recognition (see Chapter II).

In 1933 FROST and DINTSES observed the retardation of the initial hydrocarbon decomposition by its products, or by propylene admixture [56].† HINSHELWOOD [54] showed that nitric oxide produced a similar effect. His qualitative study of the fall of cracking rate-constant with NO concentration showed that, at sufficiently high NO concentrations, the rate-constant became independent of [NO], attaining some constant limiting value (the rate-constant for the "completely inhibited reaction"). It was later found that propylene had a similar effect to NO, and, which is more important, the limiting retarded rates were identical. The difference between these gases consisted solely in the need to add considerably more propylene to obtain the same effect (e.g. 12·5 times more C_3H_6 than NO had to be used to retard the cracking of n-C_5H_{12} [54] at 530°C). Fig. 20 shows HINSHELWOOD's data on NO and C_3H_6 inhibition in the cracking of n-C_5H_{12}. STEPUKHOVICH [57] made quantitative

---

* Even in this range there are important discrepancies, principally at the higher pressures, with unbranched long-chain alkanes ($n > 6$), so a law of mixed first and second orders, $Ap_0 + Bp_0^2$, has to be used. The first-order law is sufficiently accurate over a considerably wider range in branched-chain hydrocarbons.

† An exception is ethylene, admixture of which does not retard the decomposition of ethane, although this decomposition also becomes strongly retarded during the reaction. The cause of this effect with ethane has so far not been discovered.

measurements of the effect of *iso*-C_4H_8 and C_3H_6 on hydrocarbon decompositions, and showed that the retarded rates were identical.

A number of parallel studies have been made on NO- and self-inhibition (NO absent) in cracking. POLTORAK for example [58], and VOEVODSKII [59] showed that the rate of propane cracking was the same, at sufficiently large percentual reaction, whether the

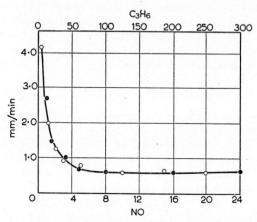

Fig. 20. Comparison of NO and propylene retardation on cracking *n*-pentane (530°C, 100 mm)

propane was pure or "completely" NO-inhibited. This means that the limiting retardation is the same for NO and cracking-products. The results are shown in Fig. 21.

This is obviously in agreement with HINSHELWOOD's view that each particular hydrocarbon has a unique limiting inhibited cracking rate, dependent only on the presence of sufficient inhibitor, and independent of its nature.

The normal point of view on inhibitor action in chain processes is that these substances react very rapidly with chain radicals, satisfying their free valencies or transforming them to extremely inactive forms. HINSHELWOOD [54] analysed the above work on cracking on this basis, and concluded that the chain was completely suppressed at high NO or C_3H_6 concentrations. The residual reaction not being subject to inhibition, was in his opinion of molecular type. Hence the constant rate for different inhibitors was explained. Since it is actually difficult to explain this important, purely experimental, fact in any other way, it is a serious argument in favour of HINSHELWOOD's assumption that the completely inhibited process is molecular.

On the other hand there are many factors which cast doubt upon this simple and apparently natural hypothesis: e.g. it is well known from the work of HINSHELWOOD and others that the product compositions from hydrocarbon pyrolyses are the same for both the uninhibited and the completely inhibited reactions. This is so in all temperature ranges in which the cracking has been studied.

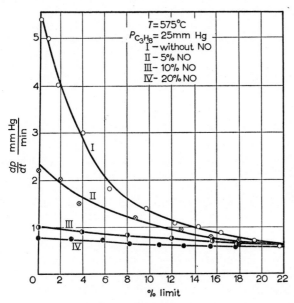

Fig. 21. Effect of NO on the cracking rate in propane.
(575°C, 25 mm Hg)

More recently, this has been confirmed by POLTORAK [58] for propane cracking. The results for one such series are given in Table 40.

If we take HINSHELWOOD's point of view, we have no explanation why the two completely different mechanisms (chain and molecular) give exactly the same products. Some perplexity is also caused by the observation that the rates of the chain and molecular reactions are in general very little different (if we follow HINSHELWOOD) for a very large number of compounds—hydrocarbons of varied structure, esters, etc. Although the activation energies for NO-retarded decomposition of the various organic compounds are very varied (50–75 kcal), the difference between the activation energies of the inhibited and uninhibited reactions is very small, being only a few kilocalories.

Table 40. Propane cracking-product compositions, NO *present and absent, at* 590°C *and* $p(C_3H_8) = 25$ mm Hg

% Transformation		% Composition of Product			
		CH$_4$	H$_2$	C$_2$H$_4$ + C$_2$H$_6$	C$_3$H$_6$
5	without NO	23·5	29	16·5	31
	+ 20% NO	22·6	29·1	22	26
20	without NO	27·3	21·7	24·7	26·4
	+ 20% NO	28	20	28	24

RICE and POLLY [60], and, in more detail, GOLDANSKII [61] have proposed a very reasonable explanation for the limiting retardation effect: all compounds capable of chain-rupture are also simultaneously capable of chain-initiation. This hypothesis explains the limiting retardation observed on adding sufficient inhibitor. The residual rate is then naturally that of the chain, and the discrepancies indicated above, being due to the assumed molecular mechanism for the limitingly inhibited reaction, disappear. This interpretation is also considered unsatisfactory though, because it does not explain the very remarkable and important fact that the limits of retardation are quantitatively the same for different inhibitors.

Thus it is necessary to determine whether the fully retarded reaction is molecular or chain-type by direct experiment. WALL and MOORE [62] made the first attempt at this. They cracked a C_2H_6/C_2D_6 mixture alone and with 2·5 per cent NO at 610°C. The H_2, HD and D_2 contents were the same in both cases, with $H_2 \simeq$ HD $\approx D_2$. It was shown that the exchange occurred in relation to the actual decomposition since at the same temperature H_2/D_2, H_2/CD_4, D_2/CH_4 and CD_2/CH_4 mixtures did not exchange so extensively when ethane was absent.

The exchange data for CH_4 and C_2H_6 given by WALL and MOORE lead one to conclude that NO does not alter the chain mechanism at all appreciably, since purely molecular reactions in C_2H_6 and C_2D_6 mixtures should give only H_2 and D_2, and no HD. HINSHELWOOD [63] analysed this work, and pointed out that the NO added was insufficient for complete inhibition. We consider that the use of 2·5 per cent NO reduces the initial rate so markedly (HINSHELWOOD assigns this to the chain mechanism) however, that if the molecular reaction occurs at all it would give a considerable reduction in the exchange.

POLTORAK and VOEVODSKII [64] studied the pyrolysis of $C_3H_8 + D_2$ to determine the nature of the completely NO-inhibited reaction, and measured the ethylene deuterium content. The chain-carriers in the radical mechanism must interact with D_2 to form deuterated products. Of itself, the molecular process cannot give deuteration. Exchange was found to occur identically, whether sufficient NO was present for complete inhibition, or if it was absent. Identical exchange in the ethylene was observed at equal degrees of transformation. This shows that the limiting retarded reaction is also a chain, and not molecular. This can be expressed as the deuterate being formed by processes independent of cracking in both cases, e.g. by surface reaction: so the independent process must be related not to the extent of reaction, but to time only. A converse result is obtained experimentally: the exchange corresponds completely with the extent of reaction, and is independent of the time required to attain it (the times required with and without NO differ by a factor 7). This work was inadequate, in that, although different temperatures and $C_3H_8:D_2$ ratios were used, the extent of reaction was always the same. It was hence essential to show that the exchange was actually proportional to the percentage reacted. RICE and VARNERIN [65] did this for the cracking of $C_2D_6 : CH_4$ mixtures. The CH_3D/CH_4 ratio was actually proportional to the percentage reacted, being the same whether NO was absent, or present in a sufficiently large amount.

This undoubtedly indicates that the limiting retarded reaction is not molecular, but chain-type. HINSHELWOOD considers that this has not been sufficiently conclusively demonstrated. In our opinion, though, HINSHELWOOD's work [66, 67] on the decomposition of CH_4 and C_4H_{10} (plus D_2), and of ^{14}C-propane, gives an additional excellent proof that the mechanisms are the same (chains) in the inhibited and unhibited reactions. His arguments against this conclusion in these papers appear to us not sufficiently telling; e.g. he considers it as being proved that butylene does not undergo chain decomposition. Because butane and butylene were found to exchange with CH_4 on decomposition, he considers this proof that there is no chain mechanism in the fully retarded butane decomposition. As we have shown above (Chapter 2), there are in our opinion many reasons for considering butylene decomposition to be a chain, and HINSHELWOOD's work may, moreover, be considered as a simple proof of this.

Also very recently KEBARLE and BRYCE [68] have studied the pyrolysis of butylene plus $Hg(CH_3)_2$. The CH_3 radicals formed when the latter decomposes accelerate the reaction, which undoubtedly shows it to be radical and not molecular.

However, if HINSHELWOOD's hypothesis had explained why the limiting effects were the same for different inhibitors simply and clearly, then, since we now know that the residual reaction is of chain type, this extremely important question would again be unsolved.

Latterly, POLTORAK and VOEVODESKII [58, 59], using experimental data on propane cracking (25–50 mm Hg, 500–600°C), have proposed that the action of inhibitors in retarding the chain reactions in alkane pyrolysis may be due to chain termination and retardation being heterogeneous. This is fairly similar to the explanation of the kinetics of chloride pyrolyses given above.

VOEVODESKII [59], considering this problem, supposed that non-reversible decomposition processes could occur at the walls, which caused radicals to be ejected into the gas, such as the reaction

$$H_2 + Cl_2 \xrightarrow{\text{wall}} HCl + Cl + (H)$$

which was considered above when analysing surface effects in the kinetics of the thermal H_2/Cl_2 reaction. These irreversible processes are stimulated by free valencies in the glass, and initially produce increased radical concentrations in the gas, which also causes an increased initial rate in the absence of the inhibitors. Concurrently with these processes the free valencies are gradually used up, and the wall goes over to a state where only the reversible processes of dissociation and a recombination occur, which correspond to some equilibrium radical concentration in the gas, as was considered in the H_2/Cl_2 reaction. So if the non-reversible wall processes are completely suppressed the rate will be independent of the state of the surface. Hence the limiting self-inhibition in the decompositions of pure hydrocarbons is explained, as well as the identical results found with various inhibitors.

From this point of view the limiting inhibited rate is the true chain rate in cracking. Then the free radical concentrations and hence the rate, will be constant and independent of the sites where radicals are generated and removed—in the volume or on the surface, or in both places at once. If so the rate should not depend on S/V.

The initial phase is then "non-equilibrium" and corresponds to introducing an initiator which is used up (in this case the initiators are wall free valencies, which are gradually blocked, in VOEVODESKII's opinion). Hence the initial rate should depend on the state of the surface. POLTORAK and VOEVODESKII [58, 59] first showed that the initial rate was dependent on the surface condition with small amounts of O_2. For example, treatment of a quartz vessel with HF + NH_4F or hot hydrofluoric acid caused the initial rate of decomposition in 25 mm C_3H_8 + 1–2 mm O_2 to increase by 4–5 times. The HF-activated surface gradually lost its activity after many experiments, and the rates finally became comparable with those for untreated vessels at the same level of O_2. It is also interesting that untreated wool introduced into a treated vessel at

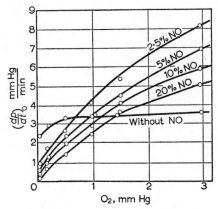

Fig. 22. Relation of reaction rate to NO and oxygen contents. (575°C, propane pressure 25 mm)

once reduced the rate to that for an untreated one. The rate remained reduced when the wool was removed.

The addition of NO to a C_3H_8/O_2 mixture does not reduce the rate, but, conversely, increases it (see Fig. 22).

POLTORAK and VOEVODSKII discovered that treatment of the vessel with MoO_3 caused NO to become a very weak inhibitor (with oxygen absent) and the reduction in initial rate on adding 20 per cent NO to be only about 20 per cent, while in a clean vessel the fall would be by a factor 8–12 in thermal conditions. LEITIS and POLTORAK have found that special wall treatments can raise the initial cracking rate [$Mg(ClO_4)_2$] or reduce it (H_2S + NO), while the rate changes do not depend on S/V and hence are not due to heterogeneous catalysis. The same independence of S/V was demonstrated for HF-treated vessels.

These experiments lead us to conclude that, at least sometimes, chains are initiated at the surface in cracking. The interdependence of the initial rate and S/V has often been remarked. This fact indicates that both initiation and termination occur at the surface of the reaction vessel.

6. FACTORS INFLUENCING THE CHAIN LENGTH

As we saw above, even very small amounts of certain extremely effective substances (oxygen, peroxides, ions of variable valency, etc.), can produce the initial free radicals comparatively readily, and thus accelerate reactions considerably.

In the rate-formula there is a factor for the rate of initiation; since accelerators increase this considerably, they also increase the overall rate. This accentuates the importance of chain modes.

Many chain reactions in liquids are known to occur at very low temperatures, particularly oxidations (e.g. aldehydes), if appropriate impurities are present, or if peroxides are amongst the primary products. ν is frequently $\sim 10^4$ under these circumstances, and the reaction may be rapid even at very low rates of initiation, i.e. if the amount of catalyst is very small.

Some factors which influence ν will now be considered. The chain length is given by the ratio of the chain rate to the rate of primary reactant dissociation, J_0. Thus, if X = halogen, then the reaction of X_2 with H_2 has $J_0 = 10^{-10} \exp{(-Q/RT)}[X_2][M]$. Since

$$w_C = 10^{-10} \exp{(-\varepsilon_1/RT)}[X][H_2]$$
$$= 10^{-10} \exp{(-\varepsilon_1/RT)}\sqrt{(J_0/k_3)}[H_2], \text{ and } k_3 = 10^{-32}[M]$$

with $[M] \simeq 10^{19}$ at $p = 1$ atm, the chain length is

$$\nu = \frac{w_C}{J_0} = \frac{10^{-10} \exp{(-\varepsilon_1/RT)}10^{19}}{\sqrt{(k_3 J_0)}}$$

$$= \frac{10^9 \exp{(-\varepsilon_1/RT)}}{\sqrt{\{10^{-32}[M]10^{-10}\exp{(-Q/RT)}[X_2][M]\}}}$$

$$= \frac{10^9 \exp{[(\tfrac{1}{2}Q - \varepsilon_1)/RT]}}{10^{19}\sqrt{10^{-23}}} \simeq 10 \exp{\left(\frac{\tfrac{1}{2}Q - \varepsilon_1}{RT}\right)}$$

For $H_2 + Cl_2$, $Q = 57$ kcal and $\varepsilon_1 = 6$ kcal, so at $600°K$ $\nu \simeq 10^9$. For $H_2 + Br_2$, $Q = 46$ kcal and $\varepsilon_1 = 17$ kcal, so $\nu \simeq 10^3$ at $700°K$; since $Q/2$ is usually greater than ε_1, ν falls with increase of T. This may seem unexpected at first sight, but it quite logical, since the recombination rate rises with the free radical concentration, i.e. as J_0 increases. The greater J_0, the greater the rate of recombination, and the shorter the chains.

Photochemically induced chains decrease in length as the inverse square root of the light intensity. The chain length naturally depends on ε_1; if this is large the chains are short, since ν decreases as ε_1 increases. The chain length is:

$$\nu = \frac{w_C}{J_0} = \frac{10^{-10} \exp{(-\varepsilon_1/RT)}[CD]}{\sqrt{(J_0 k_3)}}$$

J_0 depends solely on the number of quanta absorbed, and is temperature-independent. With fixed J_0 ν increases with T, via the factor $\exp\left(-\varepsilon_1/RT\right)$.

ν depends on ε_1 for photoreactions carried out at normal temperatures, ε_1 being the activation energy for the rate-limiting step. If $\varepsilon_1 = 6$ kcal, ν is large, while if $\varepsilon_1 > 10$ kcal, the chains are short. The chains frequently terminate after 1 cycle ($\nu = 1$), the radicals recombining. Under such conditions recombination products form a substantial part of the terminal compounds. The fraction assignable to recombination is small when ν is large. If the dissociation rate is great, ν is small, and a large fraction of the product results from chain radical combination. This is often found in low-temperature liquid reactions.

The occurrence of competing chain and molecular reactions will now be considered. w_C may be expressed as the product of the initiation rate and the chain length, $w_C = J_0\nu$. Each individual endothermic act of dissociation involves the absorption of the equivalent of Q, but the resultant radicals cause numerous molecules to react via the chain mechanism. In direct reactions, even if exothermic, each individual molecular transformation demands a high activation energy. If ν is 10^3, then even if J_0 is 10^3 times less than w_D (the rate of direct reaction), w_C will be equal to w_D. For example, if $\nu = 10^3$, and $T = 800°K$, and Q (the energy required to dissociate the molecule into radicals) is 65 kcal, then if w_C is to be equal to w_D, E for the molecular reaction must be given by

$$\exp\left[-\left(Q - E/RT\right)\right] = 10^{-3} = \exp\left(-6\cdot9\right)$$

since the pre-exponential factors will be approximately equal at $10^{13}\,\text{sec}^{-1}$. Hence $Q - E = 6\cdot9\,RT = 6\cdot9 \times 2 \times 0\cdot8 = 11$ kcal. So $E = 54$ kcal. If $Q - E > 11$ kcal, then the chain predominates, whereas if $Q - E < 11$ kcal, the direct reaction does, so chain reactions may be more rapid than molecular ones even if Q (for chains) is greater than E (for direct molecular reaction).

7. THE ELEMENTARY ACT OF DECOMPOSITION

The primary act of homogenous molecular decomposition, if not complicated by subsequent reactions such as chain propagation or heterogenous combination, is one of extreme interest. In many cases $Q < E$, and the molecule gives radicals more readily than molecular products. In such instances not only chain reactions, but also radical processes ($\nu = 1$) are energetically more favoured than molecular ones. In other cases $E < Q$, and the direct molecular decomposition is considerably more probable. Direct primary molecular decomposition may then be investigated without the trouble due to the chain reaction imitating a first-order reaction.

Unfortunately few investigations into the primary act of decomposition have so far been made. RICE and DOOLEY [69] using the mirror technique, and SZWARC [15] with the toluene method (page 12), have shown that the primary decompositions of many organic molecules give free radicals. In some cases direct decomposition to molecular products, via bond rearrangements, is energetically more favoured than the radical mode. In other cases where the two modes are energetically comparable, decomposition will then be to radicals under some conditions and to molecules under others. Differences between the mechanisms in such instances must naturally depend on the molecular structure, but so far this has not been systematically investigated.

SZWARC, together with a number of other workers, supposes that the primary decompositions of numerous compounds give radicals. His experiments were carried out by flow methods, using heated tubes at very low pressures (< 1 mm Hg) the substances under investigation being diluted with an inert gas. The issuing gas was examined for radicals. (These experiments have been described in Chapter 1.) Ethylbenzene [70] was shown to decompose almost entirely to CH_3 and benzyl, for instance, and not to styrene and hydrogen, as would have been expected from direct molecular reaction. Allyl bromide [71] gives Br and an allyl radical, instead of HBr and propadiene. Ethylene oxide [4] gives CH_3 and HCO, not CH_4 and CO.

Peroxides also decompose to two radicals via O—O bond rupture, and the primary product is thus not molecular; e.g. di-*tert*.-butyl peroxide gives two butoxyl radicals [72]:

$$(CH_3)_3COOC(CH_3)_3 \rightarrow 2(CH_3)_3\dot{C}O$$

Table 40 gives a number of compounds that have been shown by SZWARC and others to decompose primarily to radicals.

A large fraction of the compounds in Table 41 cannot decompose directly to molecular products, due to their structures. Typical instances are bromobenzene, bromonaphthalene, bromophenanthrene, bromoanthracene, the bromomethanes, etc. These compounds may naturally be expected to give radicals. SZWARC *et al.* found that ethyl bromide [30], acetyl bromide [84], and acetic anhydride [84] decomposed to molecular products. When C_2H_5Br decomposed, HBr and C_2H_4 were found, while the amount of dibenzyl, which acts as radical detector, was very small.* CH_3COBr decomposes thus:

$$CH_3COBr \rightarrow CH_3Br + CO \text{ and } CH_3COBr \rightarrow CH_2CO + HBr$$

* This paragraph deals with the primary act of decomposition, and "decomposition" should be taken as implying "primary decomposition".

Table 41

Compound	Radicals formed	$Q_{\text{C—X}}$ (where X may be either an atom or a radical)	Source
CH_3Br	$CH_3 + Br$	67·5	[73]
CH_2Br_2	$CH_2Br + Br$	62·5	[73]
$CHBr_3$	$CHBr_2 + Br$	55·5	[73]
CBr_4	$CBr_3 + Br$	49·0	[73]
CH_2ClBr	$CH_2Cl + Br$	53·5	[73]
CCl_3Br	$CCl_3 + Br$	49·0	[73]
CF_3Br	$CF_3 + Br$	64·5	[73]
C_6H_5Br	$C_6H_5 + Br$	70·9	[74]
$C_6H_5CH_2Br$	$C_6H_5CH_2 + Br$	50·5	[71]
$CH_2{=}CH{-}CH_2Br$	$CH_2{=}CH{-}CH_2 + Br$	47·5	[71]
C_6H_5COBr	$C_6H_5CO + Br$	57·0	[75]
(decalin with Br at ring-junction position)	(decalin radical) $+ Br$	69·2	[76]
(decalin with Br on side)	(decalin radical) $+ Br$	70·0	[76]
(tricyclic with Br)	(tricyclic radical) $+ Br$	67·7	[76]
(linear tricyclic with Br)	(linear tricyclic radical) $+ Br$	65·6	[76]
$C_6H_5CH_2Cl$	$C_6H_5CH_2 + Cl$	68·0	[77]
C_6H_5COCl	$C_6H_5CO + Cl$	73·6	[77]
$CH_3\overset{O}{\overset{\|}{C}}{-}O{-}O{-}\overset{O}{\overset{\|}{C}}{-}CH_3$	$2CH_3\overset{O}{\overset{\|}{C}}{-}O\cdot$	29·5	[78]
$(CH_3)_3COOC(CH_3)_3$	$2(CH_3)_3CO$	36·0	[72]
H_2NNH_2	$2NH_2$	60·0	[79]
$C_6H_5CH_2NH_2$	$C_6H_5CH_2 + NH_2$	59·0	[80]
$C_6H_5CH_2CH_3$	$C_6H_5CH_2 + CH_3$	63·2	[70]
$C_6H_5CH_2CH_2CH_3$	$C_6H_5CH_2 + CH_2CH_3$	57·5	[30]
$C_6H_5CH_2CH_2CH_2CH_3$	$C_6H_5CH_2 + CH_2CH_2CH_3$	65·0	[81]

Table 41.—continued

Compound	Radicals formed	Q_{C-X} (where X may be either an atom or a radical)	Source
$C_6H_5CH(CH_3)_2$	$C_6H_5CHCH_3 + CH_3$	61·0	[82]
$CH_3C_6H_4CH(CH_3)_2$	$CH_3C_6H_4CHCH_3 + CH_3$	60·0	[82]
$C_6H_5-C(CH_3)_2-CH_3$	$C_6H_5C(CH_3)-CH_3 + CH_3$	59·5	[82]
$CH_2=CH-CH_2CH_3$	$CH_2=CH-CH_2 + CH_3$	61·5	[83]
CH_3COCH_3	$CH_3CO + CH_3$	72·0	[14]
CH_2-CH_2 (with O)	$CH_3 + HCO$	44·0	[4]
CH_3I	$CH_3 + I$	54·0	[22]
C_2H_5I	$C_2H_5 + I$	52·2	[22]
$n\text{-}C_3H_7I$	$n\text{-}C_3H_7 + I$	50·0	[22]
$iso\text{-}C_3H_7I$	$iso\text{-}C_3H_7 + I$	46·1	[22]
$n\text{-}C_4H_9I$	$n\text{-}C_4H_9 + I$	49·0	[22]
$tert.\text{-}C_4H_9I$	$tert.\text{-}C_4H_9 + I$	45·1	[22]
$CH_2=CH-CH_2I$	$CH_2=CH-CH_2 + I$	39·0	[22]
$CH_2=CHI$	$CH_2=CH + I$	55·0	[22]
$C_6H_5CH_2I$	$C_6H_5CH_2 + I$	43·7	[22]
C_6H_5I	$C_6H_5 + I$	54·0	[22]
CH_3COI	$CH_3CO + I$	50·7	[22]
C_6H_5COI	$C_6H_5CO + I$	43·9	[22]
CH_3COCH_2I	$CH_3COCH_2 + I$	45·0	[22]

Dibenzyl is not found. Acetic anhydride also does not yield dibenzyl, the molecular products being ketene and acetic acid:

$$CH_3COOCOCH_3 \rightarrow CH_2CO + CH_3COOH$$

These are present in equal amounts.

BLADES and MURPHY [31], using the toluene carrier method, showed that the primary decompositions of C_2H_5Br, $n\text{-}C_3H_7Br$, and $iso\text{-}C_3H_7Br$ were molecular. SERGEEV's and MACCOLL's experiments also demonstrate that C_2H_5Br and $iso\text{-}C_3H_7Br$ decompose molecularly under static conditions, but the decomposition of $n\text{-}C_3H_7Br$ is of chain type. This difference between two compounds otherwise so similar was explained as being due to their respective molecular structures.

SHILOV [85, 86] has recently investigated the primary acts of decomposition in a number of compounds (at the Institute of Chemical Physics), as well as the relation between mechanism and structure. C_2H_5Br, C_2H_3Br, $C_2H_2Br_2$, C_3H_5Cl, CCl_4, $CHCl_3$, CH_2Cl_2 and CH_3Cl were studied by the toluene carrier method. Ethyl bromide decomposed to C_2H_4 and HBr, with a rate constant $k = 1.78 \times 10^{13} \exp(-53,700/RT)$ sec^{-1}, in agreement with the earlier data of SZWARC [30] and BLADES and MURPHY [31].

Vinyl bromide was investigated to elucidate the influence of double bonds. This also decomposes molecularly (dibenzyl absent). The activation energy (65 kcal) was approximately the same as Q_{C-Br}.*

If the molecule contains a second Br atom then the character of the decomposition is different. Ethylene dibromide decomposes at least partially to radicals with an activation energy of 62.8 kcal.

SHILOV found that allyl chloride, like allyl bromide, studied by SZWARC [71], decomposes to radicals giving Cl and an allyl radical by primary decomposition. The activation energy (59.3 kcal) is close to the electron-impact value for Q_{C-Cl} in C_3H_5Cl (60 $\pm$ 4 kcal) [87].

The chloromethanes are of particular interest. Unlike the bromides, which were studied by SZWARC and SEHON [73], some chlorides decompose preferentially to biradicals. According to SHILOV, $CHCl_3$ and CH_2Cl_2 give biradicals:

$$CHCl_3 \rightarrow HCl + \dot{C}Cl_2; \quad CH_2Cl_2 \rightarrow HCl + \dot{C}HCl$$

while CCl_4 and CH_3Cl give univalent radicals, e.g.

$$CCl_4 \rightarrow CCl_3 + Cl$$

$CHCl_3$ also decomposes more rapidly than CCl_4, although Q_{C-Cl} in CCl_4, is lower than in $CHCl_3$. No dibenzyl was found with $CHCl_3$, but C_2Cl_6 was present (from combination of CCl_3 radicals), in very small yield. All these facts indicate that $CHCl_3$ does not decompose by a radical mechanism. Since $CHCl_3$ cannot give molecular products directly, its primary decomposition must involve a biradical. Additional evidence has been obtained by the use of $CDCl_3$. There is an

* The reaction was of second order within the pressure range covered (7–50 mm Hg). $w = k'[C_2H_3Br][M]$, where [M] is the total number of molecules present (C_2H_3Br and toluene). Many unimolecular reactions are found to be second order at sufficiently low pressures. The rate-limiting step in these cases is molecular activation by collision.

isotope effect on the rate, which should be absent if the primary decomposition is to $CHCl_2$ and Cl.*

Dibenzyl was also absent with CH_2Cl_2.

Table 42 gives SHILOV's main results on various halo-hydro-carbons.

Table 42. Activation energies and C—X bond-dissociation energies for some halo-hydrocarbons

Compound	Mechanism	E	$Q_{C—X}$
C_2H_5Br .	Molecular	53·7	65·0
C_2H_3Br .	Molecular	65·5	70 ?
$C_2H_2Br_2$	Radical	62·8	62·8
C_3H_5Cl	Radical	59·3	60 ± 4
CCl_4 . .	Radical	55·1	68–70
$CHCl_3$ . .	Biradical	47·0	73·5 ?
CH_2Cl_2	Biradical	66·5	78·5 ?
CH_3Cl . .	Radical	85·0	83·0

The radical mechanism in CH_3Cl could not be demonstrated in any simple fashion, since the decomposition temperature is so high (800°C) that toluene decomposes rapidly, and the toluene-carrier method cannot be used. The radical nature of the decomposition was deduced from the overall kinetics; the relative amounts of the principal products (HCl, CH_4 and C_2H_2) were estimated from the radical mechanism, and found to agree quite well with analysis. Also, the activation energy (85 kcal) was practically equal to $Q_{C—Cl}$ in CH_3Cl.

The activation energy for CCl_4 (55·1 kcal) gives some cause for doubt. If CCl_4 decomposes by a radical mechanism, as the presence of dibenzyl would indicate, then the activation energy and $Q_{C—Cl}$ should be identical. However, $Q_{C—Cl}$ (68–70 kcal) [89] is some 15 kcal greater than E, $Q_{C—Cl}$ being obtained by electron impact, and also from indirect evidence (see Table 9, Chapter 1).

SHILOV's experimental data may be used in some preliminary general observations on the relation between molecular structure and mode of decomposition. The elementary acts of decomposition for some organic bromides may be considered as illustrations. The unprimed reactions are radical modes, while the primed reactions

---

* $CHCl_3$ was studied by SEMELYUK and BERNSTEIN [88] in 1954. In spite of the main products being HCl and C_2Cl_4 (from combination of CCl_2 biradicals), they assumed this decomposition was uniradical in type.

are molecular. Q_R is the energy absorbed in the radical decomposition, and is equal to Q_{C-Br}. Q_M is the energy absorbed in the molecular reaction.

(1) $CH_3CH_2Br \rightarrow CH_3—CH_2 + Br - Q_R.$

(1') $CH_3CH_2Br \rightarrow CH_2\text{---}CH_2 \rightarrow CH_2\text{=}CH_2$

$$\underset{H \text{------} Br}{} \qquad \underset{HBr}{+} \quad - Q_M.$$

(2) $CH_2\text{=}CHBr \rightarrow CH_2\text{=}CH + Br - Q_R.$

(2') $CH_2\text{=}CHBr \rightarrow HC\text{≡}CH \qquad CH\text{≡}CH$

$$\underset{H\text{---}Br}{} \rightarrow \underset{HBr}{+} \quad - Q_M.$$

(3) $CHBr\text{=}CHBr \rightarrow CHBr\text{=}CH + Br - Q_R.$

(3') $CHBr\text{=}CHBr \rightarrow BrC\text{≡}CH \rightarrow BrC\text{≡}CH$

$$\underset{H\text{---}Br}{} \qquad \underset{HBr}{+} \quad - Q_M.$$

(4) $CH_2Br—CH\text{=}CH_2 \rightarrow CH_2CH\text{=}CH_2 + Br - Q_R.$

(4') $CH_2Br—CH\text{=}CH_2 \rightarrow H_2C\text{---}C\text{=}CH_2 \rightarrow H_2C\text{=}C\text{=}CH_2$

$$\underset{Br\text{--}H}{} \qquad \underset{HBr}{+} \quad - Q_M.$$

(5) $C_6H_5Br \rightarrow C_6H_5 + Br - Q_R.$

(5')

If AHX denotes the alkyl halide, where X is the halogen atom, then A denotes the olefin. Q_M is given by:

$$Q_M = Q_{AH-Br} + Q_{A-H} - Q_{H-Br}$$

Decomposition to radicals involves a scarcely appreciable ε_0, whereas the barrier is always fairly considerable for molecular decomposition. For the radical mode, $E_R = Q_R$, but for the molecular, $E_M = E + Q_M$.

Assuming that the pre-exponential factors for the two modes are identical, at about 10^{13} sec^{-1}, the ratio of rates is:

$$\frac{\exp\left(-E_M/RT\right)}{\exp\left(-E_R/RT\right)} = \exp\left(-\frac{E_M - E_R}{RT}\right)$$

If $E_R - E_M$ is positive, molecular decomposition will predominate, whereas if it is negative the radical mode will. The complete equation for $E_R - E_M$ will take the form:

$$E_R - E_M = Q_{AH-X} - Q_{AH-X} - Q_{A-H} + Q_{H-X} - E_0$$
$$= -Q_{A-H} + Q_{H-X} - E_0$$

Since bromides are being considered, $Q_{H-X} = Q_{H-Br} = 85$ kcal. E_0 will certainly vary between bromides, since it depends on molecular structure; this dependence is not at present known, but the changes cannot be very large, and E_0 lies between 25 and 35 kcal. Exact calculation of E_M is impossible, but Q_{A-H} will have the greater effect on the balance between the reactions, even if not the decisive one; the larger Q_{A-H}, the more the radical mode will predominate. One interesting point is that Q_{AH-X} does not influence the balance of the reactions, since it does not enter into the equation for $E_R - E_M$.

SHILOV estimated Q_{A-H} for the five compounds listed above. Q_{A-H} for ethyl is known to be 38·5 kcal (Chapter 1, page 16). Q_{A-H} is not known for vinyl, but it can be estimated if $Q_{C_2H_3-H}$ is taken as 104 kcal. Thermochemical data give $Q_{CH=CH-H} = 45$ kcal. $Q_{CBr=CBr-H}$ still cannot be estimated for $C_2H_2Br_2$, since the requisite thermochemical data are not available, though it must evidently be larger than Q_{A-H} in vinyl, since the additional bromine atom reduces the energy of the π-bond as compared with that of acetylene, and must therefore raise Q_{A-H}, which latter must therefore be greater than 45 kcal. $Q_{CH_2}\!\!>\!\!C-H$ for allyl may be calculated from
$$CH_2$$

$\Delta H_{C_3H_5}$ (for allyl)

$$CH_2=CH-CH_3 \rightarrow CH_2=CH-CH_2 + H - Q$$

$Q_{C_3H_5-H}$ for the CH_3 group in C_3H_6 is 77 kcal. Then $\Delta H_{C_3H_6} = \Delta H_{C_3H_5} + \Delta H_M - Q$. Substituting for $\Delta H_{C_3H_6}$ and ΔH_M, we get

$$4·9 = \Delta H_{C_3H_5} + 57·9 - 77$$

hence $\Delta H_{C_3H_5} = 30$ kcal. Q_{A-H} may now be calculated for C_3H_5:
$$CH_2=CH-CH_2 \rightarrow CH_2=C=CH_2 + H - Q,$$

$$\Delta H_{C_3H_5} = \Delta H_{C_3H_4} + \Delta H_M - Q$$

hence, since $\Delta H_{C_3H_4}$ (allene) is 46 kcal, $Q_{CH_2\!\!>\!C-H \atop CH_2} = 67\cdot9 \sim 68$ kcal.

In phenyl $Q_{C_6H_4-H}$ must be even greater, since C_6H_4 must have an energy-rich triple bond (C_6H_4 would appear not to exist):

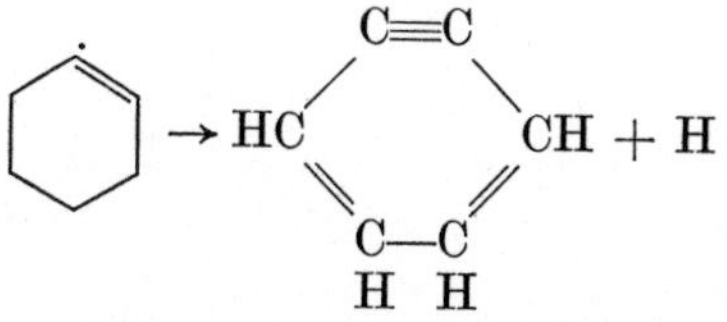

Q_{A-H} increases on ascending the series C_2H_5Br, C_2H_3Br, $C_2H_2Br_2$, C_3H_5Br, C_2H_5Br, and the relative importance of the radical mode must therefore increase correspondingly. The experimental data actually show that C_2H_5Br and C_2H_3Br decompose molecularly, $C_2H_2Br_2$ partially via a radical mechanism, and allyl bromide and bromobenzene, for which Q_{A-H} is largest, decompose solely in the radical way.

If Q_{H-X} decreases, then the radical mode tends to become dominant. SHILOV compared the three alkyl halides C_2H_5Cl, C_2H_5Br and C_2H_5I, for which Q_{A-H} is identical, assuming that the values of E_0 were not widely different. C_2H_5Br is known from the experiments of SZWARC [30], and SHILOV [85, 86] to decompose molecularly, while C_2H_5I does so via radicals. The mode of decomposition of C_2H_5Cl has not yet been established, but it would seem that it must be molecular.

So far, primary decomposition has been considered as being either to radicals or molecules. Primary decomposition can also be to biradicals, though this mode is always energetically less favourable than the molecular, since a biradical is normally an energy-rich particle. In some instances, though, primary decomposition to molecules is impossible. SHILOV showed that $CHCl_3$ and CH_2Cl_2 gave biradicals instead of radicals, as was mentioned above.

Exactly the same type of equation applies to parallel radical and biradical modes as was given above for the radical vs. molecular modes, being

$$E_R - E_B = -Q_{B-H} + Q_{H-X} - \varepsilon_0'$$

where the subscript B indicates a biradical. Accurate estimation of $E_R - E_B$ is impossible, since not only is ε_0' unknown for biradical reactions, but also Q_{B-H} is known only in a few instances.

The different mechanisms in chloromethanes may be explained for CCl_4 and $CHCl_3$. We suppose that CCl_4 also gives biradicals:

(1) $CCl_4 \rightarrow CCl_2 + Cl_2 - \Delta H_1$,

(2) $CHCl_3 \rightarrow CCl_2 + HCl - \Delta H_2$.

$\Delta H_1 - \Delta H_2$ is calculable from thermochemical data, being 24 kcal; the biradical mode is 24 kcal more favourable in $CHCl_3$ by 24 kcal. Since Q_{C-Cl} in CCl_4 is less than in $CHCl_3$, the radical mode will occur more readily in CCl_4 than in $CHCl_3$. Experimental data on the four chloromethanes indicate that the activation energies for $CHCl_3$ and CH_2Cl_2 (47 and 66·5 kcal respectively) are considerably less than the C—Cl bond energies, as calculated by VOEVODSKII (73·5 and 78·5 kcal), so these cannot decompose to radicals, in agreement with experiment. Biradical decomposition is energetically more favoured in $CHCl_3$ and CH_2Cl_2.

The E_B's for biradical decomposition may be calculated for CH_3Cl and CCl_4. Assuming that the potential barriers in (1) and (2) are approximately equal, we get $E_B(CCl_4) = E_B(CHCl_3) + \Delta H = 47 + 24 = 71$ kcal. Q_{C-Cl} is 68–70 kcal for CCl_4, i.e. slightly less than E_B. Hence, although the two routes are energetically almost identical, the radical mode is likely to predominate, other things being equal.

E_B for CH_3Cl may be calculated from the equations:

(1) $CH_3Cl \rightarrow H_2 + CHCl - \Delta H$,

(2) $CH_2Cl_2 \rightarrow CHCl + HCl - \Delta H_2$.

$\Delta H_1 - \Delta H_2 \sim 20$ kcal. Assuming that ε_{01} and ε_{02} are not widely different, we get $E_B(CH_3Cl) = E_B(CH_2Cl_2) + 20 = 66·5 + 20 = 86·5$ kcal. Q_{C-Cl} in CH_3Cl is 83 kcal. and E_R is known to be 85 kcal. Thus biradical decomposition demands slightly more energy. Experimentally, the radical decomposition occurs.

The above examples demonstrate that the primary decomposition of a molecule depends on its structure. Our work constitutes an attempt to demonstrate some of the qualitative relationships involved.

8. FREE RADICAL PRODUCTION BY REACTION BETWEEN STABLE MOLECULES

We indicated above (page 150) that it was possible, from the theoretical point of view, for molecules to react in such a way as to include radicals amongst the products, while the potential barrier height remained small. For example, $H_2 + Cl_2 \rightarrow H + HCl + Cl - 58$ kcal. There is some reason to assume that, if the four atoms are arranged in the same straight line H—H + Cl—Cl → H $\cdots$ H $\cdots$ Cl $\cdots$ Cl → H + HCl + Cl, that the height of the potential barrier will be as small as, or smaller than, that found in the reactions of free radicals with molecules (see Appendix II). Supposing that the height is only a few kilocalories (say, 5 kcal), then the activation energy will be 63 kcal. If this is actually the case, this process will generate atoms in H_2/Cl_2 mixtures, though at a lesser rate than $Cl_2 + M \rightarrow Cl + Cl + M - 57$ kcal.

That this is possible is made clear by considering the reverse process: $H + HCl + Cl \rightarrow H_2 + Cl_2$. Actually, if the two particles with free valencies—H and Cl—approach the HCl molecule from opposite sides, they will partially draw away the electrons in the H—Cl bond, and thus reinforce one another's actions, although they do not react directly. Hence, if one atom reacts with a molecule (such as $H + HCl \rightarrow H_2 + Cl$) and ε_0 is low, then ε_0 will be even lower when two are present (Appendix II). But if this is so, the reverse, endothermic, process $H—H + Cl—Cl \rightarrow H + HCl + Cl$ must also have a low potential barrier (or even none at all).

The existence of radical disproportionations such as $C_2H_5 + C_2H_5 \rightarrow C_2H_4 + C_2H_6 + \sim 60$ kcal, implies that two molecules can react to give two radicals. This disproportionation appears to have a very small activation energy; if so, the reverse reaction must also have a low potential barrier, and an activation energy of about 60 kcal.

Recent work at the Institute of Chemical Physics has also been concerned with molecular reactions that may give rise to radicals. SHILOV, PYACHKOVSKII and TIKHIMIROVA have studied the interaction of lithium ethyl with triphenylchloromethane, and have shown by paramagnetic resonance methods that free radicals are formed. At first the free radical concentrations are large, but as the radicals recombine, the concentrations fall to the equilibrium values:

$$LiC_2H_5 + (C_6H_5)_3CCl \rightarrow LiCl + \dot{C}_2H_5 + (C_6H_5)_3\dot{C}$$

It would be most interesting if the sensitivity of the method could be so increased that reactions involving less stable radicals could be studied.

9. PARTICULAR EXAMPLES

The above hypothesis may clarify some hitherto unexplained facts.

The Oxidation of Hydrogen

A possible process of this type is

$$H—H + O{=}O \rightarrow OOH + H \tag{1}$$

Q_{H-O_2} has previously been estimated as 47 kcal. Thus (1) is endothermic: $47 - 103 = -56$ kcal. The activation energy will be about 60 kcal. This process is incomparably more favourable for producing the first radicals than are the dissociations $H_2 \rightarrow 2H$ and $O_2 \rightarrow 2O$, where the bond energies are 103 and 118 kcal respectively.

It is interesting to recall that the activation energy for initiation was estimated in 1943 to be about 50 kcal by the present author, from an analysis of the kinetic data [90]. This is comparable with the value of 60 kcal quoted above.

The above process can take place still more rapidly at the walls, since adsorbed hydrogen atoms will produce HO_2 by much less endothermic processes.

The Oxidation of Hydrocarbons

It is probable that the comparative ease with which complex hydrocarbons are oxidized (particularly in the liquid state) at 100–150°C is due to the production of primary radicals by processes such as $RH + O_2 \rightarrow R + HO_2$.* Since substantially less energy is required to abstract hydrogen from a complex hydrocarbon than from hydrogen itself (Q_{C-H} is often as low as 80–90 kcal), the activation energies are likely to be about 40 kcal; such processes can proceed at low rates even near room temperature.

Since peroxides are the primary oxidation products, the chain reactions are autocatalytic, and a very small primary radical concentration produces a fairly high reaction rate, once the induction period is over. Oxygen probably really acts in this way when it initiates the combination of HBr with olefins, polymerizations, cracking, etc.

Let us consider, for instance, the pyrolysis of acetaldehyde, as initiated by oxygen, which has been studied by NICLAUSE and LETORT [92]; it was shown that traces (~ 0.05 per cent) of O_2 greatly accelerated the reaction, apparently a homogeneous one. The following probable mechanism, in which radicals are generated by the aldehyde reacting with O_2, was proposed

(0) (a) $CH_3CHO + O_2 \rightarrow HO_2 + CH_3COQ$;⎫
     (b) $HO_2 + CH_3CHO \rightarrow H_2O_2 + CH_3CO$.⎬ initiation

(1) $CH_3CO \rightarrow CH_3 + CO$,⎫
(2) $CH_3 + CH_3CHO \rightarrow CH_4 + CH_3CO$,⎬ propagation

(3) $2CH_3 \rightarrow C_2H_6$,⎫
(4) $CH_3 + CH_3CO \rightarrow CH_3COCH_3$.⎬ termination

The rate would then be

$$\omega_0 = k_2(k_0/k_3)^{\frac{1}{2}}[O_2]_0^{\frac{1}{2}} \frac{[CH_3CHO]^{\frac{3}{2}}}{(1 + \frac{k_4 k_2}{k_3 k_1}[CH_3CHO])^{\frac{1}{2}}} \tag{1}$$

ω_0 and $[O_2]_0$ being the initial rate and initial O_2 concentration.

---

* This process is proposed for initiating hydrocarbon oxidations in several schemes; the first such initiation was described for hexane by HINSHELWOOD [91]. But in all cases the $RH + O_2 \rightarrow R + HO_2$ reaction is proposed formally, i.e. without considering what the activation energy might be.

Experimentally, the rate was found to vary as $[O_2]^{\frac{1}{2}}$ and as $[CH_3CHO]^{\frac{3}{2}}$, the overall activation energy E being 22 kcal. The expression for the rate can be used to derive E_0, from

$$E = E_2 + E_0/2 - E_3/2 = 22 \text{ kcal}$$

E_2 and E_3 are known to be 6 and ~ 0 kcal respectively, so

$$E_0 = 2(22 - 6) = 32 \text{ kcal}$$

The heat of (0) (a) is then $Q_{CH_3CO-H} - Q_{H-O_2} = 33$ kcal. We thus see that (0) (a) actually occurs without involving an activation barrier and has an activation energy equal to the energy absorbed.

Fluorination

Fluorine is a highly active substance; even below 0°C it reacts rapidly (often with explosion) with many organic compounds. This high activity, coupled to the great variety of products resulting from halogenated olefins, leaves little doubt that the reactions are not direct molecular, to give molecular products. Some data indicate that free radicals are formed; F_2 cannot split up directly into free radicals because the dissociation energy is 37 kcal. It is easily shown that less than one F atom is formed by dissociation per second in one mole of F_2 at about 0°C. The sole way we can explain the activity is that the molecules react to give free radicals.

1. $F_2 + RH$ (saturated hydrocarbon) $\rightarrow F + HF + R$; since Q_{H-F} is large (134 kcal) this reaction must be exothermic for most hydrocarbons because with CH_4 it is practically neutral.

$$F_2 + CCl_3CHCl_2 \rightarrow CCl_3CCl_2 + HF + F + 13 \text{ kcal}$$

With olefins the reactions must be still more exothermic.

2. $F_2 + C_nH_{2n} \rightarrow F + C_nH_{2n}F + q$. For C_2H_4, q is about 20 kcal; the same sort of value is found with chlorinated olefins:

$$F_2 + CCl_2{=}CCl_2 \rightarrow CCl_2FCCl_2 + F + 19 \text{ kcal}$$

We have shown above that the potential barriers against such reactions may be very low, at a few kilocalories only; in most cases such reactions (two molecules $\rightarrow$ two radicals) are strongly endothermic while with fluorine they are exothermic, and so are rapid at low temperatures.

The high activity is occasioned by Q_{F-F} being small (37 kcal) relative to Q_{C-F} and Q_{H-F} (115 [93] and 134 kcal respectively). The radicals formed react further with the parent compounds; the rates of the primary processes are so great that the chains can scarcely develop, particularly below 0°C (say, at -70°C). The activation energies of the initiation steps are always comparable with, and sometimes less than, those of the propagation steps. In 1956 MILLER *et al.* [94–98] studied the fluorination of halo-olefins and supposed that such initiation steps could occur, though not because they considered the potential barriers to be low for theoretical reasons.

We can thus suppose that traces of fluorine can initiate many chain reactions in hydrocarbons; MILLER *et al.* [94] have observed this effect in oxidations and chlorinations on tetrachloroethylene and pentachloroethane. The reactions do not proceed at low temperatures in the dark if fluorine is absent, but do so if it is present; they also proceed on illumination, which dissociates Cl_2 into atoms. SCHUMACHER [9] has shown that these chlorine-photosensitized reactions are chain ones, so the fluorine merely provides an alternative way of producing the primary free radicals; this is proved by the products being the same in both cases. Thus on oxidizing pentachloroethane one obtains, for instance, CCl_3COCl and $COCl_2$ in about the same ratio.

Chlorination and Bromination of Olefins

Olefins frequently chlorinate at room temperature even in the dark. The reproducibility is normally poor, and the rate depends on the state and material of the walls. The activity of the walls may be reduced by special treatment, and the dark reaction is then very slow below 100°C. SCHMITZ *et al.* [9] naturally employed such conditions when studying the photochlorination of ethylene. The chlorination chain is initiated by photolysis of Cl_2:

(1) $Cl + CH_2{=}CH_2 \rightarrow C_2H_4Cl + 26$ kcal,

(2) $C_2H_4Cl + Cl_2 \rightarrow C_2H_4Cl_2 + Cl + 17\cdot6$ kcal.

The chain length, at 10^7, is very great. The great length is due to the small activation energies of the exothermic elementary reactions (1) and (2).

It may thus be supposed that the dark reaction is also a chain, initiation being by thermal dissociation. Homogenous initiation via $Cl_2 \rightarrow 2Cl - 57$ kcal is extremely slow, and even with a chain length of 10^7 the reaction would not be perceptible at ~ 100°C if the walls were of low activity. So the initiating step may naturally be

(3) $Cl_2 + CH_2{=}CH_2 \rightarrow Cl + CH_2Cl—\dot{C}H_2 - q_1$,

with $q_1 = 34\cdot4$ kcal.

A reaction of this type (molecule + molecule → radical + radical) may have quite a low ε_0—about 6–8 kcal in this case. The activation energy is then

$$\varepsilon = \varepsilon_0 + 34\cdot4 \simeq 41 \text{ kcal}$$

i.e. 16 kcal less than Q_{Cl-Cl}. (3) is sufficiently probable at 100°C for the chain reaction to proceed. q_1 may be calculated from the heat of the overall reaction:

$$C_2H_4 + Cl_2 \rightarrow C_2H_4Cl_2 + U$$

so

$$U = \Delta H_{C_2H_4} + \Delta H_{Cl_2} - \Delta H_{C_2H_4Cl_2} = 12\cdot5 + 0 - (-31\cdot1)$$
$$= 43\cdot6 \text{ kcal (Conn } et\ al.\ [27] \text{ give } 43\cdot653 \text{ kcal)}$$

If the overall reaction occurs via two elementary steps

(1) $Cl_2 + CH_2{=}CH_2 \rightarrow CH_2Cl-\dot{C}H_2 + Cl - q_1$,

(2) $CH_2Cl-\dot{C}H_2 + Cl \rightarrow CH_2Cl-CH_2Cl + q_2$,

then $-q_1 + q_2 = U$, or $q_1 = q_2 - U$.

The energy of the C—Cl bond formed in (2) is not known. Table 6 gives $Q_{C_2H_5-Cl}$ as 80 kcal, and Q_{C-Cl} in a —CCl$_2$ group is 4 kcal lower. In this particular case the second chlorine atom is attached to the neighbouring carbon atom, so $80 > q_2 > 76$ kcal. Assuming $q_2 = 78$ kcal, then $q_1 = q_2 - U = 78 - 43\cdot6 = 34\cdot4$ kcal.

In 1930–5 Stewart et al. [98] studied the chlorination of benzene in solution in the presence of C_2H_4; they found that C_6Cl_6 and $C_2H_4Cl_2$ were formed. If C_2H_4 was absent the C_6Cl_6 was only formed if the reaction was initiated by light, etc., while if C_2H_4 was present the reaction occurred in the dark. Shilov and Smirnov-Zamkov [99] observed a similar effect in

$$Br_2 + R-C{\equiv}C-R \rightarrow R-CBr{=}CBr-R$$

the dark reaction being typically a chain one. If toluene was added, benzyl bromide was formed; this reaction usually only occurs on illumination, via Br atoms, so we must have here a system which generates Br atoms in the dark, the source being the above reaction.

In both cases we can assume the halogen atoms generated by $X_2 + C_2H_4 \rightarrow X + CH_2X-CH_2$.

The Chlorination of Dienes

Dienes (e.g. butadiene) chlorinate even at room temperature:

$$Cl_2 + CH_2{=}CH-CH{=}CH_2 \rightarrow CH_2Cl-CH{=}CH-CH_2Cl$$

The tendency for the two chlorine atoms to be found at positions 1 and 4 is a clear indication that a chain mechanism is involved:

(1) $Cl + CH_2{=}CH-CH{=}CH_2 \rightarrow CH_2Cl-CH{=}CH-\dot{C}H_2$,

(2) $CH_2Cl-CH{=}CH-\dot{C}H_2 + Cl_2 \rightarrow CH_2Cl-CH{=}CH-CH_2Cl +$
$$+ Cl.$$

If addition of molecular chlorine occurred in one step (direct molecular reaction), then the two chlorine atoms would be expected to be found in nearly all cases at positions 1 and 2. In practice, this is found only to a slight extent, though when bromine combines with butadiene the 1,2-dibromo derivative is about 20 per cent of the product.† Chain initiation appears to be determined by the process:

$$Cl_2 + CH_2{=}CH{-}CH{=}CH_2 \rightarrow Cl + CH_2Cl{-}CH{=}CH{-}\dot{C}H_2 - q_1$$

It is shown below that q_1 is about 18 kcal. Assuming that $\varepsilon_0 \simeq$ 7 kcal, the relatively low value of 25 kcal is found for the activation energy of initiation, which explains why butadiene chlorinates easily at low temperatures.

q_1 is derived as follows. As in the case of ethylene, the overall reaction is the result of the two elementary steps (1) and (2) given above. Then

$$q_1 = q_2 - U$$

q_2 may be estimated with an accuracy of 2–3 kcal on the assumption that it is the same as $Q_{C_3H_5-Cl}$ for allyl chloride.

Table 6 gives $Q_{C_3H_5-Cl}$ as 58 kcal. U is not known, but it should be comparable with the value for the chlorination of olefins ($U \simeq$ 40 kcal), since in both cases one π-bond is broken and two C—Cl bonds are formed.

U may be calculated by splitting the overall reaction into four hypothetical stages:

(1) The electrons in butadiene are localized:

$$CH_2{=}CH{-}CH{=}CH_2 \rightarrow (CH_2{=}CH{-}CH{=}CH_2)^*$$

where * indicates that the electrons are considered as being localized. Some 6 kcal is absorbed in this process, this being the difference between $\Delta H'_{C_4H_6}$, calculated from mean bond energies, and $\Delta H_{C_4H_6}$ from thermochemical data.

(2) The biradical with localized valence electrons is formed, by breaking one π-bond: this absorbs 57 kcal:

$$(CH_2{=}CH{-}CH{=}CH_2)^* \rightarrow (\dot{C}H_2{-}CH{=}CH{-}\dot{C}H_2)^* - 57 \text{ kcal}$$

(3) The chlorine molecule is dissociated into two atoms:

$$Cl_2 \rightarrow Cl + Cl - 57 \text{ kcal}$$

† That 20 per cent of the product is the 1, 2 derivative does not necessarily indicate that direct molecular addition takes place. It only means that the Cl atom can attack the CH group as well as the CH$_2$ group, and the chain the propagates as below:

(1) $Cl + CH_2{=}CH{-}CH{=}CH_2 \rightarrow \dot{C}H_2{-}CHCl{-}CH{=}CH_2,$

(2) $\dot{C}H_2{-}CHCl{-}CH{=}CH_2 + Cl_2 \rightarrow CH_2Cl{-}CHCl{-}CH{=}CH_2 + Cl.$

(4) The two chlorine atoms combine with the biradical:

$$(\dot{C}H_2\!-\!CH\!=\!CH\!-\!\dot{C}H_2)^* + 2Cl \rightarrow CH_2Cl\!-\!CH\!=\!CH\!-\!CH_2Cl$$

Since the actual state of the dichloride is one where the electrons are practically localized, then the heat liberated by the addition of the two chlorine atoms must be twice Q_{C-Cl} in some compound such as C_2H_5Cl, the electrons being localized in the C_2H_5 radical. $Q_{C_2H_5-Cl}$ is 80 kcal. Since two atoms are involved in (4), the energy liberated will be 160 kcal. Thus, using the above hypothetical scheme, we find:

$$U = -6 - 57 - 57 + 160 = 40 \text{ kcal}$$

Hence $q_1 = q_2 - U = 58 - 40 = 18$ kcal.

Polymerization

DOLGOPLOSK *et al.* [100] have shown that a number of radical polymerizations are initiated at low temperatures $(+5°C)$ by adding two substances, one an oxidant and one a reductant; it is assumed that these interact to give free radicals. Reactions such as those between hydroperoxides and mercaptans or SO_2 initiate radical polymerizations, the radicals in all probability being formed via reactions such as

$$ROOH + R'SH \rightarrow RO + H_2O + R'S$$

The energy balance of this process can be calculated approximately. Q_{C-O} in the ROOH is probably less than 40 kcal, Q_{H-S} for the mercaptans being unknown, but is ~ 90 kcal for H_2S, so in RSH it is probably somewhat lower, say ~ 80 kcal, since Q_{H-OH} is 116 kcal. The reaction is therefore neutral or slightly exothermic, so the activation energy is fairly small, and the reaction can proceed at 5°C at a rate sufficient to initiate the polymerization.

The initiation method recently proposed by ZIEGLER [101] and developed by NATTA [102] and others is of particular interest; here the initiator is a mixture of an aluminium trialkyl with $TiCl_3$ or $TiCl_4$. With such systems ZIEGLER was able to polymerize C_2H_2, C_3H_6 and other olefins at temperatures and pressures much below those previously usable. Here we can suppose radicals formed by AlR_3 reacting with $TiCl_4$, e.g.

$$Al(C_2H_5)_3 + TiCl_4 \rightarrow AlCl(C_2H_5)_2 + TiCl_3 + C_2H_5$$

The reaction may be facilitated by complexing and radical adsorption on the catalytic surface, but the polymerization takes a different course from a normal radical one, stereospecific polymers being formed, as NATTA has shown. The reaction is clearly heterogeneous;

the initiation and propagation mechanisms being at present unclear; various contradictory views have been expressed. Many suppose it to be an ionic polymerization, though it seems to us that the role of radicals in initiating it cannot be denied.

Latterly SHILOV and BUBNOV [103] (Institute of Chemical Physics) have shown by EPR methods that the products formed when $Al(iso-C_4H_q)_3$ or $Al(C_2H_5)_3$ react with $TiCl_4$ show a resonance absorption of energy, which they relate to surface radicals forming. These radicals may be supposed to participate in the polymerization in some special way; for instance, the free valence may here not be at the end of the polymer chain but at the point where it is bound to the surface.

Doubts may arise as to whether these processes are not simple direct molecular combinations. The primary process may be the formation of a biradical, analogous to the biradical

$$\dot{C}H_2—CH_2—CH_2—\dot{C}H_2$$

formed from two ethylene molecules. The biradical may be formed in butadiene as follows:

$$CH_2{=}CH—CH{=}CH_2 + CH_2{=}CH—CH{=}CH_2 \rightarrow$$
$$\dot{C}H_2—CH{=}CH—CH_2—CH_2—\dot{C}H—CH{=}CH_2 + q \quad (B)$$

The entropy diminishes in this process, and the steric factor is thus small, $f = 10^{-4}–10^{-6}$. $q \simeq 0$, and so $\varepsilon = \varepsilon_0$. The rate of biradical formation is

$$w = f \times 10^{-10} \exp (- \varepsilon_0/RT)[C_4H_6]^2$$

The biradical cyclizes very readily, the activation energy being small. Ring closure is exothermic, and the whole heat of the overall reaction is liberated at this step, so the rate of cyclization is limited by biradical formation. This is why dimerization is more rapid than polymerization, since the latter has a large activation energy. If various polymerization accelerators, such as peroxides, are present the radicals they produce react with butadiene to give univalent radicals; since these cannot cyclize, polymerization occurs at low temperatures. There are some grounds for believing that biradical formation involves potential barriers somewhat higher (by 1·5–2 times) than those found in reactions of univalent radicals with molecules (see Appendix II). The latter energies depend on the heat of reaction, q. If $q \simeq 0$, ε_0 is usually about 11–14 kcal. So the formation of two univalent radicals or one biradical in a thermally neutral reaction may imply ε is in the range 15–22 kcal. This is precisely the activation energy typical of cyclizations.

Suppose that reaction (B) has $q \sim 0$. Two π-bonds are broken and one σ-bond is formed. If butadiene and $\dot{C}_8H_{12}$ were not conjugated, then the energy absorbed in forming this biradical would be the same as that for $\dot{C}H_2CH_2CH_2\dot{C}H_2$, formed from two molecules of ethylene, i.e. about 30 kcal. However, butadiene is conjugated, and the removal of this conjugation involves about 12 kcal. The energy of conjugation in

$$\dot{C}H_2{-}CH{=}CH{-}CH_2{-}CH_2{-}\dot{C}H{-}CH$$
$$\| \atop CH_2$$

will be approximately twice that of the allyl radical, previously calculated as being about 20 kcal (page 266). So the total heat available from biradical formation will be $-30 - 12 + 40 \simeq 0$.

The Oxidation of Oxides of Nitrogen

NO is a radical of low activity, and $NO + O_2 \rightarrow NO_2 + O$ has a high activation energy, being strongly endothermic. We may suppose that if two NO molecules and one oxygen molecule are arranged in the same straight line, with the oxygen atom in the middle, the exothermic reaction:

$$\dot{N}O + O{=}O + \dot{N}O \rightarrow 2NO_2 + 27 \text{ kcal}$$

will occur, with a low activation energy. Experimentally, these reactions are known to be termolecular, but they have slightly negative temperature coefficients, which are difficult to accomodate within the framework of the theory proposed.[*]

It is legitimate to inquire at this point whether many reactions which cannot occur via a chain might not more readily go by a purely radical reaction. $H_2 + I_2 \rightarrow 2HI$ is known not to involve a chain, but does it occur by direct molecular reaction? HI formation can occur in another way:

(1) $I_2 + M \rightarrow I + I + M - 35\cdot5$ kcal,

(2) $I + H - H + I \rightarrow 2HI$,

since the reverse reaction can occur via

$$I{-}H + H{-}I \rightarrow I + H_2 + I$$

Consider the reaction rate, starting from the assumptions made above. [I] is given by

$$[I]^2/[I_2] = 10^{24} \exp(-35\cdot5/RT)$$

[*] The reaction is often assumed to occur in two stages: $NO + NO \leftrightarrows (NO)_2$ and $(NO)_2 + O_2 \rightarrow 2NO_2$.

whence $[I] = 10^{12} \exp(-17 \cdot 75/RT)\sqrt{[I_2]} = $ The frequency of triple collisions $I + H_2 + I$ is $f \times 10^{-32}[I]^2[H_2]$ which is equal to $f \times 10^{-32} \times 10^{24} \exp(-35 \cdot 5/RT)[I_2][H_2]$. If the activation energy of (2) is ε_2, then

$$w = f \times 10^{-8} \exp[-(35 \cdot 5 + \varepsilon_2)/RT][I_2][H_2]$$

The experimental result is

$$w \simeq 10^{-10} \exp(-39/RT)[I_2][H_2]$$

If we assume that $\varepsilon_2 \simeq 4\,\text{kcal}$, and $f = 10^{-2}$, the theoretical and experimental formulae are in agreement. Values of ε_2 and f of this order are acceptable, since only some small fraction of all three-body collisions will give a linear arrangement $I \cdots H \cdots H \cdots I$. At present there is no information on whether the process is really as above, or whether it is merely a direct collision of H_2 and I_2, giving $2HI$, as is generally assumed. This new point of view cannot be discounted without resort to special experiments.

The Decomposition of Azo-methane

Two radicals are formed when a molecule decomposes by rupture of the weakest bond, but simultaneous rupture of two bonds is also possible. Two radicals and a molecule, i.e. a new bond, are formed in this case. For instance two CH_3 radicals and a molecule of nitrogen are formed when azo-methane decomposes without initiating a chain reaction. Azo-methane can decompose by two routes:

(1) $CH_3—N{=}N—CH_3 \rightarrow CH_3—N{=}N—CH_3—N{=}N—CH_3$
    decomposing to $N{\equiv}N$ and CH_3 in the second stage; and

(2) $CH_3—N{=}N—CH_3 \rightarrow CH_3 + N{\equiv}N + CH_3$ two CH_3 radicals and N_2 being formed simultaneously.

The latter seems to be more probable and is confirmed by recent published data. In the first case the activation energy should equal the C—N bond energy (53 kcal) whereas the activation energy found is 46 kcal [93] i.e. 7 kcal lower. If the second route, which involves a low ε_0, is possible, then azo-methane could be formed from two CH_3 radicals by bilateral attack on $N{\equiv}N$, a linear complex being formed. This is of course quite natural. Since ε_0 is usually low when a radical attacks a molecule there is no reason why it should be higher when the molecule is attacked from opposite sides by two radicals.

One most important question is that of the relative occurrence of chain and radical reactions on the one hand, and of direct molecular reactions on the other. We have here put forward the view that a large proportion involve chain or radical mechanisms, and that radical reactions are, like ionic reactions, one of the main types of chemical transformation.

REFERENCES

1. H. J. SCHUMACHER. *Chemische Gasreaktionen.* Leipzig 1938.
2. N. N. SEMENOV. *Usp. Khim.* **21,** 641 (1952).
3. M. LETORT. *J. Chim. Phys.* **34,** 265 (1937); A. BOYER, M. NICLAUSE, and M. LETORT. *J. Chim. Phys.* **49,** 345 (1952).
4. F. P. LOSSING, K. U. INGOLD and A. W. TICKNER. *Disc. Faraday Soc.* **14,** 34 (1953).
5. R. A. OGG. *J. Amer. Soc.* **56,** 526 (1934).
6. YA. B. ZELDOVICH, P. YA. SADOVNIKOV and D. A. FRANK-KAMENETSKII. *Oxidation of Nitrogen by Combustion.* Academy of Sciences of U.S.S.R., Moscow–Leningrad 1947 (in Russian).
7. R. N. PEASE. *J. Amer. Chem. Soc.* **54,** 1876 (1932).
8. E. W. R. STEACIE. *Atomic and Free Radical Reactions.* 1st. Ed. New York 1946.
9. H. SCHMITZ, H. I. SCHUMACHER and A. JÄGER. *Z. phys. Chem.* **B51,** 281 (1942).
10. A. M. CHAIKIN. Candidate's dissertation, Moscow State University (1955).
11. M. L. BOGOYAVLENSKAYA and A. A. KOVALSKII. *Zh. Fiz. Khim.* **20,** 1325 (1946).
12. F. F. RUST and W. E. VAUGHAN. *J. Org. Chem.* **5,** 472 (1940).
13. V. A. POLTORAK and V. V. VOEVODSKII. *Dokl. Akad. Nauk SSSR* **91** 589 (1953); D. H. R. BARTON. *J. Chem. Soc.* 148 (1949).
14. M. SZWARC and J. W. TAYLOR. *J. Chem. Phys.* **23,** 2310 (1955).
15. M. SZWARC. *Chem. Rev.* **47,** 75 (1950).
16. W. L. HADEN and O. K. RICE. *J. Chem. Phys.* **10,** 445 (1942).
17. J. R. E. SMITH and C. N. HINSHELWOOD. *Proc. Roy. Soc.* **A180,** 237 (1942).
18. A. BOYER, M. NICLAUSE and M. LETORT. *J. Chim. Phys.* **49,** 337 (1952).
19. C. N. HINSHELWOOD and P. J. ASKEY. *Proc. Roy. Soc.* **A115,** 215 (1927).
20. P. GRAY. *Fifth Symposium on Combustion,* p. 535. Reinhold, New York 1955.
21. L. B. ARNOLD and G. B. KISTIAKOWSKY. *J. Chem. Phys.* **1,** 166 (1933).
22. E. T. BUTLER and N. POLANYI. *Trans. Faraday Soc.* **39,** 19 (1943).
23. R. A. OGG and M. POLANYI. *Trans. Faraday Soc.* **31,** 482 (1935).
24. M. S. KHARASCH and F. R. MAYO. *J. Amer. Soc. Chem.* **55,** 2468, 2521, 2531 (1933).
25. V. V. MARKOVNIKOV. Data on the Mutual Influence of the Atoms in Chemical Compounds. Kazan 1869. In the symposium *Memorial to V. V. Markovnikov.* Moscow 1905.
26. V. V. MARKOVNIKOV. *C.R. Acad. Sci., Paris.* **81,** 668 (1875).
27. J. B. CONN, G. B. KISTIAKOWSKY and E. A. SMITH. *J. Amer. Chem. Soc.* **60,** 2764 (1938).
28. G. B. KISTIAKOWSKY and C. H. STAUFFER. *J. Amer. Chem. Soc.* **59,** 165 (1937).
29. A. MACCOLL and P. T. THOMAS. *J. Chem. Phys.* **19,** 977 (1951).
30. M. SZWARC and C. H. LEIGH. *J. Chem. Phys.* **20,** 403 (1952).
31. A. T. BLADES and G. W. MURPHY. *J. Amer. Chem. Soc.* **74,** 6219 (1952).
32. N. N. SEMENOV, G. B. SERGEEV and G. I. KAPRALOVA. *Dokl. Akad. Nauk SSSR* **105,** 301 (1955).
33. G. B. SERGEEV. Candidate's dissertation, Moscow State University (1955).

34. P. AGIUS and A. MACCOLL. *J. Chem. Phys.* **18**, 158 (1950).
35. A. MACCOLL. *J. Chem. Soc.* 965 (1955).
36. P. J. AGIUS and A. MACCOLL. *J. Chem. Soc.* 973 (1955).
37. A. MACCOLL and P. J. THOMAS. *J. Chem. Soc.* 979 (1955).
38. A. MACCOLL and P. J. THOMAS. *J. Chem. Soc.* 2445 (1955).
39. J. H. S. GREEN and A. MACCOLL. *J. Chem. Soc.* 2449 (1955).
40. G. D. HARDEN and A. MACCOLL. *J. Chem. Soc.* 2454 (1955).
41. J. H. S. GREEN, G. D. HARDEN, A. MACCOLL and P. J. THOMAS. *J. Chem. Phys.* **21**, 178 (1953).
42. G. B. SERGEEV. *Dokl. Akad. Nauk SSSR* **106**, 299 (1956).
43. D. H. R. BARTON and K. E. HOWLETT. *J. Chem. Soc.* **155**, (1949).
44. K. E. HOWLETT and D. H. R. BARTON. *Trans. Faraday Soc.* **45**, 735 (1949).
45. D. H. R. BARTON. *J. Chem. Soc.* 148 (1949).
46. D. H. R. BARTON and P. F. ONYON. *J. Amer. Chem. Soc.* **72**, 988 (1950).
47. R. J. WILLIAMS. *J. Chem. Soc.* 113 (1953).
48. R. J. WILLIAMS, D. H. R. BARTON and A. J. HEAD. *J. Chem. Soc.* 2033 (1951).
49. D H. R. BARTON and K. E. HOWLETT, *J. Chem. Soc.* 165 (1949).
50. D. H. R. BARTON and A. J. HEAD. *Trans. Faraday Soc.* **46**, 114 (1950).
51. D. H. R. BARTON, A. J. HEAD and R. J. WILLIAMS. *J. Chem. Soc.* 2039 (1951).
52. K. E. HOWLETT. *J. Chem. Soc.* 4487 (1952).
53. D. H. R. BARTON. *Nature, Lond.* **157**, 626 (1946).
54. C. HINSHELWOOD and F. J. STUBBS. *Proc. Roy. Soc.* A**200**, 458 (1949); *Disc. Faraday Soc.* No. 10, 129 (1951).
55. F. O. RICE and K. F. HERZFELD. *J. Amer. Chem. Soc.* **56**, 284 (1934).
56. A. I. DINTSES and A. V. FROST. *Zh. Obshch. Khim.* **3**, 747 (1933).
57. A. D. STEPUKHOVICH and E. S. SHVER. *Zh. Fiz. Khim.* **27**, 1013 (1953); A. D. STEPUKHOVICH and A. M. CHAIKIN. *Zh. Fiz. Khim.* **27**, 1737 (1953); A. D. STEPUKHOVICH and G. M. VOROBOV. *Zh. Fiz. Khim.* **28**, 1361 (1954).
58. V. A. POLTORAK. Candidate's dissertation, Moscow State University (1952).
59. V. V. VOEVODSKII. Dissertation for doctorate, Moscow, Inst. Khim. Fiz (1954).
60. F. O. RICE and O. L. POLLY. *J. Chem. Phys.* **6**, 273 (1938).
61. V. I. GOLDANSKII. *Usp. Khim.* **15**, 63 (1946).
62. L. A. WALL and W. J. MOORE. *J. Amer. Chem. Soc.* **73**, 2840 (1951); *J. Phys. Coll. Chem.* **55**, 965 (1951).
63. C. N. HINSHELWOOD, F. J. STUBBS, K. U. INGOLD, B. C. SPALL and C. J. DANBY. *Proc. Roy. Soc.* A**214**, 20 (1952).
64. V. A. POLTORAK and V. V. VOEVODSKII. *Dokl. Akad. Nauk SSSR* **91**, 589 (1953).
65. F. O. RICE and R. E. VARNERIN. *J. Amer. Chem. Soc.* **76**, 324 (1954).
66. C. N. HINSHELWOOD, C. J. DANBY, B. C. SPALL and F. J. STUBBS. *Proc. Roy. Soc.* A**228**, 448 (1955).
67. C. N. HINSHELWOOD, H. M. FRAY and C. J. DANBY. *Proc. Roy. Soc.* A**234**, 301 (1956).
68. P. KEBARLE and W. A. BRYCE. *Canad. J. Chem.* **35**, 576 (1957).
69. F. O. RICE and M. D. DOOLEY. *J. Amer. Chem. Soc.* **56**, 2747 (1934).
70. M. SZWARC. *J. Chem. Phys.* **17**, 431 (1949).
71. M. SZWARC, B. N. GHOSH and A. H. SEHON. *J. Chem. Phys.* **18**, 1142 (1950).
72. J. MURAWSKI, J. S. ROBERTS and M. SZWARC. *J. Chem. Phys.* **19**, 698 (1951).

73. M. SZWARC and A. H. SEHON. *J. Chem. Phys.* **19,** 656 (1951).
74. M. SZWARC and D. WILLIAMS. *J. Chem. Phys.* **20,** 1171 (1952).
75. M. LADACKI, C. H. LEIGH and M. SZWARC. *Proc. Roy. Soc.* A**214,** 273 (1952).
76. M. LADACKI and M. SZWARC. *J. Chem. Phys.* **20,** 1814 (1952).
77. M. SZWARC and J. W. TAYLOR. *J. Chem. Phys.* **22,** 270 (1954).
78. A. REMBAUM and M. SZWARC. *J. Amer. Chem. Soc.* **76,** 5975 (1954).
79. M. SZWARC. *Proc. Roy. Soc.* A**198,** 267 (1949).
80. M. SZWARC. *Proc. Roy. Soc.* A**198,** 285 (1949).
81. C. H. LEIGH and M. SZWARC. *J. Chem. Phys.* **20,** 407 (1952).
82. C. H. LEIGH and M. SZWARC. *J. Chem. Phys.* **20,** 844 (1952).
83. A. H. SEHON and M. SZWARC. *Proc. Roy. Soc.* A**202,** 263 (1950).
84. M. SZWARC and J. MURAWSKI. *Trans. Faraday Soc.* **47,** 269 (1951).
85. A. E. SHILOV. *Dokl. Akad. Nauk SSSR* **98,** 601 (1954).
86. A. E. SHILOV. Candidate's dissertation, Institute of Chemical Physics, Moscow (1954).
87. F. P. LOSSING, K. U. INGOLD and J. H. S. HENDERSON. *J. Chem. Phys.* **22,** 1489 (1954).
88. G. P. SAMELUK and R. B. BERNSTEIN. *J. Amer. Chem. Soc.* **76,** 3793 (1954).
89. J. B. FARMER, J. H. S. HENDERSON, F. P. LOSSING and D. G. H. MARSDEN. *J. Chem. Phys.* **24,** 348 (1956).
90. N. N. SEMENOV. *Acta phys.-Chim. URSS* **20,** 291 (1945).
91. C. F. CULLIS and C. N. HINSHELWOOD. *Disc. Faraday Soc.*, No. 2, The Labile Molecule, 117 (1947).
92. M. NICLAUSE. Contribution à l'etude du mecanisme de la reaction lente entre l'oxygene et une substance organique gazeuse (l'exemple de l'acetaldehyde), Paris, 1954.
93. V. I. VEDENEEV. Dissertation, Moscow, 1957.
94. W. T. MILLER and A. L. DITTMAN. *J. Amer. Chem. Soc.* **78,** 2793 (1956).
95. W. T. MILLER, S. D. KOCH and F. W. MCLAFFERTY. *J. Amer. Chem. Soc.* **78,** 4992 (1956).
96. W. T. MILLER and S. D. KOCH. *J. Amer. Chem. Soc.* **79,** 3084 (1957).
97. H. J. SCHUMACHER and W. THURAUF. *Z. phys. Chem.* A **189,** 183 (1941).
98. D. D. STEWART and D. M. SMITH. *J. Amer. Chem. Soc.* **52,** 2869 (1930). T. D. STEWART and W. WEIDENBAUM. *J. Amer. Chem. Soc.* **57,** 2035, (1935).
99. E. A. SHILOV and I. V. SMIRNOV-ZAMKOV. *Izv. Akad. Nauk SSSR*, Otdel. Khim. Nauk 32 (1951).
100. B. A. DOLGOPLOSK. *Trud. VNIISK** 1948.
B. A. DOLGOPLOSK, E. I. TINYAKOVA and V. N. REIKH. *Trud. VNIISK** **87** (1947–50); *Izv. Akad. Nauk SSSR*, Otdel. Khim. Nauk, No. 7 (1957). H. W. MELVILLE. *Ind. Rubb. J.* **67,** 541 (1955).
101. K. ZIEGLER, *Angew Chem.* **67,** 541 (1955).
102. G. NATTA. *Gazz. Chim. Ital.* **87,** 528, 549, 570 (1957).
103. A. E. SHILOV and N. I. BUBNOV. *Izv. Akad. Nauk SSSR*, Otdel. Khim. Nauk (1958) (in press).
104. M. PAGE, H. O. PRITCHARD and A. F. TROTMAN-DICKENSON. *J. Chem. Soc.* 3878 (1953).

* All-Union Synthetic Rubber Research Institute.

Appendix I

THE ACTIVATED COMPLEX*

LET us suppose that the purely computational difficulties in the theoretical derivation of rates of chemical reactions can be overcome, and that such calculations can be carried to completion, at least for reactions which are the simplest from the point of view of the chemist. These simple reactions are, as a rule, kinetically complex, however, since they are of chain type. Suppose that it were possible to calculate theoretically the rate of

$$2H_2 + O_2 \rightarrow 2H_2O \tag{1}$$

This calculation would clearly involve several distinct steps. The overall reaction (1) may be the result of some dozen of simple reactions, such as:

$$H + O_2 \rightarrow OH + O$$
$$O + H_2 \rightarrow OH + H$$
$$OH + H_2 \rightarrow H_2O + H$$

Each such simple reaction is the sum of numerous elementary acts due to slightly different thermal motions and relative arrangements of the atoms at the instant of collision, as well as on their relative velocities and directions of movement.

Three problems arise in the theoretical computation of reaction rates:

(1) The elementary acts in the simple reactions. The energy of the system must be determined as a function of the relative velocities and positions of the atoms. This falls within the province of quantum chemistry.

(2) Determination of the rates of the simple reactions, as being the net result of an enormous number of elementary acts. This problem, being statistical in nature, must be dealt with by the methods of statistical mechanics.

(3) Determination of the rate of the complex reaction, made up as it is of simple reactions. This problem is dealt with by chain theory.

In principle the solution of each problem involves assuming the preceding ones solved. At present methods for solving the third problem are the best developed. The quantum-chemical methods available are such that no quantitative results can be obtained for

* This section was written by M. I. Temkin.

the first. However, the approximate methods give a probably correct qualitative picture of the elementary act in the simplest cases [1]. These qualitative results will be used in the later discussion.

The situation is more satisfactory in the statistical section. The kinetic theory of gases can be applied successfully here. Further developments have taken the form of theories of the so-called transition state or activated complex, the reaction rates being calculated by the methods of statistical mechanics.

A basic assumption in the activated complex theory is that the reaction does not materially affect the equilibrium molecular distribution over the various states (Maxwell–Boltzmann distribution). We assume this to be so here, and defer discussion to a later stage.

According to the Maxwell–Boltzmann law, the probability of any state is proportional to $\exp(-\varepsilon/kT)$, where ε is the energy of that state; states of high energy are improbable. Hence the vast majority of elementary acts occur via nearly the most favourable route, i.e. the deviations from the energetically most favoured route are small. These relationships will be considered for the very simple reaction

$$H_2 + D \rightarrow H + HD \qquad (2)$$

This reaction has a small but finite activation energy. Approximate quantum-mechanical calculations show that the deuterium atom experiences the least repulsion on approaching along the molecular axis. If so, reaction will almost always involve the D atom approaching along a line close to this. Molecular elongation will reduce the repulsion experienced by the atom, but such extension must absorb energy. There must be some atomic separation for which the total energy demanded is least. The Maxwell–Boltzmann law shows that for the vast majority of acts the internuclear distance will be close to the optimum.

The change in the nuclear separation is due to thermal agitation, i.e. valence-vibration in H_2. Reaction will almost always imply collision with a vibrating molecule (naturally, one having the requisite vibrational amplitude), at the instant of maximum distension. At first sight, the simultaneous combination of all requirements may seem of extremely low probability, since the direction of approach, the amplitude and phase of vibration, and the relative velocity of the particles are all specified. But in fact this mode of reaction is considerably more probable than any other, since it will demand least energy; the probability falls off very sharply with increase in energy due to the factor $\exp(-\varepsilon/kT)$.

On the other hand, the actual route is not exactly the most

favourable one, since strictly the latter is of zero probability. Thus the elementary reaction follows a path close to the most favoured one.

For some fixed total energy of the reacting atoms, alternation between two alternative forms—kinetic and potential—will occur during the elementary act. By potential energy we here mean that part dependent solely on the relative nuclear spacing—this in fact includes the kinetic energy of the electrons with the true potential energy. Kinetic energy means the part dependent on the nuclear velocities.

In each act of reaction the atoms pass through a configuration of maximum potential energy (and minimum kinetic energy), or in other words, the system passes over the potential barrier. This configuration is called the activated (or active) complex, or alternatively, the transition state.

The basic concept in this method is that the activated complex configuration is a kind of reference point determining the reaction rate. In order to know the number of elementary acts of reaction it is sufficient for us to calculate the number of systems that have passed through that configuration.

Since we have assumed the Maxwell–Boltzmann law applicable, we do not need to consider all the detailed steps from the initial state to the activated complex. We may determine the populations of the states of interest to us, without reference to the mechanism by which the statistical equilibrium is established.

Let us suppose that the potential energy of the reacting system is expressed as a function of the atomic dispositions by a multi-dimensional surface. The potential energy corresponding to the activated complex configuration is a maximum as regards the atomic motions which result in reaction. On the other hand, since any deviation from the most favourable route involves an increase in potential energy, it is a minimum from the point of view of deviations from the most favourable route. Thus the activated complex configuration corresponds to a minimax or saddle-point on the potential surface. The activated complex differs here from stable molecules, in which the potential energy increases for any displacement of the atoms from their equilibrium positions; a stable molecule corresponds to a minimum on the potential surface.

Normal coordinates for small deviations of the configuration from that implied by the extreme point on the potential surface may now be taken. In stable molecules these coordinates correspond to the normal modes of vibration; in addition, there are three rotational coordinates (two only, in linear molecules) and three coordinates for the molecular centre of gravity, involving motion of the molecule as a whole. By analogy, the activated complex may be described by three coordinates for the centre of gravity, three rotational coordinates (or two only in a linear activated complex, as in the instance above), and a number of vibrational coordinates, which define the deviations from the most favourable route, and finally, one coordinate, to which there is no analogue in stable molecules— the "reaction coordinate," which defines the progress along the most favourable reaction route.

The terms "rotation" and "vibration" as applied to the activated complex must not be taken literally. They indicate that the potential and kinetic energies depend on the coordinates and conjugate

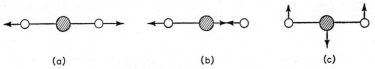

(a)   (b)   (c)

Fig. 23. Normal vibrations of CO_2: (a) symmetric valence vibration:
(b) antisymmetric valence vibration: (c) deformation vibration

momenta in the same way as for the normal coordinates of a stable molecule. These relationships, and only these, are needed in calculations using the Maxwell–Boltzmann distribution. Obviously, since the activated complex has only a momentary existence it cannot in fact either rotate or vibrate.

The number of degrees of freedom in the activated complex is readily established from the fact that a system of n atoms has $3n$, in general. For instance, a linear complex of three atoms has nine degrees of freedom; three translational, two rotational, one is that corresponding to the reaction coordinate, and there are consequently three vibrational degrees of freedom.

A comparison may be made between a triatomic linear complex and a triatomic linear stable molecule. The normal vibrations of CO_2 are set out in Fig. 23. The deformation vibration may take place in two mutually perpendicular planes; it is therefore to be reckoned as two vibrations. CO_2 therefore possesses four independent normal vibrational modes—two of deformation, one symmetric valence mode, and one antisymmetric valence mode. Motion along the reaction route corresponds to the antisymmetric valence mode in a triatomic linear activated comple. Hence there are three vibrational degrees of freedom, which define the deviations from the most favoured route; in particular, the deformational mode corresponds to deviation of the complex from a straight line form as the particles approach.

So far we have dealt only with the configuration of the activated complex. But for any given atomic configuration corresponding to the activated complex there are two possible opposite directions of motion along the reaction coordinate. One of these corresponds to the forward reaction, e.g. $H_2 + D \rightarrow H + HD$, while the other is $H + HD \rightarrow H_2 + D$. The activated complex is only completely defined if the direction of motion is given as well as the configuration.

The activated complex should be clearly differentiated from the intermediary complexes, critical complexes, etc., appearing in some earlier theories. We suppose that the change:

$$A \rightarrow B \qquad (3)$$

occurs via the formation of the intermediate X, which is unstable and short-lived, and that X can be reconverted to A. The transformation then takes the form

$$A \rightleftharpoons X \rightarrow B \qquad (4)$$

Let the changes $A \rightarrow X$ and $X \rightarrow A$ take place extremely rapidly by comparison with $X \rightarrow B$. Then the equilibrium between A and X is only inappreciably disturbed by the process $X \rightarrow B$. Equilibria of just this type have been postulated in theories involving intermediate complexes, etc. The interrelationship between A, B, and the activated complex Z is indicated thus:

$$A \rightarrow Z \rightarrow B \qquad (5)$$

The activated complex formed from A is always transformed to B, and never reverts to A.* Having attained the activated complex the atomic motion continue, due to inertia; after the complex has been formed, and the potential barrier overcome, the system continues down the far side.

The total energy of the system (kinetic plus potential) associated with the reaction coordinate will always be either greater or less than the exact height of the potential barrier. The probability that the energy of the system will be exactly equal to the barrier height is zero. Therefore there can be no pause at the summit of the barrier.

If (3) is reversible, equilibrium can be established:

$$A \rightleftharpoons B \qquad (6)$$

This equilibrium is established in accordance with the scheme

$$
\begin{array}{ccc}
 & Z^+ & \\
 \nearrow & & \searrow \\
A & & B \\
 \nwarrow & & \swarrow \\
 & Z^- & \\
\end{array}
\qquad (7)
$$

---

* The reaction is supposed adiabatic. Detailed consideration will be given below to the limitations of this concept.

Z^- is the activated complex for the reverse reaction, having the same configuration as Z^+, but with the sense of motion along the reaction coordinate reversed.

If the intermediate X is formed, then equilibrium is established when X is in equilibrium with both A and B:

$$A \rightleftharpoons X \rightleftharpoons B \qquad (8)$$

In a system in chemical equilibrium, as in (6), all possible molecular states are in statistical equilibrium. In particular, the frequency with which the states Z^+ and Z^- occur may be determined from the law governing the statistical equilibrium.

Imagine that [A] is maintained at the value corresponding to chemical equilibrium, while [B] is suddenly reduced to zero. Then only the reaction A → B will occur, and Z^- will not be formed, since this only is formed from B, and not from A. The basic assumption of the method may be formulated as the hypothesis that the rate of A → B will be unaffected when [B] → 0, or in other words that Z^+ will be present in the system just as frequently as at chemical equilibrium. We therefore suppose that the direct and reverse reactions do not influence one another. This hypothesis is scarcely new, since it occurs even in the earlier kinetic theories, as in Guldberg and Waage's demonstration of the law of mass action in chemical equilibria.

These are the basic physical premises of the activated complex method.

The computation of rates by this method may be explained as follows. Consider some small length Δl along the reaction coordinate, l, such that it includes the top of the potential barrier. Systems for which the reaction coordinate falls within Δl, and the motions of which along the coordinate are in the requisite direction, are termed activated complexes for the direct reaction. We may now speak of the concentration of activated complexes, since the number per unit volume can be defined for a chosen length Δl. This number must be proportional to Δl, if Δl is small. The concentration of complexes may then be written as $c_a \Delta l$, where c_a^+ is the coefficient of proportionality between the concentration of activated complexes and Δl, or the concentration of activated complexes per unit length of the reaction coordinate.

Let $\bar{v}$ indicate the mean rate of change of reaction coordinate with time. $\bar{v}$ is the rate of change of configuration, in essence, the relative velocities of the particles in the reacting system. The mean lifetime of the activated complex is $\Delta l / \bar{v}$, i.e. it is the time required to move a distance Δl along the reaction route, at a velocity $\bar{v}$.

Each formation of an activated complex constitutes one act of reaction. Thus there are $c_a \Delta l$ acts of reaction per unit volume in time $\Delta l/\bar{v}$, so the number of acts per unit volume in unit time (i.e. the rate) is $c_a \bar{v}$.

We have so far assumed that attainment of the activated complex guarantees reaction. This is not so in some cases (see below); an additional factor must be introduced—the transmission coefficient x, $x \leqslant 1$. The rate w^+ is then given by

$$w^+ = \kappa c_a^+ \bar{v} \tag{9}$$

Since we have assumed that statistical equilibrium is maintained between the activated complexes and the parent compounds, we may calculate c_a and $\bar{v}$ by the well-known methods of statistical mechanics. The generalized form of the Maxwell–Boltzmann law (the expression involving sums over states) is used to calculate c_a, while $\bar{v}$ is calculated by the normal methods used for computing mean velocities due to thermal motion.

We thus obtain EYRING's equation [2] for a homogenous gas reaction:

$$k_C = \kappa \frac{kT}{h} \frac{f_a'}{f} \exp\left(-\varepsilon_0/kT\right) \tag{10}$$

In this equation k_C is the rate constant (in which the concentration is expressed as molecules/unit volume), k is Boltzmann's constant, h is Planck's constant, T is the absolute temperature, f is the product of the statistical sums (sums over states) for the initial molecules, calculated for unit volume, f_a' is the sum per unit volume for the activated complex, not including the factor for the reaction coordinate, ε_0 is the height of the potential barrier, i.e. the minimum energy difference between the activated complex and the parent molecules.

There are different definitions of the average velocity along the reaction coordinate. EYRING [2, 3] defined it as

$$\bar{v} = \frac{\displaystyle\int_0^\infty v \exp\left(-m^* v^2/kT\right) dv}{\displaystyle\int_{-\infty}^\infty \exp\left(m^* v^2/kT\right) dv} \tag{11}$$

where m^* is the reduced mass of the activated complex.

EVANS and POLANYI [4] made use of

$$|\bar{v}| = \frac{\displaystyle\int_{-\infty}^\infty |v| \exp\left(-m^* v^2/kT\right) dv}{\displaystyle\int_{-\infty}^\infty \exp\left(-m^* v/kT\right) dv} = \frac{\displaystyle\int_\infty^\infty v \exp\left(-m^* v/kT\right) dv}{\displaystyle\int_0^\infty \exp\left(-m^* v^2/kT\right) dv} \tag{12}$$

which implies the usual concept of an average velocity. Evidently $\bar{v} = \frac{1}{2} |\bar{v}|$. If c_a is the concentration of activated complexes per unit length of reaction coordinate, irrespective of the direction of motion, then at chemical equilibrium $c_a^+ = \frac{1}{2} c_a$ and

$$w^+ = \frac{1}{2} \kappa c_a |\bar{v}| \tag{13}$$

which is EVANS and POLANYI's equation [4] or

$$w^* = \kappa c_a \bar{v} \tag{14}$$

which corresponds to EYRING's treatment. Unlike (13) and (14), (9) is valid at any [B] and not only at the [B] corresponding to chemical equilibrium.

The transmission coefficient κ requires separate consideration. For this purpose we must introduce the concept of adiabatic elementary acts of reaction.

The term "adiabatic" is here used in the sense first employed by EHRENFEST in his theory of "adiabatic invariants", and has nothing in common with adiabatic processes in thermodynamics.

If the parameters of the mechanical system change extremely slowly (in the limit, infinitely slowly), then the quantum number specifying its state of motion cannot change. A process of this type is termed adiabatic in quantum mechanics.

The quantities defining the relative positions of the nuclei (such as $H_2 + D$ at some stage of the reaction), play the role of parameters for the motions of the electrons in the system. Since the heavy nuclei move very much more slowly than the light electrons, it is natural to assume that the electrons are rearranged for each configuration of the nuclei, and that their motion is almost exactly the same as if the nuclei had been resting in their actual positions for an infinitely long time. This is equivalent to the assumption that the elementary act is adiabatic.

If the above assumption is fulfilled, then the point corresponding to the system moves on a definite potential surface. If the point attains the top of the potential barrier, then the reaction of necessity occurs. Hence for adiabatic processes $\kappa = 1$ (or if allowance is made for the approximate character of the activated complex concept, then we should say that $\kappa \simeq 1$).

A quantum-mechanical treatment shows, however, that the supposed adiabatic course of the elementary act may not occur in some cases. As a rule, the course will be non-adiabatic if it involves a change in the total electron spins, or if it corresponds to some other prohibited transition. The theory of non-adiabatic processes has been developed by LANDAU [5]; it shows that reaction is not guaranteed in such processes even if the top of the potential barrier is attained; in most cases the system returns to the initial state. Values of κ of the order of 10^{-5} are typical of non-adiabatic processes.

In order to decide on the relative occurrence of adiabatic and non-adiabatic reactions we return to the data on the rates of unimolecular reactions. It follows from (10) that if $\kappa = 1$, then the pre-exponential factors for unimolecular reactions must be about 10^{13}–10^{14} sec^{-1}. Chain mechanisms which also give first-order equations can only affect the activation energy, the pre-exponential factors remaining of the same order as in direct unimolecular decomposition.

Thus, no matter what the mechanism, if a reaction is of the first order, and the pre-exponential factor is 10^{13} sec^{-1} or somewhat larger, then an adiabatic course is indicated; much lower values for the pre-exponential factors, such as 10^8 sec^{-1}, indicate that the reaction is non-adiabatic. It may thus be shown that some 90 per cent of reactions are adiabatic.

Returning to the general consideration of the activated-complex method, we note that the initial basic assumption that the reaction does not affect the equilibrium Maxwell–Boltzmann distribution is not always correct. The most well-known instance of this is found in unimolecular gas reactions at low pressures, when the number of activating collisions is inadequate to maintain the equilibrium concentration of active molecules.* In such cases the reactions go more slowly than would be indicated by (10).

At one stage in the development of the chain theory great importance was attached to deviations from the Maxwell–Boltzmann distribution due to the reaction, which led to assumptions about "energy" chains. These concepts have now been abandoned. A large body of experimental data indicates that the chains are material, and not energetic. Deviations from the Maxwell–Boltzmann distribution play a much more modest role than had been assumed. The separate simple chain-carrying reactions may be quite adequately described by equations derived without allowance for deviations from the Maxwell–Boltzmann distribution.

The range of phenomena to which the basic concepts of the activated-complex method apply coincides with that to which the law of mass-action and Arrhenius' equation are applicable. Deviations from the Maxwell–Boltzmann distribution would in fact lead to the law of mass-action being violated, as is actually found for gas-phase unimolecular reactions at low pressures; the reaction is not

---

* "Active molecules" means those molecules in which the total energy present in the vibrational degrees of freedom is greater than the height of the potential barrier. A clear distinction should be drawn between the concepts "active molecule" and "activated complex".

described by an equation of the first order, and Arrhenius' equation is also not applicable.

In addition to the neglect of deviations from the Maxwell–Boltzmann distribution, which results in some errors (although not usually large ones in most cases), the method in the form in which it is usually stated still contains some inaccuracies of principle; neglect of curvature of the reaction-path, of vibrational quantization in the activated complex, etc. It should none the less be recognized that the method is successful as an approximation, quite sufficient in the present state of chemical kinetics. It may be applied successfully to rates of chemisorption of gases by solid bodies, and to heterogeneous catalytic processes [6].

The opportunities for applying the method are greatly restricted by our lack of knowledge of the potential surfaces which define the courses of the elementary acts, though some results are obtainable without detailed knowledge of the potential surface; the general form of the law of mass-action in non-ideal systems, dependence of the rate on the action of external forces, (e.g. hydrostatic pressure on liquid-phase reactions), the approximate estimation of pre-exponential factors in Arrhenius' equation, etc.

Further progress in the theoretical calculation of rates of simple reactions will primarily result from improvements in the methods of handling the quantum-mechanical part of the problem, rather than from more accurate treatment of the statistical part.

In conclusion, some errors involved in the application of the method will be dealt with.

It is sometimes suggested that the method depends on the maintenance of some specific equilibrium similar to chemical equilibria between the activated complex and the parent molecules. Then the reciprocal of the factor kT/h in (10) (which has the dimensions of a frequency) is treated as the lifetime of the activated complex, and the lifetime is thus taken to be about 10^{-13} sec.

All these ideas are based on misunderstandings. "Lifetime of the activated complex" (like the activated complex concentration) is an indefinable quantity unless we assign some small interval along the reaction route (including the top of the barrier) within which fall the configurations we agree to consider as belonging to the activated complex. The Maxwell–Boltzmann law defines the number of particles having coordinates between the limits of q_1 and $q_1 + \Delta q_1$, q_2 and $q_2 + \Delta q_2$, etc., the conjugate momenta being between p_1 and $p_1 + \Delta p_1$, p_2, and $p_2 + \Delta p_2$, etc., where Δq_1, Δp_1, etc., are small quantities. How much time does the particle spend in this state? This depends on the values chosen for Δq_1, Δq_2, . . ., Δp_1, Δp_2, . . . In the same way the time for which the system remains in the state defined by values of the reaction coordinate in the range l to $l + \Delta l$ depends on the Δl chosen, being proportional to Δl if Δl is small.

Thus the assertion that the activated complex has a lifetime of the order of 10^{-13} sec, strictly speaking, is devoid of meaning. The time for which the activated complex exists is of the nature of a differential, just as in the lifetime of the states referred to in the Maxwell–Boltzmann law. This evidently does not prevent us from using the Maxwell–Boltzmann law in calculating the concentration of activated complexes in the reacting system; for this purpose no equilibrium other than the Maxwell–Boltzmann equilibrium between states has to be assumed.

We trust that the above remarks will advance the correct appreciation of the meaning of the activated complex method, and of its field of applicability.

Appendix II

THE QUANTUM-MECHANICAL CALCULATION OF ACTIVATION ENERGIES*

ONE of the first attempts to calculate the activation energy of an elementary bimolecular reaction was that of LONDON [7]. The degree of approximation was such as to give the bond-dissociation energy of H_2 in the simple form:

$$w_0 = Q_{H-H} = A_0 + \alpha_0 \tag{1}$$

Here A_0 is the so-called Coulomb integral, numerically equal to electrostatic energy of the unperturbed electron clouds and the two hydrogen nuclei, and α_0 is the so-called exchange integral, which arises from the requirement that the molecular wave-function derived from the one-electron functions of the separate atoms, must satisfy certain definite symmetry conditions. This integral represents the specific atomic interaction; in particular, the presence of this exchange integral in the expression for the energy enables us to understand the fact that the chemical bonds are satisfied. The integrands for α_0 and A_0 contain the electrostatic interaction energy of the electrons and nuclei of the two H atoms, as well as the corresponding wave-functions. In the approximation considered, for internuclear distances close to the equilibrium value, the exchange integral comprises about 80–95 per cent of the total bond-energy.

(1) is obtained in a first approximation by perturbation theory, on the assumption that the wave-function for the two separate systems remains unchanged when they approach one another. In addition, in obtaining (1) it is assumed that the square of the so-called non-orthogonality integral (S), indicating the degree of overlap of the two atomic wave-functions in the molecule, is negligibly small as compared with unity. Neglect of this quantity means that the molecular wave-function is inaccurately normalized.

(1) is not suitable for quantitative calculations, due to the simplifying assumptions made in its derivation. If S is not neglected, the following expression is obtained for Q_{H-H}:

$$w_0 = \frac{A_0 + \alpha_0}{1 + S^2} \tag{1'}$$

w_0 computed from (1') is some 66 per cent of the actual Q_{H-H}. If S^2 is neglected, as in (1), then a value is obtained which is close to

* This section was written by N. O. Sokolov in collaboration with the author.

the experimental, due to cancelling of errors, but this does not justify the omissions made.

Consider a reaction of the type:

$$XY + ZW \rightarrow XZ + YW \tag{2}$$

where X, Y, Z and W are univalent atoms. By solving the corresponding four-electron equation with the assumptions made in

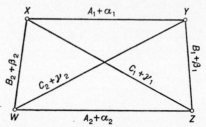

Fig. 24.   Activated complex for the reaction
XY + ZW → XW + YZ

deriving (1), it is not difficult to obtain the energy of the system of four atoms in the following form (due to LONDON):

$$w = \Sigma - \{\tfrac{1}{2}[(\alpha - \beta)^2 + (\beta - \gamma)^2 + (\gamma - \alpha)^2]\}^{\frac{1}{2}} \tag{3}$$

Σ here indicates the sum of the Coulomb integrals for all possible pairs of atoms in the system (Fig. 24)

$$\Sigma = A_1 + A_2 + B_1 + B_2 + C_1 + C_2 \tag{4}$$

while α, β, γ are the sums of the corresponding exchange integrals:

$$\alpha = \alpha_1 + \alpha_2; \ \beta = \beta_1 + \beta_2; \ \gamma = \gamma_1 + \gamma_2 \tag{5}$$

The magnitudes of the integrals α_i, β_i, γ_i ($i = 1, 2$) differ from α_0 in (1) and (1'), since the integrands contain not only terms relating to the electrostatic interactions between the given pairs of atoms (both electrons and nuclei), but also terms relating to the interaction of each of the atoms with all of the rest, and of the latter with one another.

Some important assumptions are made in the derivation of (3). Firstly, as in deriving (1), it is assumed that the wave-functions of the separate atoms remain unperturbed as they approach, and that S^2 is small by comparison with unity; secondly, (3) assumes the presence of only one electron on each atom, and therefore is not applicable to multi-electron atoms; thirdly, the permutation of more than two electrons is completely neglected, so additional quantities of the order of S^2 are omitted. Further, (3) does not take account of bond polarity, so consequently it is not applicable in ionic reactions.

Finally, (3) takes no account of changes of valency state during the reaction.

In spite of the assumptions made, (3) gives the main results as correct in a qualitative sense for the interaction of two molecules (XY and ZW) with one another, and for the interaction of one atom (Z) with a molecule (XY) (at least in the case where X, Y, Z and W are hydrogen atoms). This is readily verified by applying (3) to a triatomic system. Supposing $A_2 = B_2 = C_2 = 0$, and $\alpha_2 = \beta_2 = \gamma_2 = 0$, we find for the energy of the system XYZ

$$w' = A_1 + B_1 + C_1 - \{\tfrac{1}{2}[(\alpha_1 - \beta_1)^2 + (\beta_1 - \gamma_1)^2 + (\gamma_1 - \alpha_1)^2]\}^{\tfrac{1}{2}} \qquad (6)$$

In the case where Z is at a great distance from XY, and thus $B_1 = C_1 = \beta_1 = \gamma_1 = 0$, (6) gives

$$w_0 = A_{01} - |\alpha_{01}| = A_{01} + \alpha_{01} \; (\alpha_{01} < 0)$$

This expression is identical with (1) i.e., it is just Q_{X-Y} in the isolated molecule XY. If Z now begins to approach XY, then for distances which are sufficiently large by comparison with the equilibrium X − Y separation we may take $\beta_{1/\alpha_1} \ll 1$ and $\gamma_{1/\alpha_1} \ll 1$. Then, expanding (6) into a number of such small quantities, we get

$$w' = (A_1 + \alpha_1) + B_1 + C_1 - \tfrac{1}{2}\beta_1 - \tfrac{1}{2}\gamma_1 \qquad (7)$$

This equation means that the energy increases as the atom approaches the chemically saturated molecule, in so far as calculation for s-electrons gives

$$|B_1| < \tfrac{1}{2}|\beta_1|; \; |C_1| < \tfrac{1}{2}|\gamma_1|; \; \beta_1 < 0 \text{ and } \gamma_1 < 0$$

Consequently, there is a repulsion between the atom and the molecule. If the atom X is initially at a great distance from YZ, and then begins to approach, then by analogy the energy of the system rises from $B_{01} + \beta_{01}$ to

$$w' = (B_1 + \beta_1) + A_1 + C_1 - \tfrac{1}{2}\alpha_1 - \tfrac{1}{2}\gamma_1 \qquad (8)$$

Hence for reactions of the type

$$XY + Z \rightarrow X + YZ \qquad (9)$$

there must be some activation energy which is calculable from (6) if the values of all the integrals appearing therein are available for the appropriate interatomic spacings.

However, without performing the numerical calculation, using (6) we may make some general assumption as to the relation between the energy of the system XYZ and the interatomic distances. Let us consider the particular case of a linear arrangement of the atoms, each of which has one s-electron (Fig. 25). Then the energy will be a function of the two coordinates r_1 and r_2, and may be depicted as a potential energy surface. Taking r_1 and r_2 as the axes of the coordinate system, the energy may be expressed in the form

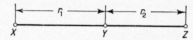

Fig. 25. Activated complex for the reaction
$$XY + Z \rightarrow X + YZ$$

of lines of equal energy (Fig. 26). Then with $r_2 = \infty$ and $r_1 = r_{01}$ (r_{01} being the equilibrium X—Y distance in the isolated molecule XY) we will be at the top left corner of the diagram, at which point the energy will be equal to the energy of atomic interaction in the equilibrium state of XY. As Z approaches (r_2 decreasing) the energy increases, and if r_1 remains constant may attain very high values. The energy will change in an analogous fashion if $r_2 = r_{02}$ and $r_1 = \infty$ initially.

The state where all three atoms are uncoupled corresponds to the upper right section of the potential surface ($r_1 = r_2 = \infty$) the energy then being zero. If, starting from this state, we bring the atoms together in such a way that $r_1 = r_2$ at all times, this will be equivalent to motion along the diagonal line PO (Fig. 26). For some value of the interatomic distances (subject to $r_1 = r_2$) the energy will have a minimum, evidently at the saddle point, indicated by a cross. The transition from the state XY + Z to the state X + YZ via this point obviously involves the least absorption of energy. It is clear from Fig. 9 that the approach of Z to XY is energetically favoured by some increase in the X—Y distance, the maximum energy being reached at the saddle point;* after passing through the gap, r_2 will continue to diminish, while r_1 will increase until the terminal state with $r_1 = \infty$ and $r_2 = r_{02}$ is reached. Thus (9) has a "most favoured route" (the broken curve in Fig. 26), in following which the system demands the least energy (the activation energy).

Using (3) we may obtain approximate relative activation energies for different mutual orientations of the colliding particles. Consider for instance the reaction:

$$H_2 + D \rightarrow HD + H \tag{10}$$

* According to EYRING and POLANYI, in reactions of the type $H_2 + D \rightarrow HD + H$ the minimum on the line PO corresponds to the bottom of a shallow depression about 2·5 kcal deep [6]. The top of the pass is then displaced somewhat to the side of the line PO. However, the presence of such a depression has not been confirmed experimentally, and has not been substantiated adequately from theory.

Assuming that $r_1 = r_2$, it is not difficult to show that the linear arrangement of the three particles gives the activation energy of (10) as being lower than for the angular arrangement (Fig. 27).

Subject to the condition $r_1 = r_2$ (6) may be put in the form $(A_1 = B_1;\ \alpha_1 = \beta_1)$:

$$w' = 2A_1 + C_1 + \alpha_1 - \gamma_1 \tag{11}$$

The difference between this energy and that of the initial state $w_0 = A_{01} + \alpha_{01}$ (1) will be equal to:

$$\varepsilon = \varepsilon_0 = 2A_1 + C_1 - A_{01} + (\alpha - \alpha_{01}) - \gamma_1 \tag{12}$$

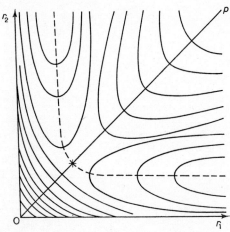

Fig. 26. Potential energy surface

If the condition $r_1 = r_2$ corresponds to the saddle-point on the potential surface, then expression (12) represents the activation energy for (10). It is readily perceived from (12) that the difference between the energies of the linear and right-angled configurations arises from atoms a and c being closer in the latter case (Fig. 27). Correspondingly, the energy of repulsion of these atoms $(-\gamma_1)$ is greater in the right-angled configuration than in the linear one. Since the exchange integral always considerably exceeds the coulomb integral in hydrogen, this increased repulsion cannot be balanced by a simultaneous increase in the Coulomb attraction (C_1). According to approximate estimates made by the so-called semi-empirical method (see below), this difference may be 20–30 kcal.

It is not difficult to demonstrate from (3) that the activation energy for the reaction of two hydrogen molecules:

$$H_2 + D_2 \rightarrow HD + HD \tag{13}$$

calculated on the assumption that the activated complex is square in form (Fig. 28) is twice as great as the energy of formation of the triangular complex with three hydrogen atoms in Fig. 11.

Assuming that $A_1 = A_2 = B_1 = B_2$ and $\alpha_1 = \alpha_2 = \beta_1 = \beta_2$ in (3) we get:

$$w = 4A_1 + 2C_1 + 2\alpha_1 - 2\gamma_1 \tag{14}$$

Computing the energy of the two isolated molecules from this

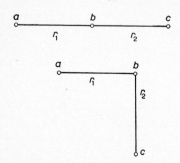

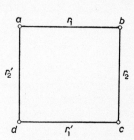

Fig. 27. Linear and right-angled arrangements of three atoms in the activated complex

Fig. 28. Square-type activated complex

expression, as being $2w_0 = 2(A_{01} + \alpha_{01})$, we get for the activation energy of (13):

$$E' = w - 2w_0 = 2[2A_1 + C_1 - A_{01} + (\alpha_1 - \alpha_{01}) - \gamma_1] \tag{15}$$

Comparison with (12) shows that E' is actually twice as great as ε. By analogy, the activation energy of

$$H_2 + D_2 \rightarrow H + HD + D \tag{16}$$

assuming a linear arrangement of the four atoms in the activated complex (Fig. 29) must be approximately equal to Q_{H-H}. On the assumption that the separations of neighbouring atoms are equal and the same as in the triatomic case, we have $A_1 = B_1 = B_2$; $C_1 = C_2$; $\alpha_1 = \beta_1 = \beta_2$; and $\gamma_1 = \gamma_2$. Inserting these relations, and neglecting the quantity $(\gamma_1 - \alpha_2)^2/6(\alpha_1 - \gamma_1)^2$ as being $\ll 1$, the activation energy of (16) is:

$$E' = Q_{H-H} + \varepsilon_0 + [C_1 + A_1 + A_2 + 0\cdot73\,(\alpha_1 - \gamma_1)] \tag{17}$$

where ε_0 is the activation energy of (10) (see formula (12)). It is not difficult to see that the quantity in square brackets is negative, since $(\alpha_1 - \gamma_1) < 0$. Hence the activation energy of (16) falls between the limits of $\varepsilon_0 + Q_{H-H}$ and Q_{H-H}, $\varepsilon_0 + Q_{H-H} > E' \geqslant$

Q_{H-H}. The activation energy E_0 for the reverse (exothermic) reaction has $\varepsilon_0 > E_0 \geqslant 0$.

The conclusion that E' in (16) is small in the linear arrangement has recently been confirmed by systematic quantum-mechanical computation of the linear H_3 complex by the method of molecular

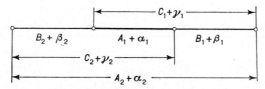

Fig. 29. Linear arrangement of four atoms in the
activated complex

orbitals; (due account being taken of the antisymmetry and inter-action of the electrons) using self-consistent field methods [10, 11].

The numerical calculation of activation energies from LONDON's formula involves great mathematical difficulties. This is why an approximate method (the so-called semi-empirical method) was proposed, deriving from the potential curves for diatomic molecules. Due to the experimental data utilized in the calculation being the ones used in the derivation of (6) or of (3), the errors are likely to cancel out to some extent. However, this same semi-empirical method also involves some fresh assumptions, which are fresh sources of error, and it introduces a substantial arbitrary element into the calculation.

In order to derive the variation of the integrals in (3) with the interatomic separations, it is assumed, firstly, that the interaction energy of the atoms in XY as expressed by (1), may be approximated by a Morse function, i.e. the equation becomes:

$$w_0 = A + \alpha\, D\{\exp\left[-2a(r-r_0)\right] - 2\exp\left[-a(r-r_0)\right]\} \qquad (18)$$

where D is the bond-energy (without allowance for the zero of energy), r_0 is the equilibrium internuclear distance X—Y, and a is a constant which can be derived from spectroscopic data. It is further assumed that the Coulomb integral A is a definite, constant, fraction n of the total bond energy. The integrals A and α may then be evaluated as:

$$A = nD\{\exp\left[-2a(r-r_0)\right] - 2\exp\left[-a(r-r_0)\right]\} \qquad (19)$$

$$\alpha = (1-n)D\exp\left[-2a(r-r_0)\right] - 2\exp\left[-a(r-r_0)\right] \qquad (19')$$

Analogous formulae may be derived for each pair of atoms in the system $(X—Y) + (Z—W)$. By evaluation of the Coulomb and exchange integrals in (3) or (6) we may evaluate the energy for any interatomic spacing, and thus determine the activation energy.

It is not difficult to derive the energy of the system $H \cdots H \cdots H$ for example, which is an intermediary state in the elementary reaction (10). The experimental activation energy of this reaction is about 7 kcal.

Assuming a linear atomic arrangement, and supposing $r_1 = r_2$ we utilize (12). The calculation shows that the minimum energy occurs when $r_1 = 0.78$ Å when $r_1 = r_2$. Taking this value, and assuming that $n = 0.14$ and $D = 108.5$ kcal, with $a = 1.94$ Å^{-1} we find from (19) and (19') that $A_{01} \simeq -15$ kcal, $A_1 \simeq -15$ kcal, $C_1 \simeq -6$ kcal, $\alpha_{01} \simeq -93$ kcal, $\alpha_1 \simeq -93$ kcal, and $\gamma_1 \simeq -34$ kcal. Substituting these in (12), we find $\varepsilon_0 \simeq 13$ kcal. EYRING and POLANYI [8] found approximately the same value for the activation energy of (10), their calculations having almost the same form. The above value exceeds the experimental one by almost a factor 2. Agreement with the experimental value may be obtained if n is raised somewhat. Actually, assuming $n = 0.17$, and multiplying the first three terms in (12) by $0.17/0.14$, and the next three by $0.83/0.86$, with the distances $r_1 = r_2 = 0.78$ Å, we find $\varepsilon_0 \simeq 7$ kcal.

This calculation introduces two errors. The first amounts to this, that the fraction n of the total bond-energy assigned to the Coulomb integral, instead of being constant, depends strongly on the internuclear distance. It is easily shown that A, for two H atoms decreases as $\exp(-2r)$ for large values of r, while the exchange integral decreases as $\exp(-r)$. Analogous discrepancies occur at small r. Thus, for molecular H_2, calculation shows that the proportion of the total bond-energy assigned to the Coulomb integral at $r = 1$ Å is 17 per cent, while at $r = 0.78$ Å, which corresponds to the H—H separation in the activated complex (reference [2], page 83, Fig. 7), it is about 5 per cent. If n is given the value 0.05 in the above calculation, then the activation energy of (10) is found to be approximately 30 kcal.

The second error is due to the fact that α for a system containing four (or three) atoms cannot be identified directly with α for the isolated bond between two atoms. They may in fact differ considerably because the operator appearing in the wave equation for the system of four (or three) atoms contains terms additional to those appearing in the case of two atoms only, which relate to the interaction of these two atoms with the rest, and of the latter with one another. If the integrals are treated as identical then errors of the order of magnitude of α are introduced.

However, the elimination of the above errors by systematic calculation of all the integrals appearing in (6), with appropriate normalization does not lead to agreement with experiment: the activation energy obtained in this way is 19 kcal [7]. This indicates that the assumptions made in the derivation of LONDON's formula involve too great an approximation. Up to the present there has been no satisfactory quantitative calculation of the activation energy. Attempts to improve the accuracy in the case of (10) by way of atomic wave-functions "distorted" by the interaction of the atoms have not given acceptable results. Thus, the introduction of two adjustable parameters into the wave-function improves the calculated energy of H_2 considerably, but has little effect on the energy of the triatomic complex $H \cdot \cdot \cdot H \cdot \cdot \cdot H$; consequently, the value of ε_0 calculated for (10), which is the difference of these quantities, deviates still further from the experimental value, becoming 25 kcal [7].

The values obtained for the energy of the non-linear H, complex by semi-empirical and perturbation methods also disagree sharply. Thus the difference between the energies of the linear and right-angled configurations with $r_1 = r_2 = 1 \cdot 05$ Å, is about 20 kcal according to the semi-empirical method, but according to the perturbation method it is greater than 50 kcal [8].

Numerical calculation of the activation energy for reaction of two H_2 molecules was only made via the semi-empirical method. Naturally, it involves just the same discrepancies as in the interaction of an atom with a molecule. GLASSTONE et al. [2] give the activation energy of (13) as 90 kcal. In view of the inaccuracies in the calculations this value can only be considered as being doubly approximate.

It must be emphasized that the semi-empirical method introduces considerable arbitrariness into the calculation of activation energies. This is due to the part of the total bond-energy assigned to the Coulomb integral in the semi-empirical method being in practice almost arbitrary. This gives considerable scope for "adjusting" the calculated activation energy to the experimental value. We have already seen above that $n = 0 \cdot 14$ for (10) was already arbitrary, and that the more correct value of $n = 0 \cdot 05$ gave a calculated ε_0 very different from the real one. The choice of n is still more arbitrary when the reactions involve atoms or molecules with p-electrons. In this case direct calculation of the Coulomb and exchange integrals shows that [11] they have similar values; in calculations analogous to the derivation of LONDON's formula it is implied that the Coulomb integral is considerably less than the exchange one. Thus in [2] the activation energy for the reaction between H_2 and ICl is in one place (page 240) calculated with $n = 0 \cdot 14$, while in another place (page 241) the value is taken to be $0 \cdot 17$ and $0 \cdot 20$. Even comparatively small changes in n affect the activation energy strongly, ε changing by 8 kcal on going from $n = 0.17$ to 0.20; this implies a divergence in the estimated rate at normal temperatures by a factor $\exp(-\Delta E/RT) \sim 10^6$ times.

Consequent to the errors introduced and the simplifications made in calculating activation energies by LONDON's formula in conjunction with the semi-empirical method; the error in E may in

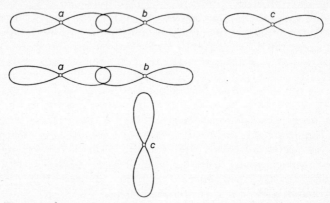

Fig. 30. Linear (top) and right angled arrangements of three atoms with p-electrons in the activated complex (schematic)

practice be even larger, amounting to several hundred per cent; the extent of the inaccuracy cannot be determined in advance from theory.

Thus we are convinced that LONDON's formula is not suitable for quantitative calculation of activation energies, and is only applicable in qualitative arguments. We have already seen previously that qualitative conclusions may be drawn about the activation energies involved in different mutual orientations of an atom and a molecule of hydrogen.

It must, however, be noted that these conclusions, and still more so the quantitative estimates, must not be transferred to many electron atoms and molecules, particularly in cases where the elementary act of reaction involves p-electrons. Calculations even on such simple diatomic molecules as Li_2 and LiH, etc., show that all relations and results strongly depend on whether or not account is taken of the electrons in the atomic cores. This is still more so in molecules in which the outer shells have electrons which do not take part in the intramolecular bonds (non-bonding electron-pairs). Further, the picture is greatly complicated by the specific distributions of the p-electron orbitals. It is evident from Fig. 30 that the conditions of interaction of three atoms having p-electrons will differ from one another in the linear and right-angled arrangements much more markedly than in atoms with s-electrons. The conditions under which the two molecules (ab) and (cd) (both having p—p bonds (Fig. 31)) interact, are themselves different from the case where three atoms with p-electrons interact in the right-angled arrangement. Here, as distinct from the case of s-electrons, it is difficult to

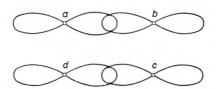

Fig. 31. Arrangement of four atoms with p-electrons with the activated complex (schematic)

discern any direct relation between the activation energies. The position is still more complicated when unshared electrons are present, the axes of the clouds in the p-state being arranged at right-angles to the bond-axis, which in all probability increases the repulsion. In cases such as these it is impossible to say anything in advance about the activation energy. Systematic calculations on similar systems may show that the activation energy itself is of a different nature from that in the interaction of atoms and molecules of hydrogen.

Thus we conclude that the theoretical calculation of activation energies in quantitative terms for gas-phase bimolecular reactions remains completely impracticable. Strictly speaking, qualitative treatments exist, relating only to atoms and molecules of hydrogen. Investigation of this range of problems must evidently take some different form. The application of automatic computing methods, as in calculations on stable molecules, may scarcely be capable of resolving the problem as a whole.

REFERENCES

1. See for instance N. N. SEMENOV. *Usp. Khim.* **1**, 19 (1934).
2. S. GLASSTONE, K. J. LAIDLER and H. EYRING. *Theory of Rate-processes* 1941. Russian edition, 1948.
3. H. EYRING. *J. Chem. Phys.* **3**, 107 (1935).
4. M. G. EVANS and M. POLANYI. *Trans. Faraday Soc.* **31**, 875 (1935).
5. L. D. LANDAU. *Phys. Z. Sowjet.* **1**, 88 (1932); *ibid.* **2**, 46 (1932).
6. M. I. TEMKIN. *Zh. Fiz. Khim.* **11**, 169 (1938).
7. F. LONDON. *Probleme der modernen Physik* (*Sommerfeld Festschrift*). p. 104. 1928; *Z. Electrochem.* **35**, 552 (1929).
8. H. EYRING and M. POLANYI. *Z. phys. Chem.* B **12**, 279 (1931).

9. J. Hirschfelder, H. Eyring and N. Rosen. *J. Chem. Phys.* **4,** 121 (1936).
10. J. Hirschfelder. *J. Chem. Phys.* **6,** 795 (1938).
11. M. F. Mamotenko. Article in the *Symposium on Physical Chemistry.* p. 1. Academy of Sciences of *U.S.S.R.*, 1947.
12. V. Criffing. *J. Chem. Phys.* **23,** 1015 (1955).
13. V. Criffing and J. T. Vanderslire. *J. Chem. Phys.* **23,** 1035 (1955).

NAME INDEX

SUBJECT INDEX

302

THE INTERNATIONAL
ENCYCLOPEDIA
OF PHYSICAL CHEMISTRY
AND CHEMICAL PHYSICS

Topic 19. GAS KINETICS

EDITOR: A. F. TROTMAN-DICKENSON

Volume 5
CHEMISTRY IN
PREMIXED FLAMES

BY

C. P. FENIMORE

THE INTERNATIONAL ENCYCLOPEDIA
OF PHYSICAL CHEMISTRY AND CHEMICAL PHYSICS

Members of the Honorary Editorial Advisory Board

THE INTERNATIONAL ENCYCLOPEDIA
OF PHYSICAL CHEMISTRY AND CHEMICAL PHYSICS

Editors-in-Chief

E. A. GUGGENHEIM   J. E. MAYER
READING   LA JOLLA

F. C. TOMPKINS
LONDON

Chairman of the Editorial Advisory Group

ROBERT MAXWELL

PUBLISHER AT PERGAMON PRESS

List of Topics and Editors

INTRODUCTION

THE International Encyclopedia of Physical Chemistry and Chemical Physics is a comprehensive and modern account of all aspects of the domain of science between chemistry and physics, and is written primarily for the graduate and research worker. The Editors-in-Chief, Professor E. A. GUGGENHEIM, Professor J. E. MAYER and Professor F. C. TOMPKINS, have grouped the subject matter in some twenty groups (General Topics), each having its own editor. The complete work consists of about one hundred volumes, each volume being restricted to around two hundred pages and having a large measure of independence. Particular importance has been given to the exposition of the fundamental bases of each topic and to the development of the theoretical aspects; experimental details of an essentially practical nature are not emphasized although the theoretical background of techniques and procedures is fully developed.

The Encyclopedia is written throughout in English and the recommendations of the International Union of Pure and Applied Chemistry on notation and cognate matters in physical chemistry are adopted. Abbreviations for names of journals are in accordance with *The World List of Scientific Periodicals*.

CONTENTS

CHAPTER 1

FLAT PREMIXED FLAMES

EVERY flame is sustained by a complex reaction involving free radicals, as far as is known, and some of its elementary steps can often be followed more cleanly in other reacting systems. Radicals from discharges or photolyses may undergo the same elementary reactions at lower temperatures with less interference from unwanted species, and shock tubes which heat the gas mechanically may allow a desired step to be isolated at high temperatures in a way which would not be possible in a fire. Such considerations have suggested to some the paradox that flames are not very suitable objects of study in order to understand combustion. There is no reason why a chemist should not own both a discharge tube and a burner, however, and results by one technique may complement those by another.

Flames are called diffusion flames if the reactants must mix as they burn, and called premixed flames otherwise. Each kind can be either laminar or turbulent, depending on the character of the gas flow. All these types are dealt with in the books by Gaydon and Wolfhard[1] or by Lewis and von Elbe[2]; but the present treatment emphasizes the simplest burning possible, the steady, flat, pre-mixed flame, and only occasional reference is made to any other type of burning. The aim here is to discuss the chemistry, and flat flames are best for this purpose. In the arrangement envisaged, the motion of the gas is ideally in only one dimension, and one hopes to follow the course of the burning.

Figure 1.1 is a sketch of a water cooled, porous burner on which a flat flame can be burnt.[3,4] A laminar stream of reactants flows from the cooled surface into a reaction zone where the products are formed and accelerated downstream. There is a small pressure drop across the flame[2], but ordinarily it is of no consequence and the system can be taken to be a constant pressure one. As long as the gas flow is not too fast, the flame is stabilized above the burner by loss of heat to the cooled surface. If it could be displaced downstream while the gas flow remained unchanged, the flame would lose less heat to the burner and become hotter and faster burning, and recover its original position. It is also stable against displacement upstream which would cool it and make it slower burning. The steady burning velocity can be expressed either as a constant mass flow per unit of area or as a linear flow which increases as the gas warms up. When burning velocity is referred to without qualification, the linear velocity of the reactants is meant, measured before the gas has been warmed appreciably. In general usage, furthermore, the adiabatic burning velocity is meant; and although this is not achieved with a flat flame on a porous burner, it can be estimated in the following way.

If the gas flow is increased, the flame is blown a little farther off the burner until it is hot enough to burn at the faster velocity. It is possible

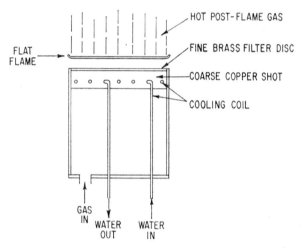

FIG. 1.1. Schematic flat flame burner, after Kaskan.[4]

to measure the decreased heat loss to the burner as the gas velocity is increased, and to extrapolate to an adiabatic burning velocity which is characteristic of the reactant composition and of its pressure and initial temperature. Measurements of the heat abstracted from flames by porous burners were first obtained by Botha and Spalding.[3] Their measurements have been criticized[5] and may have contained some errors,[6] but their extrapolation to zero heat abstraction seems valid.

Flames do not really burn without loss of heat to the surroundings, if only because of radiation. The notion of an adiabatic flame is an idealization, but it is usually a very good approximation.

Flat flames can be stabilized in other ways. The Powling burner[7] gives a flame nearer the ideal adiabatic one than a porous burner can. Instead of the cooled copper shot and porous surface shown in Fig. 1.1, the Powling burner possesses a honeycomb of columnar passages from which the gas issues with a flat velocity profile. A slight spreading of the flow occurs above the burner so that the flame can take a stable position where its burning velocity just equals the streaming velocity of the gas. A similar screen burner, in which a series of screens gives a uniform, approximately one dimensional flow, has also been used. The spreading of the gas above the burner can be measured by adding an inert dust of magnesium oxide and observing the paths of the particles. In a very fuel-lean methane flame burning as a flat, almost one dimensional flame at 1/10 atm, the spreading of the gas as it flowed from a screen burner to the downstream side of the reaction zone corresponded to a 10 per cent increase in area of a central stream tube.[8]

If the flow of gas through the burner of Fig. 1.1 is increased beyond the flat flame adiabatic burning velocity, the flame must become distorted. If the porous burner is replaced by a long open tube, a Bunsen burner, the flame remains attached to the rim of the tube and assumes a conical shape. The volume of gas supplied from the tube per second divided by the area of the flame surface is an average linear burning velocity. Such a premixed, laminar flame is still a flat flame locally, its thickness being small compared to the radius of curvature of its surface, and most published adiabatic burning velocities were measured on Bunsen type flames. Sometimes the total area of the flame is measured, sometimes the component of the flow normal to an especially suitable part of the cone.

A few experimental results may be quoted to give some feeling for the range of temperature and flammability. A stoichiometric, flat propane flame (4 per cent C_3H_8 in air) has an adiabatic burning velocity of 41·5 cm s^{-1}, measured at 289°K.[3] The velocity is slightly larger for a mixture containing a little excess fuel (4·2 per cent C_3H_8) but it decreases rapidly for compositions far from stoichiometric and is only 7 cm s^{-1} for either 2·13 or 7·1 per cent C_3H_8.[7] Linnett[9] reviewed the burning velocity measurements available for several fuels a few years ago, and discussed the errors in the various methods. His suggested values do not differ by more than about 5 per cent from some recent determinations by Scholte and Vaags,[10] obtained on Bunsen type burners, which are listed in Table 1.1. Agreement within 5 per cent is better than ought to be expected; the gas near the base of the cone is cooled by the burner wall, and that at the apex may be preheated in its passage, so the burning velocity is not really constant over the flame surface. Also the flame thickness while small is not negligible and this introduces some difficulty into determining its area. Flat flame burners possess fewer inherent sources of error, but these too always require correction or extrapolation to obtain the adiabatic velocity.

TABLE 1.1

Burning Velocities for the Fastest Burning Mixtures of Various Fuels with Air, from Scholte and Vaags[10]

Fuel	% Fuel by volume	Velocity cm s^{-1}
Hydrogen	42·4	280
Methane	10·5	40·0
Acetylene	9·45	150
Ethylene	7·3	70·0
Ethane	6·25	43·3
Propylene	4·95	45·6
Propane	4·3	41·4
But-1-ene	3·5	46·0
n-Butane	3·45	39·2

A few more burning velocities, those for the fastest burning mixtures of the five binary systems, are listed in Table 1.2. The pentaborane–air flame is the fastest burning fuel–air mixture reported so far. Its velocity was not determined on a burner, rather the growing shell of flame propagating out from a spark was photographed at various times and the burning velocity calculated from

$$\text{burning velocity} = (\mathrm{d}r/\mathrm{d}t)E$$

where $\mathrm{d}r/\mathrm{d}t$ is the rate of increase of radius of the shell with time and E a calculated expansion ratio of the burnt gas relative to the unburnt gas. The authors considered their value approximate, partly because the calculated E was used, partly because the flame front was cellular and not very well described as flat.

Hydrogen–fluorine is not listed among the halogen flames in Table 1.2 because the fastest burning mixtures cannot be burnt without detonations. Grosse and Kirschenbaum were able to mix fuel-rich compositions at 90°K which contained 6–25 per cent of F_2 and burnt about ten times faster than hydrogen–oxygen mixtures of the same initial temperature and fraction of stoichiometric strength.[256]

Fuel–air mixtures cannot burn if they contain too much of either constituent or have been diluted too much with inert gas. In general, the final flame temperature must be at least 1500°K for fuel-lean mixtures of light hydrocarbons and air to burn, and higher still for fuel-rich mixtures. Lean acetylene mixtures are exceptional in that they give flat flames with final temperatures of only around 1200°K, and both lean and rich hydrogen flames can burn with flame temperatures still lower.

There is no upper limit to flame temperatures. Among the hottest flames, that of $C_2N_2 + O_2$ is interesting because its temperature had

TABLE 1.2

Mixture	Initial T, °K	P, atm	Burning velocity cm s^{-1}	Ref
H_2–O_2, 73% H_2	room	1	~1180	a,b
H_2–Cl_2, 65% H_2	room	1	410	a
H_2–Br_2, 58% H_2	room	1	32	c
B_5H_9–air, 4% B_5H_9	room	1	540	d
H_2O–F_2, 52% H_2O	373	1	810	e
O_3	room	1	475	f
N_2H_4–H_2O, 3% H_2O	423	1	185	g
CH_3ONO	330–500	1	4–7	h
$C_2H_5ONO_2$	360	<0·2	~13	i
C_2H_4O	365	0·2–1·5	~4	j

a, Bartholomé[11]; b, Senior[12]; c, Cooley et al.[13]; d, Berl et al.[14]; e, Streng[15]; f, Streng and von Grosse[16]; g, Murray and Hall[17]; h, Gray and Williams[18]; i, Hicks[19]; j, Friedman and Burke.[20]

some bearing on the estimation of the dissociation energy of molecular nitrogen. If the energy is taken as the accepted 225 kcal mole^{-1}, the calculated equilibrium flame temperature works out to 4850°K for products mostly of $N_2 + 2CO$ plus small amounts of NO, CN, N, and O. If the old abandoned value for the dissociation energy of N_2 had been correct, 170 kcal mole^{-1}, the easier formation of N atoms would have absorbed more of the heat of combustion and the flame temperature would have been only 4325°. Thomas and co-workers[21] measured the temperature as 4800 ± 200° at a time when the dissociation energy of N_2 was still in question, and their measurement suggested that 170 kcal could not be correct. Since the high temperature of the flame is partly a consequence of the stability of its main products, it will be appreciated that the addition of more oxygen to burn the CO to CO_2 would only cool the flame because of the easy dissociation of CO_2.

The calculation of equilibrium adiabatic flame temperatures is easy in principle. A trial temperature is guessed, the equilibrium products for this temperature are calculated from thermodynamic data, and one checks that the heat released in forming the products is just sufficient to raise them to the trial temperature. If not, a new temperature is guessed and the process repeated.

Flame Equations

The equations describing steady, one dimensional flames have been formulated by Hirschfelder and co-workers[22] and by many others. They express the facts that the rate of mass flow is constant through the flame,

$$(\rho v) \text{ g cm}^{-2} \text{ s}^{-1} = \text{constant}$$

$$\rho \text{ g cm}^{-3} = \text{density}$$

$$v \text{ cm s}^{-1} = \text{linear velocity}$$

Then ignoring radiation, the rate of heat evolution in a steady flame must be balanced by an increase in the heat flow due to the motion of the gas and to thermal conduction.

$$\dot{q} \text{ cal cm}^{-3} \text{ s}^{-1} = \text{d/dz} \left\{ (\rho v) \int_{T_0}^{T} C_p \text{d}T - \lambda \frac{\text{d}T}{\text{d}z} \right\} \tag{1.1}$$

$$C_p \text{ cal g}^{-1} \, {}^{\circ}\text{K}^{-1} = \text{specific heat at constant pressure}$$

$$T = \text{temperature}$$

$$\lambda \text{ cal cm}^{-1} \text{ s}^{-1} \, {}^{\circ}\text{K}^{-1} = \text{thermal conductivity}$$

$$z \text{ cm} = \text{distance coordinate}$$

Finally, the rate of formation of any chemical species must also be balanced by an analogous increase in its flow due to the motion of the gas and to diffusion.

$$m_i R_i \text{ g cm}^{-3} \text{ s}^{-1} = \text{d/dz} \left\{ (\rho v) M_i - \rho D_i \frac{\text{d}[M_i]}{\text{d}z} \right\} \tag{1.2}$$

$$m_i \text{ g mole}^{-1} = \text{molecular weight of the } i\text{th species}$$

$$R_i \text{ mole cm}^{-3} \text{ s}^{-1} = \text{its chemical rate of formation}$$

$$M_i = \text{its mass fraction in the gas}$$

$$D_i \text{ cm}^2 \text{ s}^{-1} = \text{its diffusion coefficient.}$$

It is convenient to write equation (2) in terms of the mass fraction of the total flow carried by the ith species, G_i.

$$G_i = M_i(v + v_i)/v$$

v_i cm s^{-1} = $-D_i \, dX_i/X_i \, dz$ = diffusion velocity of the ith species

X_i = its mole fraction in the gas.

For then the content of equation (2) can be stated as follows: G_i is constant unless a chemical reaction involving the ith species occurs, and then the rate of reaction is given by

$$m_i R_i = (\rho v) \, dG_i/dz \qquad (1.3)$$

Measurement in Flames

Equation (3) allows an estimate of R_i at any point in the flame if a profile of its mole fraction, X_i vs. z, can be obtained and if D_i and v are known through the same region. Similarly, $\dot{q}$ can be inferred from a temperature profile by equation (1). Except with unusually slow, thick flames, the required profiles cannot be obtained at atmospheric pressure because the reaction zone is too thin. But reduced pressures thicken flames. At 1/20 of an atmosphere pressure, the oxygen in a relatively low temperature hydrogen–oxygen flame requires about 0·3 cm of distance in order to react. This allows adequate resolution for good flame profiles.

Most composition traverses through flames have been obtained by probe methods. Microtechniques are necessary, and very small quartz probes have been developed[23] which give faithful samples of the partially reacted gas. Their important characteristic is that they should quench the gas quickly. The sample is drawn at sonic velocity through the small probe orifice and expanded and cooled. Little reaction of stable species seems to occur in these microprobes. Radicals in the sample ordinarily recombine in the probe, but Fristrom has reported[24] that one radical at least can be measured by a scavenger probe technique. Oxygen atoms in the gas were measured by rapidly mixing the sample with NO_2, introduced separately into the probe, and the NO formed via $O + NO_2 \rightarrow NO + O_2$ was measured. In the very fuel-lean flames used, the consumption of NO_2 by other radicals was judged to be small and could be corrected for.

Thermocouples of butt-welded Wollaston wires, quartz coated to reduce surface catalysis,[4] have been used to obtain temperature traverses through flames of up to around 2000°K. The usual optical temperature measurements by line reversal, or other methods involving emission from electronically excited species, depend on an equilibrium excitation of the emitters and are suspect in the reaction zone itself. The sodium D-line reversal temperature, for example, assumes that in gas coloured by a little added sodium the ratio of excited Na* in the upper states of the transiton to ground state Na is given by the equilibrium expression

$$[Na^\star]/[Na] = 3\,e^{-h\nu/kT}.$$

A heated source of adjustable known temperature is viewed spectroscopically through the gas and the effective black body temperature of the source is the same as T in the expression when the D-lines are just reversed; that is, when seen neither in absorption nor emission. This is also the gas temperature if the sodium is equilibrated. It sometimes happens that the concentration of the excited species is much above its equilibrium value in the flame zone, and then a false "anomalous" temperature would be deduced if one supposed that the radiation reflected an equilibrium ratio of concentrations. In the post-flame gas the anomalies are rare and experience has shown that sodium D-line reversal temperatures are generally reliable. Optical temperatures can be obtained by absorption measurements of ground state OH radicals,[25,26] and these depend on the distribution of the OH among the rotational levels of the ground vibrational state. There is no reason why this distribution should not be thermally equilibrated. The temperature deduced from it is the same as a thermocouple temperature which has been properly corrected for heat loss.

The last paragraph is inexact because temperature is an equilibrium concept which is inexact in a reacting system. It can be reworded as follows: A thermocouple gives essentially a translational "temperature" of the bulk of the gas which is an appropriate T for equation (1) and (2). Measurements of the index of refraction[27] also give this "temperature", and OH rotational "temperatures" obtained in absorption are found to agree with it. But "temperatures" deduced from emission spectra are different unless the emitting species are distributed among their energy levels in accordance with the translational "temperature" of the bulk of the gas. In the post-flame gas equilibrium is approached and all "temperatures" converge on the translational "temperature".

Equation (2) neglects thermal diffusion due to the temperature gradient in the gas. Even with this simplification, the calculation of reaction rates is difficult enough because a general knowledge of the concentration diffusion coefficients does not exist. It is often possible to choose fairly reliable values in special cases. The temperature has not exceeded 2000°K in flames for which detailed composition traverses have been obtained so far, and experimenters have tried to work with mixtures in which one component made up the bulk of the gas, so that it was not unreasonable to treat it as a binary mixture of this main component with each of the other species in turn. A helpful summary of D and λ values exists with particular reference to flame studies,[28] and additional measurements for treating diffusion in fuel-lean methane–oxygen flames have been made by Walker and Westenberg. They added a flowing thread of some substance centrally to a stream of hot gas and measured its radial diffusion with time as the gas flowed downstream.[29] Ember and co-workers[30] have measured the self diffusion of carbon dioxide in this way to 1680°K by adding a stream of radioactive CO_2 to the post-flame CO_2 obtained by burning moist CO–O_2–CO_2 mixtures on a porous burner. It is possible sometimes to obtain D values from the profiles measured through flames because diffusion often changes the mole fraction of a particular species upstream of the reaction zone in a region where it is fairly certain that no chemical reaction involving it has yet occurred. If so, G_i remains unchanged for the species, and this fact together with a curve of X_i vs. z in the region in question defines D_i. If the temperature dependence of D_i can also be measured or assumed, the diffusion coefficient can be extrapolated everywhere through the flame.

The effect of erroneous transport data was discussed by Peacock and Weinberg[230] along the lines that equation (2) can be approximated by

$$R_i \sim \frac{(\rho v)}{\text{average mol. wt.}} \left\{ \frac{dX_i}{dz} - \frac{D_i}{v}\frac{d^2 X_i}{dz^2} \right\}$$

The term in $d^2 X_i/dz^2$ is of opposite sign to dX_i/dz upstream of the point where $d^2 X_i/dz^2$ equals zero and of the same sign downstream of this point. Far upstream, an error in D_i leads to a greatly magnified error in R_i so it is impossible to state exactly where R_i first becomes appreciable. In the neighbourhood of the point where $d^2 X_i/dz^2$ equals zero and farther downstream, however, errors in D_i do not give magnified errors in R_i.

In most of the flame studies published so far, thermal conductivities when needed were calculated by the method of Lindsay and Bromley[31] from the conductivities of the pure constituents.

Measurements of the detailed structure of flames have begun to appear in the literature only recently. Previously, the only experimental quantity was often a measurement of the adiabatic burning velocity and the use of equation (1) and (2) was different. It was supposed most often that the flame could be represented by some single reaction of rate R; and solutions were worked out to give the calculated burning velocity for various assumed R which could be compared with the measured burning velocity. In the absence of more experimental data, this was all that could be done. But the burning velocity is proportional to only the square root of some sort of an average reaction rate in such solutions; so it is an insensitive property for investigating flame reactions, and not much chemical insight can be expected from comparisons of calculated with measured burning velocities. The relation of burning velocity to reaction rate will be discussed in chapter 9.

The Post-Flame Region

Nothing has been said yet about the hot post-flame gas downstream of the thin flame proper. Gaydon and Wolfhard[1] call this region the "interconal gases" because it is terminated by a diffusion flame with the surrounding air when a fuel-rich Bunsen flame is burnt in the open. The post-flame gas is not always equilibrated thermodynamically and reactions of much interest may take place in it. Sufficient spatial resolution can generally be obtained to follow the reactions even at atmospheric pressure, and an approximate knowledge of the transport coefficients is adequate to correct for diffusion and thermal conductivity. In fact these corrections have often been omitted without introducing large errors, as could not possibly be done in the thin flame zone. Typically, the post-flame gas flows 100–1000 cm s^{-1} and reactions which go appreciably in times of the order of 10^{-3} s are easily followed by spectroscopic or by probe methods.

CHAPTER 2

THE POST-FLAME GAS FROM
HYDROGEN–OXYGEN FLAMES

THE accepted reaction mechanism of hydrogen–oxygen mixtures at temperatures around 800°K [2,32,33] leads to a reasonable description of their burning at higher temperatures. If this extrapolation were not true, it would be much more difficult to understand flames. The mechanism is reviewed briefly below and its consequences are developed. The immediate goal is to deduce the expected state of the post-flame gas, but this requires some consideration of the vigorous reaction zone in which the gas is made.

The Mechanism at Around 800°K

The lower temperature mechanism was worked out to account for the observation that mixtures of the reactants when run into a heated vessel either explode or do not, depending on gas composition, temperature, pressure, and vessel size and surface. It is supposed that a few radicals are generated in some slow initiation process, and that these can multiply rapidly under isothermal conditions by the sequence of reactions

$$H + O_2 \underset{k_{-1}}{\overset{k_1}{\rightleftharpoons}} OH + O \tag{2.1}$$

$$O + H_2 \rightleftharpoons OH + H \tag{2.2}$$

$$OH + H_2 \rightleftharpoons H_2O + H; \tag{2.3}$$

so that a steady, non-explosive system can exist only if terminating reactions also occur to cancel the multiplication of free radicals. k_1 cm^3 mole^{-1} s^{-1} is the rate constant for reaction (1) in the forward direction, k_{-1} the constant for the reverse, and analogous k's attach to the other reactions. The reverses are neglected in explosion limit studies where only the beginning of the consumption of oxygen and hydrogen is in question, but they must be included under more general circumstances.

The question investigated experimentally is whether the system is

11

steady under essentially isothermal conditions, and an explosion indicates that a steady system was not obtained. If all experimental variables are held constant except pressure, the system is found to be steady above a certain pressure called the upper or second explosion limit. It is also steady below a lower or first explosion limit, but at intermediate pressures the gas explodes. In addition to this bounded explosive region, a third limit exists at higher pressures above which the system always explodes, but the third limit may not represent a purely isothermal branching chain and its study has not contributed to the simple mechanism being reviewed here. Qualitatively, the explosion limits for some particular composition at a fixed temperature can be represented by Fig. 2.1. Points A and B indicate the first and second

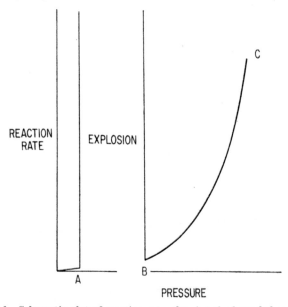

Fig. 2.1. Schematic plot of reaction rate, showing the bounded explosive region between A and B. Hinshelwood and Williamson.[34]

explosion limits and at nearby pressures outside the explosive region the steady reaction rate is very small. At sufficiently high pressures the reaction rate increases so that it becomes difficult to maintain an approximately isothermal system. The third explosion limit occurs at C.

Two different terminating processes cancel the branching chains at the two lower limits. At the second limit, the terminating reaction is

$$H + O_2 + M \rightarrow HO_2 + M \qquad (2.4)$$

The collision complex of H and O_2 must lose part of its energy in order to form a stable entity, and M is any species which accepts the energy. The HO_2 is supposed not to regenerate an active free radical, so the branching is checked. Quantitatively, $2k_1 = k_4[M]$ at the second limit, and by varying other experimental parameters, the ratio k_1/k_4 can be determined as a function of temperature and of various M species.

At pressures below the second limit, termolecular reaction (4) is too slow to quench the branching, and fresh gas mixtures prepared at lower and lower pressures still explode until the chain branching is cancelled at the first limit by a new terminating reaction. The new reaction, favoured by low pressure, is the diffusion of active free radicals to the vessel wall and their destruction there,

$$H \text{ or } O \rightarrow \text{destruction at the wall} \qquad (2.5)$$

The evidence suggests that only H or O atoms are ordinarily destroyed in this way, OH radicals reacting too rapidly by (3) for many ever to reach the wall. Reactions (5) can be written formally as first order processes of rate equal to $k_5'[H]$ or $k_5''[O]$, and the ratios k_1/k_5' and k_2/k_5'' obtained for a particular reaction vessel from determinations of the first limit. In general, (5) depends on both the diffusion of atoms and on their accommodation at the wall; but if the vessel surface is sufficiently active in capturing the atoms which strike it, (5) is controlled by diffusion alone and absolute values of k_5' and k_5'' can be calculated. In this way, absolute values of k_1 and k_2 can be derived in the H_2–O_2 system[35] or in closely related systems.[36] A value of k_1 can also be obtained from measurements within the explosive region of the rate at which the chains develop.[37] These estimates and some others which will be discussed later are plotted in Fig. 4.1, chapter 4, where the data just discussed are the segments labelled a, b, and c.

Extension of Flames

Although radicals can diffuse from the region in which they are formed, wall reactions of type (5) are unimportant in flames where there are no walls. (4) might still be important, and if so, the HO_2 formed might no longer be effectively inert. Yet an extrapolation of k_1/k_4 from 800 to 1500°K shows that (4) cannot be as fast as (1). The most efficient M species in reaction (4) is the water molecule, and in a gas at atmospheric pressure, at 1500°, k_1 is expected to be about ten times larger than $k_4[H_2O]$ when the mole fraction of water is 0·25. The fastest flame reactions therefore should be (1), (2), and (3).

Sugden and his co-workers[38] developed the consequences to be expected. If the products from the forward reactions build up to considerable concentrations, the reverses of (1), (2), and (3) must become important. Also, since these three reactions and their reverses cannot give the final equilibrium products, recombination reactions are expected to occur in order to reach equilibrium eventually. The expected recombinations are such processes as

$$H + H + M \rightarrow H_2 + M \qquad (2.6)$$

$$OH + H + M \rightarrow H_2O + M \text{ etc.} \qquad (2.7)$$

and reaction (4) might also lead to recombination eventually. It is important that all the recombinations are strongly exothermal and require third bodies to accept part of their energies of reaction, because the expected state of the post-flame gas depends on the rates of the bimolecular as compared to the termolecular processes.

Following Sugden, a reaction equilibrated with its own reverse is called a balanced reaction, and at low enough pressure bimolecular (1), (2), and (3) will be balanced before termolecular (4), (6), (7), etc., can reduce the radical concentrations to values appropriate to equilibrium products. At low pressures, therefore, a hydrogen–oxygen flame is expected to contain a zone of vigorous net reaction before the bimolecular reactions become balanced—this will be the flame proper —followed by a post-flame gas in which the bimolecular reactions are balanced while the slower termolecular recombinations continue to reduce [H], [OH], and [O]. In the post-flame gas, the radicals are expected to be related by

$$\frac{[OH][O]}{[H][O_2]} = \frac{k_1}{k_{-1}} = K_1 = 300 \ T^{-0.372} \ e^{-17.13 \text{ kcal}/RT} \qquad (2.8)$$

$$\frac{[OH][H]}{[O][H_2]} = \frac{k_2}{k_{-2}} = K_2 = 2.27 \ e^{-1.87/RT} \qquad (2.9)$$

$$\frac{[H][H_2O]}{[OH][H_2]} = \frac{k_3}{k_{-3}} = K_3 = 0.21 \ e^{15.19/RT} \qquad (2.10)$$

The numerical values for the equilibrium constants are quoted from Kaufman and Del Greco[39] who offered them as good to within a few per cent at 300–2200°K. They are based on $\Delta H_{298} = 9.33$ kcal mole^{-1} for the heat of formation of OH. This is the only quantity involved in the numerical values about which some doubt still exists, and if the choice is correct, the values are good to 3 per cent.

Experimental Tests

Schott[40] made a test of the concept of the quasi-equilibria by heating mixtures of H_2–O_2–Ar to temperatures of 1200–2800°K in a shock tube. He found that OH, measured by its ultraviolet absorption, rapidly developed to about the concentration expected on the basis of reversible reactions (1), (2), and (3) if no recombination took place at all. The recombination reactions were evidenced by a subsequent slower decay of [OH]. In the remainder of this section, the evidence from steady flames is reviewed.

Kondratiev and co-workers showed long ago that low pressure hydrogen flames at 0·3–2·5 cm of Hg pressure contained large [OH].[41,42] When gas of composition $2H_2$ plus O_2 was run through a vessel heated to 750–820°K, it burnt with the generation of much larger [OH] than corresponded to equilibrium in the products. The [OH] was estimated spectroscopically in absorption. These experiments did not differentiate between reaction zone and post-flame gas.

Sugden and co-workers[38] inferred large radical concentrations in fuel-rich post-flame gas even at atmospheric pressure by adding lithium salts to the reactants and determining [Li] in the products from the emitted resonance lines. The additive proved to be present mostly as a compound rather than as free metal atoms and by varying gas composition and temperature separately, [Li] at 2200–2400°K was found to agree with the assumed equilibrium

$$\text{Li} + \text{H}_2\text{O} = \text{LiOH} + \text{H}_{\text{equ}} \qquad (2.11)$$

where H_{equ} represents the calculated equilibrium H for the known composition and measured temperature. The temperature dependence of this equilibrium being known, the expected [Li] at any lower temperature could be calculated for a smaller $[\text{H}]_{\text{equ}}$, but the [Li] actually found in the gas from lower temperature flames was much larger than that calculated. The interpretation was that the equilibrium (11) was still maintained, but that $[\text{H}] > [\text{H}]_{\text{equ}}$ at lower temperatures. [H] could then be estimated from measurements of [Li]. In this way, and subsequently by other methods also, the decrease of [H] with increasing distance downstream into the post-flame gas could be measured and shown to conform to the expected occurrence of reactions (6) and (7), as far as this could be judged at a fixed pressure of one atmosphere.

The most direct proof that radicals in low temperature post-flame gases are much above their equilibrium concentrations comes from Kaskan's determination of [OH] by absorption in the ultraviolet.[25] At 1/2 and at 1 atm, he found that [OH]/[OH]$_{\text{equ}}$ just downstream of the flame varied from a few thousand at around 1340°K to a few hundred at around 1550°; which may be compared with the ratio from the lithium method, [H]/[H]$_{\text{equ}}$ having been found about 100 at 1600° and about 10 at 1850° in similar gas. The ratios follow a uniform trend with temperature, as they ought. In fuel-rich gas, the bulk products H_2O and H_2 cannot differ much from their equilibrium concentrations, and equation (10) implies therefore that

$$[OH]/[OH]_{\text{equ}} = [H]/[H]_{\text{equ}}$$

Accepting this relation, Kaskan estimated the decay rate of H atoms from the fall of [OH], and observed the characteristic pressure dependence expected for a termolecular recombination.

Fenimore and Jones[43] estimated [H] from measurements of the rate of formation of HD in rich post-flame gas containing added D_2O. It was supposed that the rate of exchange was determined by the reactions

$$H + D_2O \underset{\frac{1}{2}k_3}{\overset{k_{-3}}{\rightleftharpoons}} HD + OD \underset{\frac{1}{2}k_{-3}}{\overset{\frac{1}{2}k_3}{\rightleftharpoons}} HDO + D \underset{k_3}{\overset{\frac{1}{2}k_{-3}}{\rightleftharpoons}} D_2 + OH$$

and also by the similar set obtained by exchanging H and D in these formulae. It could be shown that

$$H + D_2 = HD + D \text{ and } D + H_2 = HD + H$$

were equilibrated in the post-flame gas, and it was assumed that reactions of the type of (2) would not contribute much to the exchange in fuel-rich gas. Then $k_{-3}[H]$ should have been given by

$$k_{-3}[H] = \frac{-2[H_2] \, d \ln \{[D_2O]_0/[H_2]_0 - [HD]/2[H_2]\}}{[H_2]_0 \, dt} \tag{2.12}$$

where $[H_2]/[H_2]_0$ was the fraction of hydrogen fed which remained unburnt, and $[D_2O]_0/[H_2]_0$ the ratio of added D_2O to the original H_2. Equation (12) could give only relative [H] until k_{-3} was known. It was found that the relative [H] was decreased strongly by the addition of simple hydrocarbons to fuel-rich H_2 flames; and in the post-flame gas from fuel-rich CH_4 or C_2H_2 flames, it varied over a small temperature range in the same way as the calculated [H]$_{\text{equ}}$ if k_{-3} was assumed to have an activation energy of about 25·5 kcal mole^{-1}. Supposing

[H] = [H]$_{equ}$ in these special cases, k_{-3} was obtained and estimates of [H] in the post-flame gas from pure fuel-rich H_2 flames agreed well with those by other methods. The activation energy assumed for k_{-3} has since been proved too large, 21·3 kcal mole^{-1} appears nearer the truth.[44] But all subsequent work has confirmed that [H] in post-flame gas containing hydrocarbons is approximately equal to [H]$_{equ}$, and the absolute value of k_{-3} at around 1600°K was not badly chosen.

From the experiments just described, it seems very probable that (3) is balanced in fuel-rich gas during the recombination processes. That it is also balanced in lean post-flame gas is more or less obvious in particular cases; with the approximate value of k_{-3}, it can be calculated that even the small equilibrium [H] in many hot lean gases would be enough to cause a very appreciable decrease in [H_2O] unless (3) was at least approximately balanced.

Reactions (2) and (1) can be discussed more briefly. From equations (9) and (10)

$$[O] = K_3[OH]^2/K_2[H_2O] \tag{2.13}$$

and experimental evidence for this relation was obtained by Kaskan[45] in lean post-flame gas. [OH] was again measured by ultraviolet absorption. About one per cent of nitric oxide, known to be stable against decomposition to nitrogen and oxygen under the conditions used, was present in the gas; and by measuring the intensity of the greenish emission due to

$$O + NO \rightarrow NO_2 + h\nu$$

a quantity proportional to [O] could be obtained at each point where [OH] was measured. The form of equation (13) was satisfied experimentally, [O] was proportional to [OH]^2. By estimating the absolute intensity of the O + NO emission, a collision efficiency for radiation could be deduced which agreed moderately well with independent estimates. This indicates that the difference at least of (2) and (3) is balanced. A proportionality of the form of (13) was reported to hold in rich gas containing added nitric oxide at temperatures up to about 2100°K.[46]

Reaction (1) is almost obviously balanced in lean gas because the net d[O_2]/dt is zero when some gross generation of oxygen must be occurring. In a typical one of Kaskan's lean gases just discussed, his measured [OH] and [O] would have formed by the reverse of reaction (1) more [O_2] per millisecond than was present in the gas unless the reaction of (1) in the forward direction had cancelled it. In rich gas, of course, both $[O_2]$ and $[O]$ are small and it would be harder to prove (1) balanced.

To sum up: in the post-flame gas from hydrogen flames, $[H]$, $[OH]$, and $[O]$ may be much above their equilibrium concentrations, and related to one another by the balanced reactions (1), (2), and (3) while they decay relatively slowly towards their equilibrium values. This behaviour is quite consistent with the lower temperature reaction mechanism. As the temperature of the post-flame gas is raised, equilibrium radical concentrations increase greatly but the actual radical concentrations do not increase very much; so that at sufficiently high temperatures, the radical concentrations no longer exceed equilibrium. In the post-flame gas from some H_2-rich flames at 1 atm, the concentrations approached equilibrium values at around 2200–2400°K.

As for the mechanism of balancing, equation (3) seems established in rich gas for $[H]$ vs. $[OH]$ by the tracer experiments. It is not certain that (2) and (3) need actually occur to maintain the balance of $[O]$ vs. $[OH]$ in lean gas, however, for they are equivalent to $2OH \rightleftarrows O + H_2O$ as far as the quasi-equilibria are concerned. This latter reaction is known to be very fast in the forward direction even at room temperature,[39] and it may maintain the balance in lean gas.

CHAPTER 3

REACTIONS IN THE POST-FLAME GAS FROM HYDROGEN FLAMES

A FEW years ago, Steacie[47] could say of flames, "The systems are so complex and our knowledge of them so slight that they cannot be used in practice as reliable sources of atoms and radicals." The last chapter showed that this statement is no longer altogether true, and some uses to which the post-flame gas has been put are now considered. The work to be described usually involves measuring the change in some property of the burnt gas as it flows downstream. The velocity of the gas is known, so the change of the property with time can be obtained.

Radical Recombinations

The radicals are related by the balanced reactions and decay as a pool. An expression to represent the pool can be obtained by noting that from equations (2.1), (2.2), and (2.3),

$$d\{[H] + [OH] + 2[O] + 2[O_2]\}/dt = \text{zero}$$

Therefore $\{[H] + [OH] + 2[O] + 2[O_2]\}$ is constant as far as the action of these reactions is concerned, and the recombinations must be supposed to decrease this sum rather than any single member of it. The species are all present in only small concentrations in fuel-rich gas, and the sum is a representation of the pool for rich gas.

The notion of a pool of species which decays towards equilibrium does not depend on the balancing reactions, however, and the expression just found can also be obtained by specifying which species are present and which are formed as the system approaches equilibrium. It was shown by Kaskan and Schott[48] that if a system containing H, OH, O, H_2, O_2, H_2O decays in such a way that H_2 and H_2O are formed, as should be the case in fuel-rich gas, the conservation of chemical elements requires that

$$-d\{[H] + [OH] + 2[O] + 2[O_2]\}/dt = \text{recombination rate} \quad (3.1)$$

19

If equilibrium is approached by a formation of O_2 and H_2O, as should be the case in fuel-lean gas, the corresponding equation is

$$-d\{3[H] + [OH] + 2[O] + 2[H_2]\}/dt = \text{recombination rate}$$
(3.2)

Equation (2) can be obtained from the balancing reactions, but it can also be considered a consequence of the stoichiometry and the requirement that the chemical elements cannot be formed or destroyed.

In studies of the recombination of radicals in fuel-rich gas it was supposed that the contributions of [O] and $[O_2]$ to the pool of radicals could be neglected and this assumption was justified by equations (2.8), (2.9), and (2.10). The recombination reactions considered were

$$H + H + M \xrightarrow{k_6} H_2 + M \qquad (2.6)$$

$$OH + H + M \xrightarrow{k_7} H_2O + M \qquad (2.7)$$

so that equation (1) became

$$-d\{[H] + [OH]\}/dt = 2k_6\{[H]^2[M]\} + 2k_7[H][OH][M] \qquad (3.3)$$

The factors 2 are introduced in (3) because H atoms and OH radicals are consumed at twice the rate of the elementary processes. M was assumed to represent the same third body in both terms on the right side of (3). Writing [OH] as a function of [H] by equation (2.10), Bulewicz and Sugden[49] put (3) in the form

$$\frac{1}{[H]} - \frac{1}{[H]_0} = k'(t - t_0) \qquad (3.4)$$

where

$$k' = \frac{2[M]\{k_6 + k_7[H_2O]/K_3[H_2]\}}{\{1 + [H_2O]/K_3[H_2]\}}$$

Then estimating [H] as the gas flowed downstream by a method calibrated against their Li method, they could determine k' for various ratios of $[H_2O]/[H_2]$ and split k' between k_6 and k_7. They assumed that $[M] = [H_2O]$ and that no other species was nearly as efficient as a third body, to obtain at 1650°K

$$2k_6 = 2 \cdot 3 \times 10^{16} \text{ cm}^6 \text{ mole}^{-2} \text{ s}^{-1}$$

if $[M] = [H_2O]$ only

$$2k_7 = 55 \times 10^{16}$$

A marked decrease in k_6 and k_7 at temperatures above 2000° was discounted as possibly due to $[H] - [H]_{equ}$ having become rather small.

Kaskan's[25] measurement of the same process, by OH absorption, gave approximately $2k_6 = 0 \cdot 4 \times 10^{16}$ cm^6 mole^{-2} s^{-1}, if $[M] =$ the whole gas and would have been about three times larger if he had supposed that $[M] = [H_2O]$ only. His data indicated that $k_7/k_6 > 1$ but were not extensive enough to give more than an approximate k_6. Dixon-Lewis and Williams[50] added water to various fuel-rich flames but found no special efficiency for this molecule as a third body and reported $2k_6 = 0 \cdot 6 \times 10^{16}$ for $[M] = [H_2]$, and $0 \cdot 4 \times 10^{16}$ when $[M] = [H_2O]$ or $[N_2]$. The estimates in flames are not inconsistent with the measurements of Farkas and Sachsse[51] who found $2k_6$ about 10 times larger near room temperature; nor with the smaller values from shock tube studies at 3000°K or more,[52–55] obtained by combining measured dissociation rates with equilibrium constants. The shock tube studies were interpreted to mean that k_6 varies inversely with temperature.

The decay of radicals in fuel-lean gas was investigated by Kaskan[45] under conditions where [OH] was considerably larger than any of [H], [O], or $[H_2]$. He simplified equation (2) to

$$-d[OH]/dt = \text{recombination rate},$$

and reported that

$$-d[OH]/dt \sim 4 \times 10^{10}[OH]^2 \text{ mole cm}^{-3} \text{ s}^{-1} \qquad (3.5)$$

at 1 and at $0 \cdot 45$ atm. He could suggest no satisfactory interpretation for (5) and pointed out that a production of $O + H_2O$ or of $O_2 + H_2$ from 2OH is no recombination because it only exchanges species in the pool. Recently he remarked that a decay of [OH] proportional to $[OH]^3$ would also agree with his measurements. If the recombination had actually involved the process, known to occur at lower temperatures,

$$H + O_2 + H_2O \xrightarrow{k_4} HO_2 + H_2O \qquad (2.4)$$

and if this had been followed by a destruction of HO_2 by any of

$$HO_2 + (O, OH, H) \rightarrow O_2 + (OH, H_2O, H_2)$$

or by

$$HO_2 + H \rightarrow 2OH$$

then

$$-d[OH]/dt = 4k_4[H][O_2][H_2O] = 4k_4 \left\{ \frac{K_3}{K_1K_2} \right\} [OH]^3 \qquad (3.6)$$

The factor 4 is the number of OH radicals or the equivalent which are recombined for each occurrence of (2.4), and the equilibrium constants are from equations (2.8), (2.9), and (2.10). The reported values of the constant in equation (5) can be converted into values of k_4 since the range of [OH] was given for each run. Using the average [OH] in each of the 22 leanest runs to make this conversion, one finds that the data are consistent with

$$k_4 \sim 1 \text{ to } 2 \times 10^{16} \text{ cm}^6 \text{ mole}^{-2} \text{ s}^{-1}$$

which is some five times smaller than the known value of k_4 at 800°K.[56] The possible error in [OH] could give a compounded error in k_4 of a factor of five.

A value for k_4 of the same order can also be inferred from Fristrom's[24] work in the post-flame gas of a very fuel-lean CH_4–O_2 flame at 1/20 atm. This gas should not differ from the burnt gas of an H_2–CO–O_2 flame except for a lower level of radical concentrations and the possibility that the balancing reactions might become established more slowly. In particular, the CO analog of (2.3) which will be discussed in the next section,

$$CO + OH \rightleftarrows CO_2 + H$$

might balance more slowly. To estimate k_4 from his data, it must be supposed that [H], [OH], and [O] were related by the three balanced reactions (2.1), (2.2), and (2.3); and while Fristrom himself did not think these reactions balanced, they must not have been badly out of balance either. A really serious imbalance is equivalent to saying that O_2 or H_2O were still being rapidly formed or destroyed, and such was not observed. At 1600°K, he reported the measurements.

$$-d[O]/dt = 3{\cdot}7 \times 10^{-7} \text{ mole cm}^{-3} \text{ s}^{-1}$$
$$-d[H_2]/dt = 1{\cdot}7 \times 10^{-7}$$
$$-d[CO]/dt = 14 \times 10^{-7}$$

On the balancing assumption, it can be calculated that

$$-d[OH]/dt = 1{\cdot}7 \times 10^{-7}$$
$$-d[H]/dt = \text{zero}$$
$$[H][O_2][H_2O] = 9 \times 10^{-24} \text{ mole}^3 \text{ cm}^{-9}$$

For his gas, the data do not suggest that (2) can be simplified to $-d[OH]/dt$ only. Writing equation (2) as

$$-d\{[OH] + 2[O] + 2[H_2]\}/dt = 4k_4[H][O_2][H_2O]$$

the data give

$$k_4 = 3 \times 10^{16} \text{ cm}^6 \text{ mole}^{-2} \text{ s}^{-1}$$

If the CO reaction had been balanced, $-2 \, d[\text{CO}]/dt$ would have had to be included in the pool, and k_4 would then have been 11×10^{16}. Probably the CO reaction was neither balanced nor yet irreversible, and k_4 lay between the extreme values. Fristrom's work therefore suggests a k_4 which agrees approximately with the recalculation of Kaskan's data, though it refers to a much leaner gas and to a pressure only $1/10$ as large.

It is concluded that the radicals decay primarily by reactions (2.6) and (2.7) in H_2-rich gas and perhaps at a rate proportional to (2.4) in lean gas. For (2.4) to lead to recombination, however, it must be followed by another reaction which consumes the HO_2; and since such a process remains unproven in flames, the decay of the radicals in lean gas is uncertain.

Carbon Oxides in Post-Flame Gas

By adding CO_2 to fuel-rich H_2–O_2 flames of final temperature only 1200–1350°K, the water gas reaction

$$H_2 + CO_2 = H_2O + CO \tag{3.7}$$

was found not to be equilibrated in the post-flame gas, and the approach towards equilibrium could be followed by sampling the gas as it moved downstream.[57] If the mechanism of this reaction is a combination of

$$OH + H_2 \rightleftarrows H_2O + H \tag{2.3}$$

which is known to be balanced, at least over most of this temperature range, and of (8)

$$OH + CO \underset{k_{-8}}{\overset{k_8}{\rightleftarrows}} CO_2 + H \tag{3.8}$$

$$K_8 = k_8/k_{-8}$$

the establishment of the water gas equilibrium is only the establishment of a balance for (8), and can be represented by

$$-d[\text{CO}_2]/dt = k_{-8}[\text{H}][\text{CO}_2]\left\{1 - \frac{K_8[\text{CO}][\text{H}_2\text{O}]}{K_3[\text{H}_2][\text{CO}]}\right\}$$

From measurements of all other quantities in this expression, Fenimore and Jones obtained $k_{-8}[\text{H}]$, and from simultaneous determinations of $k_{-3}[H]$ by equation (2.12) when heavy water was added to the reactants, the ratio was found

$$k_{-8}/k_{-3} \sim 0 \cdot 11 - 0 \cdot 17 \text{ at } 1200 - 1350°K$$

At temperatures above 1350°, the water gas equilibrium was established too quickly to be followed very conveniently at 1 atm, and it appeared that reaction (8) would always be quickly balanced in rich post-flame gas from H_2–O_2–CO_2 flames when the temperature was 1500°K or more.

The work of Friedman and Nugent[58] suggests that (8) also becomes balanced in lean gas at 1600–1800°K. They probed low pressure, lean CO–O_2–H_2 and CO–O_2–H_2O flames, and concluded,

> *The flame reaction consists of a rapid step associated with intense luminosity, followed by a much slower process in which the last of the CO is consumed. An assumption that the reaction rate decreases linearly with decreasing [CO] does not account for this effect. . . . Traverses show the temperature to be rising through the region in question, so the effect cannot be attributed to cooling. . . .*

This quotation describes very well the observations to be expected if (8), initially unbalanced, becomes balanced in the post-flame gas so that the last of the CO is a part of a pool of species decaying at a rate determined by the recombination of radicals.

In two papers Kaskan investigated carbon oxides in post-flame gas by optical methods, using the blue emission attributed to

$$CO + O \rightarrow CO_2 + h\nu$$

First[59] he measured [OH] in absorption in rich gas from H_2–CO–O_2 flames, and simultaneously measured the emitted intensity. [O] was calculable from

$$[O] = K_3[OH]^2/K_2[H_2O]$$

by virtue of (2.9) and (2.10). [CO] was calculated from the water gas equilibrium which must have held, the gas temperature being 1520–1880°. He could then compare the emitted intensity with the product [O][CO]. A very good proportionality was observed and, supposing that the total quanta emitted were twice those between 3500 Å and 6000 Å, he concluded that about 5×10^{-10} of the collisions of CO with O atoms radiated.

In a second paper,[60] he measured the intensity emitted from lean gas where CO was no longer a major constituent. If (8) were balanced,

$$[CO] = [CO_2][H]/K_8[OH] = \frac{K_3[CO_2][OH]^2}{K_1K_2K_8[O_2][H_2O]}$$

The intensity, being proportional to [CO][O], should now depend on $[OH]^4$ rather than on $[OH]^2$ as in fuel-rich gas. Measurements of intensity and of [OH] were in fact related in this way in lean gas from 1510 to 2000°K, 1/3–1 atm, and independently of whether the flame reactants were H_2–air–CO or H_2–air–CO_2. A gas at 1440°K did not fit the relation and might have reflected the incipient breakdown of the balance of (8) as the temperature became too low.

Estimates of the product [O][CO] by the emitted intensity have been used[61] to investigate the state of the gas behind detonations under more extreme conditions, to about 3400°K and 4 atm.

The work summarized above indicates that in the post-flame gas from H_2 flames containing CO or CO_2, (8) is quickly balanced at 1500°K or more, but not at somewhat lower temperatures. CO is a universal intermediate in hydrocarbon–oxygen flames, and it seems appropriate to add that radical concentrations are generally larger in gas from H_2 flames than in gas from hydrocarbon flames, so it is not necessarily true that a balance of (8) would be established as easily in the post-flame gas from hydrocarbon flames. It was mentioned above that Fristrom finds it unbalanced in gas from lean CH_4 flames.

In the studies of the O + CO radiation, it was not clear if the reaction involved a third body. Clyne and Thrush[62] investigated the emission at lower temperatures with particular reference to this point by mixing O atoms from a discharge with CO and various inert gases. The intensity was always proportional to [O][CO] and the proportionality constant was independent of the pressure of any particular inert gas, but different for different inert gases. The relative intensity was 1·0, 0·9, 0·7, or 0·5 when the inert gas was O_2, N_2, Ar, or He respectively. They concluded that the emission could be explained by

$$O + CO + M \xrightarrow{k'} CO_2^\star + M$$

$$CO_2^\star + M \xrightarrow{k''} CO_2 + M$$

$$CO_2^\star \xrightarrow{k} CO_2 + h\nu;$$

and that the quenching of excited $CO_2^\star$ was always much more frequent than emission. Hence the emitted intensity

$$I = k \left\{ \frac{k'}{k''} \right\} [O][CO]$$

was independent of [M] for any particular species, but the ratio $\{k'/k''\}$ might change when [M] was changed from one species to another. Their intensities depended on temperature,

$$k\{k'/k''\} = 10^{6 \cdot 6 \pm 0 \cdot 4}\, e^{-(3 \cdot 7 \pm 0 \cdot 5)\text{kcal}/RT}\ \text{cm}^3\ \text{mole}^{-1}\ \text{s}^{-1}$$

when $[M] = [O_2]$. An extrapolation of this expression to flame temperatures gives a rate constant of 10^6 as compared to Kaskan's observed value in flames of about 2×10^5 with different M species. The discrepancy is within the combined experimental error; but agreement between these estimates is meaningless unless the radiation has the same origin in both experiments. The blue radiation is a discrete system of "CO flame bands" at low temperatures, but is largely the "CO continuum" in flames on which the flame bands are merely superimposed; and the implication of agreement is that the continuum is an unresolved band system. Colloman and Gilby[270] have confirmed that this is so; under high resolution, the "CO continuum" in flames shows dense rotational fine structure with no evidence for a true continuum at all.

The overall process involves a spin reversal and Clyne and Thrush suggested that the $CO_2^\star$ is formed initially in a stable triplet state which undergoes a radiationless transition to an excited singlet $CO_2^\star$. In the mechanism above, therefore, $CO_2^\star$ means two different things. In the stabilization of excited $CO_2^\star$ by a third body it is the stable triplet, but in the other two reactions it stands for excited singlet $CO_2^\star$. The transition between the two multiplicities, though forbidden by the spin conservation rule, was thought to be easy and not rate determining.

Previous work on the radiation was discussed by Gaydon[63], who favoured the alternate interpretation that the spin reversal might occur at some other time than that proposed by Clyne and Thrush. He thought the emission might be a transition between a triplet state and the singlet ground electronic state of CO_2. The most recent study of the CO flame bands, however, suggests that the upper state of the transition is singlet.[271] It is a bent molecule of equilibrium angle $123 \pm 3°$, and of energy about 8 ± 1 kcal higher than the energy of $CO + O(^3P)$. The emission arises from transitions into high vibrational levels of the linear ground electronic state; and is associated with the absorption spectrum of carbon dioxide at about 1500 Å which occurs far in the ultraviolet because the absorption originates from low vibrational levels of the ground electronic state.

Nitrogen Oxides

The use of the greenish O + NO emission as a test for O atoms in flames was proposed by Gaydon, who has also described the qualitative observations.[63] Kaskan's work referred to in the last chapter[43] led to a rate constant for $I = k[O][NO]$ of about $1\cdot2 \times 10^6$ cm^3 mole^{-1} s^{-1}. This is twelve times smaller than the yield observed by Kaufman[64] at room temperature, but the difference may be partly explained by Clyne and Thrush's[62] finding that the emission from NO + O differed from that of CO + O chiefly in having a small negative activation energy of $-1\cdot2 \pm 0\cdot4$ kcal mole^{-1}. The pre-exponential factor for the emitted intensity was about the same as for CO + O and the emission was thought to go by the same kind of mechanism as that just outlined except that spin reversal was not necessary for NO + O.

Nitric oxide is very stable against decomposition to N$_2$ in the post-flame gas from hydrogen flames.[1,65] Even in the flames themselves, the evidence suggests that it decomposes only at high temperatures by a mechanism the same as or very similar to the thermal decomposition of pure nitric oxide.[65] The gas phase thermal decomposition of nitric oxide has been worked out by other means not involving flames; there are two mechanisms. One of these is[66,67,68]

$$O + NO \rightleftharpoons N + O_2 \tag{3.9}$$

$$N + NO \rightleftharpoons O + N_2 \tag{3.10}$$

the other is[69]

$$2NO \rightarrow \ldots \rightarrow \text{eventually } N_2 + O_2 \tag{3.11}$$

which predominates at temperatures below about 1600°K when [N] is extremely small and (9) and (10) therefore unimportant. The detailed course of (11) will be discussed below. The reactions (9), in the reverse direction, and (10), as written, can be studied at low temperatures with N atoms generated in discharges. The over-all process represented by (11) can be studied in static systems. From such experiments, the expected rate of either mechanism can be calculated at flame temperatures and compared with the decomposition rate observed.

Small amounts of NO when present in post-flame gas at 2200°K or more suffer a slow decomposition[70] which is much faster, however, than that expected to occur by (11). The decomposition has the dependence on gas composition and about the rate expected if it could be supposed that (9), or some indistinguishable equivalent reaction such as $H + NO = N + OH$, was balanced; so that

$$[N] = K_9[O][NO]/[O_2]$$
$$-d[NO]/dt = 2k_{10}[N][NO]$$

There is considerable doubt, however, whether (9) or one of its variants could have been balanced in fuel-rich post-flame gas, and more work in such mixtures would be worthwhile.

Nitrous oxide cannot be obtained in the post-flame gas from fuel-rich mixtures, for it reacts in the flame about as quickly as molecular oxygen does. It can be readily obtained in moderately low temperature fuel-lean gas, however, where it decomposes partly by

$$O + N_2O \rightarrow 2NO \tag{3.12}$$

and mostly by other reactions. (12) can be followed independently of the other processes because NO is inert under the conditions used. By measuring [O], [N_2O], and d[NO]/dt, k_{12} can be obtained,

$$d[NO]/dt = 2k_{12}[O][N_2O]$$

The result was[71]

$$k_{12} = 1 \times 10^{14} e^{-28 \text{ kcal}/RT} \text{ cm}^3 \text{ mole}^{-1} \text{ s}^{-1}$$

with estimated uncertainties of about a factor of two in the absolute value of 1700°K, and ± 3 kcal in the activation energy. Reaction (12) has also been examined[72] by mixing O atoms from a discharge with N_2O and running the mixture through a furnace heated to various temperatures in the range 770–1070°K. The reaction was followed by the glow due to the interaction of $O + NO$. The experiment was considered inaccurate because of the many corrections required; and the 21 kcal mole^{-1} obtained for the activation energy was judged not to be inconsistent with the 28 ± 3 from flames.

The numerical value obtained for k_{12} has a bearing on the detailed mechanism of reaction (11). This bimolecular decomposition of nitric oxide might go either by a direct formation of the final products in a four-centre reaction, $2NO \rightarrow N_2 + O_2$, or might be controlled by the rate of the reverse of reaction (12), $2NO \rightarrow N_2O + O$, with a subsequent decomposition of N_2O and recombination of O atoms. In the latter case, the rate constant found experimentally[69] for (11) should also be calculable from the measured value of k_{12} and from the equilibrium constant k_{12}/k_{-12}. The experimental and calculated rate constants do agree and therefore it seems that the bimolecular NO decomposition goes at the rate of the reverse of reaction (12).

Some other Chemiluminescent Effects

When the radiation from flames is studied, the question comes up whether the emitting species are thermally equilibrated with species in the lower state of the transition or if the emitters are formed chemically in the excited state which then radiates; in short, whether the radiation is thermal or chemiluminescent. A decision is possible if the concentrations of the species in both states of the transition can be measured—for thermal excitation, the concentrations are related by the equilibrium constant. H_2-O_2 flames offer examples of both kinds of radiation. The emitters seem to be equilibrated[63] in the ultraviolet radiation from electronically excited O_2 and in the vibration–rotation infrared radiation from hot H_2O, both of which extend into the visible. But other radiations are observed which are not thermal.

The radiation of excited $OH^{\star 2}\Sigma^+$ in hydrogen flames is an example of non-thermal radiation. Charton and Gaydon[73] had suggested the association $O + H \rightarrow OH^\star$ as a source of excitation of the $v' = 2$ and 3 vibrational states of the electronically excited level. Kaskan[74] attempted a quantitative test of the source of $OH^\star$ by measuring ground state $OH^2\pi$ in absorption and also the emission intensity from the first four vibrational levels of $OH^\star$. In each case the intensity was found to be proportional to $[OH]^3$. A sample of his data in Fig. 3.1 shows the intensity of the O—O band as a function of ground state $[OH]$ in nine flames. The post-flame gases were followed 0·5–1·5 cm downstream to get the variation in I_{00}/l as $[OH]$ decayed. The temperatures were 1260–1610°K in these runs. The open symbols refer to measurements at 1 atm, the solid ones to 1/3–1/6 atm. The lines on the log–log plot are drawn with a slope of three, and it is seen how well the proportionality is obeyed. If $OH^\star$ had been thermally excited, the lines would have had a slope of one. Using the relations among the balanced radicals, $[H]$, $[OH]$, and $[O]$, Kaskan could list all possible reactions which would be energetic enough to excite $OH^\star$ and would also be proportional to $[OH]^3$. He supposed that $OH^\star$ would be quenched by $OH^\star + M \rightarrow OH + M$ much more often than it could radiate,[75] and could then write out the expected dependence of the emission on the concentrations of $[H_2]$ and $[H_2O]$ for each possible reaction. The expressions obtained were so much alike that a choice among them was impossible, except that definite evidence was obtained for an excitation by reaction (13) to the $v' = 2$ vibrational level. On

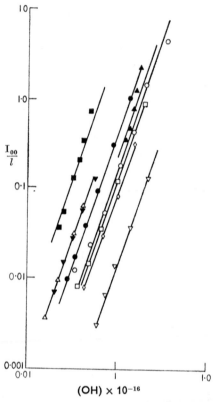

Fɪɢ. 3.1. Intensity of the OH★ → OH, O—O band per unit of optical path as a function of ground state [OH], in molecules cm^{-3} (Kaskan[74]).

the grounds that only the most exothermic reactions would give the non-equilibrium population ratios observed in the vibrational levels, reactions (14) and the odd looking (15) would be preferred; and it was suggested that (14) excites most of the emission except for that due to (13).

$$O + H \rightarrow OH\star \qquad (3.13)$$

$$H + OH + OH \rightarrow OH\star + H_2O \qquad (3.14)$$

$$O + H_2 + OH \rightarrow OH\star + H_2O \qquad (3.15)$$

Another example of chemiluminescent radiation is the blue continuum of H_2–O_2 flames, investigated most recently by Padley.[272] It extends from about 2200–6000 Å with a broad maximum in intensity around 4500 Å. In a variety of fuel-rich post-flame gases, it decayed with time in the same way as $[H]^2$ did—or as quantities proportional to $[H]^2$. Its dependence on $[H_2]$ and $[H_2O]$ suggested that the intensity was proportional to $[OH][H]$ or to the indistinguishable $[O][H_2]$, of which the former was thought more reasonable. It was not determined if the preferred $H + OH \rightarrow H_2O + h\nu$ required a third body. Similar continua can be obtained[200] by adding small amounts of halogens to hydrogen flames; and if it is supposed that $H + HZ = H_2 + Z$ is balanced, where Z represents a halogen atom, the intensity is found to correlate with the product $[H][Z]$.

Examples of both thermal and chemiluminescent excitation are shown by Fig. 3.2 from Padley and Sugden[76] in which measurements

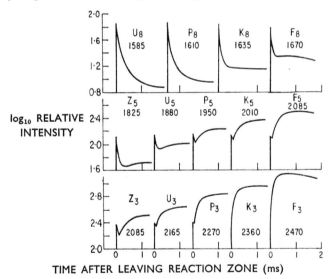

FIG. 3.2. Sodium D-line intensity vs. time for post-flame gases containing a constant trace amount of added NaCl. The reversal temperature for each flame is given, as estimated when the curve became horizontal. The letters and subscripts give the composition of the H_2–N_2–O_2 mixtures fed to the burner. For F, K, P, U, Z, H_2/O_2 fed was 2·5, 3·0, 3·5, 4·0, 4·5 respectively. The subscript gives the ratio of N_2/O_2 fed. From Padley and Sugden.[76]

of the intensity of the sodium D-lines in H_2-rich post-flame gas are plotted against time. About 1 ms from the reaction zone, a nearly steady intensity was reached and the reversal temperature measured at this time is quoted for each flame. This was considered the actual gas temperature as would be measured by a thermocouple. Before the steady intensities were reached, most flames showed a short region of increasing intensity which was attributed to heat evolved in exothermic radical recombinations. In the lower temperature flames, where the final thermal emission was small, strong spikes became predominant. These could scarcely arise from thermal excitation. The peak intensity of the spikes varied by a factor of less than four in all the flames, while the final thermal intensity varied by a factor of 400. The small change in the intensity of the spikes resembles the slight change in the actual radical concentrations in H_2 post-flame gas at various temperatures, and the authors showed that the spikes could be accounted for by the excitation processes,

$$H + H + Na \rightarrow H_2 + Na\star \qquad (3.16)$$

$$OH + H + Na \rightarrow H_2O + Na\star \qquad (3.17)$$

If [H] was balanced with [OH], the non-thermal radiation should have depended on $[H]^2$ for either process. Estimates of [H] and of the emitted intensity at low temperatures satisfied this proportionality. The relation (18) has been used to estimate relative [H] in some very low temperature flames where any thermal emission was negligible,[50]

$$I_{Na} \text{ proportional to } [H]^2 \qquad (3.18)$$

In the experiments represented by Fig. 3.2, it was supposed that all the added NaCl was present as free metal atoms in the gas. Hence the thermal emission of the D-lines should depend only on temperature and not on the gas composition, as is shown for flames F_5 and Z_3 in the figure. Contrary evidence exists in the literature; Minkowski et al.[77] found that a part of added NaCl did not appear in rich gas as free Na atoms, though the fraction is not enough to call the interpretation of Fig. 3.2 into question. When lithium or gallium was added to fuel-rich flames under high temperature conditions where thermal excitation was probable, Sugden and his co-workers found that the intensity of the atomic lines depended markedly on gas composition and it was concluded that much of the metal was present as a compound. Thus as discussed in the last chapter, the variation of intensity of lithium lines was explained by the equilibrium

$$LiOH + H = Li + H_2O$$

In fuel-lean gas, even sodium must be mostly a compound; anyone who has measured reversal temperatures in lean gas from low temperature flames knows how difficult it is to get enough Na atoms to see the D-lines clearly.

Padley and Sugden suggested that processes analogous to (16) and (17) also accounted for the chemiluminescent excitation of other added metals. No energy level was excited, from iron for example, which required much more than the 118 kcal available from (17). The chemiluminescent excitation of low energy radiation was always swamped by equilibrium thermal excitation, as in Fig. 3.2, when the temperature was raised enough. But it was not possible to raise the temperature sufficiently if the excitation required nearly the whole 104–118 kcal available.

Molecular spectra obtained in emission when metals are added to H_2-rich flames often depend strongly on the gas composition and the probable nature of the emitter can be inferred from the dependence. The familiar flame colours, orange from added calcium, red from strontium, green from barium, were suggested to be due to triatomic CaOH, etc., on this basis,[78] and the suggestion was subsequently confirmed in other ways.[79] Also in this way, the green copper bands were identified as due to CuOH. The intensity of the CuH bands was found[49] to be proportional to the product [Cu][H], added Cu being considered present mostly as free atoms and [H] being determined by the Li method; and the CuH emission has been much used as a secondary means of estimating [H]. It was believed at first that the molecular spectra were thermally excited; but this notion has been abandoned. The spectra are considered to be excited by chemiluminescence and to have nothing to do with the amount of CuOH, CaOH, MnOH, etc., present in the gas.[80]

The Boron "Fluctuation" Bands

Kaskan and Millikan[81] demonstrated that the green bands characteristic of flames containing boron compounds are emitted by the BO_2 radical. In the post-flame gas from mixtures containing trimethyl borate, they could show by infrared emission spectra that most of the boron was present as HBO_2, with about 3 per cent present as B_2O_3 in typical cases, as would be expected from equilibrium considerations. This distribution of the bulk of the boron was almost independent of time as the gas flowed downstream, and was essentially the same in fuel-rich as in fuel-lean gas. The concentration of the emitter depended markedly on gas composition, however. It was measured by absorption in one of the stronger of the fluctuation bands, [OH] was measured by absorption also, and these two concentrations were always proportional to one another over the 50-fold or so change in [OH] which could be obtained in various post-flame gases. Changes of this magnitude in the concentration of the emitter were inconsistent with its identification as B_2O_3, but were compatible with its identification as BO_2 and the equilibrium

$$HBO_2 + OH = H_2O + BO_2 \qquad (3.19)$$

or with indistinguishable variants of (19) such as $OH + B_2O_3 = HBO_2 + BO_2$ or $HBO_2 + H = H_2 + BO_2$. The assignment to BO_2 was checked by experiments in which the green bands were studied in the gas over molten, dry B_2O_3 in a furnace and shown to depend on the oxygen pressure according to[82, 83]

$$\tfrac{1}{2}B_2O_{3\text{(liquid)}} + \tfrac{1}{4}O_2 = BO_{2\text{(gas)}}$$

From the temperature dependence of BO_2, ΔH for reaction (19) was estimated to be roughly -16 kcal mole^{-1}, and therefore $\Delta H_{BO_2} \sim -84$ kcal mole^{-1}. From the furnace experiment,[82] $\Delta H_{BO_2} \sim -74$ kcal mole^{-1}. Johns[273] has presented a detailed analysis of the flame bands, obtained by flash photolysis of mixtures of boron trichloride and oxygen, and shown that they arise from two electronic transitions in the linear symetric BO_2 molecule.

The chemical applications of the post-flame gas from H_2–O_2 flames are due to its content of one or a few per cent of free radicals; to the balancing reactions which allow one radical concentration to be inferred from another, and also allows considerable variation in relative [H], [OH], and [O]; and to the possibility of controlling the temperature independently of the gas composition. The chief limitation is that one radical species cannot be obtained cleanly. Hence in studying the recombinations of $H + H$ and $H + OH$, it was impossible to distinguish between

$$H + OH + H_2 \rightarrow H_2O + H_2$$

$$H + H + H_2O \rightarrow H_2O + H_2$$

because of the nature of the balancing reactions.[49] Also, a reaction such as

$$O + O + M \rightarrow O_2 + M$$

has not been measured in the post-flame gas, nor is it apt to be because of interference by the reactions of O atoms with other species present.

CHAPTER 4

RATE CONSTANTS IN HYDROGEN–OXYGEN FLAMES

THE constants for the elementary reactions in H_2–O_2 mixtures can be measured in flames. In this chapter, the values obtained are compared

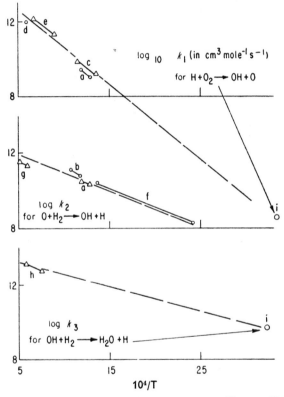

FIG. 4.1. Some recent estimates of rate constants. Key: a, Baldwin[35]; b, Azatian, Voevodskii, and Nalbandian[36]; c, Karmilova, Nalbandian, and Semenov[37]; d, Schott and Kinsey[88]; e, Fenimore and Jones[87]; f, Clyne and Thrush[90]; g, Fenimore and Jones[91]; h, Fenimore and Jones[43]; and i, Del Greco and Kaufman.[44]

with those found by other techniques, and a list is given in Table 4.1 for occasional reference hereafter. The data for three of the constants are also plotted in Fig. 4.1 in Arrhenius form.

Values of k_3

$$OH + H_2 \underset{k_{-3}}{\overset{k_3}{\rightleftharpoons}} H_2O + H \qquad (2.3)$$

Fenimore and Jones[43] measured the product $k_3[H]$ in the post-flame gas by the exchange of H_2 with D_2O as was described in chapter 2; the k_3 deduced from their k_{-3} when $[H] \sim [H]_{equ}$ is probably correct within the limits $k_3 = 1 \cdot 5 \pm 0 \cdot 8 \times 10^{13}$ cm^3 mole^{-1} s^{-1} at 1600°K. They did not determine the temperature dependence, but assumed $E_3 \sim 10$ kcal mole^{-1} from experiments at lower temperatures[84] in which OH from a discharge through water vapour was allowed to react with H_2. Del Greco and Kaufman[44] have proved the water discharge a treacherous source for OH, however, so $E_3 \sim 10$ kcal has no valid basis. These authors prepared OH in a dependable way, by mixing H atoms from a discharge with NO_2,

$$H + NO_2 \rightarrow NO + OH$$

and measured various reactions of OH near room temperature, reaction (2.3) among them. Their estimate of $k_3 = 4 \pm 1 \times 10^9$ at 310°K combines with the result near 1600° to give the rate constant listed in Table 4.1 which is probably good to a factor of two at flame

TABLE 4.1

Rate Constants, probably Valid within a Factor of Two at Flame Temperatures

$k = A\,e^{-E\,\text{kcal}/RT}$; units are mole cm^{-3} and s

Rate constant	Reaction	A	E
k_1	$H + O_2 \rightarrow OH + O$	4×10^{14}	18
k_2	$O + H_2 \rightarrow OH + H$	9×10^{12}	9
k_3	$OH + H_2 \rightarrow H_2O + H$	7×10^{13}	6·1
k_8	$OH + CO \rightarrow CO_2 + H$	$k_8 \sim 0 \cdot 08\,k_3$ at 1200–1350°K	
k_4*	$H + O_2 + H_2O \rightarrow HO_2 + H_2O$	$\sim 5 \times 10^{16}$	~ 0
k_6†	$H + H + M \rightarrow H_2 + M$	$\sim 0 \cdot 2 \times 10^{16}$	~ 0
k_7‡	$H + OH + M \rightarrow H_2O + M$	$\sim 5 \times 10^{16}$	~ 0
k_α	$H + N_2O \rightarrow N_2 + OH$	3×10^{14}	16

* This is of the order of k_4 at 800°,[56] and not incompatible with the rough value suggested in chapter 3. But it certainly might be worse than right to a factor of two.

† $-d[H]/dt = 2 \times k_6[H]^2[M]$. [M] is considered to be the whole gas concentration.

‡ $-d[H]/dt = -d[OH]/dt = k_7[H][OH][M]$. [M] considered to be the whole gas, and the constant taken to be $\sim 24 \times k_6$.

temperatures. Dixon-Lewis and Williams[50] also obtained an approximate estimate of k_{-3} at 1072°K. They measured $k_{-3}[H]$ late in a flame by the exchange reaction with D_2O, and [H] early in the same flame from the exchange of H with D_2, the latter reaction having a known rate constant.[85] These two regions did not overlap, but were bridged by measuring relative [H] in both regions from the chemiluminescent excitation of sodium according to equation (3.18). Their value, $k_{-3} = 5 \times 10^9$, is consistent with the other data; although they thought this an upper limit, while from Table 4.1 and the equilibrium constant in equation (2.10), $k_{-3} = 8 \times 10^9$ at 1072°.

Values of k_1

$$H + O_2 \underset{k_{-1}}{\overset{k_1}{\rightleftharpoons}} OH + O \qquad (2.1)$$

The experimental data for k_1 in flames are temperature and composition profiles obtained by fairly standard methods,[23] and there is no difficulty in evaluating $-d[O_2]/dt$ and $[O_2]$. On the condition that only reaction (2.1) is important in consuming O_2 and that the reverse of (2.1) is negligible, as can be assured through most of the reaction zone by using fuel-rich mixtures, $-d[O_2]/dt = k_1[H][O_2]$ and k_1 can be inferred if [H] is known. In any estimate published so far, only approximate values of [H] have been obtained by assumptions which could not be strictly true. The assumption made here is that [H] is constant through the reaction zone of a low pressure H_2-O_2 flame.

This assumption is not a very bad one. Gaydon and Wolfhard[86] concluded that the diffusion of H atoms should be easy over distances of the order of the flame thickness though not over a much greater distance. Some experimental support for it can be obtained from estimates of [H] on both sides of the flame;[87] by the fast exchange of H with D_2 early in the reaction zone, and by the slow exchange with D_2O in the post-flame gas. The two [H] are not very different and a much greater value between the regions of measurement seems unlikely.

Figure 4.2 shows traverses through a fuel-rich H_2-N_2O–air flame containing added N_2, burnt at 6 cm of mercury pressure. A diffusion coefficient from Ref. 28 appropriate to a gas entirely of N_2 was used in calculating G_{N_2}, and one appropriate to a binary mixture of N_2-O_2 was used in calculating G_{O_2}. The G are plotted at the bottom of the figure, and $-d[O_2]/dt$ and $-d[N_2O]/dt \sim d[N_2]/dt$ were computed from them by equation (1.3). The curves for HD, which extend into the post-flame gas, gave $k_{-3}[H]$ just downstream of the reaction zone; and by hypothesis [H] was the same in the flame zone also. The k_1 obtained for a k_{-3} which conforms to the k_3 of the last section are plotted as segment "e" at the top of Fig. 4.1.

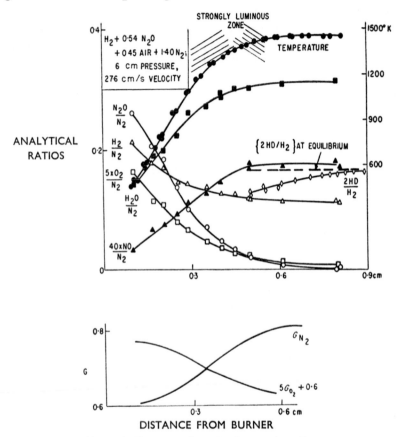

FIG. 4.2. Traverses through a low-pressure flame
(Fenimore and Jones[87]).

A possible complication which was not considered is that reaction (2.4)

$$H + O_2 + M \xrightarrow{k_4} HO_2 + M \qquad (2.4)$$

might also consume oxygen and lead to too large an estimate of k_1. However, if k_4 has a value of 5×10^{16} cm^6 mole^{-2} s^{-1} when $[M] = [H_2O]$, and is $1/10$ as large for other $[M]$, $k_4[M]$ would be negligible compared to k_1 at $1200°$ in the flame described by Fig. 4.2. At much lower temperatures or higher pressures, (2.4) would have to be taken into account.

Other estimates of k_1 are also plotted in Fig. 4.1. The segments labelled "*a*" and "*c*" were obtained from explosion studies and were discussed very briefly in chapter 2. "*d*" is from estimates of the rate of branching in H_2–O_2–Ar mixtures heated in a shock tube. Schott and Kinsey[88] found experimentally that the time required for [OH] to develop sufficiently in the heated gas to be detectable by ultraviolet absorption was related to $[O_2]$ and to temperature by the equation

$$[O_2]t = 2.3 \times 10^{-14} e^{(18.1 \pm 2.9)\text{kcal}/RT} \text{ mole cm}^{-3} \text{ s} \qquad (4.1)$$

Assuming that during this induction period, the chains developed by reactions (2.1), (2.2), and (2.3), of which the first was supposed to be much the slowest,

$$d[H]/dt = 2k_1[H][O_2]$$

This integrates to

$$2k_1[O_2]t = 2.3 \log \left\{ \frac{[H]}{[H]_0} \right\} \sim 2.3 \log \left\{ \frac{[OH]}{[OH]_0} \right\} \qquad (4.2)$$

Where $[H]_0$ is the concentration at zero time when the generation of radicals by reaction (2.1) was equal to their generation by some poorly understood initiation process. From (1) and (2),

$$k_1 = 0.5 \times 10^{14} e^{-18.1/RT} \times \log \left\{ \frac{[H]}{[H]_0} \right\} \qquad (4.3)$$

The measurements were made over the range 1100–2600°K. Those at 1650° were thought to be most free of complications; and the value plotted as "*d*" was obtained when $\log \{[H]/[H]_0\}$ was set equal to 7.1, this choice being more or less arbitrary. For an approximate estimate of k_1, however, any conceivable choice is all right; the k_1 would be unchanged within a factor of two if [H] or [OH] increased by any factor between 10^4 and 10^{14} during the induction period. The assumption $k_1 \ll k_2$, made to derive (2) is now known to be false at 1650° but k_1 should still be approximately correct.

The complication encountered by Schott and Kinsey was that at temperatures above 1700°K the values of $[O_2]t$ were not really independent of mixture composition as stated by (1). A partial explanation is that reaction (2.1) was not sufficiently slow compared to (2.2) at higher temperatures; but the authors suggested a more interesting origin since the complication appeared when the induction times were comparable to the times which might be required to excite molecular oxygen vibrationally. If oxygen must be excited to undergo (2.1),

4

this would never be known under ordinary circumstances but the rate of reaction might become limited by vibrational relaxation of O_2 when reaction was sufficiently fast. While the shock tube results do not provide real evidence for it, the suggestion is interesting because it requires that the reverse of (2.1) be written as forming vibrationally excited oxygen, $O + OH \rightarrow O_2^* + H$; and a number of exothermal atom reactions of this type are known already where the energy released appears initially as vibrational excitation of the newly formed molecule.[89]

Schott's suggestion might possibly be proved by studying the reverse reaction as Del Greco and Kaufman did.[44] They prepared OH radicals, which were not vibrationally excited, from $H + NO_2$, mixed them with O atoms from a second discharge, and measured the reverse rate constant. The equilibrium constant being known, k_1 could be obtained at about 300°K. This estimate, indicated by "i" in Fig. 4.1, is smaller by a factor of 10^7 than any other, but is consistent with the rest. It would be interesting if the vibrational state of the O_2 formed could be determined.

The equation of the dashed line through the various results in Fig. 4.1 is given in Table 4.1. It would be possible to change E_1 by 2 kcal and still have as good agreement as that obtained with $E_1 = 18$ kcal.

Values of k_α

The rate of consumption of N_2O in various flames[87] of quite different [H], the flame portrayed by Fig. 4.2 is one example, could always be described by

$$-d[N_2O]/dt = k_\alpha[H][N_2O]$$

with k_α very near k_1 in magnitude. This was interpreted to mean that most of the N_2O decomposed by

$$H + N_2O \xrightarrow{k_\alpha} N_2 + OH$$

and that the rate constant had the value listed in Table 1.2 within a factor of two at flame temperatures. Pure N_2O–H_2 mixtures cannot be burnt at as low temperatures as O_2–H_2 because they do not involve rapidly branching reactions and therefore possess smaller radical concentrations. The reaction above, and also the formation of NO, N_2, and O_2 from $O + N_2O$, are not particularly slow reactions in flames, however, and there is no difficulty in burning N_2O–H_2 as there is in burning NO–H_2.

Value of k_2

$$O + H_2 \underset{k_{-2}}{\overset{k_2}{\rightleftarrows}} OH + H \tag{2.2}$$

The rate constant has been determined in three different ways. Baldwin[35] found that at the lower explosion limit of H_2–O_2 mixtures, either the destruction of O atoms at the wall competed with (2.2) or the destruction of OH competed with (2.3). The ambiguity arose because (2.2) and (2.3) involve [H_2] in the same way; but it is now known that (2.3) is too fast for much OH to have been destroyed at the wall under the conditions used, and his result is plotted in Fig. 4.1 as "a". Azatian and co-workers[36] replaced most of the [H_2] by [CO]. The substitution does not affect the reactions of OH very much since $CO + OH \rightarrow CO_2 + H$, (3.8), duplicates reaction (2.3), though at a slower rate; but no reaction analogous to (2.2) was thought to exist for CO and, if so, the ambiguity which troubled Baldwin was removed. Their k_2 is plotted as "b".

Clyne and Thrush[90] mixed O atoms from a discharge with H_2 and used the O + NO emission to follow the decrease in [O]. This straightforward method gives the long segment "f".

The values "g" were obtained from profiles through H_2–N_2–O_2–N_2O flames, using the ratios of rate constants already determined.[91] It was supposed that the decomposition of N_2O could be adequately described by the processes

$$H + N_2O \overset{k_\alpha}{\longrightarrow} N_2 + OH$$

$$O + N_2O \longrightarrow 2NO \tag{3.12}$$

$$M + N_2O \underset{k_\beta}{\longrightarrow} M + N_2 + O$$

of which the reaction with H atoms was the fastest by far. The straight thermal decomposition of N_2O, the last reaction, was only important at the highest temperature, and the reaction $O + N_2O \rightarrow N_2 + O_2$ could be disregarded because this is known[72] to be slower than (12). In the region in which (2.2) was measured, its reverse could be shown to be small, although neither (2.1) nor (2.3) was irreversible. [O] was near its maximum value and its net rate of formation was approximately zero. The consumption of O atoms by reaction (2.2) could then be written in terms of the observed $-d[O_2]/dt$, $d[NO]/dt$, and the calculated thermal decomposition of nitrous oxide

$$d[O]/dt \sim \text{zero} = -d[O_2]/dt - k_2[O][H_2]$$
$$-d[NO]/2\,dt + k_\beta[M][N_2O]. \tag{4.4}$$

Since k_α, k_1, and k_3 were known, equation (5), (6), and (7) could be solved in turn from the profiles of nitrous oxide, water, and molecular oxygen to get an independent value of [O].

$$[H] \sim -d[N_2O]/k_\alpha[N_2O]\,dt \tag{4.5}$$

$$[OH] = \frac{\{d[H_2O]/dt + k_{-3}[H_2O][H]\}}{k_3H_2} \tag{4.6}$$

$$[O] = \frac{\{k_1[H][O_2] - d[O_2]/dt\}}{k_{-1}[OH]} \tag{4.7}$$

The [O] from (4) and (7) were equated to get the k_2 plotted as "g" in Fig. 4.1. The result does not depend on the absolute values of k_1, k_3, and k_α but only on their ratios.

Within a factor of about two, all estimates of k_2 agree with the dashed line drawn in Fig. 4.1. The equation of this line is given in Table 4.1.

Value of k_8

$$OH + CO \underset{k_{-8}}{\overset{k_8}{\rightleftharpoons}} CO_2 + H \tag{3.8}$$

If it is accepted that $k_{-8}/k_{-3} = 0\cdot11\text{--}0\cdot17$ at 1200–1350°K, as stated in chapter 3, it follows that $k_8/k_3 \sim 0\cdot08$ in this temperature range with no marked dependence on temperature.

The simple Arrhenius expressions for the bimolecular constants in Table 4.1 might not be expected really to hold over the wide temperature ranges of Fig. 4.1 but within the scatter of the data they seem good enough.

CHAPTER 5

REACTIONS IN SIMPLE HYDROCARBON
OXYGEN FLAMES

H_2–O_2 flames were discussed in terms of an accepted lower temperature mechanism, but a similar approach to hydrocarbon flames is opposed by much evidence. For example, hydrocarbons which differ by orders of magnitude in their rates of oxidation at around 500–700°K[92,93] have almost the same burning velocities.[94] The common opinion is that oxidation in a steady hydrocarbon flame differs in some fundamental way from the low temperature oxidation, and one had best study the flame directly to understand its reactions. In general, fuel-rich flames are more complex than lean ones. The fuel is consumed in the latter without any considerable formation of other hydrocarbons; but sufficiently rich flames are mixtures of oxidation and pyrolytic reactions which can give large yields of hydrocarbons not present in the original fuel. The oxidation of a hydrocarbon is studied most simply therefore in a lean flame. Under lean conditions, the relative radical concentrations favour large [OH] and [O] at the expense of [H], and it is difficult to deduce much about reactions involving H atoms. It is possible to burn fuel-rich flames of mixed H_2–hydrocarbon fuel in which large [H] can be obtained; and if only a little hydrocarbon is present, most of the complexities of pure hydrocarbon-rich mixtures are avoided. Thus in a CH_4-rich flame the oxidation of CH_3 radicals competes with a rapid formation of C_2 hydrocarbons presumably via $2CH_3 \rightarrow C_2H_6$ which is known to be a fast reaction.[95] But if only a little CH_4 is added to a fuel-rich H_2 flame, not much formation of C_2 hydrocarbons occurs.

Similarities of Hydrocarbon–O_2 to H_2–CO–O_2 Flames

The data of Fristrom and co-workers[96,97] furnish a good starting point for a discussion of hydrocarbon flames. Figure 5.1 shows a traverse for CH_4 through a very fuel-lean CH_4–O_2 flame burnt at 1/20 atm. M_{CH_4} is the measured mass fraction, G_{CH_4} the fraction of the mass flow carried by CH_4 as obtained after the diffusion correction was made. The slope of G is proportional to reaction rate; and while

43

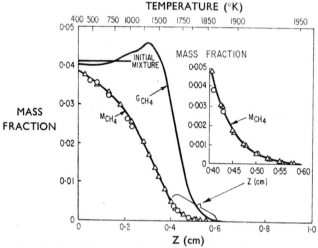

FIG. 5.1. Profile of the mass fraction of methane, M_{CH_4}, through a fuel-lean flame at 1/20 atm. The G_{CH_4} curve derived from the measurements is also shown (Fristrom[97]).

some uncertainties cloud the farthest upstream values of G, the difficulties are less later in the flame. From a set of curves such as Fig. 5.1, one for each constituent, the reaction rates of Fig. 5.2 were obtained by

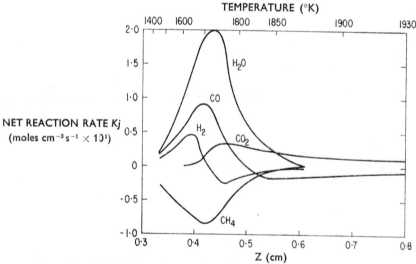

FIG. 5.2. Net reaction rates in CH_4-O_2 flame at 1/20 atm (Westenberg and Fristrom[97]).

equation (1.3). A curve for $-d[O_2]/dt$ is missing, but this was measured and was consistent with

$$-d[O_2]/dt = 1/2\{d[H_2O]/dt + d[CO]/dt\} + d[CO_2]/dt$$

as would be required by the conservation of atoms. The net rate measured for a little formaldehyde was too small to be shown in the figure. Table 5.1 lists the initial conditions and the final state of the gas when reaction had almost ceased. The column of observed mole fractions has vacancies because the radical concentrations were not determined.

It can be seen from Fig. 5.2 that CO was formed before CO_2 was. Much of the CO_2 must have been made by reaction (3.8), and it is generally supposed that all of it was,

$$CO + OH \overset{k_8}{\rightleftharpoons} CO_2 + H \tag{3.8}$$

Some but not all of the H_2O was formed from H_2 by

$$H_2 + OH \overset{k_3}{\rightleftharpoons} H_2O + H \tag{2.3}$$

The presence of CO and H_2 had been observed before in fuel-lean mixtures of C_3H_8–air burning at low pressures;[98] and by now it has been confirmed repeatedly that the last stage of a hydrocarbon flame is a CO–H_2–O_2 flame. In fuel-lean gas, the H_2 is always rather small compared to CO, partly because k_3 is larger than k_8 and partly because not all the hydrogen in the hydrocarbon goes through a stage of H_2.

In the post-flame gas from H_2–CO–O_2 flames, [H], [OH], and [O] were balanced among themselves, and one naturally asks if this is true in the gas from hydrocarbon flames. Reaction (2.1) must have been balanced in the final gas described by Table 5.1.

$$H + O_2 \overset{k_1}{\underset{k_{-1}}{\rightleftharpoons}} OH + O \tag{2.1}$$

for taking k_1 from Table 4.1 and $[H]_{equ}$ and $[O_2]$ from Table 5.1, one finds that in the final gas $k_1[H][O_2]$ was about 3/4 of the maximum $-d[O_2]/dt$ observed in the reaction zone itself. Since $-d[O_2]/dt$ was really negligible in the final gas, the forward reaction of (2.1) must have been cancelled by the reverse. Similarly, $d[H_2]/dt \sim d[H_2O]/dt \sim$ zero in the final gas implies that (2.2) and (2.3) were balanced.

[H] may have been larger than $[H]_{equ}$ and therefore (2.1) faster than just estimated in both directions. According to Table 5.1, $[H_2]/[H_2]_{equ}$ was ~ 3 in the final gas; and since in a balanced lean gas,

$$[H]/[H]_{equ} = \{[H_2]/[H_2]_{equ}\}^{3/2}$$

$[H]/[H]_{equ}$ might have been about 5. Even without this factor of 5, [H] in the final gas was of the order required in the reaction zone to account for the consumption of O_2 at the rate of $k_1[H][O_2]$. The inference from these comparisons, that the O_2 may have been consumed mostly by H atoms, was shown to be true by direct measurements in other flames. Fenimore and Jones[99] probed a number of fuel-rich or only moderately lean flames where the reverse of (2.1) could be assumed small early in the reaction zone. The [H] was computed which would be

TABLE 5.1

Initial and Final States of the Gas for the Flame Illustrated by Fig. 5.2

	Initial	Final	
		Calc*	Obs
T, °K	400†	1990	1980
V, cm s^{-1}	93†	323	312
X_{CH_4}	0·079	0	0
X_{O_2}	0·919	0·756	0·763
X_{H_2}	0	0·00023	0·0008
X_{H_2O}	0·0004	0·153	0·154
X_{CO}	0	0·00056	0·00305
X_{CO_2}	0·0015	0·0792	0·0788
X_H	0	0·00011	—
X_{OH}	0	0·00626	—
X_O	0	0·00285	—

* Calculated assuming the final equilibrium state.
† The flat flame was stabilized on a screen burner surface temperature 400°K.

required to make $k_1[H][O_2]$ equal to the observed $-d[O_2]/dt$, and this calculated [H] was compared with that measured by exchange reactions of H with added D_2 or D_2O. The two [H] agreed within about 30 per cent in various flames of CH_4, C_2H_4, and C_3H_8 over a 20-fold variation of [H].

The discussion to this point has shown that hydrocarbon flames are partly H_2–CO–O_2 flames, and that O_2 is consumed largely by reaction (2.1); these two conclusions being opposite sides of the same coin.

The Formation of CO in Methane Flames

From what was said above, the real problem in the methane flame is evidently to specify how the fuel is broken up to give CO and H_2 with more or less water. It is widely accepted that the only reactions of CH_4 itself are those forming a CH_3 radical,

$$CH_4 + X \rightleftarrows CH_3 + HX \qquad (5.1)$$

which is written as a reversible reaction because if X were H, it would be possible to reform CH_4 in the presence of much H_2; though if X were OH or O, the reverse would seem unlikely. The formation of CO in low temperature, slow oxidations has usually been ascribed to

$$CH_3 + O_2 + M \rightarrow CH_3O_2 + M \rightarrow \ldots \rightarrow H_2CO + \ldots \qquad (5.2)$$

with a subsequent break up of the H_2CO to CO—and this has sometimes been suggested to account for the CO formed in CH_4 flames also, though without any evidence. In this section it will be suggested that the CO usually results from a reaction of CH_3 with O atoms rather than with O_2 molecules.

The formation of CO can be symbolized in a general way by

$$CH_3 + \text{oxidant} \rightarrow \ldots \rightarrow CO + (H_2 \text{ and/or } H_2O) \qquad (5.3)$$

Reaction (3) is considered irreversible because it forms a bond between the C atom in CH_3 and an O atom in the oxidant species, and the C—O bond is probably never broken once it is made. For example, no one has ever obtained appreciable hydrocarbons or soot by burning fuel-rich mixtures of methyl alcohol and O_2. Some information about the identification of the "oxidant" in (3) can be obtained by studying flames containing isotopically tagged atoms. On adding H_2O^{18} to the reactants of CH_4–O_2 flames,[100] it was found that the CO_2 formed contained considerable O^{18} but the CO did not. Since the CO_2 was supposed to be formed by reaction of CO with OH, the OH must have contained $O^{18}H$, and of course, the water contained H_2O^{18}. Therefore the CO did not derive its O atoms from either OH or H_2O. It can be concluded that if the "oxidant" in (3) is one of the species known to be present or formed in the flame, O_2, O, OH, H_2O, it must be O or O_2.

The $[O]_{equ}$ in the final products of a very lean flame, say that described in Table 5.1, was 0·38 per cent of $[O_2]$; the ratio $[H_2]/[H_2]_{equ}$ suggests that the actual $[O]$ was about 1 per cent of $[O_2]$ in the final products, and $[O]$ was perhaps of this order in the reaction zone too. In flames richer in fuel the ratio $[O]/[O_2]$ is generally larger than in very lean flames. Now the reaction of CH_3 with O_2 to form the methylperoxy radical is termolecular at 290 to 470°K,[101,102] with a rate constant of 2×10^{16} cm^6 $mole^{-2}$ s^{-1} when M in equation (2) is acetone or methyl iodide, and about 10 times smaller when M is CO_2. The constant has little temperature dependence and is roughly the same even at $1370°$.[103] Reaction (2) is therefore a slow process for flame zones, being about as fast as other termolecular recombinations. It was found in the last two chapters that such termolecular processes often cannot keep up with the faster bimolecular reactions; and if CH_3 radicals reacted bimolecularly with O atoms with a collision efficiency of 10^{-3} or greater, it would outrun termolecular (2) even though [O] was only one per cent of $[O_2]$.

If CO was formed from CH_3 radicals at the rate of their reaction with O atoms,

$$CH_3 + O \xrightarrow{k_\gamma} \dots \to \text{eventually CO} \dots \tag{5.4}$$

it should follow that

$$d[CO]/dt + d[CO_2]/dt = k_\gamma[O][CH_3] \tag{5.5}$$

where the left side gives the total rate of formation of CO, as opposed to the net observed rate. Experiments have been made[100] to see if (5) applied to fuel-rich H_2–CH_4–O_2 flames containing a little added NO. The left side of (5) was measured from composition traverses, and [O] was approximated from an extension of equation (4.4). CH_3 was estimated from the partial decay of the added NO which is quite inert in H_2–CO–O_2 flames at the temperatures and pressures used. In the presence of reacting CH_4, however, NO decomposed with a roughly equivalent formation of HCN. It was supposed that the NO consumption was due to

$$CH_3 + NO \xrightarrow{k} CH_3NO \to \dots \to HCN + \dots$$

and that Christie's estimate[104] of the limiting value of the apparent second order constant, 7×10^{11} cm^3 mole^{-1} s^{-1}, could be used to infer $[CH_3]$ from $-d[NO]/dt$. The value of this constant is about the same at $1170°K$[105] as at room temperature, so the assumption that it remains unchanged at temperatures a few hundred degrees higher seems reasonable.

Some profiles through a typical flame and the estimates of reaction rate derived from them are shown in Fig. 5.3. The fall in NO and the formation of HCN during the oxidation of the CH_4, and the stability of the remaining NO thereafter are obvious. The consumption of CH_3 by NO was only an indicator reaction, most of the CH_3 underwent the usual oxidation to give CO.

Supposing that [CH$_3$] of the right order at least had been measured, and substituting [O] and [CH$_3$] into equation (5), values of

$$k_\gamma \sim 4 \times 10^{13} \text{ cm}^3 \text{ mole}^{-1} \text{ s}^{-1}$$

were found in various flames at 1210–1560°K. The evidence for the oxidation of CH$_3$ by O atoms seemed fairly good, and since termolecular (3) could not have accounted for the observed formation of carbon

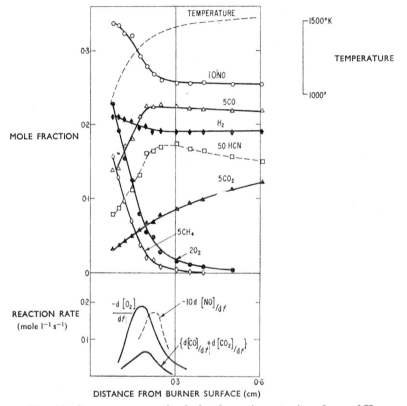

FIG. 5.3. Some traverses and calculated reaction rates in a flame of H$_2$ + 0·17 CH$_4$ + 0·54 O$_2$ + 0·105 NO + 1·05 Ar burnt at 8 cm of mercury P with a mass flow of 3·7 × 10^{-3} g cm^{-2} s^{-1} (Fenimore and Jones[100]).

oxides, it was concluded that CO was formed by reaction (4). The primary product was unproven; the obvious O + CH$_3$ → H + H$_2$CO would account for the little formaldehyde observed in the region where CH$_4$ was consumed.

Hoare[106] did not believe that the reaction of CH$_3$ + NO was a second order reaction. He thought it termolecular CH$_3$ + NO + M → CH$_3$NO + M; whence the termolecular constant would be about

10^{18} cm^6 mole^{-2} s^{-1} in Christie's experiments at room temperature when M was CH_3I, or in Bryce and Ingold's experiments at 1170° when M was He. From his own work at 470°K, Hoare suggested a termolecular constant of 0.3×10^{18} when M was acetone. It should be added therefore that if the consumption of NO by CH_3 in the flames studied had been a termolecular process with rate constant 10^{18}, the $[CH_3]$ deduced would have been unchanged within 50 per cent and the conclusion unchanged.

The impression should not be left that general agreement exists about the fate of CH_3 radicals in methane flames. Fristrom[24] considers the question open whether the reaction is

$$CH_3 + O \rightarrow H + H_2CO$$

or

$$CH_3 + O_2 \rightarrow OH + H_2CO$$

or perhaps the former in moderately rich flames and the latter in very fuel-lean ones. McKellar and Norrish[107] flash photolysed CH_3I–O_2 mixtures and discussed their spectroscopic observations on OH and H_2CO in terms of the reaction of $CH_3 + O_2$, considered to be fast and bimolecular even when the combustion was explosive. If a fast bimolecular reaction does occur, it would obviously be wrong to reject $CH_3 + O_2$ on grounds that it was too slow. It is fair to add that no evidence for such a fast reaction has been presented as yet.

The Formation of CH_3 Radicals in Methane Flames

CH_3 radicals are formed as fast as CH_4 disappears. Westenberg and Fristrom[97] assumed that the process in very lean flames was the irreversible reaction,

$$CH_4 + OH \xrightarrow{k_\delta} CH_3 + H_2O \tag{5.6}$$

and supposed that the reverse of (3.8)

$$CO + OH \xrightarrow{k_8} CO_2 + H \tag{3.8}$$

could be neglected in regions where CH_4 reacted, as is certainly true. From the local measured ratios of $[CO]/[CH_4]$ and the ratios of $d[CO_2]/dt$ to $-d[CH_4]/dt$, read off Fig. 5.2, they obtained

$$k_\delta/k_8 \sim 15 \text{ at } 1660\text{–}1840°K, \ 3.8 \text{ cm Hg pressure.}$$

A larger ratio of rate constants from another flame at twice the pressure was considered less accurate. Fenimore and Jones[108] confirmed the choice of equation (6) and found $k_\delta/k_8 \sim 22$ at 1450–1800°K, 5–14 cm Hg pressure. The k_8 in Table 4.1, chapter 4, does not differ significantly from the value assumed by Westenberg and Fristrom; it gives

$$k_\delta = 1 \text{ to } 2 \times 10^{13} \text{ cm}^3 \text{ mole}^{-1} \text{ s}^{-1} \text{ at } 1750°$$

but the 9 kcal mole^{-1} activation energy reported by Fenimore and Jones is doubtless too large in view of the discussion of k_3 and k_8 in chapter 4. Table 4.1 implies $E_\delta \sim 6$ kcal, but this is based on very scanty evidence for E_8. It seems certain that the reactions of OH with CO and with CH_4 have nearly the same activation energies. Karmilova and co-workers[109] added isotopically tagged CO to slowly oxidizing CH_4–O_2 mixtures at 745°K and showed that CO_2 was mostly formed from CO, presumably by equation (3.8). Accepting that CH_4 is also destroyed by (6) under such circumstances, it follows from their observations that

$$k_\delta/k_8 \sim 30 \text{ at } 745°K;$$

so this ratio is nearly unchanged over an 1100° interval.

In fuel-rich H_2–CH_4–O_2–N_2O flames, [H]/[OH] is 30–100 times larger than in lean flames, and the k_δ just given cannot account for $-d[CH_4]/dt$. It was found[108] that the consumption could be correlated by

$$CH_4 + H \xrightarrow{k_\varepsilon} CH_3 + H_2 \qquad (5.7)$$

and that k_ε could be evaluated by comparison with

$$N_2O + H \xrightarrow{k_\alpha} N_2 + OH$$

if care was taken to avoid situations where the reverse of (7) was important. Accepting the k_α from Table 4.1, chapter 4,

$$k_\varepsilon = 1.5 \times 10^{14} \, e^{-11 \text{ kcal}/RT} \text{ cm}^3 \text{ mole}^{-1} \text{ s}^{-1}$$

at 1220–1790°K and 3–5 cm Hg pressure, but the 11 kcal could be changed by 2 or 3 kcal if compensating changes were made in the pre-exponential factor. k_ε has been measured often at lower temperatures. The earlier estimates[47] favoured an activation energy of 12–13 kcal and a pre-exponential factor of $\sim 10^{14}$ or larger, but more recent ones suggest an activation energy of about 8 kcal, or even less,[110–112] and a smaller pre-exponential factor, sometimes much smaller.[111] One cannot say much about the activation energy from work in flames alone when a difference of only a few kcal mole^{-1} is in question. If both the flame work and the lower temperature values are approximately correct in absolute magnitude, E is probably not less than 10 kcal and the pre-exponential factor is of order 10^{14}.

This concludes the description of the present situation for the burning mechanism of CH_4. The probable consumption of CH_3 by reaction with O atoms, and of O_2 by reaction with H atoms in flames contrasts with the low temperature oxidation of methane[113] when methyl radicals are thought to be oxidized by reaction with O_2 molecules. An important reason for the difference must be that reaction (2.1), $H + O_2 \rightarrow OH + O$, with its 18 kcal mole^{-1} of activation energy is 1000 times faster at 1500° than at 700°K, but the rate of $CH_3 + O_2 + M \rightarrow CH_3O_2 + M$ does not increase significantly with temperature. The products from $O + CH_3$ are uncertain but formaldehyde seems reasonable. If formed, its subsequent destruction should go very readily; for formaldehyde resembles a mixture of $H_2 + CO$ as a fuel and its breakup cannot be a difficult step in the overall oxidation. The ease of oxidation of formaldehyde will be commented on in chapter 8.

Radical Concentrations in Hydrocarbon Flames

Methane flames, particularly fuel-rich ones, possess smaller radical concentrations than do H_2–O_2 or H_2–CO–O_2 flames. The radicals recombine by termolecular processes in the absence of hydrocarbons, but methane flames may have a fast bimolecular reaction of $CH_3 + O$ which also terminates free valencies. Figure 5.4, which has not been published elsewhere, illustrates the point with some traverses through two H_2–O_2–Ar flames; one containing a little added CO, the other an equal concentration of CH_4. In the CO flame, the temperature continued to rise after the O_2 was all consumed because of the continued recombination of free radicals, as had been found before by Padley and Sugden.[114] In the gas from the CH_4 flame the radicals must have been considerably smaller because no continued large heat release is apparent. From the rates of consumption of oxygen in the two flames, assuming that the reverse of reaction (2.1) was negligible over most of the region where $-d[O_2]/dt$ is plotted, it can be inferred that [H] was about 4 times larger in the CO than in the CH_4 flame. If a ratio of this order holds in the post-flame gas also, the difference in the temperature traverses is very reasonable because the rate of heat release by recombination depends on the square of the radical concentrations.

Flames of other simple hydrocarbons resemble those of methane in that they too appear to be H_2–CO–O_2 flames fed by the breakup of the

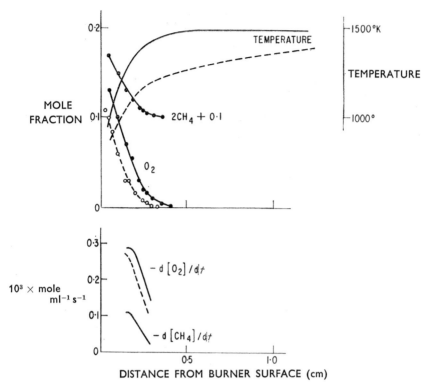

Fig. 5.4. Profiles through two flames, both burnt at 7 cm Hg pressure. For the dotted curves, the reactants were $H_2 + 0.27 O_2 + 0.14 Ar + 0.06$ CO; for the solid curves, an equal amount of CH_4 was substituted for the CO. Lower half gives some calculated rates of reaction.

hydrocarbon. The temperature traverses suggest that the breakup of the other hydrocarbons also consumes free valencies and decreases the large excess radical concentrations which would otherwise be expected from the H_2–CO–O_2 flames. The effectiveness of hydrocarbons in decreasing excess radicals is most noticeable in fuel-rich gas, and [H] is near $[H]_{equ}$ whenever any hydrocarbon survives into the post-flame gas. This allowed a calibration in early determinations of [H] by exchange with added D_2O, as was mentioned in chapter 2, and it has been confirmed several times since then, e.g. by Reid and Wheeler in propane flames.[115]

The Decomposition of C_2H_6 in Flames

Much as with CH_4, the measured values of $-d[C_2H_6]/[C_2H_6]\,dt$ in fuel-lean C_2H_6–O_2 or fuel-rich C_2H_6–H_2–O_2 flames can be correlated with

[OH] and [H] respectively.[116] In neither type of flame is there evidence for a significant attack of O atoms on C_2H_6. In lean flames, the relative rates of

$$C_2H_6 + OH \xrightarrow{k_\delta'} \text{presumably } C_2H_5 + H_2O \qquad (5.8)$$

and

$$CO + OH \xrightarrow{k_8} CO_2 + H \qquad (3.8)$$

gave

$$k_\delta'/k_8 \sim 34 \text{ at } 1400-1600°K, \text{ 2--3 cm Hg pressure}$$

which is little different from the corresponding ratio for CH_4. In rich flames with small ratios of $[C_2H_6]/[H_2]$, the relative rates of

$$C_2H_6 + H \xrightarrow{k_\varepsilon'} \text{presumably } C_2H_5 + H_2 \qquad (5.9)$$

and

$$O_2 + H \xrightarrow{k_1} OH + O \qquad (2.1)$$

when measured in regions where the reverse of (2.1) could be assumed negligible, and interpreted by the k_1 from Table 4.1, gave

$$k_\varepsilon' \sim 1 \times 10^{14} e^{-9.7/RT} \text{ cm}^3 \text{ mole}^{-1} \text{ s}^{-1} \text{ at } 1000-1400°K$$

$$3-5 \text{ cm Hg pressure.}$$

This agrees very well with the estimate by Darwent and Roberts[117] at 300–580°, but not so well with that of Berlie and LeRoy[118] who interpreted their results at 250–430° by a 30-fold smaller pre-exponential factor and a 3 kcal smaller activation energy. The ratio k_ε'/k_1 has also been estimated at 793° [119] and at 753° [120] from shifts of the explosion limit of H_2–O_2 mixtures. A little added C_2H_6 shrank the bounded explosion region, and the additional chain terminating reaction was found to be proportional to $[C_2H_6]$ and probably to [H] by consideration of the reasonable kinetic possibilities. By identifying the new terminating reaction with (9), the ratio of k_ε'/k_1 could be obtained. The two determinations from explosion limits agreed with each other and with an extrapolation of the ratio from flames.

Baldwin[121] has carried out additional work at 813°K to obtain from explosion limits an absolute value of k_1 and then of k_ε', and has also recalculated the experiments of Darwent and Roberts using more recent estimates for the velocity of exchange of $D + H_2$ which was involved in their calculation. He plotted the results of the various investigations over the temperature range 300–1500°K, reproduced as Fig. 5.5, and concluded that

$$\log_{10}k'_s = 14 \cdot 0 \pm 0 \cdot 4 - 9 \cdot 5 \pm 1 \cdot 0 \text{ kcal}/2 \cdot 3 \text{ } RT.$$

It is probable that in flames the subsequent reactions of C_2H_5 radicals include bimolecular processes which terminate free valencies, analogous

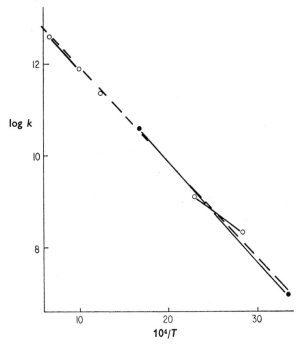

FIG. 5.5. Estimates of the rate constant, in cm^3 $mole^{-1}$ s^{-1}, for $H + C_2H_6$ $\rightarrow C_2H_5 + H_2$. From the top of the curve downwards, the data are: the flame results; Baldwin's estimate at 813°K; his recalculation of Darwent and Roberts' results; Berlie and LeRoy's results. The equation of the dotted line is given in the text.

to and even the same as those of CH_3—but they have not been worked out.

Decomposition of C_2H_4 in Flames

By probing a number of ethylene flames,[116] the specific decay rate of this fuel was measured in mixtures containing various concentrations of [H], [OH], and [O]. The radical concentrations were approximated in ways already discussed, using the constants from Table 4.1 of chapter 4 and supposing that molecular oxygen and carbon monoxide

5

were consumed only by reactions with H and OH radicals respectively. The specific decay rate of the fuel was found to increase markedly towards the downstream end of the reaction zone: [H] and [OH] did not increase in the same region, but [O] did. This suggested that C_2H_4 was destroyed mostly at the rate of its reaction with O atoms,

$$C_2H_4 + O \xrightarrow{k''} C_2H_4O^\star \rightarrow \ldots \qquad (5.10)$$

and if so, the data for all flames would be consistent with

$$k'' = 2\text{–}3 \times 10^{13} \text{ cm}^3 \text{ mole}^{-1} \text{ s}^{-1} \text{ at } 1400\text{–}1600°\text{K}$$

The k'' from flames would then be of the same order as the constant obtained at much lower temperatures for reaction (10); agreeing moderately well with Ford and Endow's[122] calculation of Cvetanovic's[123] photolytic work, or with Elias and Schiff's[124] estimates by discharge tube methods. A partial consumption of C_2H_4 by reaction with OH could not be excluded, however, in the flame work.

At low temperatures, the excited $C_2H_4O^\star$ formed in (10) are thought to break up partly to give CH_3 radicals,[125] and these may well have formed in flames too. Fuel-rich mixtures of a little C_2H_4 in much H_2 gave a transient yield of CH_4 in the reaction zone which was compatible with the occurrence of

$$H + CH_4 \rightleftarrows CH_3 + H_2 \qquad (5.7)$$

if it was supposed that CH_3, formed at the rate of $k''[O][C_2H_4]$ and destroyed just as in methane flames at the rate $k_\gamma[O][CH_3]$, could also undergo a transient formation of CH_4 by the reversible reaction (7). The transient CH_4 was only large in the presence of much added H_2 and therefore was thought not to have been formed directly in the destruction of C_2H_4.

Studies of Acetylene Flames

When a little fuel-rich C_2H_2–O_2 mixture in much inert gas was heated suddenly in a shock tube, Kistiakowsky and co-workers[126,127,128,128a] observed that the induction time until appreciable reaction began was the same function of temperature and [O_2] as had been reported when H_2–O_2 was heated, equation (4.1). They concluded that the branching reaction

$$H + O_2 \rightarrow OH + O \qquad (2.1)$$

which controls the build up of free radicals for H_2–O_2 did so for C_2H_2–O_2

also. In H_2–O_2, O atoms and OH radicals were supposed to react rapidly with hydrogen by (2.2) and (2.3) to regenerate the H atom consumed in (2.1) and to form two new H atoms besides. The subsequent reactions must be different in rich acetylene mixtures where much carbon monoxide and smaller amounts of water, diacetylene, and doubtlessly other products are formed,[128] but these must also make two new H atoms per molecule of oxygen consumed by (2.1) if branching is to be equally rapid. Bradley and Kistiakowsky[128] were primarily interested in the diacetylene. They suggested it was formed by

$$O + C_2H_2 \rightarrow C_2H + OH$$

$$OH + C_2H_2 \rightarrow C_2H + H_2O$$

$$C_2H + C_2H_2 \rightarrow C_4H_2 + H,$$

and noted that if all the O and OH radicals formed in (2.1) reacted this way, two new H atoms would be returned to the system per molecule of oxygen consumed in (2.1). However, the fraction of acetylene which simultaneously formed carbon monoxide was much larger than that forming diacetylene; so if the build up of free valencies is attributed to (2.1) plus the equivalent occurrence of reactions forming diacetylene, it must also be supposed that much more oxygen is consumed simultaneously in some other way to form carbon monoxide from acetylene. This is unlikely; in steady flames at least molecular oxygen is mainly consumed by (2.1).[99] If it is mainly consumed by (2.1) in shock tubes also, the bulk of the O and OH formed must react with acetylene, or with intermediates derived from it, to give carbon monoxide from its carbon. There is no obvious reason why the induction times should not still conform approximately to equation (4.1)—but this point of view relegates diacetylene formation to an unessential side reaction as far as the main branching mechanism is concerned. The importance of diacetylene is that it suggests the presence of C_2H radicals which may be important in processes of electronic excitation[127] and ionization,[128a] though of little importance in the development of the bulk of the free radicals.

That acetylene does not react mainly with OH radicals in some mixtures at least was shown[274] by probing low pressure flames of CO–O_2–Ar–C_2H_2 and comparing the rate of disappearance of the hydrocarbon with the formation of carbon dioxide. In one example it was found that the ratio of the specific rate of consumption of acetylene, $-d[C_2H_2]/[C_2H_2]\ dt$, to the specific rate of formation of carbon dioxide,

$d[CO_2]/[CO]$ dt, increased from 30 at 1150° to 300 at 1380°K. If both processes were irreversible reactions with OH radicals,

$$OH + CO \xrightarrow{k_8} CO_2 + H$$

$$OH + C_2H_2 \xrightarrow{k'} \text{products},$$

k' must have had around 30 kcal more of activation energy than k_8 and a pre-exponential factor about 10^6 times larger—which is judged to be impossible. An analogous comparison with $-d[O_2]/[O_2]$ dt in regions where the oxygen consumption could be considered unaffected by the reverse of (2.1) showed that acetylene could not have been mainly destroyed by an irreversible reaction with H atoms either. Crude estimates of [O] were possible in a narrow region of the reaction zone, similar to those obtained in ethylene flames, and these [O] were proportional to $-d[C_2H_2]/[C_2H_2]$ dt; so acetylene is probably destroyed in such flames by reaction with O atoms. The rate constant for the attack of O on acetylene was estimated to be 1 to 2 $\times$ 10^{13} cm^3 mole^{-1} s^{-1} and of essentially zero temperature dependence. The value is near that found for the attack of O on ethylene.

It is interesting that ethylene and acetylene both seem to be destroyed by O atoms. Methane and ethane are not, but are attacked by H atoms and OH radicals which doubtlessly abstract H from the saturated fuels. A plausible reason for the difference is that carbon is attacked directly in the unsaturated fuels; and such an attack on carbon has been directly demonstrated by Haller and Pimentel,[129] though under conditions about as different from flames as could be imagined. They photolysed a solid argon matrix containing nitrous oxide and acetylene, and found that the O atoms from nitrous oxide formed ketene. Ketene was not observed in samples probed from flames, but has been reported formed when a mixture of acetylene plus about 1·5 per cent of oxygen was run through a tube heated to 750°K.[130]

The course of reaction in flames is unknown. The formation of methylene or a ketyl radical is not unlikely,

$$O + C_2H_2 \rightarrow CH_2 + CO, \text{ or } HCCO + H,$$

but other suggestions might be advanced. Whatever the primary products, other than H atoms, they should not react largely with molecular oxygen if this is mostly consumed by (2.1). At lower temperatures methylene reacts considerably faster with many other species than with molecular oxygen;[275,276] and if it reacted 100 times or so faster with O or OH than with oxygen molecules, it need not consume much molecular oxygen in flames either.

Cool Flames

Steady reactions in a flow system can be obtained in fuel-rich mixtures of oxygen with higher hydrocarbons, or with ethers, alcohols, aldehydes, etc., which have a much smaller temperature rise across the reaction zone than the flames just described. These cool flames occur spontaneously[92] with most higher hydrocarbons at around 500–700°K and at pressures which depend on the particular fuel molecule. Townend and co-workers[131,132] stabilized the flame in a mixture of ether and oxygen flowing in a diverging conical tube, and Bailey and Norrish[133] using a similar tube heated to 528–538°K stabilized a cool flame of n-hexane–O_2–N_2. Similar flames of ether-air fed at room temperature[134,135] or of pre-heated n-hexane–air and n-heptane–air[134] have also been stabilized on a Powling burner.

These low temperature flames are very different from the hot ones described above. The emitted light from them is the same as from fluorescing formaldehyde.[136] The flame temperatures of various stabilized $(C_2H_5)_2O$–O_2 cool flames lies in the range 600–800°K.[131,134] The intermediate reaction products include aldehydes, etc., most of which, except for formaldehyde, may be destroyed again with the formation of considerable unsaturated hydrocarbons. They are certainly not associated with H_2–CO–O_2 flames, and the O_2 in them doubtlessly reacts with larger radicals and molecules rather than with H atoms. In unsteady systems, however, and in the presence of enough oxygen they sometimes ignite the hot flame.[2]

CHAPTER 6

IONIZATION AND ELECTRONIC EXCITATION IN HYDROCARBON FLAMES

ELECTRONICALLY excited molecules are the most obvious species in the visible reaction zone of hydrocarbon flames. They decay rapidly and do not persist into the post-flame gas. It was conceivable once that they might be accounted for on equilibrium considerations; that in some instances, an excited molecule A* might be thermally equilibrated with ground state A which was formed and then burnt up in the reaction zone. The A* have been found too numerous for this interpretation, however, and the excited species are now thought to originate in chemiluminescent or chemi-ionization processes. Though too many to be accounted for on equilibrium considerations, they are too few to affect the main course of the combustion.

The excitation processes are quite energetic in hydrocarbon flames. When a little iron carbonyl is added to hydrogen, the most energetic line excited requires 122 kcal,[76] very near the 118 kcal available from the recombination of H + OH; but a line requiring 174 kcal is excited in hydrocarbon flames.[137] The larger energy must often derive from forming in some way the strong C–O bond from species like C, CH, etc.;[137] and it may be that a process of this kind is directly visible in the emission from the excited HCO* radical.[138] More often the excited species which is observed does not contain the C—O group.

It is difficult to get quantitative evidence about excitation processes in hydrocarbon flames because the species suspected to be involved are only present in small concentrations. The way in which these are formed is unknown, though of course it is not unreasonable that hydrocarbon radicals should include traces of C_2 and CH, for example. Only traces are involved; until recently, neither of these species could be measured in steady flames. Both of them have now been found by absorption spectroscopy.[139] Yet no reaction attributed to the species C_2, CH, etc., has been shown to depend on the concentrations $[C_2]$, [CH], etc.; and the chemiluminescent and chemi-ionization processes in hydrocarbon flames are therefore not understood very well.

Ions in Flames

Ions have been studied by Langmuir probes, by the effect of free electrons on high frequency circuits, and by mass spectroscopy. In the probe method[140,141] a fine wire is introduced in the flame and the current to it measured as a function of applied voltage. The other, non-saturating, grounded electrode is the burner itself and a screen placed above the flat flame. At sufficiently negative voltages the electrons are repelled and all the positive ions diffusing to the wire are captured.

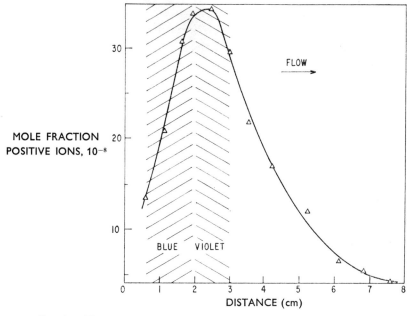

FIG. 6.1. Variation of positive ions through a C_2H_4–O_2 flame burning at 0·3 cm Hg (Calcote[141]).

The method can be checked by measurements in post-flame gas containing easily ionizable alkali metals, when the calculable equilibrium ionization swamps any residual ionization of the pure flame. Probes cannot identify ion species but can give the total ion concentration with high spatial resolution.

Figure 6.1 from Calcote[141] shows the mole fraction of positive ions through a low pressure C_2H_4–O_2 flame. There is no species known to be present in such a flame which would have a sufficiently low ionization potential to account for the peak value by the equilibrium process,

$$A \rightleftarrows A^+ + e^-$$

When mixture strength was varied, the greatest ion concentration occurred in the neighbourhood of stoichiometric mixtures. When pressure was varied the mole fraction of ions was essentially constant between 10 cm Hg and atmospheric pressure.[142] CH_4, C_3H_8, and C_2H_4 fuels gave about the same mole fraction of ions in their flames, but C_2H_2 gave more.[141]

Measurements by high frequency methods of the concentration of electrons in fuel-rich hydrogen flames containing added cesium showed that negative ions were not very numerous compared to electrons.[143] Some probe measurements which imply that negative ions are important in stoichiometric and lean flames have not been confirmed by the mass spectrometer,[144] and the weight of the evidence is that $[e^-]$ is about the same as the concentration of positive ions in the flame itself and immediately downstream of it.

By mass spectroscopy, Van Tiggelen and co-workers[145,146] and Knewstubb and Sugden[147] proved that the principal ion in hydrocarbon flames was H_3O^+, although a large number of other species also exist in smaller concentrations. The preponderance of H_3O^+ was confirmed in other studies[144,148] and the disappearance of ions in Fig. 6.1 must have been chiefly a disappearance of H_3O^+ and may have involved the dissociative recombination

$$H_3O^+ + e^- \rightarrow H_2O + H \qquad (6.1)$$

If it was supposed that only recombination was significant along the descending curve downstream of the flame zone, Fig. 6.1 could be corrected for diffusion and fitted to the expression

$$-d[n^+]/dt \sim 1 \times 10^{17}[n^+]^2 \text{ mole cm}^{-3} \text{ s}^{-1}$$

which conforms to (1) if $[n^+] = [H_3O^+] = [e^-]$. A diffusion coefficient appropriate to the neutral N_2 molecule was used in the correction, the electrons being constrained by electrical forces from diffusing faster than the heavy positive ions. About the same rate constant was observed in the pressure range, 3 cm Hg to atmospheric pressure.[141] Since ion recombination was a second order reaction and the maximum mole fraction of ions independent of pressure, it is probable that the formation of ions was second order also. The assumption in this conclusion is that the mole fractions of ion precursors were independent of pressure. Considering the possible reactions among species known to be present in the reaction zone, Calcote[141] suggested that the ionization might be explained by such reactions as

$$O + CH \xrightarrow{k} HCO^+ + e^-, \qquad \Delta H = 0 \qquad (6.2)$$

$$H_2O + HCO^+ \xrightarrow{k'} H_3O^+ + CO \qquad \Delta H = -34 \text{ kcal} \qquad (6.3)$$

$$e^- + H_3O^+ \xrightarrow{k''} H_2O + H \qquad \Delta H = -145 \qquad (6.1)$$

with a formation of other ions by charge transfer from the HCO^+ or H_3O^+. The ΔH are quoted from Green and Sugden[148] who used the same reactions to interpret a study of fuel-rich H_2–N_2–O_2 flames containing 1 per cent or less of added acetylene. In their work at atmospheric pressure, a flame of purified H_2 gave an insignificant yield of ions but added C_2H_2 caused much ionization. $[HCO^+]$ and $[H_3O^+]$ were the smallest and largest ion concentrations observed by mass spectroscopy, $[H_3O^+]/[HCO^+] = 4 \times 10^5$ for 1 per cent acetylene. When ion concentrations were varied by changing the added acetylene, $[HCO^+]$ was proportional to $[H_3O^+]^2$ in the region of maximum ionization—as would be consistent with reactions (3) and (1) if $d[H_3O^+]/dt$ were zero in this region. No other ion was found with concentration proportional to $[H_3O^+]^2$, and this was taken to support (3) and (1) as written. If the $k'' \sim 10^{17} \text{ cm}^3 \text{ mole}^{-1} \text{ s}^{-1}$ is accepted from Fig. 6.1, the observed ion ratios give k' of order 10^{15} to 10^{16}. The evidence so far is consistent with (3) and (1), but there is no experimental evidence yet for equation (2) for the $[CH]$ in the flames studied was unknown. The reason for proposing it is that few other reactions can be imagined which would be sufficiently energetic, and none which also involve species definitely known to be present in the flame.

Kistiakowsky and co-workers[126–128a] have studied ionization in shock heated C_2H_2–O_2–Ar mixtures. Their mass spectrometric results led them to propose that C_2H was a major intermediate under the conditions used and that it was partly oxidized according to $C_2H + O \rightarrow CO + CH$, where the CH might well be formed as electronically excited $CH^\star$. CH (or excited $CH^\star$) was considered to react with O to form ions, equation (6.2), or to form electronically excited $CO^\star$ which gave the short ultraviolet radiation observed. The yield of short UV photons was estimated as about 10^{-5}, and of ion pairs as about 10^{-6} of the acetylene molecules reacting.

A charge exchange from the flame ions to added metals was proposed[143] as the most reasonable explanation for the ionization of lead in acetylene flames to a greater extent than corresponded to equilibrium. The ionization of the metals persisted into the post-flame gas because no fast recombination process such as (1) could operate; and this differentiated it from the ionization of the pure flame. An exchange process was also thought to contribute to the ionization of sodium in flames, which did not ionize above equilibrium but reached equilibrium faster in hydrogen flames containing one per cent of acetylene than in nominally pure hydrogen flames. Other data from the same school are plotted in Fig. 6.2, which gives the degree of ionization,

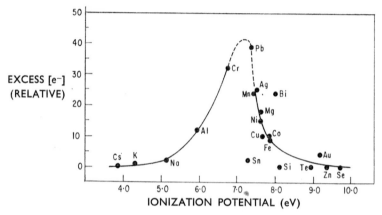

FIG. 6.2. $[e^-]/[e^-]_{equ}$ for various metals in a fuel-rich acetylene flame at 2500°K (Bulewicz and Padley[138]).

relative to equilibrium, for various metals added in traces to acetylene flames. The extent of non-equilibrium ionization evidently depends on the ionization potential of the metal and is consistent with the ΔH quoted for (2), (3), and (1), which could give as much as 7·8 eV.

Electronically Excited Species

Added lead and iron[137] and probably chromium[149] undergo a non-equilibrium excitation in the reaction zone of hydrocarbon flames. The effect is described sometimes by quoting the excitation temperature which would be required to give the populations observed in the excited levels if these conformed to an equilibrium distribution. The excitation temperature is often higher than the calculated adiabatic flame temperature. Gaydon and Wolfhard[1] commented on the parallel between the ionization of pure hydrocarbon flames and the non-thermal excitation of metals added to them, and King[150] and then in more detail Bulewicz and Padley[138] have shown that the correlation is very good indeed.

An excitation deriving its energy from the reaction partners, $O + CH$,[151] could parallel ionization via reaction (2).[152]

The visible and ultraviolet radiation from the reaction zone of hydrocarbon flames free of added metals is mostly due to excited $OH^\star$, $CH^\star$, $C_2^\star$, and sometimes to $HCO^\star$.[63] Bands of $CO^\star$ are also obtained in the far ultraviolet which require over 8 eV for their excitation. The origin of none of these species is established, though plausible conjectures can be put forward for some.

Ground state [OH] is smaller in low pressure stoichiometric CH_4-O_2 flames than in H_2-O_2, yet the peak $[OH^\star]$ is some hundreds of times larger.[26] Furthermore, the OH formed in H_2-O_2 has a rotational energy distribution more or less appropriate to the gas temperature; but that in hydrocarbon flames has a distribution appropriate to a temperature several times higher than the actual gas temperature. The exchange of rotational energy with other molecules is very rapid for $OH^\star$, as Carrington[153] showed by exciting a single rotational level and studying the fluorescence from this and from nearby rotational levels populated from the level excited. Despite the rapid rotational exchange, the electronic quenching by $OH^\star + M \rightarrow OH + M$ is also so fast that no very large shift of energy occurs, and the emission from $OH^\star$ is a fairly faithful representation of the states in which it is made. Gaydon[63] is of the opinion that the formation of $OH^\star$ in hydrocarbon flames requires the presence of ground state CH radicals. If the recently proposed ionization mechanism (2) and (3) is correct, the hints linking $OH^\star$ to CH might link it just as well to H_3O^+; and oddly enough, a marked similarity exists between the rotational energy distribution of $OH^\star$ in hydrocarbon flames and in discharges through water vapour.[154]

The emission from $C_2^\star$ and $CH^\star$ has been studied for its dependence on mixture strength, pressure, and the fuel burnt.[63] Both molecules in their ground states have been observed weakly in absorption in an equimolecular C_2H_2-O_2 flame at 0·4 cm Hg pressure.[139] $[C_2^\star]/[C_2]$ was about 70 times the equilibrium ratio. The CH absorption was not found in the stronger emission bands of $CH^\star$ at 4315 and 3900 Å but in the 3143 Å band which is only weakly emitted by $CH^\star$; and this is evidence that $CH^\star$ is not thermally excited since the lower state for all three systems is the ground state of CH.[63] Absorption by these molecules can also be observed in the products obtained by flash photolysing C_2H_2-O_2 mixtures [155] and in those behind detonation waves.[156]

Using acetylene with isotopically tagged carbon atoms, Ferguson showed that excited $C_2^\star$ in C_2H_2-O_2 flames did not preserve the pairing of C atoms in the fuel[157]. The formation of $C_2^\star$ in other systems also seems to involve carbon atoms in separate entities. Miller and Palmer[158] swept various organic halides by a carrier gas into an atmosphere of potassium vapour at 670°K and observed $C_2^\star$ radiation in the resulting diffusion flame. From $CHCl_3$ or $CHBr_3$ plus K, the $C_2^\star$ was found preferentially in the $v' = 1$ and 2 vibrational levels of the excited electronic state. They suggested the reactions

$$2CH \rightarrow C + CH_2$$
$$C + CH \rightarrow C_2^\star + H$$

the second of which is energetic enough to give $C_2^\star$ in $v' = 1$ of the excited state. Conceivably the same process could take place in flames, though the distribution of $C_2^\star$ among its vibrational levels is not the same for the halogen diffusion flames as it is for premixed hydrocarbon flames. The reactants $CFCl_3$–K, CCl_4–K, and CCl_4–Na all gave $C_2^\star$ excited preferentially into higher vibrational states, $v' = 7$ and 8, and were thought to involve analogous reactions of CCl radicals. From a diffusion flame of C_2Cl_4–K, $C_2^\star$ was not observed.

In diffusion flames of $ClF_3 + (CH_4$ or $C_2H_2)$, CH* was not found when oxygen was rigorously excluded, but was obtained otherwise.[159] Its excitation is therefore presumed to require oxygen and probably to involve the simultaneous formation of CO. Such possibilities as $C_2 + OH \rightarrow CO + CH^\star$, favoured by Gaydon,[63] or $O + C_2H \rightarrow CO + CH^\star$ by Hand and Kistiakowsky,[128a] would satisfy the facts known at present. The former suggestion uses only species known to be present but is a four-centre reaction which are rare among fast gas phase processes.   While C_2H has not been identified in flames, its existence is suggested by the interpretation of the reaction of fuel-rich C_2H_2–O_2–Ar mixtures heated in shock tubes.

HCO* radiation is said[63] not to occur as commonly in flames as that from OH*, $C_2^\star$, or CH*. The spectrum can also be obtained in fluorescence by illuminating formaldehyde vapour with light in the far ultraviolet, the exciting wave lengths possibly lying in absorption bands of H_2CO at 1287 and 1223 Å.[160]

The ultraviolet radiation from CO occurs in hot C_2H_2–O_2 flames and is almost certainly the same as the far ultraviolet radiation observed from C_2H_2–O_2 or from CH_4–O_2 mixtures heated by shocks[127]. In shock tubes, the radiation intensity was slight from CH_4 and much larger in the C_2H_2 mixtures where it developed with about the same exponential time constant as characterized the development of the branching chains during the induction period. The formation of CO was appealed to for the excitation of this high energy radiation; and the same reactants as those for equation (2), O + CH, are plausible.

Although the hints reviewed above suggest that the electronic excitation, including ionization, in hydrocarbon flames depends fundamentally on only a few radical–radical interactions, the particular processes involved are not identified very well. This state of affairs may not be true for long, however, because the subject interests a number of active investigators.

CHAPTER 7

SOOT IN PREMIXED FLAMES

THE formation of soot in the gas from a premixed flame is usually a form of disequilibrium. Solid carbon could not exist under equilibrium conditions unless the over-all atom ratio of the reactants, O/C, was about unity or less, and while soot contains a large proportion of H atoms and some O and is not solid carbon, bodies of its composition should not exist either. Street and Thomas[161] determined the critical O/C ratios at which many fuel–air mixtures would just form a luminous carbon zone in Bunsen burner flames at atmospheric pressure. They observed soot when the over-all atom ratio was O/C < 1·2 for acetylene fuel; when O/C < 1·7–1·9 for C_2H_4, C_3H_6, or C_4H_8; or when O/C < 2·2 for C_2 to C_4 paraffins.

Figure 7.1, taken from Macfarlane,[162] shows how the soot yield in premixed flames varies with wide changes in burning conditions. If equilibrium had obtained for these flames, soot should not have

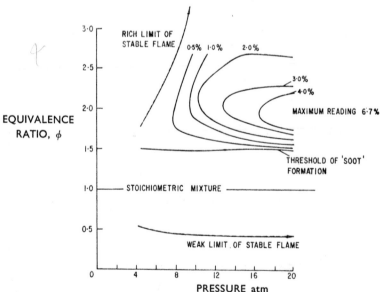

FIG. 7.1. Percent by weight of isopentane fed in a premixed flame which was recovered in the product as filterable solids and tars (Macfarlane[162]).

separated until an equivalence ratio of nearly 3·2 was reached; but the threshold occurs at much leaner mixtures, at an equivalence ratio of about 1·5 or for atom ratios of O/C < 2·1. As the mixtures are made richer at constant pressure, the soot yield goes through a maximum and decreases again in the cooler flames near the rich limit. The region of very rich flames has not been investigated much by other experimenters—most have worked nearer the threshold of soot formation.

The ratios quoted above and Fig. 7.1 prove the lack of equilibrium, but the different tendencies of various fuels to give soot in their flames is not very direct information, because the soot need not form from the original fuel. When fuels containing 1–4 carbon atoms are burnt, the blue-green flame is followed by a clear non-luminous space of thickness comparable to the flame thickness; and the soot condenses downstream of the clear space. Aromatic fuels do not possess a clear space, in Bunsen flames at least[161], and the soot region follows directly on the flame proper. In either case, the soot forms in the post-flame gas and it is the conditions here which are really relevant. Some attempts to correlate conditions in the post-flame gas with the presence of soot will be described.

Most of the carbon fed in the fuel is present as CO in rich post-flame gas and does not participate in soot formation. Ferguson[163] exploded rich mixtures of $C^{13}O$–C_3H_8–O_2 and found that no significant amount of C from the $C^{13}O$ was incorporated in the soot.

The post-flame gas from sooty flames often contains hydrocarbons equivalent to 10 per cent or more of the carbon fed, though the original fuel may no longer be an important constituent.[164,165] The rapid formation of CO in the flame involves species such as O atoms and is much slower once these active oxidants are exhausted. The hydrocarbons in the post-flame gas are themselves non-equilibrium species, and in view of its hydrogen content, the soot can also be considered a hydrocarbon of sorts. Acetylene is the hydrocarbon present in largest concentration in the burnt gas from most flames, methane flames excepted; and Porter[265] suggested that soot forms directly from acetylene in most flames.

Millikan[166] studied the conditions when soot first appeared in the post-flame gas from C_2H_4–air flames burning at atmospheric pressure on a porous burner. The [OH] in the reaction zone was about 5 times $[OH]_{equ}$ calculated for the post-flame gas and decayed rapidly through the clear region between the flame proper and the carbon zone. It was found that soot, deposited on a small wire immersed in the carbon zone, would burn off when the wire was moved upstream into the clear space. The clear space was therefore an oxidizing region which terminated when [OH] had decayed to its equilibrium value and only then could soot deposit. $[C_2H_2]$, which was 2–3 times greater than $[CH_4]$, was measured by infrared absorption, the necessary corrections for the underlying water bands and the absorption coefficient for C_2H_2 at flame temperatures having been worked out previously[167]. The gases contained at most only a thin cloud of carbon particles, and the temperature from the spectral distribution of its emissivity was proved the same as the gas temperature by sodium D-line reversal.[168] Since OH radicals in the clear zone seemed to oppose soot growth, it was postulated that the visible onset of soot farther downstream was opposed by oxidation processes (assumed proportional to $k_{ox}[OH]_{equ}$) and made possible by growth processes (proportional to $k_g[C_2H_2]$); and that soot appeared when

$$\frac{[C_2H_2]}{[OH]_{equ}} > \frac{k_{ox}}{k_g} = 0 \cdot 05 \times e^{34 \text{ kcal}/RT} \tag{7.1}$$

The numerical constant was determined to fit the data at 1720–1820°K. It may be that at lower temperatures (1) would not fit as well, for the heterogeneous deposition of soot from hydrocarbons on to a carbon surface, and its consumption by O_2 or CO_2, cannot be expressed by an Arrhenius equation at 1000–1500°K.[169] The particle or precursor which is supposed to grow or to be destroyed, depending on $[C_2H_2]/[OH]$ and the temperature, was not identified. If it were some sort of a nucleus, such identification would be very difficult for the nucleus need be only a small part of the soot particle.

There is evidence that moderately short polymers of C_2H_2 may be intermediates in soot formation from acetylene. Aten and Greene[170] found diacetylene, C_4H_2, and vinyl acetylene, C_4H_4, along with higher boiling unidentified materials, in C_2H_2–Ar mixtures which had been heated briefly in reflected shock waves to 1400–2500°K; and Bradley and Kistiakowsky showed by sampling into a time-of-flight mass spectrometer that C_4, C_6, and C_8 hydrocarbons were present in the hot gas itself.[128] In the latter work, the concentration of polymers decreased at about the same time that appreciable quantities of soot should have appeared according to Hooker's[171] measurements of the time lag for carbon deposition in similar shocked gas. The question whether such precursors are necessary intermediates or if acetylene itself deposits directly on a growing soot particle has not been answered conclusively.

The choice of OH and C_2H_2 as the chief species to consider was reasonable for Millikan's C_2H_4 flame where acetylene was the principal hydrocarbon species present. For other flames, it is possible that other hydrocarbons could be important. Fenimore, Jones, and Moore[164] also used the notion that the onset of soot in premixed flames might be determined by a balance between processes of growth (proportional to one or more hydrocarbons) and oxidation processes (proportional to $[H_2O]/[H_2]^{1/2} = [OH]_{equ}$). If so, it was necessary to suppose that not only $[C_2H_2]$ contributed to soot growth, as was assumed in equation (1), but that $[CH_4]$ could also make some smaller contribution, and that whenever it was present, $[C_6H_6]$ in the post-flame gas was around 50 times as effective as $[C_2H_2]$ in causing the onset of visible soot. $[C_6H_6]$ was always very small in the post-flame gas from simple hydrocarbon fuels, however, unless it was added in the fuel. Such experiments suggest that the importance of acetylene to soot growth is that it is often the most plentiful hydrocarbon species present. Other hydrocarbons may be as important if present in large amounts, or even certain ones in small amounts. In diffusion flames of light paraffins or ethylene, Cole and Minkoff[172] found no correlation between soot formation and acetylene in the reaction zone. But in such flames, C_2H_2 would not have been the chief hydrocarbon present in the region of soot growth; as was proved for methane flames at least by Gordon and co-workers.[173] No correlation should have been found if other hydrocarbons than acetylene could deposit soot.

When the soot formed in premixed flames is examined in the electron microscope[165], it is found to be filaments if caught on metal grids, or sometimes aggregates of various sizes if caught on quartz or mica slips. These may be artifacts of the mode of collection. Samples obtained by sucking a slightly sooty gas through a probe[168] contained no filaments and were rather uniform in size—about 400 Å in diameter collected well out in the soot zone and considerably smaller when collected some 10 ms earlier, farther upstream, from an ethylene–air post-flame gas at about 1800°K. As estimated by the extinction of light at the two levels, about 3 times as much soot was in the cloud at the downstream as at the upstream station. If a given number of particles had grown to contain 3 times as much soot, the particle diameter should have increased by only $\sqrt[3]{3} = 1\cdot4$–$1\cdot5$, but it appeared that the particle diameter increased several times between the two stations; so some of the particle growth may have been an aggregation of small particles into fewer large ones. Particles of the order of a few hundred angstroms diameter are the most frequently observed size in other premixed flames and even in diffusion flames.[174] Streznewski and Turkevitch[175] found that soot from a benzene diffusion flame had an average diameter of 450 Å and a size distribution agreeing with a symmetrical Gaussian curve of half width 195 Å.

The extinction of a beam of light by a cloud of particles is partly due to scattering, partly to absorption. For soot particles smaller than about 600 Å, the extinction by scattering of light of 6000 Å or more is not important compared to absorption. The extinction can be expressed empirically[176] as a function of wavelength of the light by

$$\log (I_0/I) = C/\lambda^n \qquad (7.2)$$

where C depends on the concentration of carbon in the cloud but n does not. n can be determined either in the flame or by catching a thin soot deposit on a cooled glass plate.[177] If the plate is allowed to become hot as the soot is collected, the n value subsequently measured is decreased. The value of n was found to be quite variable, 0·7–1·43 for a variety of fuels,[178] and not constant even for the same fuel. Millikan[177] then found that n depended on the composition of the soot, and increased about linearly with the H/C atom ratio from $n = 0·66$ for H/C = zero (carbon evaporated in a vacuum from a spectroscopic electrode) to $n = 1·9$ for H/C = 0·53 (soot from a low temperature C_2H_4–air flame). A measurement of C and n from extinction curves of the soot cloud at various levels in a post-flame gas may tell something about the soot. The estimate given in the last paragraph, that the total concentration of carbon in the cloud increased threefold between two stations was read from Millikan's data.[168] At the same time, n in equation (2) decreased from about 2·4 to 1·8 ± 0·2; which implies that the H/C ratio in the soot decreased from around 0·7 to around 0·5. The soot, initially containing 2/3 or more of the hydrogen in the C_2H_2, must have changed in composition by stewing out hydrogen as it flowed downstream.

Hydrocarbon flames are not the only ones which can form a condensed phase, of course. The post-flame gas from trimethyl borate–air flame[179] was found to contain boric oxide droplets of about 1200 Å diameter when first observed by light scattering experiments. They grew as the gas flowed downstream to about 1800 Å in 30 ms or so, mostly by aggregation of smaller into larger droplets. This condensation resembles soot formation in that a gas, H_2O in this instance, was presumably lost at some point of the process. In the vapour phase, most of the boron was present as HBO_2; but the condensed phase must have been nearer B_2O_3 in composition.

CHAPTER 8

FLAME INHIBITION

Flammability Limits

A CH_4–air mixture containing about 10 per cent of fuel burns faster than any other composition of these reactants. If the mixture is diluted by air or fuel, compositions are reached while the burning velocity is still a few cm s^{-1} which no longer propagate flame. These flammability limits occur at about 5 and 14 per cent of CH_4, and corresponding limits are found with other fuels. The standard method[180] of measuring them is to attempt to ignite a large volume of quiescent gas in a long tube of 5 cm or more diameter, open at the lower end so that the gas remains at atmospheric pressure during the upward passage of the flame. If the flame travels the length of the tube, the mixture is called flammable. It is specified that the flame should propagate upwards because many mixtures will burn upwards but not downwards. Fuel-rich hydrocarbon flames are notably sensitive to the direction of flame propagation, though CH_4–air is an exception with rich limits about 14 per cent CH_4 for upwards burning and about 13 per cent for downwards. The ethylene–air rich limit occurs at 28–32 per cent C_2H_4 for upward burning but only 15 per cent for downwards.

Egerton and co-workers[7,181] found that they could burn leaner mixtures on flat flame Powling burners than were flammable in tubes. Fuel-rich flames were difficult to stabilize and rich mixtures, flammable by the standard test, could not be burnt as steady flat flames.[7] Table 8.1 gives some limits determined by flat flames and in tubes.

There are two notions at present why limits occur. One view is that the limit is an inherent property of a one dimensional flat flame and that diluting the reactants to slower burning and cooler compositions eventually brings one to some catastrophic point where flame propagation breaks down. The catastrophe suggested by Van Tiggelen[182] and by Burden et al.[183] was that the generation of free radicals in branching chain reactions could no longer outrun their consumption in terminating reactions. Spalding[184] and Mayer,[185] independently, based a more general theory of inherent limits on the consideration that a strictly adiabatic flame is an idealization. They considered that

TABLE 8.1

Flammability Limits and Burning Velocities at the Limits of some Fuel–Air Mixtures

Fuel	% H_2O in mix	Flat flames*		Upward propagation† in tubes	
		% fuel at lean limit	Burning velocity cms s^{-1}	% fuel at lean limit	% fuel at rich limit
CH_4	—	5·31	3·40	5·4	14·0
C_2H_6	—	2·53	3·50	3·0	12·5
C_3H_8	—	1·89	3·82	2·2	9·5
C_4H_{10}	—	1·40	3·72	1·9	8·5
C_2H_4	—	2·72	3·74	3·1	32·0
CO	0·12	15·89	3·12	—	—
	0·50	14·18	4·20	—	—
	1·35	12·79	3·52	—	—
	2·1	—	—	12·5	74·0
$(CN)_2$	1·90	5·05	3·38	6	32·0

* From Badami and Egerton.[181]
† From Coward and Jones.[180]

the hot gas radiates and consequently possesses a falling temperature gradient in the post-flame region which cools the reaction zone the more the smaller the burning velocity. But a cooler reaction zone gives a slower burning rate and therefore the temperature of the reaction zone might be lowered still more. The reciprocal action of a greater fraction of heat lost as radiation and of slower burning velocity becomes catastrophic at a low enough flame temperature for simple theoretical reaction models, and a flammability limit is predicted at a finite burning velocity.

It is probable that inherent limits exist, and an example will be given presently in which it was supposed that they were approximated experimentally. The observed limit need not necessarily be an inherent one, however, as was pointed out by Linnett and Simpson.[186] These authors noted that Egerton's work had extended the lean limits found in tubes, and that the burning velocities in Table 8.1 were approximately constant. They inferred that the observed limit might be fixed by the least burning velocity which was stable under the conditions used. Recalling how it is necessary to pay attention to suppressing instabilities in order to establish a slow flame at all, they thought that convective effects might blow out the flames at flows of 3–4 cm s^{-1}.

Their opinion that a limit mixture is just a slowly burning one which is easily extinguished by convective forces or perhaps by heat losses to the apparatus used was also favoured by Dixon-Lewis and Isles.[187]

How close an observed limit is to an inherent theoretical one need not be specified in order to use the observation as an indication of the ease of the overall reaction. Limits obtained by diluting stoichiometric mixtures with inert nitrogen, until they will only just propagate flames have been used for this purpose. A "limiting oxygen index of combustion" was defined as $[O_2]/([O_2] + [N_2])$ in a mixture containing the maximum of added nitrogen which will burn. Hall and co-workers[188] quoted some of these indices; 0·056 for H_2, 0·069 for moist CO, 0·130 for CH_4, 0·118 for C_2H_6. They inferred from the values that hydrocarbons inhibit their own combustion in a way which hydrogen and carbon monoxide do not, and went on to show that the index for formaldehyde was about the same as for moist CO and therefore this substance did not inhibit its own combustion either. The conclusion is borne out by the observations of Legrand *et al.*[189] that the flammability limits of H_2CO–air mixtures are about as wide as those of H_2–CO–air.

The same point about the self inhibition of hydrocarbons is suggested by the calculated adiabatic flame temperature of 1500°K for lean limit mixtures of CH_4–air or for other light saturated hydrocarbons; this temperature is about 1600° for the hexanes and octanes.[190] By contrast, 10 per cent of H_2 in air, with an adiabatic flame temperature of less than 1100°K, propagates a coherent flame.[180] Even leaner H_2–air mixtures burn, but the light H_2 molecules diffuse preferentially into regions where burning occurs and the flame is not a flat flame in any approximation. At the H_2-rich limit, a similar preferential diffusion would have to be by the heavier O_2 molecule, and it does not occur noticeably. The rich H_2–air limit mixture has a low flame temperature, only about half the 1800°K of the rich CH_4–air limit. The self inhibition of the hydrocarbons is probably to be attributed to the fewer free valencies present in their flames than in H_2–CO flames. It has been already remarked in chapter 5 that this is particularly true of the rich hydrocarbon flames. In rich CH_4 mixtures, more than in lean ones, the generation of O atoms and of free valencies by $H + O_2 \rightarrow OH + O$ is more nearly equal to their consumption by $O + CH_3 \rightarrow \ldots \rightarrow CO + \ldots$, and a greater fraction of the free valencies is necessarily consumed in the burning. An equality between the rate of formation of O atoms and their rate of consumption by CH_3 radicals might give a fundamental limit of the sort envisaged by Van Tiggelen.

A characteristic of hydrocarbon–air limits is that, while the lean limit is not very dependent on pressure, the fuel-rich limit is displaced strongly towards richer mixtures by increasing pressures; e.g. the isopentane limits in Fig. 7.1 in the last chapter. Such a displacement does not occur for H_2–air limits. The rich limit of CH_4–air, about 14 per cent CH_4 at 1 atm, is displaced to 35–40 per cent CH_4 at 100 atm[180]. This shift is not understood, though one may suspect that something like a cool flame is being approached which involves reactions of hydrocarbon radicals with O_2 molecules in very fuel-rich mixtures. For CH_4, it is possible that at high pressures there might be an increasing role of termolecular $CH_3 + O_2 + M$ (rate constant $= 2 \times 10^{15}$ $cm^6 mole^{-2} s^{-1}$) as compared to $CH_3 + O$ (rate constant $= 4 \times 10^{13}$ $cm^3 mole^{-1} s^{-1}$), the constants being taken from chapter 5 with M assumed to be CO_2. If [O] were 1 per cent of $[O_2]$, the two reactions would be comparable at 10 atm.

In addition to composition limits at fixed pressure, flames of fixed composition can be extinguished by reducing the pressure sufficiently in a given apparatus. Although the radiation theory predicts an intrinsic limit at low enough pressures, the extinction of flames of hydrocarbons with air or oxygen are probably quenching effects which can be avoided, as far as is known, by scaling up the dimensions of the apparatus as the pressure is reduced. The special case of the decomposition flame of acetylene may be an exception; Cummings and coworkers[191] thought that a limit might be approached for this flame because of radiation losses. When ignited in tubes, acetylene propagated flame upwards with burning velocities of 2·8–8·5 cm s^{-1} at pressures of 2·02–10·2 atm respectively and with measured brightness temperatures of the hot soot of 1620–2140°K. In the faster flame, about 2 per cent of the C_2H_2 remained undecomposed; in the slower about 28 per cent. It was considered that at still lower pressures, a flammability limit was encountered because the slower flames lost more of their energy by radiation. The more usual non-sooty flames are less luminous, and the radiation losses are much smaller. Wolfhard[192] has stressed that an intrinsic limit due to increased radiation losses at decreasing pressures has never been observed for near stoichiometric flames of hydrocarbons with air or oxygen.

Le Chatelier's Rule

The rule states that mixtures of lean or of rich limit mixtures are themselves limit mixtures. A numerical example is given in the next paragraph. The rule is often obeyed fairly well by the common fuels, quantitatively by the flat flame hydrocarbon limit mixtures in Table 8.1. When it is not obeyed, the separate limit mixtures are inferred to possess strong mutual interaction. Thus mixtures of the hydrocarbon–air with the CO–air mixtures in Table 3.1 do not obey it very well,[181] and this is explained by the assumption that CO flames require H atoms to consume the O_2 molecules and OH radicals to form CO_2. Another example of mutual interaction is Simmons and Wolfhard's[193] observation that the H_2–air limits are contracted much more sharply by added Br_2 than corresponds to the rule. Le Chatelier's rule is not a very sensitive criterion for mutual interaction of two reacting systems, however; because even when it is approximately obeyed, the systems may still interact. For example, fuel-rich H_2–air and CH_4–air limit mixtures obey it approximately,[180] but CH_4 is considered to inhibit H_2 burning as will now be discussed.

Inhibition of Burning Velocity

Figure 8.1 from Scholte and Vaags[194] shows some burning velocities for various H_2–CH_4–air mixtures at room temperature and atmospheric pressure. The fuel mixture for curve E is composed of 0·101 CH_4, for which the rich fuel–air limit is 14 per cent fuel, and 0·882 H_2 for which the fuel–air limit mixture is 75 per cent fuel. According to Le Chatelier's rule, the percentage of mixed fuel, L, in the limit mixture is given by

$$\frac{1}{L} = \frac{0\cdot101}{14} + \frac{0\cdot882}{75} = \frac{1}{53}$$

and in Fig. 8.1, it looks possible that curve E would approach its rich limit at 53 per cent fuel. It is not very surprising therefore that the burning velocity of very rich H_2–air flames should be reduced by the addition of CH_4.

The maximum of curve E is near the maximum burning velocity for any CH_4–H_2–air mixture which contains 3·1 per cent of CH_4; and its burning velocity, 2/3 of the maximum burning velocity of pure H_2–air mixture, can be viewed as an inhibition of H_2 burning by CH_4. Lask and Wagner[195] showed that the same reduction could be obtained by a smaller addition of bromine; 1·5 per cent of Br_2 added to H_2–air mixtures reduces the maximum burning velocity to 2/3 of the un-inhibited maximum.

Methyl bromide, a combination of both inhibitors just mentioned, was studied by Burden and co-workers[183] who did not measure burning

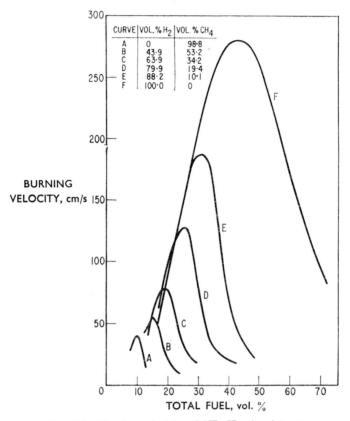

CURVE	VOL.% H$_2$	VOL.% CH$_4$
A	0	98·8
B	43·9	53·2
C	63·9	34·2
D	79·9	19·4
E	88·2	10·1
F	100·0	0

FIG. 8.1. Burning velocities of CH$_4$–H$_2$–air mixtures
(Scholte and Vaags[194]).

velocities but only the flammability limits of H$_2$–air–CH$_3$Br mixtures. They found that the initial ratios of [O$_2$]/[CH$_3$Br] in near limit mixtures were related to the calculated adiabatic temperature, T_{ad}, by:

$$[O_2]/[CH_3Br] = 0.05 \, e^{14 \, \text{kcal}/RT_{ad}}$$

and proposed that the branching reaction of H atoms with O$_2$ was opposed by terminating processes which occurred at the rate of:

$$H + CH_3Br \xrightarrow{k} CH_3 + HBr$$

Then the branching chains could only develop when:

$$k_1[H][O_2] \gg k[H][CH_3Br]$$

and the ratio [O$_2$]/[CH$_3$Br] at the limit was roughly k/k_1 at T_{ad}. The actual inhibition by added methyl bromide was perhaps due to the consumption of free valencies by the methyl radical, and to the action of HBr in ways not yet understood; but the sum of these was supposed to equal the rate of formation of methyl radicals. The interpretation could be only roughly true because the ratio of reactants in the cold gas could not have been the mean ratio in the flame, nor could T_{ad} have been a mean reaction temperature. Furthermore, it may be only approximately true that the limit was an inherent property of the reaction. The competing rates of branching and terminating reactions may have needed to be only roughly equal for extinction of the flame. Despite these reservations, the interpretation seems valid. If one accepts the k_1 from Table 4.1 of chapter 4, Burdon's treatment gives a rate constant for the reaction of H atoms with methyl bromide which is not inconsistent with the observations at much lower temperatures.[47] In unpublished work, the writer has checked the rate constant by probing some H_2–NO–N_2O flames containing a little added CH_3Br. [H] was estimated from the nitrous oxide profile, using the k_α of Table 4.1, and the rate constant determined from $-d[CH_3Br]/[CH_3Br]dt = k[H]$ was found to have only a small temperature dependence and to equal $1 \cdot 4 \times 10^{13}$ cm^3 mole^{-1} s^{-1} at 1900°K. This is twice the value deduced from the data of Burdon and co-workers—and the agreement is good enough to suggest their view is essentially correct.

When CH_4 or Br_2 are added to CO flames, the effects induced depend on the moisture or H_2 content of the CO. CH_4 added to quite dry CO–air increases the burning rate until the ratio of $CH_4/CO = 1/10$; further additions inhibit.[194] Doubtlessly, this reflects a need for H and OH radicals for CO to burn with air. When Br_2 is added to stoichiometric CO–O_2 of uninhibited burning velocity 20 cm s^{-1}, it has little effect.[196] Such a mixture contains only a few hundredths of 1 per cent of H_2 as judged by the effect of traces of H_2 on the burning velocity.[197] The inhibition of the burning velocity by added Br_2 is pronounced, however, if the CO contains 0·75 or 4·5 per cent H_2 and is faster burning initially.[196,198] When only one part in 10^4 or so of hydrogen containing substance, say $[H_2O]_0$, is present, it seems likely that the level of [OH] depends more on $[H_2O]_0$ than on the total free radicals present, which are mostly [O] atoms in any case. If added Br_2 inhibits by decreasing the concentration of free valencies, the inhibition does not affect [H] and [OH] very much when $[H_2O]_0$ is small enough. Consider as an illustration the equilibrium $H_2O + O = 2 OH$ at 2000°K and ignore all other radicals except O and OH; so that $[H_2O] = [H_2O]_0 - [OH]/2$. When $[H_2O]_0$ is 1 per cent or so of the total gas, [OH] is proportional to $[O]^{\frac{1}{2}}$ and decreasing the total free valencies by a factor of four essentially decreases $[O]$ by a factor of four and $[OH]$ by a factor of two. But if $[H_2O]_0$ is only $0 \cdot 01$ per cent of the total gas, most of the $[H_2O]_0$ is present as OH and remains so despite large changes in $[O]$. If $[O]$ is now decreased by a factor of four, say from 2 to $0 \cdot 5$ per cent, $[OH]$ decreases by only 20 per cent of its original value. The assumption in this illustration, that $O + H_2O = 2OH$ is equilibrated, was believed to be true by Semenov; it will be discussed further in the next chapter.

The effect of CH_3Br in inhibiting CH_4–air flames resembles that of an equivalent amount of Br_2,[193] about $2 \cdot 4$ per cent of Br_2 or twice as much CH_3Br being required to suppress flammability altogether. Rosser, Wise, and Miller[199] found the same effect to hold when smaller amounts of inhibitors were added; the addition of equal small mole fractions of molecules containing 1, 2, or 3 Br atoms (HBr, CH_3Br, CH_2ClBr, CF_3Br), (Br_2, CH_2Br_2, CF_2BR_2), or $CHBr_3$ decreased the burning velocity of a CH_4–air flame containing 10 per cent fuel in the ratio of approximately $1 : 2 : 3$. For CH_4–air compositions other than 10 per cent CH_4, the proportionality of inhibition to bromine content of the additive did not hold. This was ascribed to the non-bromine moiety of the inhibitors; for example, CH_3 from CH_3Br exercises its own inhibition in fuel-rich mixtures. The effectiveness of a little added Br_2 or HBr was reported not to change markedly with changes in mixture strength of the CH_4–air flame, and the effect of halogen on radical concentrations could perhaps be studied best with added Br_2 or HBr. No such studies have been reported so far. In connection with other work, Phillips and Sugden[200] found that 1/4 of 1 per cent of added Br_2 did not significantly affect radical concentrations in a fuel-rich H_2–O_2–N_2 flame; but this was not enough to inhibit H_2–air flames very decidedly anyway.

It is not certain why added bromine compounds inhibit—Wise and Rosser[201] discussed how the addition of any Br compound might decrease the rate of reaction in oxygen flames by substituting inactive atoms for part of the active free radicals. The partial substitution of H by Br would hinder the branching reaction, $H + O_2 \rightarrow OH + O$, of O by Br would hinder the oxidation of CH_3 radicals, etc. A considerable effect is expected because a branching reaction is among those hindered, and a non-branching mechanism should not be so susceptible.

More effective inhibitors have been reported than the substances discussed above, but they are even less understood. Lask and Wagner[198] stated that 0·02 per cent or less of added $Fe(CO)_5$, CrO_2Cl_2, or $Pb(C_2H_5)_4$ was as effective as 0·7 per cent of Br_2 in decreasing the burning velocity of stoichiometric n-hexane–air mixtures at atmospheric pressure. Bonne, Jost, and Wagner[202] attempted to study the effect of $Fe(CO)_5$ on temperature and OH traverses in low pressure CH_4 flames; but it was found that the inhibiting action of a constant mole fraction of $Fe(CO)_5$ decreased markedly as the pressure was lowered, and at pressures low enough for a detailed investigation of the reaction zone of the flame, its effect was very small. The [OH] and the temperature in the reaction zone were then little different with or without added $Fe(CO)_5$.

Miller and co-workers[283] have measured the burning velocity of the fastest burning hydrogen–air mixture when small amounts of eighty different substances were added. For this flame, hydrocarbons as a group were comparable to brominated hydrocarbons as inhibitors, and even iron carbonyl was not tremendously more effective. They suggested that the destruction of radicals by methane was due to

$$2CH_3 \rightarrow C_2H_6,$$

rather than to the reaction of methyl radicals with O atoms as was suggested earlier in this chapter and in chapter 5. The rate constants are about the same[95,100] and either reaction destroys two free valencies in fuel-rich flames. The relative importance should depend on the relative concentrations of CH_3 vs. O; and the first process be more important the more the added methane.

CHAPTER 9

SOME FLAME CALCULATIONS

It is debatable if measurements of burning velocity alone can give enough information to establish a conclusion of much chemical interest. Even so, people have wanted to know if a measured burning velocity was consistent with one or another suspected reaction mechanism. For a simple enough mechanism, the question can be answered by calculating the mass burning velocity (ρv) from equation (1.1) and (1.2),

$$\dot{q} \text{ cal cm}^{-3} \text{ s}^{-1} = (\rho v) C_p \mathrm{d}T/\mathrm{d}z - \mathrm{d}(\lambda \mathrm{d}T/\mathrm{d}z)/\mathrm{d}z \qquad (1.1)$$

$$m_i R_i \text{ g cm}^{-3} \text{ s}^{-1} = (\rho v)\mathrm{d}M_i/\mathrm{d}z - \mathrm{d}(\rho D_i \mathrm{d}M_i/\mathrm{d}z)/\mathrm{d}z \qquad (1.2)$$

If the generation of heat and products can be represented by a single chemical process of known dependence on temperature and on one reactant, the equations can be solved as accurately as one pleases. Hirschfelder and co-workers[22] obtained solutions for such cases, by numerical integration. These seem to be accepted as standards for checking simpler approximations. Their treatment does not give an explicit relation between reaction rate and burning velocity; and when something is suggested about the reactions merely from a knowledge of the burning velocity, it can be brought out by explicit approximations of which the most commonly used has been the Zeldovich, Frank–Kamenetsky, Semenov equation.[203]

The Zeldovich equation is an approximate solution for equation (1.1) when $\dot{q}$ is assumed to depend so strongly on temperature that it can be neglected between the initial temperature, T_0, and some intermediate T_i which is supposed to be near to the final temperature, T_f. The temperature gradient is zero both at T_0 and at T_f. It can be obtained at T_i either by integrating equation (1.1) from T_0 up to T_i, or by integrating from T_i on up to T_f. The solution is obtained by equating the two estimates of the temperature gradient at T_i. Thus in the region from T_0 to T_i, where $\dot{q} =$ zero, (1.1) gives

$$(\mathrm{d}T/\mathrm{d}z)_{T_i} = \overline{C}_p(\rho v)(T_i - T_0)/\lambda_f \qquad (9.1)$$

$\overline{C}_p$ = mean specific heat from T_0 to T_i, or approximately from T_0 to T_f

λ_f = value of λ at T_i, or approximately the value at T_f.

In the region from T_i on up to T_f, the first term on the right side of equation (1.1) is less important, compared to the second term, the nearer T_i is to T_f. If the first term is omitted altogether in this region

$$\int_{T_1}^{T_f} \dot{q} \, dT = \int_{T_0}^{T_f} \dot{q} \, dT = \frac{\lambda_f}{2} (dT/dz)^2 T_i \tag{9.2}$$

From (1) and (2), one gets for the constant mass flow

$$(\rho v)^2 = \frac{2\lambda_f \int_{T_0}^{T_f} \dot{q} \, dT}{\overline{C}_p^2 (T_f - T_0)^2} \tag{9.3}$$

Equation (3) is a limiting law, valid when $\dot{q}$ is appreciable only near T_f. Spalding[204] has shown, however, that even if $\dot{q}$ is appreciable over a larger temperature interval, the equation is still useful. He examined several forms of $\dot{q}$ for which equation (1.1) could be solved exactly and concluded that for any probable curve of $\dot{q}$ vs. T, $(\rho v)^2$ calculated from (3) would be correct to within a factor of three. He gave a modification of (3) which should be more accurate, the modified version being

$$(\rho v)^2 = \frac{\int_{T_0}^{T_f} \lambda \dot{q} \, dT}{\beta \overline{C}_p^2 (T_f - T_0)^2} \tag{9.4}$$

λ is now the local value, a function of T

$$\beta = 1/2 - 0.6604(1 - \tau) - 0.4823(1 - \tau)^2$$

$$\tau = \frac{\int_{T_0}^{T_f} (T - T_0)\lambda \dot{q} \, dT}{(T_f - T_0) \int_{T_0}^{T_f} \lambda \dot{q} \, dT}$$

In simple cases, the local rate of heat evolution, $\dot{q}$, can be written in terms of the initial reactants. The simplest case of all is when an initial concentration of $[a]_0$ moles cm^{-3}, and of initial mass fraction $(M_a)_0$, is consumed in the flame and $\dot{q}$ is proportional to its rate of reaction. Any other reactant, say species b, is present in excess and is supposed to be related to a by the stoichiometry. The mass fraction, M_a, is obtained from equation (1.2) at any point; but if

$$\rho D_a C_p / \lambda = \delta_a = 1 \tag{9.5}$$

(1.2) gives the same description of the decrease of M_a as (1.1) does of the increase of T, and (1.2) merely states that M_a decreases linearly with increasing temperature,

$$M_a = (M_a)_0 \frac{(T_f - T)}{(T_f - T_0)} \tag{9.6}$$

Equation (5) is a fairly good approximation unless species a is relatively light or heavy; but δ_a equals about 3·3 for H_2 in air, and about 1/2 for C_3H_8 in air[204]. If (6) is true and [b] calculable, $\dot{q}$ can be evaluated,

$$\dot{q} = Q[a][b]k_0 e^{-E/RT} \tag{9.7}$$

Q = heat released by the reaction per mole of species a

$k_0 e^{-E/RT}$ = rate constant

and the integration in (3) or (4) can be performed graphically. Finally, if the rate constant is not known, it might be evaluated from an explicit solution of the integral in (3). For example, if in equation (7)

$$Q = \overline{C}_p \rho_0 (T_f - T_0) / [a]_0$$

$$[a] = [a]_0 \left(\frac{T_0}{T} \right) \left(\frac{T_f - T}{T_f - T_0} \right)$$

[b] $\sim$ unconsumed excess in the burnt gas,

an approximate integration of equation (3) is[203]

$$(\rho v)^2 = \frac{2 \lambda_f \rho_0 [b] k_0 e^{-E/RT_f} \left(\dfrac{T_0}{T_f} \right) \left(\dfrac{RT_f^2}{E} \right)^2}{\overline{C}_p (T_f - T_0)^2} \tag{9.8}$$

When one speaks of getting a rate constant by applying the Zeldovich equation to measurements of burning velocity, what is meant is that the measurements as a function of flame temperature have been fitted to equation (8), or to a similar equation appropriate to the assumed order of the reaction, and k_0 and E inferred. The variation in flame temperature is often obtained by adding diluents, or changing T_0.

An Application of the Foregoing Equations

Levy and Weinberg[27] used the equations to discuss temperature profiles through lean, flat C_2H_4–air flames at atmospheric pressure. T was deduced from measurements of the index of refraction, and then $\dot{q}$ calculated from equation (1.1). Substitution of the experimental $\dot{q}$ into (3) gave (ρv) too small by 30 per cent. The use of (4) decreased the discrepancy to only 8 per cent. The authors then[205] used their local values of $\dot{q}$ to consider the following question. If some species, $[x]$ was present which reacted with C_2H_4 at the rate of

$$\dot{q} = \text{constant } [C_2H_4][x]\, e^{-E/RT} \qquad (9.9)$$

what must the profile of $[x]$ have been through the reaction zone? Supposing that $M_{C_2H_4}$ and hence $[C_2H_4]$ could be obtained from (6) at each point where T and $\dot{q}$ was known, they could solve for a quantity proportional to $[x]\,e^{-E/RT}$. It then appeared that if E was large, about 40 kcal mole^{-1}, $[x]$ must have decreased far too drastically for it to have been $[O_2]$. If E was small, about 5 kcal mole^{-1}, $[x]$ must have increased markedly through the reaction zone. For intermediate E, $[x]$ must have gone through a minimum. They could not choose among these possibilities, or even decide if (9) were approximately true. In view of the subsequent work on hydrocarbon flames, already described in chapter 5, (9) could have been only approximately true. The lagging oxidation of the CO would have supplied more heat towards the downstream side of the reaction zone than would have been expected according to (9), although most of the heat would have been evolved at about the rate of the destruction of the hydrocarbon. It is interesting that one of their possibilities, E small and $[x]$ increasing through the reaction zone, agrees qualitatively with the more detailed studies; and this is the only one of their three possibilities which is very reasonable chemically. The identification of the O atom as the chief reactant for C_2H_4 in chapter 5 was based on the observation that the species which reacted with the hydrocarbon must have increased its concentration rapidly in the reaction zone, and [O] was the radical concentration which did so most markedly.

Burning velocities are easy to correlate by an incorrect assumption about the chemistry and give less reliable information than can be deduced from temperature traverses. Levy and Weinberg went on to show this by fitting their (ρv) values to an equation of the type of (8) with $[a] = [C_2H_4]$, $[b] = [O_2]$, $E = 42$ to 49 kcal mole^{-1} over the range in T_f available with Powling burners.[205] That is, they showed that

(ρv) could be fitted very well by a fundamentally meaningless correlation because their local values of $\dot{q}$ in the same flames proved that the C_2H_4 did not disappear by a reaction with O_2 of activation energy around 40 kcal. Many correlations of just this kind have been made for hydrocarbon flames, and doubtlessly none of them has any more fundamental significance than the one proved meaningless by Levy and Weinberg.

Such correlations may have practical utility; Brokaw and Gerstein[257] showed how burning velocities of hydrocarbon–air flames, or properties depending on burning velocity such as the quenching distance, could be expressed by equations resembling (8) with activation energies around 40 kcal mole^{-1}. The concentration terms were varied in order to get the best empirical fit, and no fundamental significance was attached to the correlations.

Moist CO–O_2 Flames

CO flames tell something of their chemistry from their burning velocities alone; namely, that pure CO–O_2 or CO–air mixtures may not be able to maintain a steady flame. The burning velocity of stoichiometric CO–O_2 at one atmosphere pressure has been reported[197] to be less than 3 cm s^{-1}; and even this was considered characteristic of mixtures containing less than one part in 10^5 of H_2, rather than of pure mixtures. A little added H_2 or H_2O greatly speeds the burning and furnishes good evidence that the chief oxidation process is not a reaction of CO with O_2. It is assumed here that the main process is

$$d[CO_2]/dt = k_8[CO][OH] - k_{-8}[CO_2][H] \tag{9.10}$$

and the flame work is examined from this point of view.

In the flame studies it was supposed from theory that

$$(\rho v)^2 \text{ was proportional to } \int_{T_0}^{T_t} \left(\frac{d[CO_2]}{dt} \right) dT$$

and the aim of the experiment was to determine the reaction rate, $d[CO_2]/dt$, as a function of [CO], [O_2], [H_2O], and the temperature. The reaction rate was expressed

$$d[CO_2]/dt = \text{constant } [CO]^s[O_2]^u[H_2O]^w \, e^{-E/RT}$$

and the coefficient for each concentration term was estimated in flames of constant T_f in which that species was present in excess. In this way in fuel-rich flames, s was found to be one;[206,207] in fuel-lean flames,

u was zero[206,208] or perhaps $0\cdot25$;[207] and w was $1/2$–1 according to various workers with the lower values seemingly determined most reliably.[208] If it is postulated, as Semenov did twenty years ago,[203] that equation (2.2) and (2.3) are balanced,

$$O + H_2 = OH + H \qquad (2.2)$$

$$OH + H_2 = H_2O + H \qquad (2.3)$$

and if the reverse reaction in equation (10) is neglected; one can re-write (10) as

$$d[CO_2]/dt = k_8 \left(\frac{K_2}{K_3}\right)^{\frac{1}{2}} [CO][O]^{\frac{1}{2}}[H_2O]^{\frac{1}{2}} \qquad (9.11)$$

Semenov also assumed that the rate of (2.1), $H + O_2 \to OH + O$, was equal to that of both $O + CO \to CO_2$ and of the reaction of OH with CO; so that steady state concentrations of the radicals existed. Then [O] in (11) could be written in terms of the initial reactants. The new expression for (11) was multiplied by the heat released per mole of CO_2 formed and substituted into the Zeldovich equation to get the burning velocity of carbon monoxide flames. The process destroying O atoms, $O + CO \to CO_2$, would not be considered very important nowadays; if it is omitted, (11) remains but [O] can no longer be written in terms of the initial reactants. One can ask from experiment, how-ever, what the order of [OH] or [O] in a typical moist flame must be, relative to $[OH]_{equ}$ or $[O]_{equ}$, if (11) is true. Writing $[O]^{\frac{1}{2}}$ as a multiple of the equilibrium $[O]^{\frac{1}{2}}_{equ}$ in the post-flame gas, one has

$$[O]^{\frac{1}{2}} = \alpha[O]^{\frac{1}{2}}_{equ} = \alpha 2\cdot2\, e^{29\cdot7\ \text{kcal}/RT}[O_2]^{\frac{1}{4}}$$

the equilibrium constant being known. Substituting this in (11) along with the equilibrium constants K_2 and K_3 from equation (2.9) and (2.10), and with the approximate value of k_8 from Table 4.1 of chapter 4,

$$d[CO_2]/dt = 4 \times 10^{13}\, e^{-44/RT} \alpha[CO][O_2]^{\frac{1}{4}}[H_2O]^{\frac{1}{2}} \qquad (9.12)$$

The right side of (12) is of course only $k_8\alpha[CO][OH]_{equ}$—but it shows the temperature and composition dependence expected if α were constant. The order of α can be obtained by comparison with Sobolev's[207] result by the Zeldovich equation. For fuel-lean mixtures containing 2 per cent moisture, burnt at one atmosphere with measured flame temperatures of 1900–2400°K, he obtained

$$d[CO_2]/dt = 9\cdot5 \times 10^7\, e^{-(30\pm4)/RT}[CO]$$

where the concentrations of O_2 and H_2O were absorbed into the constant. A smaller activation energy than 44 kcal is expected because the ratio $\alpha = [OH]/[OH]_{equ}$ decreases with rising temperature. His absolute value of $d[CO_2]/[CO]\,dt$ was about 10^5 s^{-1} at $2200°K$, and if this is substituted in (12) and $[O_2]^{1/4}$ and $[H_2O]^{1/2}$ inserted, α comes out around 10 which seems a reasonable value.

Sobolev probed the post-flame gas downstream of the flame and found $d[CO_2]/[CO]\,dt$ a few hundred times smaller than he had deduced it from burning velocity in the flame. Friedman and Nugent[58] observed at lower temperatures about a ten-fold decrease in the specific rate of consumption of CO between a flame at 3 cm Hg and its post-flame gas. As was explained in chapter 3, most of this decrease was due to the growth of the second term on the right side of (10)—the decrease being more sharply defined for Sobolev at higher temperatures and pressures.

Flames of cyanogen–oxygen–inert gas resemble carbon monoxide in their sensitivity to moisture. Despite a calculated flame temperature of $2600°K$, the stoichiometric mixture with air burns at only around 10 cm s^{-1} when prepared as free as it can be of H-containing compounds. Addition of moisture or hydrogen increases this velocity markedly— for all mixture strengths according to Brokaw and Pease[269] but not for very fuel-rich mixtures according to Rutner and co-workers.[268] From rich flames the products are mostly $CO + N_2$, and it is plausible that CO is an intermediate in lean flames. The mode of consumption of the cyanogen is unknown and one cannot say whether it is directly catalysed by H compounds or if only CO oxidation and the consumption of O_2 are.

Burning Velocity and Radical Concentrations

In the examples above, the rate of reaction and hence approximately the square of the burning velocity was thought to be proportional to $[C_2H_4][O]$ in ethylene flames or to $[CO][OH]$ in carbon monoxide flames. It was impossible to test this dependence by measurements of burning velocity alone because the radical concentrations were not expressed in terms of the initial reactants and the temperature. The failing is usual in flames which are all radical reactions as far as it known. Some years ago, Tanford and Pease[258] attempted to circumvent the problem. They proposed that radicals were present in equilibrium concentrations in the burnt gas, and diffused upstream into the reaction zone where they attacked the species fed initially. The chief result of Tanford and

Pease was the suggestion that if the reaction depended on the concentration of some radical to the first power, the burning velocity would be proportional to the square root of the equilibrium concentration of this species as calculated in the burnt gas. It is now known that the proposed radical concentrations and distribution do not occur generally, so their suggestion cannot be generally true. For very hot flames, however, the equilibrium concentrations are so large that they might approach the actual values—and burning velocity might then correlate with the equilibrium concentration of a radical on which the reaction rate depends.

The moist carbon monoxide–air flame was a favourite reaction for attempting such correlations because $[H]_{equ}$ and $[OH]_{equ}$ can be varied by adding water while maintaining a fixed ratio of $[CO]/[O_2]$ in the reactants and a fixed flame temperature. For many studies, however, the temperature must have been too low for $[H]$ and $[OH]$ to be approximated by the equilibrium values. It may be remembered from chapter 2 that temperatures of 2200–2400°K were necessary for $[OH]_{equ}$ to approximate the actual $[OH]$ in the post-flame gas from fuel-rich hydrogen flames; and higher temperatures would be necessary for the same approximation to be reasonable in the reaction zone. According to the last section, $[OH]$ was about $10[OH]_{equ}$ in the reaction zone of moist carbon monoxide flames at 2200°.

Pickering and Linnett[259] found for approximately constant temperature fuel-lean C_2H_4–O_2–N_2 flames that burning velocities increased with $[O]_{equ}$ or $[OH]_{equ}$, but did not correlate with $[H]_{equ}$. In mixtures containing 30–60 per cent of oxygen initially, $[O]_{equ}$ increased from 0·84 to 1·84 per cent of the post-flame gas, thus by a factor of $(1·48)^2$, as $[OH]_{equ}$ increased by a factor of $(1·19)^2$ and burning velocity by a factor of 1·50. The result could be consistent with an attack of O atoms on ethylene; and the approximately constant flame temperature of 2690°K may have been high enough for $[O]_{equ}$ to approach the actual $[O]$.

A more reasonable way of writing radical concentrations in terms of the initial reactants is by means of the hypothesis of the chemical steady state. The reaction mechanism is supposed to be known, and the radicals are assumed to be destroyed chemically as fast as formed, or almost as fast, at every point in the reaction zone. The chemical steady state could hardly apply everywhere throughout flames involving rapid branching processes. But flames are known which are believed to react by non-branching processes, and the hypothesis has been applied to these as will be discussed below.

The Hydrazine Decomposition Flame

Murray and Hall[17] measured the steady burning velocity at atmospheric pressure for N_2H_4 vapour containing 3 per cent H_2O. At $423°K$, it was about 185 cm s^{-1}. The flame products corresponded to the over-all reaction

$$2N_2H_4 \rightarrow 2NH_3 + H_2 + N_2$$

with a calculated adiabatic temperature of about $1900°K$ as was also roughly measured. If equilibrium products had been formed, all N_2 plus H_2, the temperature would have been only $1340°$. Gray and co-workers[209] and Hall and Wolfhard[210] measured the burning velocity at lower pressures and proved (ρv) proportional to P. A flame can also be obtained above liquid N_2H_4 in glass tubes and (ρv) estimated by the rate at which the liquid burns down. When the results are corrected for quenching by the walls, this (ρv) is also proportional to P up to 1 atm.

The pressure dependence of (ρv) suggests that the rate of the reactions in the flame depends on the square of the pressure. In equation (3) the integral of $\dot{q}$ should vary with pressure in the same way that $(\rho v)^2$ does, and the reaction rates should also vary as $(\rho v)^2$ if corresponding mass fractions and temperatures occur at corresponding points when the pressure is changed. Indeed if these conditions are satisfied, it can be shown[22] from the form of equation (1.1) and (1.2) that if all the R_i vary as P^{2n}, (ρv) and $1/z$ both vary as P^n—which is the reason why low pressure thickens flames. The difficulty with determining reaction order from the pressure dependence of the burning rate is that it is not known if the conditions for a valid test are satisfied. By traverses through the reaction zone, it can be determined if the conditions are met: but then one has better evidence about the reactions than can be inferred from the pressure dependence of (ρv) and the test is no longer needed.

The suggestion for hydrazine is that since (ρv) varies with P, the decomposition may be controlled by second order reactions. The temperature dependence[209,211] implies from the Zeldovich equation an over-all activation energy of 30–45 kcal mole^{-1} for the flame decomposition, with a value of 36 kcal most probable. If a steady state concentration of radicals can be assumed, the observations would be consistent with a second order initiation process,

$$N_2H_4 + M \rightarrow 2R + M \qquad (9.13)$$

followed by a decomposition of most of the N_2H_4 in non-branching chain reactions, and terminated by second order processes. Assuming all propagating and terminating reactions to have identical rate constants, $k \sim 10^{13} e^{-7/RT}$, Gilbert[213] deduced from the burning velocity that the constant for (9.13) should be about $3 \times 10^{18} e^{-60/RT}$ cm^3 mole^{-1} s^{-1}. An apparent difficulty for this interpretation was that the gas phase decomposition of N_2H_4 at lower temperatures had been reported to be first order.[212] But Gilbert re-examined the lower temperature data and showed that they could be interpreted better as evidence for a second order reaction of rate constant just quoted than for the original interpretation of a first order decomposition. Profiles of species or temperatures have not been obtained, however, and the general type of mechanism cannot be considered settled.

The rate constant assumed by Gilbert for all propagating and terminating reactions was Birse and Melville's[260] measured value for the attack on H atoms on hydrazine at 400–500°K. A more recent measurement by Schiavello and Volpi[261] does not agree very well with the older work. In neither study was any evidence found for chain decomposition reactions of considerable length. Indeed, Schiavello and Volpi claimed a quantitative titration of H atoms according to the overall reaction, $H + N_2H_4 \rightarrow NH_3 + \frac{1}{2}N_2 + H_2$. The long chains which are the heart of the proposed flame mechanism seem to have been found at higher temperatures by Michel and Wagner[277] who heated a little hydrazine in much argon in a shock tube to 1100–1400°K, 3–7 atm pressure, and followed its decay by absorption spectroscopy. The time for half the initial hydrazine, $[N_2H_4]_0$ in mole cm^{-3}, to decompose was approximately

$$t_{\frac{1}{2}} = \frac{10^{-14 \cdot 4} e^{40\text{kcal}/RT}}{[N_2H_4]_0^{\frac{1}{2}}} \text{ seconds}$$

which suggests chain reactions of overall 3/2 order in hydrazine and independent of argon. This does not confirm the overall second order decomposition inferred from steady flames at low pressures; but it is very possible that steady flames at 3–7 atm possess a smaller pressure dependence.

The radicals involved are unknown. Lord and Sederholm[278] studied the infrared emission from the hydrazine flame under high resolution and observed many lines which could be assigned neither to N_2H_4 nor NH_3—nor to any other definite species because of the many possibilities all containing only N and H atoms and hence having their infrared bands in the same region. Lines observed in the hot ammonia of NH_3–O_2 diffusion flames and assigned tentatively to the NH_2 radical were not observed in the N_2H_4 decomposition flame, so [NH_2] was perhaps smaller in the latter.

The Hydrogen–Bromine Flame

The classical reaction law for hydrogen and bromine is[262]:

$$d[HBr]/dt = \frac{2kK^{\frac{1}{2}}[H_2][Br_2]^{\frac{1}{2}}}{1 + k''[HBr]/k'[Br_2]}$$

where a steady state of [H] and [Br] is assumed and the constants refer to the elementary steps:

$$Br_2 \rightleftharpoons 2Br, \; K = [Br]_{equ}^2/[Br_2]_{equ}$$

$$Br + H_2 \xrightarrow{k} HBr + H$$

$$H + Br_2 \xrightarrow{k'} HBr + Br$$

$$H + HBr \xrightarrow{k''} H_2 + Br.$$

This has been confirmed repeatedly in studies not involving flames, most recently by Britton and Cole.[229] Steady state concentrations of chain carriers were also predicted to be a fairly good assumption in flames by Gilbert and Altman[263] who compared the expected time to establish them with the residence time of the gas in the flame. This was disputed by Campbell, however.[279] The mass burning velocity of mixtures containing 45–60 per cent of bromine gives (ρv) proportional to about $P^{0.73}$ and therefore the reaction may be of about $1.46 \sim 1.5$ order as would be consistent with the slow reaction.[264]

Peacock and Weinberg[230] obtained preliminary traverses of temperature and of Br_2 through slowly burning mixtures at atmospheric pressure by optical methods but considered them of limited value because the transport properties necessary to interpret them could not be confidently assigned. With the values they did choose, and assuming steady state [Br], they worked out [H_2] and [HBr] from their data and then calculated the rate of heat release if d[HBr]/dt was given by the classical expression. The rate of heat release could also be calculated from the temperature traverse by equation (1.1), but the two $\dot{q}$ disagreed rather badly. Wehner and Frazier[231] examined the flame at lower pressure with thermocouples and quartz probes to obtain profiles of temperature, [H$_2$], [Br$_2$], and [HBr]. They treated their measurements as Peacock and Weinberg had done to get $\dot{q}$ by substituting their measured concentrations into the assumed rate law. The values were again in poor agreement with $\dot{q}$ from the temperature traverse. The $\dot{q}$ from the temperature traverse, when integrated through the flame, accounted adequately for the enthalpy difference of products and reactants, so the cause of the disagreement lay probably with the d[HBr]/dt assumed. More interesting results will probably be obtained when more measurements have been made in various flames, e.g. d[HBr]/dt from the HBr traverse itself, and when the preoccupation is dropped with merely checking extrapolations of the lower temperature kinetic data.

Decomposition Flames of Nitrate Esters

It was found by Belayev[217] that glycol dinitrate, (H$_2$CONO$_2$)$_2$, which decomposed at moderate temperatures and low pressures with a first order rate constant of $\sim 10^{14} e^{-35\ \text{kcal}/RT}$ s^{-1}; burnt as a steady flame above its liquid with a temperature dependence still appropriate to an activation energy of about 35 kcal, but with (ρv) proportional to pressure and therefore possibly with a second order reaction in the flame. The interpretation was that the ester decomposed under both circumstances by the mechanism

$$(\text{H}_2\text{CONO}_2)_2 + \text{M} \underset{k'}{\overset{k}{\rightleftarrows}} (\text{H}_2\text{CONO}_2)_2^{\star} + \text{M} \qquad (9.14)$$

$$(\text{H}_2\text{CONO}_2)_2^{\star} \overset{k''}{\longrightarrow} \text{products} \qquad (9.15)$$

but that at lower temperatures the activation step (14) was balanced so that $-\text{d}[(\text{H}_2\text{CONO}_2)_2]/\text{d}t = (k''k/k')[(\text{H}_2\text{CONO}_2)_2]$; while in the flame, the formation of the activated (H$_2$CONO$_2$)$_2^{\star}$ controlled the rate and a second order reaction was therefore observed. This interpretation is not inconsistent with unimolecular reaction theories;[218] according to which the transition pressure where the decomposition changes from more-or-less second order to first order ought to increase with rising temperature for complex molecules. Not enough is really known about any nitrate ester flame, however, for the interpretation to carry much conviction. It is not certain that the reaction rate really was second order in the flame—first order in the ester and first order in M—because the conditions may not have been satisfied for the reaction order to be reflected accurately by the pressure dependence of the burning rate.

The steady decomposition flame of methyl nitrate was observed by Gray, Hall, and Wolfhard at 1·3 cm Hg pressure.[219] It consisted of a blue zone about 0·1 cm thick emitting formaldehyde bands followed by a thin dark gap and then an orange red region emitting continuous radiation. Adams and Scrivener[220] measured its burning velocity by photographing the growing shell of primary flame in a closed vessel after igniting the reactant by a central spark. The primary flame was followed by a secondary burning of the initial products, NO, CO, H₂CO, etc., and their conclusions about the primary decomposition were necessarily indirect.

More has been learned about ethyl nitrate. Wolfhard[221] found (ρv) proportional to P for this flame at 0·6–20 cm Hg pressure. Needham and Powling[222] probed the steady flame at one atmosphere pressure; and Hicks[19] did the same with the greater resolution afforded by low pressures. At 3·5 cm Hg pressure, only a trivial reduction of NO formed in the reaction took place and the final measured temperature was 800°K. Ethyl nitrite to the extent of 10 per cent of the nitrate fed was observed as an intermediate, which is also a major product in the slower thermal decomposition at lower temperatures. The final flame products per mole of $C_2H_5ONO_2$ included 0·85 NO, 0·8 H₂CO, 0·35 H₂O, 0·2 CO, 0·2 CH₃CHO, 0·14 CH₃OH, 0·1 C₂H₅OH, plus smaller amounts of other species.

Hicks made no use of his composition traverses except to show that the mass fraction of $C_2H_5ONO_2$ varied inversely with the fractional increase in temperature through the flame; that is, that equation (6) applied. Thereafter he worked only with the temperature traverse to calculate $\dot{q}$ from equation (1.1) and inferred the rate of consumption of $C_2H_5ONO_2$ from $\dot{q}$. The maximum rate of heat release occurred at 750°K; and if the reactions were assumed to be controlled by

$$C_2H_5ONO_2 + M \rightarrow C_2H_5O + NO_2 + M \qquad (9.16)$$

$$-d[C_2H_5ONO_2]/dt = k[M][C_2H_5ONO_2]$$

where [M] = total gas concentration, the temperature traverse gave

$$k = 4 \times 10^9 \text{ cm}^3 \text{ mole}^{-1} \text{ s}^{-1} \text{ at } 750°K$$

or

$$k[M] = 3 \times 10^3 \text{ s}^{-1}.$$

The temperature dependence was consistent with the process envisaged, corresponding to an activation energy of $\sim$38 kcal mole⁻¹. The mass burning velocity was proportional to P; and assuming the reaction to be of the form of (16), the same rate constant and temperature dependence as the values just stated could also be inferred from the Zeldovich equation.

In isothermal decomposition studies at temperatures 300° lower, the decomposition of $C_2H_5ONO_2$ is believed to measure the same process; and here the decomposition is first order in the pressure range used by Hicks. A long extrapolation of these lower temperature results to 750° would predict specific decomposition rates of

$$-d[C_2H_5ONO_2]/[C_2H_5ONO_2]\,dt = 16 \times 10^3\ s^{-1} \qquad \text{Adams and Bawn}[223]$$
$$68 \times 10^3 \qquad \text{Levy}[224]$$

The difference between these figures is that Adams and Bawn did not correct for any re-association of the $C_2H_5O + NO_2$ fragments into which the molecules split, but Levy aimed to get the true value of the breakup free of any re-association. The observed rate in the flame was smaller than those extrapolations by a factor of 5–23. If the flame was controlled by a bimolecular activation process, it ought to have exhibited a slower decomposition rate than the extrapolated values of the high pressure limiting rate; so as far as the evidence goes, it is consistent with the assumption of reaction (16). Furthermore, above 15 cm Hg pressure, at which point $k[M]$ would presumably have been about $13 \times 10^3\ s^{-1}$, the pressure dependence of (ρv) decreased considerably according to Hicks; so the flame may have been controlled by a bimolecular activation process only as long as the specific decay rate was smaller than the expected high pressure limiting rate. This seems very reasonable. Yet the evidence for reaction order comes entirely from the pressure dependence of burning velocity, and one wishes that it had come from measurements of $-d[C_2H_5ONO_2]/dt$ from profiles of the ester in a variety of flames.

Some Other Flames

A few other types of premixed or decomposition flames have been studied but in less detail than those discussed above. Flames known to require a reduction of nitric oxide are put off to the next chapter.

It is known that N_2O decomposes by a thermal explosion when it is quickly heated in a static system to 1100–1300°K, the temperature required depending on pressure.[214] Brandt and Rozlovskii[215] investigated what pressure was necessary to obtain flame propagation through

N_2O initially at room temperature. It was found that flame would propagate upwards in a cylindrical bomb 6 cm diameter by 54 cm long when the initial pressure was 1·6 atm, and downwards when the pressure was 10 atm; but flames would not propagate at lower pressures. If it was supposed that (ρv) must be about 5×10^{-3} g cm^{-2} s^{-1} in order to have a flame at all; that is, that the linear burning velocity must be about 3 cm s^{-1} at atmospheric pressure, but less at higher pressures, then it could be calculated from the Zeldovich equation that the required (ρv) would have been expected to occur at 1·2–3·1 atm, depending on whose low temperature kinetics were used in the calculation. A critical (ρv) was considered to define the limit because of the notion that it was determined by radiation losses—but the same criterion could have been suggested on other grounds. For example, a criterion for quenching a flame by heat losses to the wall of a tube of diameter d, that

$$(\rho v) = 30 \text{ to } 50 \times \lambda/dC_p'\text{[266]}$$

would also give a critical (ρv) of the same order.

Rozlovskii[216] has calculated the expected yield of NO in this flame, formed by reaction (3.12), $O + N_2O \rightarrow 2NO$. Under a number of assumptions, he concludes that the measured yield is probably too small to be consistent with the rate constant given in chapter 3 for (3.12) and that a smaller constant which he quotes is more probable. It seems unlikely that the calculation could do more than suggest the order of magnitude of the NO yield; and the constant rejected and that preferred predict yields of the same order. The smaller constant is no longer favoured by Kaufman[72] who determined it.

The burning velocity of hydrogen peroxide vapour was measured by Satterfield and Kehat[225] for mixtures of 0·45–0·6 mole fraction of H_2O_2 with H_2O; the results seem to be consistent with the lower temperature decomposition studies. The temperature dependence of the burning velocity was estimated to be rather smaller than that expected from work on the slow isothermal decomposition, but the difference was within the error of the flame result. The pressure dependence of the burning rate was not positively determined.

Luft[280] maintained a yellow orange decomposition flame over a concentrated aqueous solution of hydroxylamine, 0·6 mole fraction of NH_2OH. The flame products included ammonia but not nitric oxide. The liquid burnt back about 0·1 cm s^{-1}, faster than liquid hydrazine or hydrogen peroxide do even when more nearly anhydrous. He commented on the possible relation of the decomposition of NH_2OH to those of N_2H_4 and H_2O_2—and the series may prove an interesting one when more experimental data are gathered.

A flat decomposition flame of ethylene oxide was studied by Friedman and Burke[20] over the pressure range 0·2–1·5 atm. The decomposition products at 1 atm were 44 per cent CO, 26 per cent CH_4, 20 per cent H_2, 10 per cent unsaturates. The flame temperature was about 1200°K when the reactant was initially at 365°. The linear burning velocity was only around 4 cm s^{-1}, and not very dependent on pressure; that is, (ρv) varied as P^n where n was less than but almost equal to one. Increasing the initial temperature of the reactant by 30° gave a very moderate activation energy by the Zeldovich equation, 14 kcal mole^{-1}. The authors mistrusted the pressure dependence as evidence for a second order reaction and the temperature dependence as a measure of the activation energy of the propagating reactions; and showed how a small increase in the final temperature with pressure might have given an apparent dependence of (ρv) on P appropriate to a second order reaction even though the reactions had really been controlled by a first order process. Nothing could be positively inferred about the flame reactions from measurements of burning velocity.

The slow decomposition rate of ozone has been measured[226] as has the burning velocity at atmospheric pressure for a wide range of O_2–O_3 mixtures.[16] Hirschfelder and co-workers,[227] by numerical integration, and Von Karman and Penner,[228] by an elaboration of the Zeldovich equation equivalent to (4), computed velocities which agreed closely with experiment; and there is general agreement that the burning rate is consistent with the reaction rate, $-d[O_3]/dt = 2k[O_3]M$, where k is the rate constant for the reaction

$$O_3 + M \rightarrow O_2 + O + M$$

The computations were made with a value of k about ten times smaller, for $M = O_3$, and five times smaller, for $M = O_2$, than the more recent value quoted by Benson.[226] If the larger k is correct, the agreement of calculated with measured velocities is within a factor of two or three rather than within the stated 20 per cent. No chemical conclusions need follow if this discrepancy exists. Perfect agreement does not prove the mechanism and disagreement by a factor of two or three need not disprove it. If reasons for or against it are sought from flames, a more intimate knowledge of the reaction zone is required than has yet been obtained.

Low Temperature Hydrogen Flames at Atmospheric Pressure

The possible formation of HO_2 by reaction (2.4),

$$H + O_2 + M \xrightarrow{k_4} HO_2 + M \tag{2.4}$$

was touched on in chapter 3 where it was shown that (2.4) might determine the rate of the recombination of radicals in the post-flame gas of fuel-lean flames if the HO_2 reacted subsequently with some other radical, no matter which. At low pressures, or in moderately hot gas even at atmospheric pressure, (2.4) is expected to be slow compared to (2.1) in the forward direction

$$H + O_2 \xrightarrow{k_1} OH + O \tag{2.1}$$

but this is not so at low enough temperatures and at atmospheric pressure. Furthermore if (2.4) occurs in the reaction zone at a rate comparable to (2.1), the subsequent fate of the HO_2 matters a great deal; a reaction with O or OH would terminate free valencies but a formation of 2OH from HO_2 + H, which was also a terminating reaction in the post-flame gas from lean flames, need not terminate free valencies in the reaction zone of fuel-rich flames. Dixon-Lewis and Williams[50] attempted to test two plausible fates for HO_2 by calculating the profiles of [H] and of the temperature for different reaction schemes involving HO_2 and comparing the calculated profiles with experiment. The calculation was done by the arduous method[232-234] of setting up unsteady, time-dependent equations corresponding to (1.1) and (1.2), one for temperature and one for each species considered. Starting from some arbitrary distribution of temperature and of the mass fractions, the equations were integrated numerically until the steady state profiles and burning velocity were reached.

A fuel-rich near limit H_2–O_2–N_2 flame was burnt at one atmosphere pressure on a Powling burner; burning velocity 9·2 cm s^{-1}, measured flame temperature 1072°K. By methods discussed previously, traverses were obtained for stable species, H atoms, and temperature. It was supposed that reaction (2.1) would always be followed by the reactions of O and of OH with H_2, so that (2.1), (2.2), and (2.3) could be combined into

$$H + O_2 + 3H_2 \rightarrow 2H_2O + 3H, \quad -\Delta H = 11 \cdot 4 \text{ kcal} \tag{9.17}$$

$$\text{rate} = k_1[H][O_2]$$

Among H, OH, and O, the most important recombination was assumed to be

$$2H + M \xrightarrow{k_6} H_2 + M, \quad -\Delta H = 104 \text{ kcal} \tag{2.6}$$

With values of k_1 and k_6 about the same as those listed in Table 4.1 of chapter 4, a mechanism composed of (17) and (6) was integrated repeatedly until the steady state was obtained. The work was lightened by assuming $\rho D_{O_2} C_p = \lambda$ so that the profile of O_2 was equivalent to the temperature profile. The steady state arrived at gave a maximum rate of heat release about 1/3 of that observed experimentally, a calculated burning velocity 2/3 of that observed, and a calculated maximum [H] about 5/2 of that observed. The general shape of the calculated traverses was consistent with those observed.

The agreement between observed and calculated traverses when HO_2 was omitted from consideration altogether was probably as good as ought to have been expected for a complete mechanism. Omitting HO_2 from consideration, however, ignores the implication of the relative size of $k_4[M]$ vs. k_1, that considerable HO_2 should have formed. An attempt was therefore made to include HO_2 in the reaction scheme. Two cases were considered: first that the HO_2 reacted with H atoms with no net consumption of free valencies,

$$H + O_2 + M \rightarrow HO_2 + M$$
$$H + HO_2 \rightarrow 2OH$$
$$2(OH + H_2 \rightarrow H_2O + H)$$

which were summed up as

$$H + O_2 + 2H_2 \rightarrow H + 2H_2O$$
$$\text{rate} = k_4[H][O_2][M] \tag{9.18}$$

The second case was to suppose that the formation of HO_2 was a terminating reaction,

$$2H + O_2 + H_2 \rightarrow 2H_2O$$
$$\text{rate} = k_4[H][O_2][M]/2 \tag{9.19}$$

It was found that the addition of (9.19) to the previously assumed mechanism of (9.17) and (2.6) led to a calculated burning velocity of almost zero, which seems to assert that (9.19) cannot be the only important course of reaction for HO_2. Addition of (9.18) did not look very promising either; for it gave 9 times too fast a burning velocity and 6 times too great a maximum rate of heat release. However, it is impossible to say how badly such a calculation must disagree with experiment before its proposed mechanism can be reliably abandoned. When the authors took a more direct approach,[281] accepting their experimental profile for [H] rather than calculating it, they concluded that the addition of (9.18) to (9.17) and (2.6) was more consistent with the observed rate of heat release than was (9.17) and (2.6) alone. There seems to be little merit in *ab initio* calculations of burning velocities and profiles through the reaction zone as compared to observations of the local rates of reactions as functions of the locally observed concentrations.

CHAPTER 10

DECOMPOSITION OF NITRIC OXIDE IN FLAMES

FLAMES of hydrogen, moist carbon monoxide, hydrocarbons, and probably ammonia burning with oxygen all have a family resemblance because the oxidant is destroyed in every case by the same fairly easy reaction with H atoms. H atoms do not destroy nitric oxide as easily and a similar family resemblance is not easy to see among the more difficult nitric oxide flames.

Three types of behaviour can be recognized when nitric oxide is mixed with H atoms or H_2 molecules. (i) Clyne and Thrush[235] found that NO was merely a recombination catalyst when mixed with H atoms at low temperatures, $H + NO + M \rightarrow HNO + M$, $H + HNO \rightarrow H_2 + NO$. (ii) At 1100–1400°K, NO–H_2 mixtures undergo a slow reaction which was originally believed[236] to be termolecular, involving binary collision complexes of different lives, but which has since been found to be of fractional order in $[H_2]$ and almost certainly in [NO] also.[237,238] It is possible that this reaction may involve HNO and reactions such as $NO + HNO \rightarrow N_2O + OH$, but the interpretation of the experimental results is uncertain.[238] (iii) At much higher temperatures around 3100°K, the H_2–NO flame resembles the decomposition flame of preheated NO so much that nitric oxide was thought to disappear by very similar mechanisms in both.[65] If so, there are at least two types of decomposition which might occur in flames.

The more reasonable path is a decomposition by

$$O + NO \rightarrow N + O_2 \tag{3.9}$$

$$N + NO \rightarrow O + N_2 \tag{3.10}$$

or by some variant of (3.9) in the presence of H atoms such as $H + NO \rightarrow N + OH$, which is indistinguishable whenever $H + O_2 = OH + O$ is balanced. Gaydon and Wolfhard[1] rejected this path, for NO–H_2 flames at least, because they thought that electronically excited NH* should be formed if the flames contained free N atoms; and NH* is absent. However, Garvin and Broida[239] found that NH* was not formed when N atoms from a discharge were run into mixtures of H, H_2, and

NO_2 at room temperature and low pressures so the absence of $NH^\star$ in flames may not be a very strong objection. The probably less reasonable path for NO decomposition is the second order process which was formulated in chapter 3 as

$$2NO \rightarrow N_2O + O \qquad \text{reverse of (3.12)}$$

followed by a decomposition of the N_2O and recombination of the O atoms. Since small additions of N_2O cause emission of $NH^\star$ from NO–H_2 flames,[65] the absence of $NH^\star$ from pure NO–H_2 flames would seem a better argument against the reverse of (3.12) than against (3.9) or its variants and (3.10). The reverse of (3.12) is too slow to account for the decomposition of NO in hot post-flame gas and might be too slow in flames too.

Ammonia Flames

Adams, Parker, and Wolfhard[65] found that the burning velocity of the stoichiometric NH_3–NO mixture is twice as large as the 30 cm s^{-1} of H_2–NO. The flame temperature is 170° less for NH_3. This implies a faster decomposition in the NH_3 flame, and since NO reacts rapidly with NH_2 radicals even at room temperature[240,241] by

$$NO + NH_2 \xrightarrow{k} \ldots \rightarrow N_2 + H_2O \qquad (10.1)$$

they suggested that the same process occurs in flames, or that NH radicals which were also present in the flame might react with NO. NH_2 radicals would be expected to be formed more readily in flames of NH_3–NO than N atoms in H_2–NO flames, and the ammonia mixture might therefore burn faster.

The reaction of ammonia with nitric oxide has been studied by mixing these species into the reactants of low pressure, fuel-rich H_2–N_2O flames, and obtaining traverses through the reaction zones.[242] The flames had final temperatures of 1700–1900°K, under which conditions all of the N_2O reacted with part of the H_2 but any added NO was stable. If a little NH_3 was also added, it was rapidly destroyed with the simultaneous consumption of an equimolecular amount of NO. The destruction of NO ceased when NH_3 was consumed; and it seemed very likely that NO reacted with some radical derived from NH_3, though it was not possible to measure the concentrations of these radicals. It was assumed that NH_2 radicals and H atoms were equilibrated according to

$$H + NH_3 = NH_2 + H_2 \qquad (10.2)$$
$$[NH_2] = K[H][NH_3]/[H_2]$$

[H] could be estimated from the N_2O profile by means of the known k_α from Table 4.1 in chapter 4, or in other ways. The consumption of NO in flames of varying [H], and therefore of varying $[NH_2]$ if (2) was true, could be correlated by

$$-d[NO]/dt = k[NO][NH_2] = kK[NO][H][NH_3]/[H_2]$$

$$kK = 5 \times 10^{13} \text{ cm}^3 \text{ mole}^{-1} \text{ s}^{-1} \text{ at } 1700–1900°K$$

The correlation is evidence, though not proof, for the truth of (2). The equilibrium constant, K, is expected to be of order unity and to have little temperature dependence, so the interpretation suggests that k is a large constant with little temperature dependence, as of course it must be in view of the results at room temperature. No other literature value of k exists with which to compare the numerical estimate from flames.

Because NO decomposes faster in flames with NH_3 than in flames with H_2 or in its decomposition flame, it is possible to obtain a set of reaction zones on a porous burner of 30 cm² area when a mix of NH_3 + 2·6NO + 1·2Ar is burnt at one atmosphere pressure with a burning velocity of about 9 cm s⁻¹. Close to the burner surface, the NH_3 plus about one mole of NO are consumed in a zone coloured yellow by emission from the bands of excited NH_2^*. Downstream of this, a colourless region extends to about 0·5 cm from the burner until $[H_2]$ falls to a low value and $[O_2]$ begins to rise. At this point a bluish-white emission sets in as the remaining NO continues to decompose and $[O_2]$ builds up. Corresponding multiple reaction zones are better known in flames of hydrocarbons with nitrogen oxides.

Reaction (1), or whatever reaction consumes NO in NO–NH_3 flames, is also important in NH_3–O_2 flames, the NO then being generated by oxidation of part of the NH_3. By probing relatively low temperature NH_3–H_2–O_2 flames,[242] it was found that the values of [H], $[O_2]$, and of $-d[O_2]/dt$ were consistent with the notion that all the O_2 was consumed by reaction (2.1), $H + O_2 \rightarrow OH + O$; and therefore there was no considerable reaction of O_2 with NH_3 or with N-containing radicals derived from NH_3. NO was always found in the reaction zone, formed possibly by the attack of O atoms on NH_3 since this occurs at room temperature when O atoms from a discharge are mixed with NH_3.[243] If a large excess of NH_3 was fed in the reactants, NO was only a transient species which was quickly destroyed again and the excess NH_3 in the fuel-rich post-flame gas was relatively stable. When small ratios of $[NH_3]/[O_2]$ were fed, more NO was formed in the flame than could be consumed, and the excess NO was stable at the temperatures used. It was concluded that the NH_3–O_2 flame was a combination of the H_2–O_2 and the NH_3–NO flames, coupled through a fast formation of NO by attack of O atoms on NH_3. The nature of the reaction of O with NH_3 is unknown, however.

The interpretation of the NH_3–O_2 flame does not agree with Husain and Norrish's views of the high temperature reaction.[282] They flash photolysed equimolecular or leaner NH_3–O_2 mixtures at about 2 cm of mercury pressure; the main function of the flash being to heat the gas to a temperature which was undetermined but less than 1500°K, the upper limit for the NH vibrational temperature. About 0·5 milliseconds after the flash, OH and NH radicals became visible in absorption; and a few milliseconds later, NH disappeared again and NH_3 disappeared with the onset of strong absorption by NO. They believed that oxygen was mostly consumed by the reaction of NH_2 + O_2, not by H + O_2 as in steady flames; and believed that nitric oxide was also formed eventually in consequence of NH_2 + O_2, not in consequence of NH_3 + O as suggested in the last paragraph. Neither [NH_2] nor [H] were estimated in the flash photolysis, however, so no real evidence was possible for the mode of consumption of O_2. The eventual formation of much nitric oxide and a little nitrous oxide resembles the products from fuel-lean steady flames, but flames also form considerable nitrogen by the partial consumption of NO before the ammonia is exhausted. The yield of nitrogen in the photolysis was not stated; if it was very small, as was implied, there must be a real difference between flash photolyses and steady flames.

Hydrazine–NO flames resemble NH_3–NO in giving an easy reduction of nitric oxide. By contrast with ammonia, the decomposition of hydrazine is fast at flame temperatures; and a hydrazine flame containing only a little added O_2 may be essentially a hydrazine decomposition flame still.[244] Larger additions of O_2 cause a marked formation of NO—as seems reasonable because O atoms at room temperature give NO more readily from N_2H_4 than from NH_3.[243]

Hydrocarbon Flames

In low temperature, fuel-rich flames of H_2–CH_4–O_2–NO, CH_3 radicals react in part with NO and a roughly equivalent formation of HCN is observed as is shown in Fig. 5.3 of chapter 5. HCN is also formed in hotter flames but decays again. A similar consumption of NO with formation of transient HCN can be observed by probing fuel-rich flames of C_2H_4 or C_2H_2 containing some O_2. Pure hydrocarbon–NO flames have not been probed and there is nothing to add to Wolfhard and Parker's[245] accounts of their qualitative features—that NO is reduced by hydrocarbon radicals, and perhaps by other species generated in the flame, and that any excess NO may decompose more slowly in a subsequent second reaction zone if the flame is hot enough. NO_2 is easily reduced to NO, and fuel-rich flames of NO_2 may possess an additional reaction zone, upstream of the NO-radical reaction zone, in which the easy reduction takes place. Otherwise, NO_2 flames seem to differ little from NO flames.

Nitric acid–hydrocarbon mixtures burn to give most of their nitrogen as NO; butane–nitric acid flames so rich that the NO would have to be reduced in order to consume the hydrocarbon are not stable.[246] The flames, on small burners at least where cooling by the surroundings is easy, seem not quite hot enough to decompose NO at atmospheric pressure. Propane–nitric acid mixtures preheated to 400°K give most of the nitrogen as NO, but if the reactants are preheated to 600° a secondary reaction zone appears in which additional NO is thought to be decomposed.[247]

Methyl Nitrite Decomposition

The decomposition flame of this substance cannot give a hot gas except by reducing much of its nitrogen to N_2O or N_2. The flame temperature is low even when about half the nitrogen is reduced, and the path by which the easy reduction occurs is a puzzle.

Gray, Hall, and Wolfhard[219] established a steady decomposition flame in CH_3ONO at one atmosphere pressure. Moderate preheating[18] increased the burning velocity from 3.2 cm s^{-1} when the reactant was initially at 288°K to 7 cm s^{-1} at 483°. On preheating to 550°, most of the reactant was decomposed before it reached the flame, and a little stronger preheating extinguished the fire because the pyrolysis products cannot support a similar flame. Arden and Powling[248] found that half of the nitrogen remained as NO in the products at the flame temperature of about 1370°K, the rest having been reduced mostly to N_2 and partly to N_2O. In the reaction zone, more of the nitrogen was present as NO and large quantities of H_2CO and CH_3OH were present. The fraction of nitrogen reduced past the stage of NO was no larger in flames of 80 per cent CH_3ONO plus 20 per cent of either H_2CO or CH_3OH than in a flame of the pure ester; but addition of NO caused a greater reduction of nitrogen.

The main point of interest is the path by which N_2O or N_2 is formed at so low a temperature. This has not been found out. It has been assumed with some evidence[18] that the flame reactions are very much like the slow decomposition reactions of the ester at lower temperatures. According to Phillips[249] and by analogy with Levy's[250] work with ethyl nitrite, this mechanism as far as nitrogen is concerned is

$$CH_3ONO \rightleftarrows CH_3O + NO \qquad (10.3)$$

$$NO + CH_3O \rightarrow H_2CO + HNO \qquad (10.4)$$

$$HNO + CH_3O \rightarrow CH_3OH + NO \qquad (10.5)$$

or
$$2CH_3O \rightarrow CH_3OH + H_2CO \qquad (10.6)$$

$$2HNO \rightarrow N_2O + H_2O \qquad (10.7)$$

or
$$NO + HNO \rightarrow N_2O + OH \qquad (10.8)$$

and some thermal decomposition of various species might occur and lead to $H + N_2O \rightarrow N_2 + OH$. Good evidence exists for (3) and its reverse:[251] but there is no evidence as yet for (7) or (8). At lower temperatures, the work of Clyne and Thrush[235] indicates that the HNO formed when H atoms are mixed with NO reacts much faster with H to regenerate $NO + H_2$ than with NO or with another HNO molecule to form N_2O. At higher temperatures, some unpublished work by W. E. Kaskan shows that HNO is also formed when much NO is added to fuel-rich H_2-air flames burning on porous burners. The HNO was identified by comparison of its red emission with the spectrum given by Dalby.[252] No significant reduction of NO occurs in these flames either, though the concentration of HNO was unknown and probably small. Other modes of reduction than (7) and (8) have been suggested. Arden and Phillips[267] believed that at low temperatures

$$HNO + 2NO \rightleftarrows HN(NO)ONO \rightarrow H + N_2 + NO_3$$

where the first stage was supposed to be a reversible equilibrium which was strongly displaced to the left with rising temperature. The process presumably would not have been observed by Clyne and Thrush at their lower pressures. The yield of N_2 was considerable at 368°K, but very small at temperatures only 40° hotter and the scheme would not seem important therefore in the decomposition flame of methyl nitrite.

It is not ruled out that the reduction of the nitrogen in flames may involve reactions of the nitrite ester itself with nitric oxide. Kuhn and

8

Günthard[253] proposed the exchange process for primary nitrite esters labelled by N^{15}

$$N^{14}O + RON^{15}O \rightleftarrows RON^{15}(N^{14}O)O \rightleftarrows RON^{14}(N^{15}O)$$

$$\rightleftarrows N^{15}O + RON^{14}O$$

and such an intermediate compound might react at higher temperatures to give N_2O or N_2.

Other flames exist which involve easy reduction of NO, but by unknown mechanisms. Mixtures of $CS_2 + 3NO$[254] ignite spontaneously at 45 cm Hg pressure when run into a 5 cm diameter vessel at 1070°K; at 18 cm pressure, ignition occurs at 1170°. The steady flame burns readily, velocity about 45 cm s^{-1} at 5 cm pressure, and its colour consists mainly of S_2 bands.[245] B_2H_6–NO mixtures[255] are readily ignited by sparking and NO present in excess of the stoichiometric ratio is largely decomposed, possibly because of the high temperature. The radiation includes BO_2 bands and, if [NO]/[B_2H_6) > 3, OH bands.

REFERENCES

References to the volumes of the Combustion Symposia are given as 3rd *Symposium*, etc. These volumes are:

Third Symposium on Combustion (Williams & Wilkins, Baltimore, 1949).
Fourth Symposium on Combustion (Williams & Wilkins, 1953).
Fifth Symposium on Combustion (Reinhold Publ. Co., New York, 1955).
Sixth Symposium on Combustion (Reinhold, 1957).
Seventh Symposium on Combustion (Butterworths Scientific Publ., London, 1959).
Eighth Symposium on Combustion (Williams & Wilkins, 1962).
Ninth Symposium on Combustion (Academic Press, New York, 1963).

1. GAYDON, A. G. and WOLFHARD, H. G., *Flames* (Chapman & Hall, London, 1960)
2. LEWIS, B. and VON ELBE, G., *Combustion, Flames, and Explosions of Gases* (Academic Press, New York, 1960)
3. BOTHA, J. P. and SPALDING, D. B., *Proc. roy. Soc.*, 1954, **A.225**, 71.
4. KASKAN, W. E., *6th Symposium*, p. 134.
5. KASKAN, W. E., *Combustion and Flame*, 1960, **4**, 285.
6. FINE, B., *Combustion and Flame*, 1961, **5**, 111.
7. EGERTON, A. and THABET, S. K., *Proc. roy. Soc.*, 1952, **A.211**, 445.
8. FRISTROM, R. M., GRÜNFELDER, C., and FAVIN, S., *J. Phys. Chem.*, 1960, **64**, 1386.
9. LINNETT, J. W., *4th Symposium*, p. 20.
10. SCHOLTE, T. G. and VAAGS, P. B., *Combustion and Flame*, 1959, **3**, 495.
11. BARTHOLEMÉ, E., *Z. Elektrochem.*, 1949, **53**, 191.
12. SENIOR, D. A., *Combustion and Flame*, 1961, **5**, 7.
13. COOLEY, S. D., LASATER, J. A., and ANDERSON, R. C., *J.A.C.S.*, 1952, **74**, 739.
14. BERL, W. G., GAYHART, E. L., MAIER, E., OLSEN, H. L., and RENICH, W. T., *Combustion and Flame*, 1957, **1**, 420.
15. STRENG, A. G., *Combustion and Flame*, 1962, **6**, 89.
16. STRENG, A. G. and GROSSE, A. V., *6th Symposium*, p. 264.
17. MURRAY, R. C. and HALL, A. R., *Trans. Faraday Soc.*, 1951, **47**, 743.
18. GRAY, P. and WILLIAMS, A., *8th Symposium*, p. 496.
19. HICKS, J. A., *8th Symposium*, p. 487.
20. FRIEDMAN, R. and BURKE, E., *5th Symposium*, p. 596.
21. THOMAS, H., GAYDON, A. G., and BREWER, L., *J. chem. Phys.*, 1952, **20**, 369.
22. HIRSCHFELDER, J. O., CURTISS, C. F., and CAMPBELL, D. E., *4th Symposium*, p. 190.
23. FRISTROM, R. M., PRESCOTT, R., and GRUNFELDER, C., *Combustion and Flame*, 1957, **1**, 102.
24. FRISTROM, R. M., *9th Symposium*, p. 560.
25. KASKAN, W. E., *Combustion and Flame*, 1958, **2**, 229.
26. BONNE, U., GREWER, T., and WAGNER, H. G., *Z. Phys. Chem.*, 1960, **26**, 93.
27. LEVY, A. and WEINBERG, F. J., *7th Symposium*, p. 296.
28. WESTENBERG, A. A., *Combustion and Flame*, 1957, **1**, 346.
29. WALKER, R. E. and WESTENBERG, A. A., *J. chem. Phys.*, 1960, **32**, 436.
30. EMBER, G., FERRON, J. R., and WOHL, K., *J. chem. Phys.*, 1962, **37**, 891.
31. LINDSAY, A. L. and BROMLEY, L. A., *Industr. Engng. Chem.*, 1950, **42**, 1508.
32. HINSHELWOOD, C. N., *Proc. roy. Soc.*, 1947, **A.188**, 1.
33. BALDWIN, R. R. and BRATTAN, D., *8th Symposium*, p. 110.
34. HINSHELWOOD, C. N. and WILLIAMSON, A.T., *The Reaction Between Hydrogen and Oxygen*, 1934, Oxford.

35. BALDWIN, R. R., *Trans. Faraday Soc.*, 1956, **52**, 1344.
36. AZATIAN, V. V., VOEVODSKII, V. V., and NALBANDIAN, A. B., *Docklady*, 1960, **132**, 864.
37. KARMILOVA, L. V., NALBANDIAN, A. B., and SEMENOV, N. N., *Zhur. Fiz. Khim.*, 1958, **32**, 1193.
38. BULEWICZ, E. M., JAMES, C. G., and SUGDEN, T. M., *Proc. roy. Soc.*, 1956, **A.235**, 89.
39. KAUFMAN, F. and DEL GRECO, F. P., *9th Symposium*, p. 659.
40. SCHOTT, G. L., *J. chem. Phys.*, 1960, **32**, 710.
41. KONDRATIEV, V. and ZISKIN, M., *Acta Phys.-chim. URSS*, 1937, **6**, 307.
42. AVRAMENKO, L. and KONDRATIEV, V., *Acta Phys.-chim. URSS*, 1937, **7**, 567.
43. FENIMORE, C. P. and JONES, G. W., *J. Phys. Chem.*, 1958, **62**, 693.
44. DEL GRECO, F. P. and KAUFMAN, F., *Disc. Faraday Soc.*, 1962, **33**, 128.
45. KASKAN, W. E., *Combustion and Flame*, 1958, **2**, 286.
46. BULEWICZ, E. M. and SUGDEN, T. M., Special Publication No. 9, p. 81, The Chemical Society (London) 1957.
47. STEACIE, E. W. R., *Atomic and Free Radical Reactions* (Reinhold, New York, 1954).
48. KASKAN, W. E. and SCHOTT, G. L., *Combustion and Flame*, 1962, **6**, 73.
49. BULEWICZ, E. M. and SUGDEN, T. M., *Trans. Faraday Soc.*, 1956, **52**, 1475.
50. DIXON-LEWIS, G. and WILLIAMS, A., *9th Symposium*, p. 576.
51. FARKAS, L. and SACHSSE, H., *Z. Phys. Chem.*, 1934, **B.27**, 111.
52. GARDINER, W. C., Jr. and KISTIAKOWSKY, G. B., *J. chem. Phys.*, 1961, **35**, 1765.
53. RINK, J. P., *J. chem. Phys.*, 1962, **36**, 262.
54. PATCH, R. W., *J. chem. Phys.*, 1962, **36**, 1919.
55. SUTTON, E. A., *J. chem. Phys.*, 1962, **36**, 2923.
56. HOARE, D. E. and WALSH, A. D., Special Publication No. 9, p. 17, The Chemical Society (London) 1959.
57. FENIMORE, C. P. and JONES, G. W., *J. Phys. Chem.*, 1958, **62**, 1578.
58. FRIEDMAN, R. and NUGENT, R. G., *7th Symposium*, p. 311.
59. KASKAN, W. E., *Combustion and Flame*, 1959, **3**, 39.
60. KASKAN, W. E., *Combustion and Flame*, 1959, **3**, 49.
61. WHITE, D. R., *Phys. Fluids*, 1961, **4**, 465.
62. CLYNE, M. A. A. and THRUSH, B. A., *Proc. roy. Soc.*, 1962, **269A**, 404.
63. GAYDON, A. G., *Spectroscopy of Flames* (Chapman and Hall, London, 1957).
64. KAUFMAN, F., *Proc. roy. Soc.*, 1958, **A.247**, 123.
65. ADAMS, G. K., PARKER, W. G., and WOLFHARD, H. G., *Disc. Faraday Soc.*, 1953, **14**, 97.
66. KAUFMAN, F. and DECKER, L. J., *7th Symposium*, p. 57.
67. KISTIAKOWSKY, G. B. and VOLPI, G. G., *J. chem. Phys.*, 1957, **27**, 1141.
68. GLICK, H. G., KLEIN, J. J., and SQUIRE, W, *J. chem. Phys.*, 1957, **27**, 850.
69. KAUFMAN, F. and KELSO, J., *J. chem. Phys.*, 1955, **23**, 1702.
70. FENIMORE, C. P. and JONES, G. W., *J. Phys. Chem.*, 1957, **61**, 654.
71. FENIMORE, C. P. and JONES, G. W., *8th Symposium*, p. 127.
72. KAUFMAN, F., *Progress in Reaction Kinetics* (Pergamon, New York, 1961).
73. CHARTON, M. and GAYDON, A. G., *Proc. roy. Soc.*, 1958, **A.245**, 84.
74. KASKAN, W. E., *J. chem. Phys.*, 1959, **31**, 944.
75. BROIDA, H. P. and CARRINGTON, T., *J. chem. Phys.*, 1955, **23**, 2202.
76. PADLEY, P. J. and SUGDEN, T. M., *7th Symposium*, p. 235.
77. MINKOWSKI, R., MULLER, H. G., and WEBER-SCHAFER, M., *Z. Phys.*, 1935, **94**, 145.
78. JAMES, C. G. and SUGDEN, T. M., *Nature*, 1955, **175**, 252.
79. GAYDON, A. G., *Proc. roy. Soc.*, 1955, **A.231**, 437.
80. REID, R. W. and SUGDEN, T. M., *Disc. Faraday Soc.*, 1962, **33**, 213.
81. KASKAN, W. E. and MILLIKAN, R. C., *8th Symposium*, p. 262.
82. KASKAN, W. E., MILLIKAN, R. C., and MACKENZIE, J. D., *J. chem. Phys.*, 1961, **34**, 570.
83. MAL'TSEV, A. A., MATVEEV, V. K., and TATEVSKII, V. M., *Doklady*, 1961, **137**, 1.

84. AVRAMENKO, L. and LORENTSO, R., *Zhur. Fiz. Khim.*, 1950, **24**, 207.
85. BOATO, G., CARERI, G., CIMINO, A., MOLINARI, E., and VOLPI, G. G., *J. chem. Phys.*, 1956, **24**, 783.
86. GAYDON, A. G. and WOLFHARD, H. G., *Proc. roy. Soc.*, 1949, **A.196**, 105.
87. FENIMORE, C. P. and JONES, G. W., *J. Phys. Chem.*, 1959, **63**, 1154.
88. SCHOTT, G. L. and KINSEY, J. L., *J. chem. Phys.*, 1958, **29**, 1177.
89. POLANYI, J. C., *J. chem. Phys.*, 1959, **31**, 1338.
90. CLYNE, M. A. A. and THRUSH, B. A., *Nature*, 1961, **189**, 135.
91. FENIMORE, C. P. and JONES, G. W., *J. Phys. Chem.*, 1961, **65**, 993.
92. POPE, J. C., DYKSTRA, F. J., and EDGAR, G., *J. Amer. Chem. Soc.*, 1929, **51**, 2203.
93. CULLIS, C. F., HINSHELWOOD, C. N., MULCAHY, M. F. R., and PARTINGTON, R. G., *Disc. Faraday Soc.*, 1947, **2**, 111.
94. GERSTEIN, M., LEVINE, O., and WONG, E. L., *J. Amer. Chem. Soc.*, 1951, **73**, 418.
95. KISTIAKOWSKY, G. B. and ROBERTS, E. K., *J. chem. Phys.*, 1953, **21**, 1637.
96. FRISTROM, R. M., GRUNFELDER, C., and FAVIN, S., *J. Phys. Chem.*, 1961, **65**, 587.
97. WESTENBERG, A. A. and FRISTROM, R. M., *J. Phys. Chem.*, 1961, **65**, 591.
98. FRIEDMAN, R. and CYPHERS, J. A., *J. chem. Phys.*, 1956, **25**, 448.
99. FENIMORE, C. P. and JONES, G. W., *J. Phys. Chem.*, 1959, **63**, 1834.
100. FENIMORE, C. P. and JONES, G. W., *J. Phys. Chem.*, 1961, **65**, 1532.
101. CHRISTIE, M. I., *Proc. roy. Soc.*, 1958, **A.244**, 411.
102. HOARE, D. E. and WALSH, A. D., *Trans. Faraday Soc.*, 1957, **53**, 1102.
103. INGOLD, K. U. and BRYCE, W. A., *J. chem. Phys.*, 1956, **24**, 360.
104. CHRISTIE, M. I., *Proc. roy. Soc.*, 1959, **A.249**, 248.
105. BRYCE, W. A. and INGOLD, K. U., *J. chem. Phys.*, 1955, **23**, 1968.
106. HOARE, D. E., *Canad. Chem. J.*, 1962, **40**, 2012.
107. MCKELLAR, J. F. and NORRISH, R. G. W., *Proc. roy. Soc.*, 1961, **263A**, 51.
108. FENIMORE, C. P. and JONES, G. W., *J. Phys. Chem.*, 1961, **65**, 2200.
109. KARMILOVA, L. V., ENIKOLOPYAN, N. S., and NALBANDIAN, A. B., *Zhur. Fiz. Khim.*, 1961, **35**, 1458.
110. WHITTLE, E. and STEACIE, E. W. R., *J. chem. Phys.*, 1953, **21**. 993.
111. BERLIE, M. R. and LEROY, D. J., *Canad. Chem. J.*, 1954, **32**, 650.
112. KLEIN, R., MCNESBY, J. R., SCHEER, M. D., and SCHOEN, L. J., *J. chem. Phys.*, 1959, **30**, 58.
113. SEMENOV, N. N., *Some Problems of Chemical Kinetics and Reactivity* (Vol. 2, Pergamon, New York, 1959).
114. PADLEY, P. J. and SUGDEN, T. M., *Proc. roy. Soc.*, 1958, **A.248**, 248.
115. REID, R. W. and WHEELER, R., *J. Phys. Chem.*, 1961, **65**, 527.
116. FENIMORE, C. P. and JONES, G. W., *9th Symposium*, p. 957.
117. DARWENT, B. DE B. and ROBERTS, R., *Disc. Faraday Soc.*, 1953, **14**, 55.
118. BERLIE, M. R. and LEROY, D. J., *Disc. Faraday Soc.*, 1953, **14**, 50.
119. BALDWIN, R. R., CORNEY, N. S., and SIMMONS, R. F., *5th Symposium*, p. 502.
120. GORBAN, N. I. and NALBANDIAN, A. B., *Doklady*, 1960, **132**, 1335.
121. BALDWIN, R. R., *9th Symposium*, p. 600.
122. FORD, H. W. and ENDOW, N., *J. chem. Phys.*, 1957, **27**, 1277.
123. CVETANOVIĆ, R. J., *J. chem. Phys.*, 1960, **33**, 1063.
124. ELIAS, L. and SCHIFF, H. I., *Canad. Chem. J.*, 1960, **38**, 1657.
125. CVETANOVIĆ, R. J., *J. chem. Phys.*, 1955, **23**, 1375.
126. GARDINER, W. C., *J. chem. Phys.*, 1961, **35**, 2252.
127. KISTIAKOWSKY, G. B. and RICHARDS, L. W., *J. chem. Phys.*, 1962, **36**, 1707.
128. BRADLEY, J. N. and KISTIAKOWSKY, G. B., *J. chem. Phys.*, 1961, **35**, 264.
128a. HAND, C. W. and KISTIAKOWSKY, G. B., *J. chem. Phys.*, 1962, **37**, 1239.
129. HALLER, I. and PIMENTEL, G. C., *J. Amer. chem. Soc.*, 1962, **84**, 2855.
130. ROBERTSON, W. W. and MATSEN, F. A., *Combustion and Flame*, 1957, **1**, 94.
131. MACCORMAC, M. and TOWNEND, D. T. A., *J. chem. Soc.*, 1940, 151.
132. SPENCE, K. and TOWNEND, D. T. A., *3rd Symposium*, p. 404.
133. BAILEY, H. C. and NORRISH, R. G. W., *Proc. roy. Soc.*, 1952, **A.212**, 311.
134. FORESTI, R. J., *5th Symposium*, p. 582.
135. AGNEW, W. G., *Combustion and Flame*, 1960, **4**, 29.

136. Topps, J. E. C. and Townend, D. T. A., *Trans. Faraday Soc.*, 1946, **42**, 345.
137. Gaydon, A. G. and Wolfhard, H. G., *Proc. roy. Soc.*, 1951, **A.205**, 118.
138. Bulewicz, E. M. and Padley, P. J., *Combustion and Flame*, 1961, **5**, 331.
139. Gaydon, A. G., Spokes, G. N., and Suchtelen, J. Van, *Proc. roy. Soc.*, 1960, **A.256**, 323.
140. Calcote, H. F. and King, I. R., *5th Symposium*, p. 423.
141. Calcote, H. F., *8th Symposium*, p. 184.
142. King, I. R., *J. chem. Phys.*, 1958, **29**, 681.
143. Padley, P. J. and Sugden, T. M., *8th Symposium*, p. 164.
144. Calcote, H. F., *9th Symposium*, p. 622.
145. Deckers, J. and Van Tiggelen, A., *7th Symposium*, pp. 254 and 283.
146. Jaegere, S. De, Deckers, J., and Van Tiggelen, A., *8th Symposium*, p. 155.
147. Knewstubb, P. F. and Sugden, T. M., *7th Symposium*, p. 247.
148. Green, J. H. and Sugden, T. M., *9th Symposium*, p. 607.
149. Gaydon, A. G. and Hurle, I. R., *Proc. roy. Soc.*, 1961, **A.262**, 38.
150. King, I. R., *J. chem. Phys.*, 1959, **31**, 855.
151. Broida, H. P. and Shuler, K. E., *J. chem. Phys.*, 1957, **27**, 933.
152. Bulewicz, E. M. and Padley, P. J., *9th Symposium*, p. 638.
153. Carrington, T., *8th Symposium*, p. 257.
154. Ferguson, R. E. and Broida, H. P., *5th Symposium*, p. 754.
155. Norrish, R. G. W., *Disc. Faraday Soc.*, 1953, **14**, 16.
156. Lyon, R. K. and Kydd, P. H., *J. chem. Phys.*, 1961, **34**, 1069.
157. Ferguson, R. E., *J. chem. Phys.*, 1955, **23**, 2085.
158. Miller, W. J. and Palmer, H. B., *9th Symposium*, p. 90.
159. Skirrow, G. and Wolfhard, H. G., *Proc. roy. Soc.*, 1955, **A.232**, 78 and 577.
160. Dyne, P. J. and Style, D. W. G., *Disc. Faraday. Soc.*, 1947, **2**, 159.
161. Street, J. C. and Thomas, A., *Fuel*, 1955, **34**, 4.
162. Macfarlane, J. J., *Combustion and Flame*, 1962, **6**, 56.
163. Ferguson, R. E., *Combustion and Flame*, 1957, **1**, 431.
164. Fenimore, C. P., Jones, G. W., and Moore, G. E., *6th Symposium*, p. 242.
165. Singer, J. M. and Grumer, J., *7th Symposium*, p. 559.
166. Millikan, R. C., *J. Phys. Chem.*, 1962, **66**, 794.
167. Millikan, R. C., *Combustion and Flame*, 1961, **5**, 349.
168. Millikan, R. C., *J. opt. Soc. Amer.*, 1961, **51**, 535.
169. Tesner, P. A., *8th Symposium*, p. 807.
170. Aten, C. F. and Greene, E. F., *Combustion and Flame*, 1961, **5**, 55.
171. Hooker, W. J., *7th Symposium*, p. 949.
172. Cole, D. J. and Minkoff, G. J., *Proc. roy. Soc.*, 1957, **A.239**, 280.
173. Gordon, A. S., Smith, S. R., and McNesby, J. R., *7th Symposium*, p. 317.
174. Parker, W. G. and Wolfhard, H. G., *J. chem. Soc.*, 1950, 2038.
175. Streznewski, J. and Turkevitch, J., *Proceedings of the Third Conference on Carbon*, p. 273 (Pergamon, New York, 1959).
176. Becker, A., *Ann. Physik.*, 1909, **28**, 1017.
177. Millikan, R. C., *J. opt. Soc. Amer.*, 1961, **51**, 698.
178. Rossler, F. and Behrens, H., *Optik*, 1950, **6**, 145.
179. Kaskan, W. E., *Combustion and Flame*, 1961, **5**, 93.
180. Coward, H. F. and Jones, G. W.,* Bulletin 503, U.S. Bureau of Mines, Washington (1952).
181. Badami, G. N. and Egerton, A., *Proc. roy. Soc.*, 1958, **A.228**, 297.
182. Tiggelen, A. Van and Deckers, J., *6th Symposium*, p. 61.
183. Burdon, M. C., Burgoyne, J. H., and Weinberg, F. J., *5th Symposium*, p. 647.
184. Spalding, D. B., *Proc. roy. Soc.*, 1957, **A.240**, 83.
185. Mayer, E., *Combustion and Flame*, 1957, **1**, 438.
186. Linnett, J. W. and Simpson, C. J. S. M., *6th Symposium*, p. 20.

* The late George William Jones is not the same man as the co-author of several papers with C. P. Fenimore, George Wallace Jones.

187. DIXON-LEWIS, G. and ISLES, G. L., *7th Symposium*, p. 475.
188. HALL, A. R., McCOUBREY, J. C., and WOLFHARD, H. G., *Combustion and Flame*, 1957, **1**, 53.
189. LEGRAND, J., DELBOURGO, R., and LAFFITTE, P., *Comptes rend.*, 1959, **249**, 1514.
190. ZABETAKIS, M. G., LAMBIRIS, S., and SCOTT, G. L., *7th Symposium*, p. 484.
191. CUMMINGS, G. A. McD., HALL, A. R., and STRAKER, R. A. M., *8th Symposium*, p. 503.
192. WOLFHARD, H. G., *Selected Combustion Problems, II*, p. 328, Butterworths (London) 1956.
193. SIMMONS, R. F. and WOLFHARD, H. G., *Trans. Faraday Soc.*, 1955, **51**, 1211.
194. SCHOLTE, T. G. and VAAGS, P. B., *Combustion and Flame*, 1959, **3**, 511.
195. LASK, G. W. and WAGNER, H. G., *Forschungsh Wes. Ing.*, 1961, **27**, 52.
196. JOST, W. and WAGNER, H. G., Special Publication No. 9, p. 197, The Chemical Society, London (1957).
197. WIRES, R., WATERMIER, L. A., and STREHLOW, R. A., *J. Phys. Chem.*, 1959, **63**, 989.
198. LASK, G. W. and WAGNER, H. G., *8th Symposium*, p. 432.
199. ROSSER, W. A., WISE, H., and MILLER, J., *7th Symposium*, p. 175.
200. PHILLIPS, L. F. and SUGDEN, T. M., *Canad. Chem. J.*, 1960, **38**, 1804.
201. WISE, H. and ROSSER, W. A., *9th Symposium*, p. 733.
202. BONNE, U., JOST, W., and WAGNER, H. G., *Fire Research Abstracts and Reviews*, 1962, **4**, 6.
203. SEMENOV, N. N., *Progress of Physical Science (USSR)*, 1940, **34**, 433; Translated as NACA TM 1026, Washington (1942).
204. SPALDING, D. B., *Combustion and Flame*, 1957, **1**, 287.
205. LEVY, A. and WEINBERG, F. J., *Combustion and Flame*, 1959, **3**, 229.
206. BEHRENS, H., *Z. Phys. Chem.*, 1950, **195**, 225.
207. SOBOLEV, G. K., *7th Symposium*, p. 386.
208. FRIEDMAN, R. and CYPHERS, J. A., *J. chem. Phys.*, 1956, **25**, 448.
209. GRAY, P., LEE, J. C., LEACH, H. A., and TAYLOR, D. C., *6th Symposium*, p. 225.
210. HALL, A. R. and WOLFHARD, H. G., *Trans. Faraday Soc.*, 1956, **52**, 1520.
211. ADAMS, G. K. and STOCKS, G. W., *4th Symposium*, p. 239.
212. SZWARC, M., *Proc. roy. Soc.*, 1949, **A.198**, 267.
213. GILBERT, M., *Combustion and Flame*, 1958, **2**, 137.
214. ZELDOVICH, Y. B. and JACOLEV, B. I., *Doklady*, 1938, **19**, 699.
215. BRANDT, B. B. and ROZLOVSKII, A. I., *Doklady*, 1960, **132**, 1129.
216. ROZLOVSKII, A. I., *Kinetics and Catalysis*, 1961, **2**, 809.
217. BELAYEV, A. F., *Acta Phys.-chima. URSS*, 1941, **14**, 523.
218. TROTMAN-DICKENSON, A. F., *Gas Kinetics*, 1955, Butterworths, London.
219. GRAY, P., HALL, A. R., and WOLFHARD, H. G., *Proc. roy. Soc.*, 1955, **A.232**, 389.
220. ADAMS, G. K. and SCRIVENER, J., *5th Symposium*, p. 656.
221. WOLFHARD, H. G., *Fuel*, 1955, **34**, 60.
222. NEEDHAM, D. P. and POWLING, J., *Proc. roy. Soc.*, 1955, **A.232**, 337.
223. ADAMS, G. K. and BAWN, C. E. H., *Trans. Faraday Soc.*, 1949, **45**, 494.
224. LEVY, J. B., *J. Amer. chem. Soc.*, 1954, **76**, 3790.
225. SATTERFIELD, C. N. and KEHAT, E., *Combustion and Flame*, 1961, **5**, 273.
226. BENSON, S. W., *The Foundations of Chemical Kinetics*, (McGraw-Hill Book Co., New York, 1960).
227. HIRSCHFELDER, J. O., CURTISS, C. F., and CAMPBELL, D. E., *J. Phys. Chem.*, 1953, **57**, 403.
228. VON KARMAN, T., MILLER, G., and PENNER, S. S., *6th Symposium*, p. 1.
229. BRITTON, D. and COLE, R. M., *J. Phys. Chem.*, 1961, **65**, 1302.
230. PEACOCK, F. and WEINBERG, F. J., *8th Symposium*, p. 458.
231. WEHNER, J. F. and FRAZIER, G. C., Johns Hopkins University Report, Sept. (1962) Baltimore.
232. SPALDING, D. B., *Phil. Trans.*, 1956, **249**, 1.
233. ZELDOVICH, Y. B. and BARENBLATT, G. I., *Combustion and Flame*, 1959, **3**, 61.
234. ADAMS, G. K. and COOK, G. B., *Combustion and Flame*, 1960, **4**, 9.

235. CLYNE, M. A. A. and THRUSH, B. A., *Trans. Faraday Soc.*, 1961, **57**, 1305.
236. HINSHELWOOD, C. N. and MITCHELL, J. W., *J. chem. Soc.*, 1936, 378.
237. GRAVEN, W. M., *J. Amer. chem. Soc.*, 1957, **79**, 3697.
238. KAUFMAN, F. and DECKER, L. J., *8th Symposium*, p. 133.
239. GARVIN, D. and BROIDA, H. P., *9th Symposium*, p. 678.
240. BAMFORD, C. H., *Trans. Faraday Soc.*, 1939, **35**, 568.
241. SEREWICZ, A. and NOYES, W. A., Jr., *J. Phys. Chem.*, 1961, **65**, 298.
242. FENIMORE, C. P. and JONES, G. W., *J. Phys. Chem.*, 1961, **65**, 298.
243. MOORE, G. E., SHULER, K. E., SILVERMAN, S., and HERMAN, R., *J. Phys. Chem.*, 1956, **60**, 813.
244. GRAY, P. and LEE, J. C., *7th Symposium*, p. 61.
245. WOLFHARD, H. G. and PARKER, W. G., *5th Symposium*, p. 718; *4th Symposium*, p. 420.
246. BOYER, M. H. and FRIEBERTSHAUSER, P. E., *Combustion and Flame*, 1957, **1**, 264.
247. MERTENS, J. and POTTER, R. L., *Combustion and Flame*, 1958, **2**, 181.
248. ARDEN, E. A. and POWLING, J., *Combustion and Flame*, 1958, **2**, 229.
249. PHILLIPS, L., *J. chem. Soc.*, 1961, 3082.
250. LEVY, J. B., *J. Amer. chem. Soc.*, 1956, **78**, 1780.
251. LEVY, J. B., *J. Amer. chem. Soc.*, 1953, **75**, 1801.
252. DALBY, F. W., *Canad. Phys. J.*, 1958, **36**, 1336.
253. KUHN, L. P. and GÜNTHARD, HG. H., *Helv. chim. acta*, 1960, **43**, 607.
254. ROTH, W. and RAUTENBERG, T. H., *J. Phys. Chem.*, 1956, **60**, 379.
255. ROTH, W., *J. chem. Phys.*, 1958, **28**, 668.
256. GROSSE, A. V. and KIRSCHENBAUM, A. D., *J. Amer. chem. Soc.*, 1955, **77**, 5012.
257. BROKAW, R. S. and GERSTEIN, M., *6th Symposium*, p. 66.
258. TANFORD, C. and PEASE, R. N., *J. chem. Phys.*, 1947, **15**, 861.
259. PICKERING, H. S. and LINNETT, J. W., *Trans. Faraday Soc.*, 1951, **47**, 1101.
260. BIRSE, E. A. and MELVILLE, H. W., *Proc. roy. Soc.*, 1940, **175A**, 164.
261. SCHIAVELLO, M. and VOLPI, G. G., *J. chem. Phys.*, 1962, **37**, 1510.
262. BODENSTEIN, M. and LIND, S. C., *Z. Phys. Chem.*, 1907, **57**, 168.
263. GILBERT, M. and ALTMAN, D., *6th Symposium*, p. 222.
264. DZAMOURANIS, I. and COMBOURIEU, J., *Compt. rend.*, 1962, **255**, 1933.
265. PORTER, G., *4th Symposium*, p. 248.
266. POTTER, A. E., *Progress in Combustion Science and Technology*, 1960, I, p. 145, Pergamon, London.
267. ARDEN, E. A. and PHILLIPS, L., *Proc. Chem. Soc.*, 1962, 354.
268. RUTNER, E., SCHELLER, K., and McLAIN, W. H., *J. Phys. Chem.*, 1960, **64**, 1891.
269. BROKAW, R. S. and PEASE, R. N., *J. Amer. chem. Soc.*, 1953, **75**, 1454.
270. COLLOMON, J. H. and GILBY, A. C., *J. chem. Soc.*, 1963, 1471.
271. DIXON, R. N., *Disc. Faraday Soc.*, 1963.
272. PADLEY, P. J., *Trans. Faraday Soc.*, 1960, **56**, 449.
273. JOHNS, J. W. C., *Canad. Phys. J.*, 1961, **39**, 1738.
274. FENIMORE, C. P. and JONES, G. W., *J. chem. Phys.*, 1963.
275. KISTIAKOWSKY, G. B. and SAUER, K., *J. Amer. chem. Soc.*, 1956, **78**, 5699.
276. RABINOVITCH, B. S. and SETSER, D. W., *J. Amer. chem. Soc.*, 1960, **83**, 750.
277. MICHEL, K. W. and WAGNER, H. Gg., *Z. Phys. Chem.*, 1962, **35**, 392.
278. LORD, R. C. and SEDERHOLM, C. H., *Spectrochim Acta*, 1959, **15**, 605.
279. CAMPBELL, E. S., *6th Symposium*, p. 213.
280. LUFT, N. W., *Monatsh.*, 1963, **94**, 330.
281. DIXON-LEWIS, G. and WILLIAMS, A., *Nature*, 1962, **196**, 1309.
282. HUSAIN, D. and NORRISH, R. G. W., *Proc. roy. Soc.*, 1963, **A.273**, 145.
283. MILLER, D. R., EVERS, R. L., and SKINNER, G. B., *Combustion and Flame*, 1963, **7**, 137.

AUTHOR INDEX

SUBJECT INDEX

119